PLANE AND SOLID GEOMETRY

WITH TECHNICAL GRAPHICS

D. GREEN

Aspull High School, Wigan

Stanley Thornes (Publishers) Ltd

First published in 1984 by
Stanley Thornes (Publishers) Ltd
Old Station Drive
Leckhampton
CHELTENHAM GL53 0DN

British Library Cataloguing in Publication Data

Green, D.
    Plain and solid geometry with technical graphics.
    1. Geometry, Descriptive
    I. Title
    516'.9   QA501

ISBN 0−85950−136−1

Typeset by Tech-Set, Gateshead.
Printed by Cambus Litho, Glasgow.

CONTENTS

Analysis of Examination-Style Questions: Plane Geometry

Analysis of Examination-Style Questions: Solid Geometry

Supplementary Material for Technical Graphics

PREFACE

The book aims to cover the syllabus for the Plane and Solid Geometry section of both C.S.E. and G.C.E. examining boards in the subjects of Geometrical and Engineering Drawing and Geometrical and Building Drawing. The book also covers the core syllabus for the proposed 16+ Graphical Communication Subjects in Engineering Drawing, Building Drawing and Technical Illustration. Some topics have been developed to a higher standard and should provide a useful source book for both Tech. 1 and Tech. 2 courses in Further Education and other Technology based subjects in Secondary Education.

No formal text has been included as it is felt that the order of work, notes and proofs accompanying the drawings are sufficient to provide a sound understanding of the principles. The principles of communication by drawing and the graphical expression of ideas are thus embodied and reinforced in the approach which emphasises the visual impact on the processes of analysis and synthesis of ideas. Superficial rote learning of constructions is not recommended (hence the provision of proofs) as most examination-type questions reflect the infinite variety of possible problems which not only require the knowledge of the basic elements of construction but the more profound concepts required in problem-solving which can only be realised through understanding.

The aims in the approach to the subject are:

(i)   that the student will appreciate the mathematical relationships which are involved in both the plane and solid geometry and through the logical graphical approach develop a thought process that both analyses and synthesises ideas, thus providing a basis for developing a problem-solving technique.

(ii)   that the students will develop a spatial awareness to such an extent that they will have the ability to understand another person's concepts when described by Orthographic Projections and to be able to complete the communications process by expressing their own concepts in the same universal language — Orthographic Projection.

(iii) that the student is given the opportunity to develop mathematical principles through the practical applications that a geometrical drawing environment affords. This provides an alternative method of stimulating an interest in mathematics to that provided by the established courses, thus furthering the concept of mathematics across the curriculum. Much of the mathematics in C.S.E. and G.C.E. courses is involved, together with topics only dealt with mathematically at a higher level.

An attempt has been made to provide an analysis of examination-type questions (from the author's own experience as an examiner) together with a breakdown of marks and a reference to the principles used. It must be emphasised however, that the questions, solutions and mark values are the author's own and are not necessarily those awarded by a particular board for examination questions of a similar nature. A detailed mark scheme is given for some examples but the author has generally used a block marking scheme which can easily be broken down for identification of the finite elements involved.

The drawings in the book follow the guidelines laid down in BS 308: Parts 1–3: 1972. Further material, based on the contents of publications from the British Standards Institution, is used in the sections on electrical networks and pipe networks: in particular BS 3939, BS 1553 and BS 1646. Copies of the complete British Standards may be obtained from the Institution.

The author would like to express appreciation to the publisher, for the friendly cooperation and helpful advice received.

STUDENT-TEACHER NOTES

The form of presentation has been chosen to illustrate a series of construction elements and the relationships that exist between these elements. These are developed and reinforced without a formal text. Development of the material occurs in a logical progression putting related elements into a common, general environment whilst providing a wide range of examples for the student to experience.

The recommended sequence of working is that the plane and solid sections are developed in parallel not in the tandem form presented in the book. The student may follow the book's progression from example to example and attempt questions at will since an immediate check is available with a solution provided to every problem. Many problems do not have a unique method of solution hence the individual should refer to his/her tutor if uncertain of the validity of the method when it does not compare with one provided. Some alternative methods have been provided or hinted at but it is impossible to cover every contingency.

The author's experience has shown that a written description of a construction method can be both confusing and irrelevant and therefore, has chosen to use the medium of graphical communication of ideas through a logical progression of annotated diagrams. This is very much in line with Dr. E. de Bono's ideas on the development of thinking.

Pictures and diagrams convey complex information by a far more easily absorbed medium than words and where it has been necessary to show a sequence of operations, the sequence has been designated by a letter order (ABC or abc) but it has been left to the student to analyse the process described by each letter. From past experiences the pupil should recognise the construction annotated by the letter. The letter may describe an individual element of a construction or a simple construction process comprising several elements. Proofs should also be referred to when given.

All the problems provided on the worksheets have a solution. A scale has been incorporated with these solutions which were initially prepared full-size on A2 paper but later were reduced during the printing process. This scale may be used to assimilate the dimensioned information given on the worksheets with the solutions provided.

To analyse a process, i.e. break it down into recognisable elements, one must ask oneself questions. It is important to ask the right question in order to get the right answer. The examples shown in T12 (pp 353–5) provide a guide to problem-solving and may provide a useful tool in the development of the thinking process.

PLANE GEOMETRY

Worksheets for G1 to G8

G1 BASIC CONSTRUCTIONS. INTRODUCING ANGLES.

G1-1 Produce the petal shape as shown in drawing G1-1.

G1-2 Produce the 6-pointed star as shown in G1-2.

G1-3 Divide a circle of diameter 80 mm into 6 equal parts with radial lines from the centre of the circle. Illustrate the angle to each line using one of the radial lines as a datum.

G1-4 Draw a line 64 mm long and mark the ends A and X. Construct a line at 60° to the given line at the end marked A.

G1-5 Draw a line AX, 55 mm long, and construct a line which meets the given line at A and forms a 120° angle.

G1-6 Draw a line AX, 75 mm long, and using a protractor draw a line AY which is at 67° to AX. Bisect the angle XAY.

G1-7 Draw a line AX, 60 mm long, and construct a line AY which forms a 30° angle XAY.

G1-8 Draw a line AX, 65 mm long, and construct a perpendicular to the line at end A.

G1-9 Draw a line AX, 70 mm long, and construct a line at 45° to the given line at end A.

G1-10 Draw a line AX, 60 mm long, and construct a line at 75° to the given line at end X.

G1-11 Draw a line AX, 70 mm long, and construct a line at 105° to the given line at end A.

G1-12 Illustrate the special types of angle, i.e. acute, obtuse, right angle and reflex angle.

G2 BISECTION: EQUAL AND PROPORTIONAL PARTS.

G2-1 Analyse and reproduce the construction shown in G2-1.

G2-2 Draw a line AB, 92 mm long, and construct a line XY which is parallel to, and 36 mm from, the given line.

G2-3 Draw 2 lines XY and XZ with an included angle of 67°. Plot the locus of a point which is always equal in distance to both XY and XZ.

G2-4 Draw any acute angle ABC and by construction repeat the angle.

G2-5 Draw any obtuse angle XYZ and by construction repeat the angle.

G2-6 Draw a line AB, 74 mm long, and bisect it.

G2-7 Draw a line AB and mark a point P anywhere above it. Now construct a perpendicular to AB which passes through point P.

G2-8 Practise drawing a series of parallel lines as shown in G2-8.

G2-9 Draw a line AB, 79 mm long, and by construction divide it into 5 equal parts.

G2-10 Draw a line 94 mm long and divide it into 6 equal parts.

G2-11 Draw a line AB, 85 mm long, and divide it into 2 parts in the proportion of 4:3.

G2-12 Draw a line 74 mm long and divide it into 3 parts having ratios of 2:5:3.

G2-13 Construct a triangle having a perimeter of 126 mm and sides in the ratio of 3:4:5.

G3 TRIANGULATION: THE CIRCLE AND ITS CENTRE.

G3-1 Note the special properties of the triangles shown in G3-1.

G3-2 Analyse the notes on construction of triangles shown in G3-2.

G3-3 Construct a scalene triangle ABC which has sides AB = 77 mm, BC = 80 mm and AC = 48 mm.

G3-4 Construct an obtuse-angled triangle ABC with AB = 42 mm, AC = 100 mm and ∠ABC = 120°.

G3-5 Analyse and reproduce the terminology and construction shown in G3-5.

G3-6 Draw a circle ∅65 mm using a template and by construction determine its centre.

G3-7 Draw a circle ∅46 mm using a template and also draw, with compasses, a circle ∅80 mm which is concentric to it.

G3-8 Draw a circle ∅78 mm using a template and mark a point P anywhere on it. Construct a tangent to the circle at point P.

G3-9 Circumscribe the triangle shown in Fig 1.

G3-10 Inscribe the triangle shown in Fig 2.

G3-11 Circumscribe the triangle shown in Fig 3.

G3-12 Inscribe the triangle shown in Fig 4.

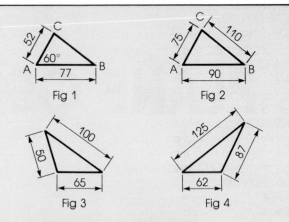

Fig 1

Fig 2

Fig 3

Fig 4

G4 CONSTRUCTION OF TRIANGLES.

G4-1 Construct a triangle ABC given AB = 52 mm, CB = 58 mm and CA = 40 mm. Then construct a similar triangle with AB increased to 65 mm.

G4-2 Construct a triangle ABC given AC = 55 mm, BC = 75 mm and the vertical height of C above AB is 50 mm.

G4-3 Construct a right-angled triangle ABC with ∠BAC = 90°, BA = 70 mm and hypotenuse of 85 mm.

G4-4 Construct a triangle ABC given that the angle at A is 90°, the angle at B is 60° and AC = 75 mm.

G4-5 Construct a right-angled triangle with ∠ABC = 90°, AC = 80 mm and ∠ACB = 30°.

G4-6 Construct a right-angled triangle where the hypotenuse AC = 87 mm and the vertical height of B above AC is 40 mm.

G4-7 Construct an equilateral triangle of given side AB = 70 mm.

G4-8 Construct an equilateral triangle with a vertical height of 68 mm.

G4-9 Construct an isosceles triangle given that AB = 40 mm and AC = 67 mm = BC.

G4-10 Construct an isosceles triangle ABC. The vertical height of C above AB is 77 mm and AC = BC = 86 mm.

G4-11 Construct an isosceles triangle ABC given that the vertical height of C above AB is 75 mm, AB = 50 mm, and AC = BC.

G4-12 Construct a scalene triangle ABC given that AB = 68 mm, BC = 74 mm and the included angle is 30°.

G5 TRIANGLES (PERIMETER AND VERTICAL ANGLES).

G5-1 Construct a scalene triangle ABC given that AB = 35 mm, BC = 67 mm and the altitude of C above AB is 62 mm.

G5-2 Construct an obtuse-angled triangle ABC given ∠BAC = 120°, AB = 45 mm and the altitude of C above AB is 60 mm.

G5-3 Construct an obtuse-angled triangle which has a base of 55 mm and base angles of 30° and 120°.

G5-4 Construct a triangle with a perimeter of 105 mm and angles of 60° and 30°.

G5-5 Construct an isosceles triangle given that the perimeter is 160 mm and the altitude is 53 mm.

G5-6 Construct a triangle with a perimeter of 170 mm, a base of 50 mm and a base angle of 50°.

G5-7 Take note of the theorems shown in G5-7.

G5-8 Construct a triangle whose base AB = 70 mm, vertical height of C above AB is 50 mm and the vertical angle ACB is 60°.

G5-9 Construct a triangle ABC given AB = 65 mm, BC = 58 mm, and the angle at C is 55°, i.e. ∠ ACB.

G5-10 Construct a triangle with a base AB = 62 mm, a base angle ABC = 60° and a vertical angle ACB = 40°.

G5-11 Construct a triangle given that the perimeter is 180 mm, ∠ A = 42° and the vertical height of A above BC is 40 mm.

G6 CONSTRUCTION OF QUADRILATERALS.

G6-1 Note the special properties of the quadrilaterals shown in G6-1.

G6-2 Construct a square given that it has a side of 54 mm.

G6-3 Construct a square given that it has a diagonal of 76 mm.

G6-4 Construct a rectangle ABCD with AB = 80 mm and BC = 55 mm.

G6-5 Construct a rectangle ABCD with AB = 75 mm and the diagonal AC = 90 mm.

G6-6 Construct a rectangle ABCD with AB = 78 mm and ∠BAC = 30°.

G6-7 Construct a rectangle ABCD given that the diagonal AC = 90 mm and ∠ CAB = 30°.

G6-8 Construct a rhombus ABCD with AB = 58 mm and the diagonal AC = 95 mm.

G6-9 Construct a rhombus ABCD given that the diagonals AC = 103 mm and BD = 44 mm.

G6-10 Construct a parallelogram ABCD given that AB = 70 mm, BC = 50 mm, and AC = 65 mm.

G6-11 Construct a parallelogram ABCD given that AB = 54 mm, AD = 44 mm and the included angle 45°.

G7 EQUIVALENT AREAS (TRIANGLES AND QUADRILATERALS).

G7-1 Construct a parallelogram ABCD given the diagonals AC = 110 mm, BD = 76 mm and the side AB = 60 mm.

G7-2 Construct a trapezium ABCD given that AB is parallel to CD and they are 44 mm apart. CD = 50 mm with ∠BAD = 60° and ∠ABC = 90°.

G7-3 Construct a trapezoid ABCD given AB = 72 mm, BC = 50 mm and AC = 60 mm. Angle ACD = 30°, AD = 32 mm and ∠BAD is obtuse.

G7-4 Construct a trapezoid ABCD given AB = 60 mm, BC = 80 mm and the included angle is 60°. CD = 34 mm and diagonal BD = 89 mm.

G7-5 Construct a triangle having a base of 52 mm and base angle of 30° which also has the same area as a triangle ABC with AB = 52 mm, BC = 60 mm and AC = 54 mm.

G7-6 Construct a triangle having an altitude of 68 mm and one side of 100 mm, equal in area to a triangle ABC with AB = 60 mm, AC = 50 mm and BC = 67 mm.

G7-7 Construct a triangle having an altitude of 70 mm and a base angle of 60°, equal in area to a triangle ABC with AB = 55 mm, AC = 45 mm and BC = 65 mm.

G7-8 Construct a triangle with a base of 40 mm and base angle of 60°, equal in area to a triangle ABC with AB = 65 mm, BC = 75 mm and AC = 45 mm.

G7-9 Construct any triangle ABC which is equal in area to a polygon PQRST with PQ = 45 mm, SQ = 70 mm, SP = 52 mm, PR = 48 mm, RQ = 33 mm and PT = ST = 30 mm.

G7-10. Reduce the triangle ABC determined in G7-9 to a rectangle which has the same area.

G7-11 Construct a rectangle which has one side of 105 mm and the same area as a rectangle ABCD with sides AB = 80 mm and BC = 55 mm.

G8 PYTHAGORAS' THEOREM, ROOTS AND AREAS.

G8-1 Analyse the information and reproduce the figure shown in G8-1.

G8-2 Two pipes A and B form a tee junction as shown in Fig 1. Determine the diameter of pipe C which is required to have the same cross-sectional area (CSA) as both A and B combined.

G8-3 Fig 2 shows several pipes feeding together at varying intervals. Determine the diameters of the intermediate pipes A ,B and C if the velocity of the fluid in the pipes is to remain constant.

G8-4 A pipe A splits into 2 pipes B and C which have a combined CSA equal to pipe A, as shown in Fig 3. Determine the diameter of pipe C.

G8-5 Analyse and reproduce the figures shown in G8-5.

G8-6 By construction determine the square root of 54, i.e. $\sqrt{54}$.

G8-7 By construction determine $\sqrt{155}$.

G8-8 Draw a rectangle 65 mm × 28 mm and by construction reduce it to a square of equivalent area.

G8-9 Draw a triangle ABC, AB = 70 mm, BC = 112 mm and AC = 66 mm. Reduce it to a square of equal area.

G8-10 Reduce the irregular hexagon shown in Fig 4 to a square of equal area.

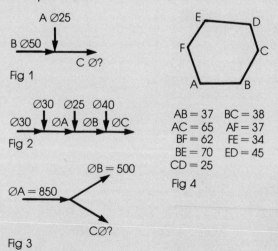

Fig 1

Fig 2

Fig 3

AB = 37	BC = 38
AC = 65	AF = 37
BF = 62	FE = 34
BE = 70	ED = 45
CD = 25	

Fig 4

G1-1: Division of a circle into 6 equal parts

Produce the petal shape as shown.

Draw a circle of diameter 80 mm and radius 40 mm. Use the same radius to produce the 6 petals.

Diameter 80 mm may be written as ∅80 on diagrams.

Radius 40 mm may be written as R40 mm (R40 on diagrams).

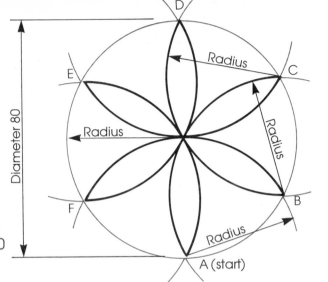

G1-2: 6-pointed star

Produce the 6-pointed star as shown.

Draw a circle of diameter 80 mm. Use the radius R40 mm and step off points A, B, C, D, E and F. Join alternate points.

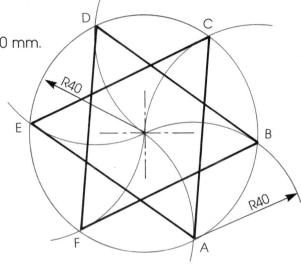

G1-3: Angles in a circle

Divide a circle of diameter 80 mm into 6 equal parts with radial lines from the centre of the circle. Illustrate the angle to each line using one of the radial lines as a datum.

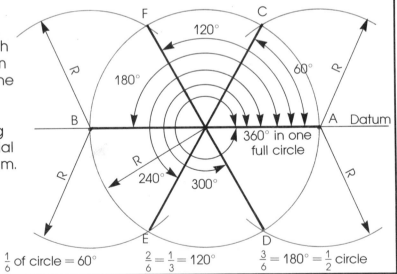

$\frac{1}{6}$ of circle = 60° $\frac{2}{6} = \frac{1}{3} = 120°$ $\frac{3}{6} = 180° = \frac{1}{2}$ circle

G1-4: To construct a 60° angle to a line AX at A

Draw a line 64 mm long and mark the ends A and X. Construct a line at 60° to the given line at the end marked A.

Draw a circle of any radius R and centre A. Mark the intersection of the circle with AX as B. With centre B step off an arc with the same radius R to intersect the circle at C. Draw a line from A through C.

B to C is $\frac{1}{6}$ of a circle, therefore angle BAC is $\frac{1}{6}$ of 360° = 60°

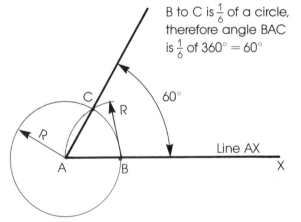

Drawing No. **G1**

TITLE: **Basic constructions. Introducing angles.**

NOTE: **Letter sequence gives order of construction.**

SCALE:

4

G1-5: To construct a 120° angle to a line AX at A

Draw a line AX, 55 mm long, and construct a line which meets the given line at A and forms a 120° angle.

─────

Proceed as in G1-4 to obtain 60° and step off the radius R once again from C to give point D. Draw a line from A through D.

B to C plus C to D $= \frac{2}{6}$ of circle
$= \frac{2}{6} \times 360°$
$= 120°$

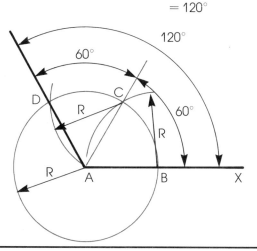

G1-6: To bisect an angle (cut it into 2 equal parts)

Draw a line AX, 75 mm long, and using a protractor draw a line AY which is at 67° to AX. Bisect the angle XAY.

─────

To bisect angle XAY, draw an arc centre A and radius R_1* to cut AX and AY at B and C. Step off R_2* from B and C to give the intersection point D. Draw a bisector from A through D.

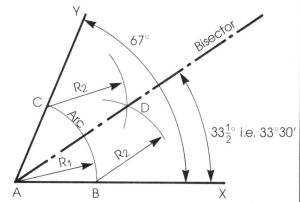

*R_1 and R_2 may be of any reasonable radius

G1-7: To construct a 30° angle to a line

Draw a line AX, 60 mm long, and construct a line AY which forms a 30° angle XAY.

─────

Produce a 60° angle as in G1-4 and bisect it as in G1-6.

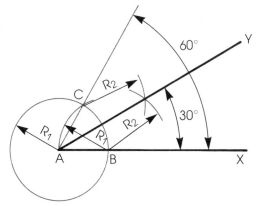

G1-8: To construct a 90° angle to a line

Draw a line AX, 65 mm long, and construct a perpendicular to the line at the end A.

─────

$90° = 60° + 30°$ i.e. $60° + (60°$ bisected).

Produce 120° as in G1-5 and bisect second 60° to give $60° + 30° = 90°$.

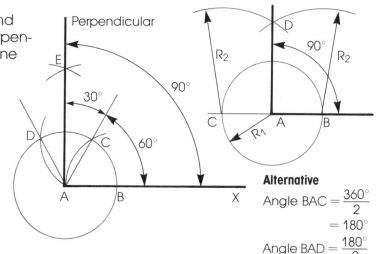

Alternative

Angle BAC $= \dfrac{360°}{2}$
$= 180°$

Angle BAD $= \dfrac{180°}{2}$
$= 90°$

| Drawing No. **G1** | TITLE: **Basic constructions. Introducing angles.** | NOTE: **Letter sequence gives order of construction.** | SCALE: |

G1-9: To construct a 45° angle to a line

Draw a line AX, 70 mm long, and construct a line at 45° to the given line at end A.
___

$45° = 30° + 15°$,
i.e. ($\frac{1}{2}$ of 60°) + ($\frac{1}{2}$ of 30°).
Construct a 60° angle and bisect to give 30°.
Bisect second 30° to give 15°.

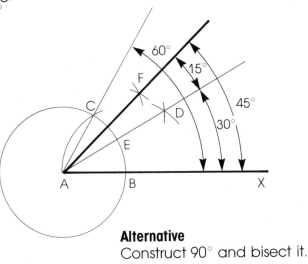

Alternative
Construct 90° and bisect it.

G1-10: To construct a 75° angle to a line

Draw a line AX, 60 mm long, and construct a line at 75° to the given line at end X.
___

$75° = 60° + 15°$, i.e. $60° + (\frac{1}{2}$ of 30°).

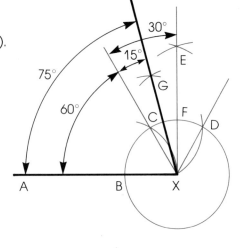

G1-11: To construct a 105° angle to a line

Draw a line AX, 70 mm long, and construct a line at 105° to the given line at end A.
___

$105° = 60° + 30° + 15°$.

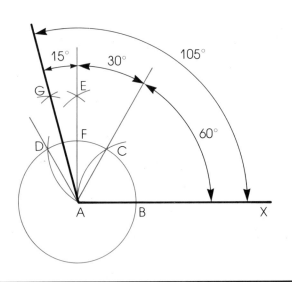

G1-12: Special types of angle; acute, obtuse, right angle and reflex angle

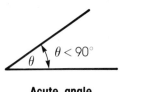

Acute angle

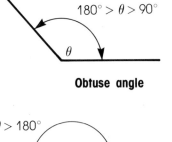

Obtuse angle

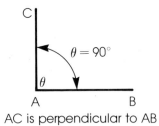

AC is perpendicular to AB

Right angle

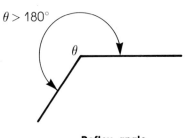

Reflex angle

Drawing No. G1	TITLE: **Basic constructions. Introducing angles.**	NOTE: **Letter sequence gives construction.**	SCALE:

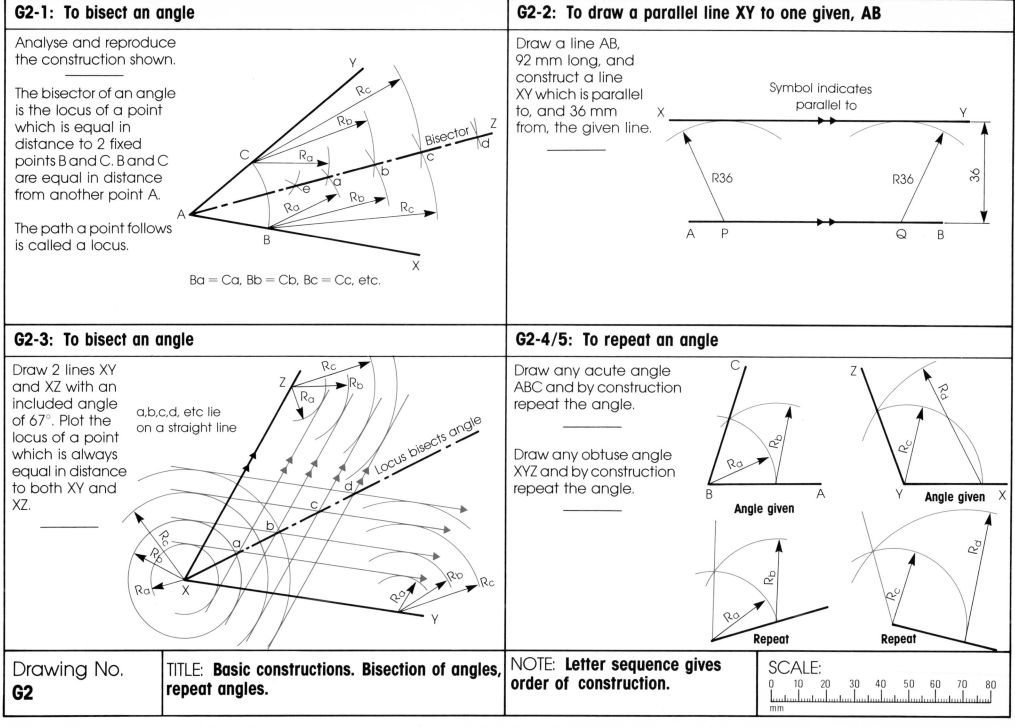

G2-1: To bisect an angle

Analyse and reproduce the construction shown.

———

The bisector of an angle is the locus of a point which is equal in distance to 2 fixed points B and C. B and C are equal in distance from another point A.

The path a point follows is called a locus.

Ba = Ca, Bb = Cb, Bc = Cc, etc.

G2-2: To draw a parallel line XY to one given, AB

Draw a line AB, 92 mm long, and construct a line XY which is parallel to, and 36 mm from, the given line.

———

Symbol indicates parallel to

G2-3: To bisect an angle

Draw 2 lines XY and XZ with an included angle of 67°. Plot the locus of a point which is always equal in distance to both XY and XZ.

———

a,b,c,d, etc lie on a straight line

Locus bisects angle

G2-4/5: To repeat an angle

Draw any acute angle ABC and by construction repeat the angle.

———

Draw any obtuse angle XYZ and by construction repeat the angle.

———

Angle given

Angle given

Repeat

Repeat

| Drawing No. **G2** | TITLE: **Basic constructions. Bisection of angles, repeat angles.** | NOTE: **Letter sequence gives order of construction.** | SCALE:
0 10 20 30 40 50 60 70 80
mm |

G2-6: Bisection of a line

Draw a line AB, 74 mm long, and bisect it.

Can you see a relationship between bisecting a line and bisecting an angle?

Note: 2 points are enough to determine the bisector, e.g. c-c.

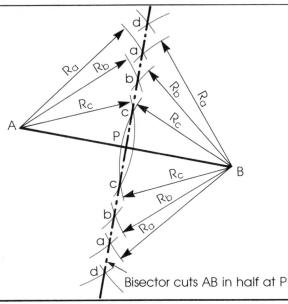

Bisector cuts AB in half at P

G2-7: To construct a perpendicular to a line from a point P

Draw a line AB and mark a point P anywhere above it. Now construct a perpendicular to AB which passes through point P.

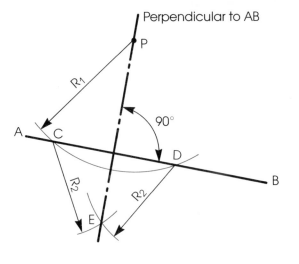

G2-8: To set up a set square to draw parallel lines

Practise drawing a series of parallel lines as shown.

Slide

Straight edge

Set square

G2-9: Division of a line into equal parts

Draw a line AB, 79 mm long, and by construction divide it into 5 equal parts.

Draw a line AY at any angle to AB and mark off the required number of increments from A, spacing them equally, e.g. A-to-1 = 1-to-2 = 2-to-3 etc. The increments can be any convenient length provided the last mark is somewhere under line end B. Join the last point, i.e. 5, to line end B and draw lines from each of the other points parallel to 5B.

Construction uses principle of similar triangles

$$\frac{AB}{AC} = \frac{AD}{AE} = \frac{BD}{CE}$$

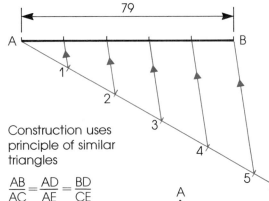

| Drawing No. **G2** | TITLE: **Basic constructions. Bisection of lines and division of lines.** | NOTE: **Letter sequence gives order of construction.** | SCALE:
0 10 20 30 40 50 60 70 80
mm |

G2-10: Division of a line into equal parts

Draw a line 94 mm long and divide it into 6 equal parts by construction.

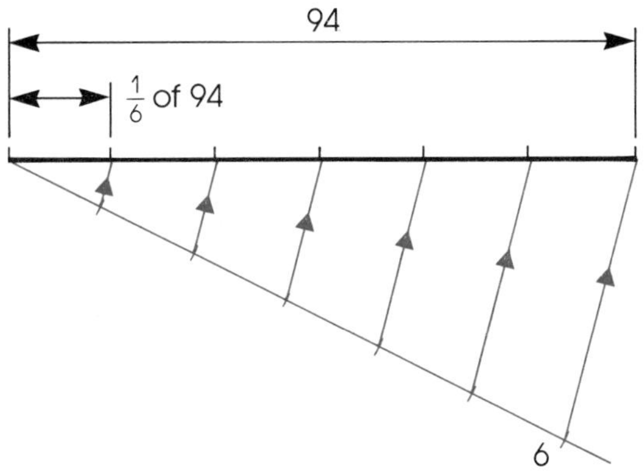

94

$\frac{1}{6}$ of 94

6

G2-11: Division of a line into proportional parts

Draw a line AB, 85 mm long, and divide it into 2 parts in the proportion of 4:3.

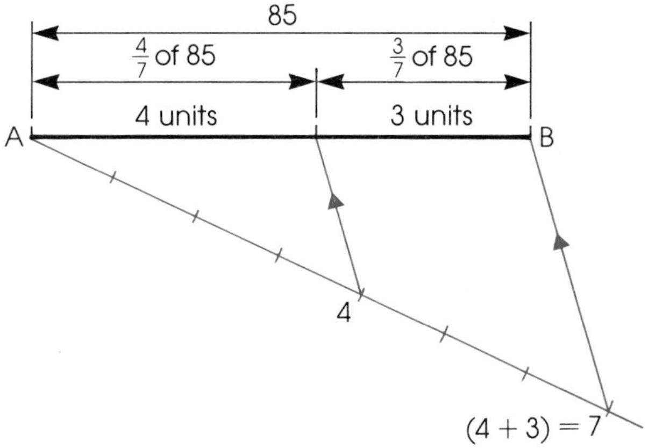

85

$\frac{4}{7}$ of 85 $\frac{3}{7}$ of 85

4 units   3 units

A   B

4

$(4 + 3) = 7$

G2-12: Division of a line into proportional parts

Draw a line 74 mm long and divide it into 3 parts in the proportions of 2:5:3.

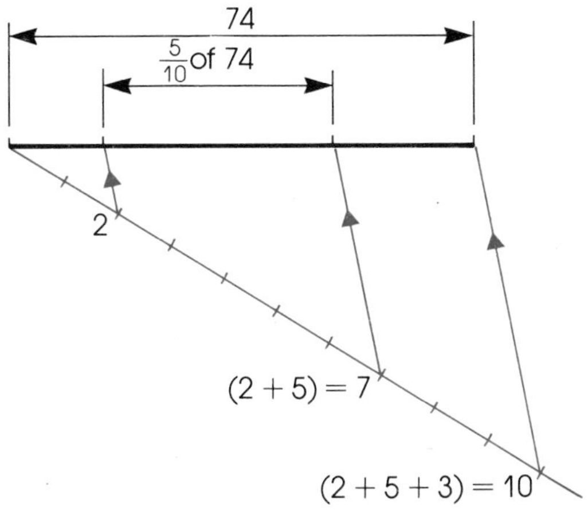

74

$\frac{5}{10}$ of 74

2

$(2 + 5) = 7$

$(2 + 5 + 3) = 10$

G2-13: To construct a triangle from a line divided into porportional parts

Construct a triangle having a perimeter of 126 mm and sides in the ratio of 3:4:5.

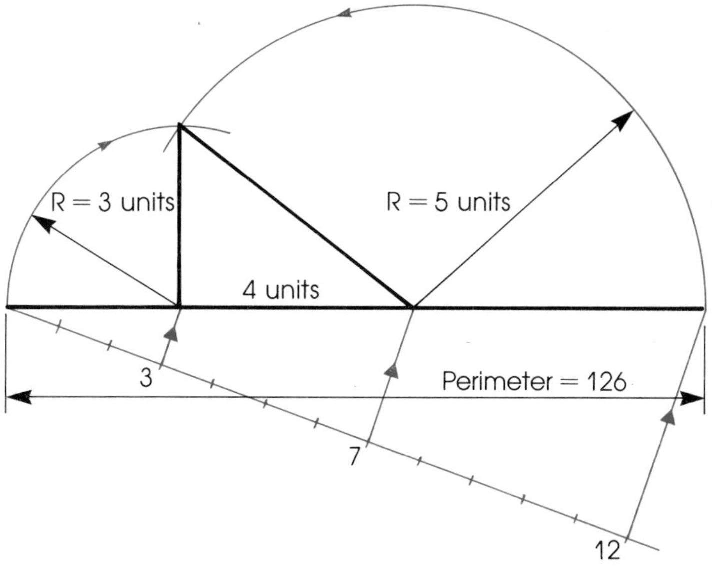

R = 3 units   R = 5 units

4 units

3

Perimeter = 126

7

12

| Drawing No.
G2 | TITLE: **Basic constructions. Division of lines into equal and proportional parts.** | | SCALE:
0 10 20 30 40 50 60 70 80
mm |

G3-1: Special properties of triangles

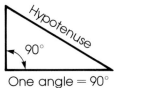

One angle = 90°

Right-angled triangle

3 sides equal
3 angles equal
i.e. 60° each

Equilateral triangle

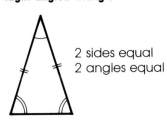

2 sides equal
2 angles equal

Isosceles triangle

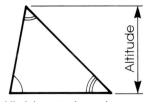

Altitude

All sides and angles
are unequal

Scalene triangle

G3-2: Construction of triangles

Before attempting to construct a triangle — or any other figure — from a written description it can be extremely helpful to make a simple sketch first. The sketch more easily allows the relationships within the construction to be analysed.

For example, in G3-3 the corner C has been located in the sketch by noting (from the written description) its distance from A and from B. In G3-4, C is located in the sketch by its given distance from A and its direction in relation to B and A.

C can also be located by the directions from both A in relation to B (i.e. the angle at A) and B in relation to A (i.e. the angle at B). This process is known as triangulation.

The intersection of medians gives point P which is the centre of gravity of the triangle:
Bd = Cd, Af = Bf, Ac = Ce.

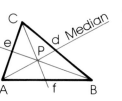

G3-3: Construction of a scalene triangle

Construct a scalene triangle ABC with sides AB = 77 mm, BC = 80 mm and AC = 48 mm.

Sketch any scalene triangle

Analyse the information given and assemble it on the sketch

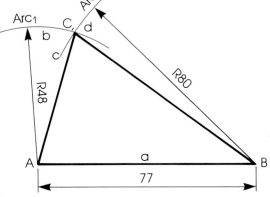

Any point on Arc₁ is 48 mm from A. Any point on Arc₂ is 80 mm from B. Point C must satisfy both of the conditions, i.e. it must lie on both arcs. The intersection of Arc₁ with Arc₂ gives C.

G3-4: Construction of an obtuse-angled triangle

Construct an obtuse angled triangle ABC with AB = 42 mm, AC = 100 mm and angle ABC = 120°

Sketch any obtuse angled triangle

Analyse the information and assemble it on the sketch

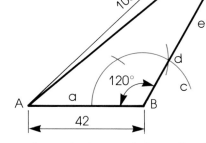

Any point on the arc is 100 mm from A. Any point on the line leading from B is at 120° to AB from B. Point C is the intersection of the arc with the line and satisfies both conditions.

Drawing No.
G3

TITLE: **Properties and construction of triangles.**

SCALE:
0 10 20 30 40 50 60 70 80
mm

G3-5: The construction of circles

Analyse and reproduce the terminology and construction shown.

―――――

The symbol for a centre line is ℄.

Circumference: distance around circle = $\pi \times D$
Area: $\pi \times R^2$ or $\pi \times D^2/4$ where $\pi = 3.142$ or $\frac{22}{7}$.

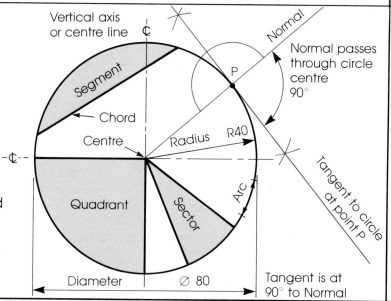

Normal passes through circle centre 90°

Tangent is at 90° to Normal

G3-6: To find the centre of a circle

Draw a circle of diameter 65 mm using a template and by construction determine its centre.

―――――

Draw any 2 chords and bisect them. As AB shortens to become one point P (see G3-5) the chord takes the form of a tangent. The chord bisector assumes the role of a normal.

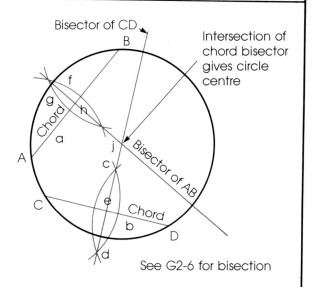

Intersection of chord bisector gives circle centre

See G2-6 for bisection

G3-7: To draw a circle concentric to one given

Draw a circle of diameter 46 mm using a template and also draw, with compasses, a circle of diameter 80 mm which is concentric to it.

―――――

Find the centre of the given circle as in G3-6 and use it for a compass point.

Concentric circles have the same centre.

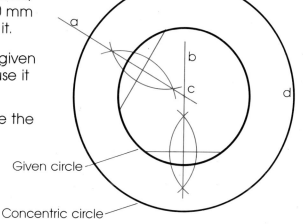

Given circle

Concentric circle

G3-8: To draw a tangent to a point on a circle

Draw a circle of diameter 78 mm using a template and mark a point P anywhere on it. Construct a tangent to the circle at point P.

―――――

To construct the tangent, find the circle centre and draw a normal from the centre through P.

The tangent is perpendicular to the normal.

Drawing No. G3	TITLE: **Parts of a circle.**	NOTE: **Lower case letter sequence gives order of construction.**	SCALE:

SCALE:
0 10 20 30 40 50 60 70 80
mm

11

G3-9: To circumscribe a triangle

Circumscribe the triangle shown below.

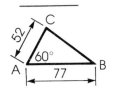

Given ABC, bisect any 2 sides. The intersection of the bisectors gives the centre of the circle.

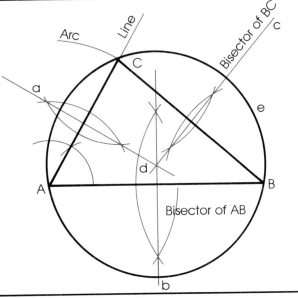

G3-10: To inscribe a triangle

Inscribe the triangle shown below.

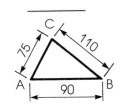

Given ABC, bisect only 2 angles. The intersection of the bisectors gives the centre of the circle.

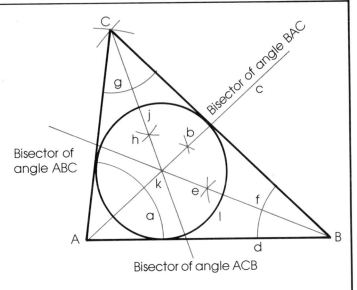

G3-11: To circumscribe a triangle

Circumscribe a triangle given that the triangle has sides of 65 mm, 50 mm and 100 mm.

Note: The sides of the triangle are chords of the circle.

The intersection of the bisectors gives the centre of the circle.

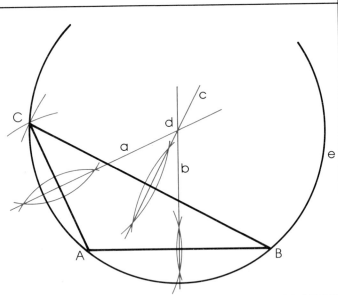

G3-12: To inscribe a triangle

Inscribe a triangle given that the triangle has sides of 62 mm, 87 mm and 125 mm.

The angle bisector is the locus of a point whose distance to 2 lines is always equal (see G2-3). A circle may be drawn to touch both AB and BC if it has its centre anywhere on the bisector b.

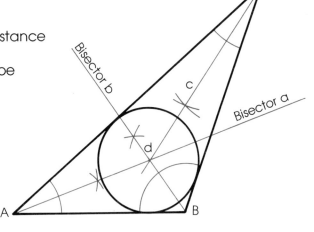

Drawing No.
G3

TITLE: **Circumscribed and inscribed triangles.**

NOTE: **Lower case letter sequence gives order of construction. Sketches of triangles from the worksheet descriptions are not to scale.**

SCALE:

0 10 20 30 40 50 60 70 80

mm

G4-1: To construct a similar triangle

Construct the triangle ABC given AB = 52 mm, CB = 58 mm and CA = 40 mm. Then construct a similar triangle with AB increased to 65 mm.

"Similar" means having the same shape, i.e. the same angles (see G2-4 for repeat angles).

Can you produce an alternative solution based on the principles shown in G2-9 to G2-13 for the construction of the similar triangle?

G4-2: To construct a triangle using a given vertical height

Construct a triangle ABC given AC = 55 mm, BC = 75 mm and the vertical height of C, above AB, is 50 mm.

See G2-2 for parallel line construction to give vertical height. Can you construct the triangle using a slightly different sequence of operations?

G4-3: To construct a right-angled triangle

Construct a right-angled triangle ABC with angle BAC = 90°, BA = 70 mm and hypotenuse of 85 mm.

Note: The hypotenuse is the side opposite the right angle.

G4-4: To construct a right-angled triangle

Construct a triangle ABC given that the angle at A is 90°, angle at B is 60° and AC = 75 mm.

See G2-7 for the construction of a perpendicular to a line to pass through a point.

Drawing No.	TITLE: **Construction of triangles.**	NOTE: **Lower case letter sequence gives order of construction.**	SCALE:
G4			0 10 20 30 40 50 60 70 80 mm

G4-5: To construct a right-angled triangle

Construct a right-angled triangle with angle ABC = 90°, AC = 80 mm and angle ACB = 30°.

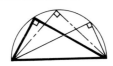

Theorem 1: The angle in a semi circle is a right angle. Note that the diameter is the hypotenuse and the third corner must lie on the circle.

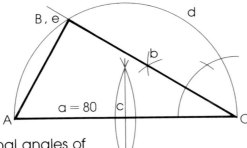

Theorem 2: The internal angles of a triangle add up to 180°.
Angles A + B + C = 180°.
Therefore angle A = 180° − (B + C).

G4-6: To construct a right-angled triangle

Construct a right-angled triangle where the hypotenuse AC = 87 mm and the vertical height of B above AC is 40 mm.

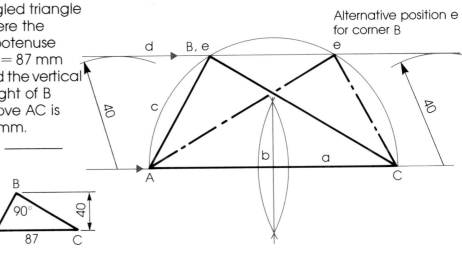

Alternative position e for corner B

G4-7: To construct an equilateral triangle from a given side

Construct an equilateral triangle given side AB = 70 mm.

Can you construct the triangle using theorem 2 in G4-5?

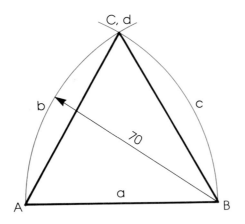

Note: Angle A = angle B = angle C = $\frac{180°}{3}$.

G4-8: To construct an equilateral triangle from a given vertical height

Construct an equilateral triangle with a vertical height of 68 mm.

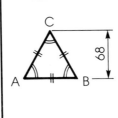

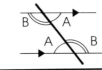

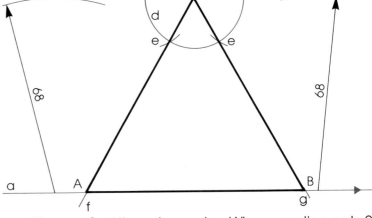

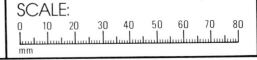

Theorem 3: Alternate angles. When any line cuts 2 parallel lines, alternate angles are equal; angle A + angle B = 180°.

Drawing No. **G4**

TITLE: **Construction of triangles.**

NOTE: **Lower case letter sequence gives order of construction.**

SCALE:
0 10 20 30 40 50 60 70 80
mm

14

G4-9: To construct an isosceles triangle

Construct an isosceles triangle given AB = 40 mm and AC = 67 mm = BC.

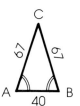

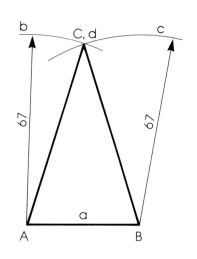

G4-10: To construct an isosceles triangle

Construct an isosceles triangle ABC. The vertical height of C above AB is 77 mm and AC = BC = 86 mm.

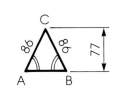

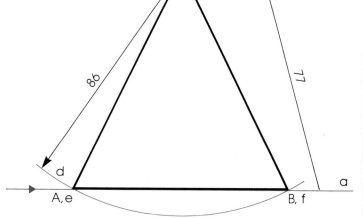

G4-11: To construct an isosceles triangle

Construct an isosceles triangle ABC given that the vertical height of C above AB is 75 mm, AB = 50 mm and AC = BC.

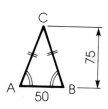

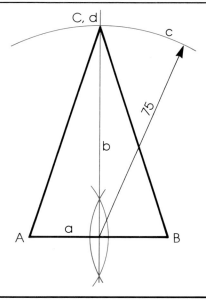

G4-12: To construct a scalene triangle

Construct a scalene triangle ABC given AB = 68 mm, BC = 74 mm and the included angle is 30°.

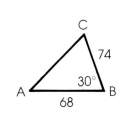

Note: "included angle" is the angle included or contained between the 2 given sides.

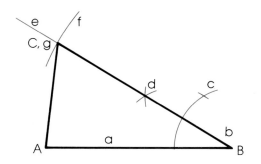

| Drawing No. G4 | TITLE: **Construction of triangles.** | NOTE: **Lower case letter sequence gives order of construction.** | SCALE: |

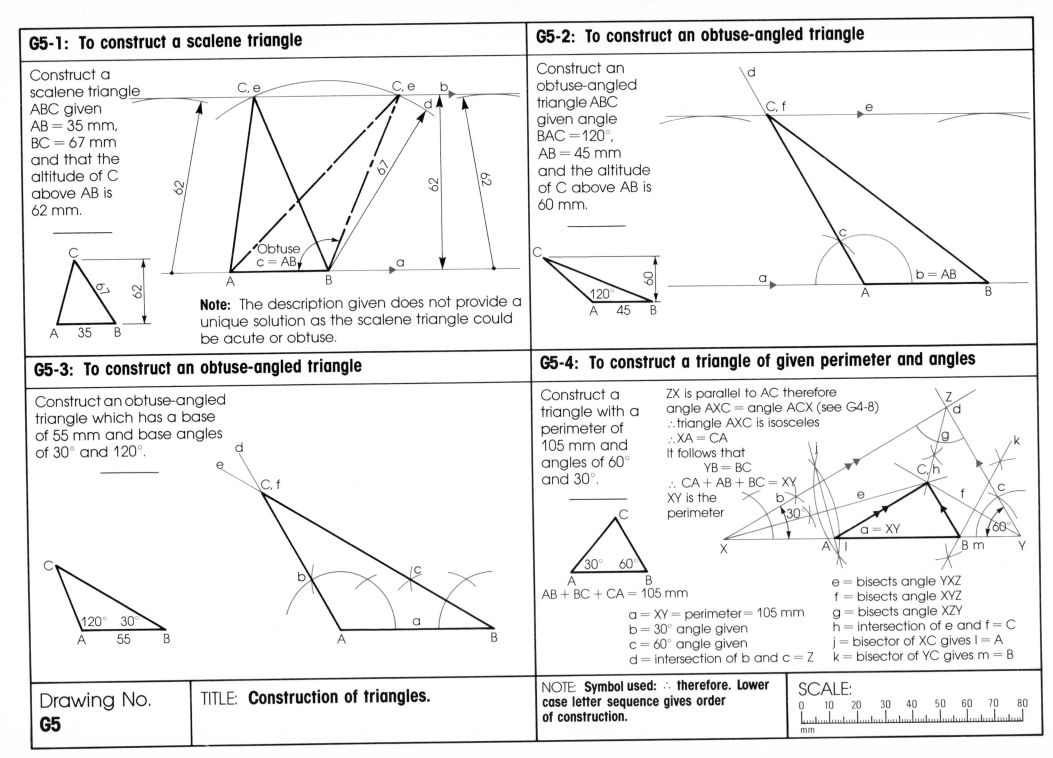

G5-1: To construct a scalene triangle

Construct a scalene triangle ABC given AB = 35 mm, BC = 67 mm and that the altitude of C above AB is 62 mm.

Note: The description given does not provide a unique solution as the scalene triangle could be acute or obtuse.

G5-2: To construct an obtuse-angled triangle

Construct an obtuse-angled triangle ABC given angle BAC = 120°, AB = 45 mm and the altitude of C above AB is 60 mm.

G5-3: To construct an obtuse-angled triangle

Construct an obtuse-angled triangle which has a base of 55 mm and base angles of 30° and 120°.

G5-4: To construct a triangle of given perimeter and angles

Construct a triangle with a perimeter of 105 mm and angles of 60° and 30°.

ZX is parallel to AC therefore angle AXC = angle ACX (see G4-8)
∴ triangle AXC is isosceles
∴ XA = CA
It follows that
  YB = BC
∴ CA + AB + BC = XY
XY is the perimeter

AB + BC + CA = 105 mm

a = XY = perimeter = 105 mm
b = 30° angle given
c = 60° angle given
d = intersection of b and c = Z

e = bisects angle YXZ
f = bisects angle XYZ
g = bisects angle XZY
h = intersection of e and f = C
j = bisector of XC gives I = A
k = bisector of YC gives m = B

Drawing No.	TITLE: **Construction of triangles.**	NOTE: **Symbol used: ∴ therefore. Lower** case letter sequence gives order of construction.	SCALE:
G5			0 10 20 30 40 50 60 70 80 mm

16

G5-5: To construct an isosceles triangle of given perimeter and vertical height

Construct an isosceles triangle given that the perimeter is 160 mm and the altitude is 53 mm.

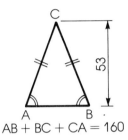

AB + BC + CA = 160

$a = PQ = \frac{1}{2}$ perimeter

$b = \perp$ to PQ at Q

c = apex, QC given.

Sequence continued on drawing.

AP = AC (triangle PCA is isosceles)

$AC + AQ = \frac{1}{2}$ perimeter $\therefore$ AP + AQ = $\frac{1}{2}$ perimeter.

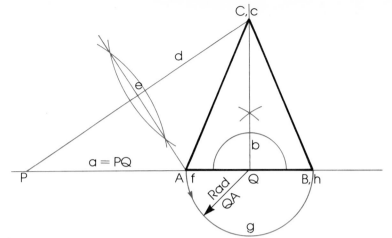

G5-6: To construct a triangle of given perimeter, base and base angle

Construct a triangle with a perimeter of 170 mm, a base of 50 mm and a base angle of 50°.

AT = length of remaining sides

AB + AC + CB = perimeter

$\therefore$ AT = AC + CB since CT = CB

i.e. triangle BCT is isosceles, given by construction.

$\therefore$ AT = perimeter − AB

a = base AB

b = base angle

c = AT = perimeter − AB

d = BT

e = bisector of BT

f = c, e intercept = C

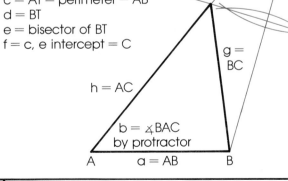

G5-7: Some useful theorems

Theorem 1: $\angle ADB = 2(\angle ACB)$

The angle subtended at the centre of a circle is twice the angle subtended at any point on the circumference when it is based on the same chord.

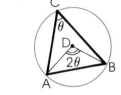

Theorem 2: $\angle A = \angle B = \angle C$

Angles on the same chord are equal.

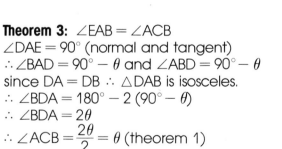

Theorem 3: $\angle EAB = \angle ACB$

$\angle DAE = 90°$ (normal and tangent)

$\therefore \angle BAD = 90° - \theta$ and $\angle ABD = 90° - \theta$

since DA = DB $\therefore \triangle DAB$ is isosceles.

$\therefore \angle BDA = 180° - 2(90° - \theta)$

$\therefore \angle BDA = 2\theta$

$\therefore \angle ACB = \frac{2\theta}{2} = \theta$ (theorem 1)

$\therefore \angle EAB = \angle ACB$.

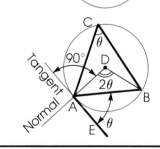

| Drawing No. **G5** | TITLE: **Construction of triangles.** | NOTE: **Symbols used:** $\perp$ perpendicular, $\angle$ **angle,** $\triangle$ **triangle. Lower case letter sequence gives order of construction.** | SCALE: |

G5-8: To construct a triangle of given base, vertical height and vertical angle

Construct a triangle having a base AB = 70 mm, a vertical height of C above AB of 50 mm and the vertical angle ACB of 60°.

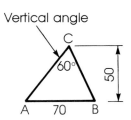

Vertical angle

a = draw AB
b = ∠ EAB = vertical angle
c = ⊥ to b at A
d = bisector of AB
e = d, c intercept
f = circle, radius eB

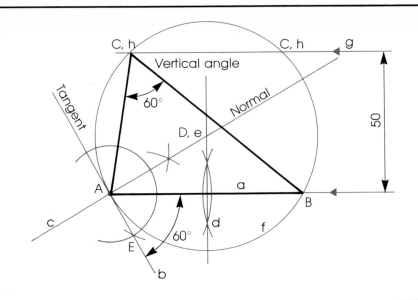

Construction based on theorem 3, G5-7.

G5-9: To construct a triangle from two given sides and one angle

Construct a triangle ABC given that AB = 65 mm, BC = 58 mm and the angle at C is 55°, i.e. angle ACB.

_____

See G5-8 for a description of the construction method.

See theorem 3, G5-7.

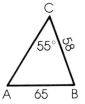

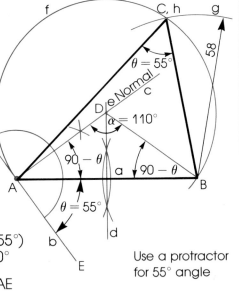

∠BAE = 55°, ∠DAE = 90°
∠BAD = 90° − 55° = 35°
∠ABD = 90° − 55° = 35°
Since △ DAB is isosceles
∠ADB = 180° − 2 (90° − 55°)
∴ ∠ADB = 180° − 70° = 110°
$\angle ACB = \dfrac{110°}{2} = 55° = \angle BAE$

Use a protractor for 55° angle

G5-10: To construct a triangle from a given base, base angle and vertical angle

Construct a triangle with a base AB = 62 mm, a base angle ABC = 60° and a vertical angle ACB = 40°.

_____

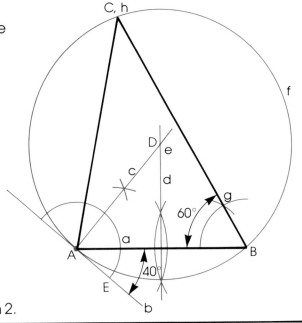

Can you construct the triangle by an easier method? See G4-5 theorem 2.

Drawing No.
G5

TITLE: **Construction of triangles.**

NOTE: **Lower case letter sequence gives order of construction.**

SCALE:

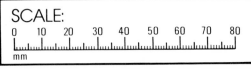

G5-11: **To construct a triangle from a given perimeter, vertical height and one angle**

Construct a triangle given that the perimeter is 180 mm, the
angle at A is 42° and the vertical height of A above BC is 40 mm.

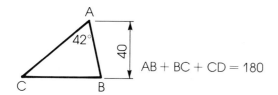

AB + BC + CD = 180

$AX = AY = \frac{1}{2}$ perimeter (given by method)
AB + BX = AX and AC + CY = AY
Since θ = angle OpX = angle OXp and OX = Op = radius P
Also angle OpB = 90° ∴ angle XpB = 90°− θ ⎤ Normals, chord
and angle OXB = 90° ∴ angle pXB = 90°− θ ⎦ and tangents
Then triangle pXB is isosceles ∴ XB = pB.
Also YC = Cp (proof same as above).
∴ AB + pB = AB + XB and AC + Cp = AC + CY
∴ Perimeter = AX + AY.

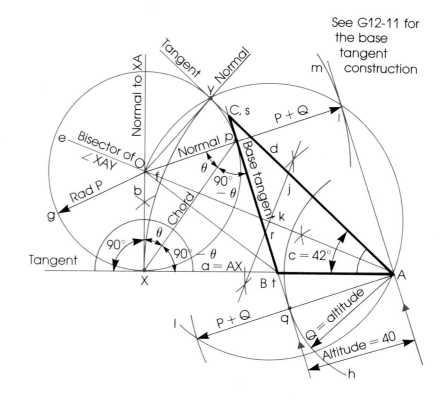

See G12-11 for
the base
tangent
construction

CONSTRUCTION SEQUENCE

a = AX = $\frac{1}{2}$ perimeter (given)
b = ⊥ to AX at X
c = 42° ∠ at A (given)
d = AY = AX
e = bisector of ∠XAY
f = intercept of b with e = 0
g = circle radius P = OX
h = arc radius = altitude (given)
j = bisector of OA
k = intercept of j with OA
l = circle radius = kO = kA

m = arc radius P + Q,
     centre O
n = arc radius P + Q, centre A
p = line (lm) intercept of
     O with g
q = (ln) intercept of A with h
r = pq produced
s = intercept of pq with AY
t = intercept of pq with AX
s = C and t = B

Drawing No.	TITLE: **Construction of triangles.**	NOTE: **Lower case letter sequence gives order of construction.**	SCALE:
G5			0 10 20 30 40 50 60 70 80 mm

19

G6-1: Special properties in quadrilaterals

Square

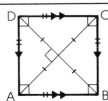

Has four equal sides.
Adjacent sides are at 90° to each other.
Diagonals are equal and bisect each other at 90°.
Opposite sides are parallel.

Rhombus

Has four equal sides.
Opposite sides are parallel.
Opposite angles are equal.
Diagonals bisect each other at 90°.

Trapezium

Has four sides one pair parallel.

Trapezoid

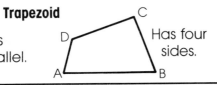

Has four sides.

Rectangle

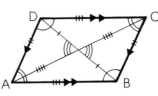

Has four sides.
Adjacent sides are at 90° to each other.
Opposite sides are equal and parallel.
Diagonals are equal and bisect each other but not at 90°.

Parallelogram

Has four sides.
Opposite sides are equal and parallel.
Opposite angles are equal.
Diagonals are not equal but bisect each other.

Cyclic Quadrilateral

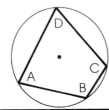

The sum of the two opposite angles of a cyclic quadrilateral is 180°.
$(\angle A + \angle C) = 180° = (\angle B + \angle D)$.

G6-2: To construct a square of given side

Construct a square given that it has a side of 54 mm.

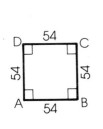

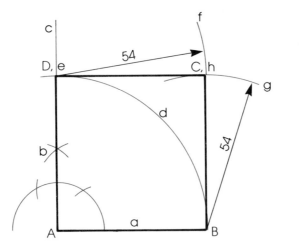

G6-3: To construct a square of given diagonal

Construct a square given that it has a diagonal of 76 mm.

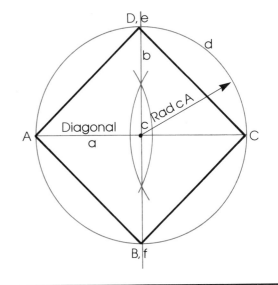

Drawing No.
G6

TITLE: **Special quadrilaterals and their construction. Squares.**

NOTE: **Lower case letter sequence gives order construction.**

SCALE:
0 10 20 30 40 50 60 70 80
mm

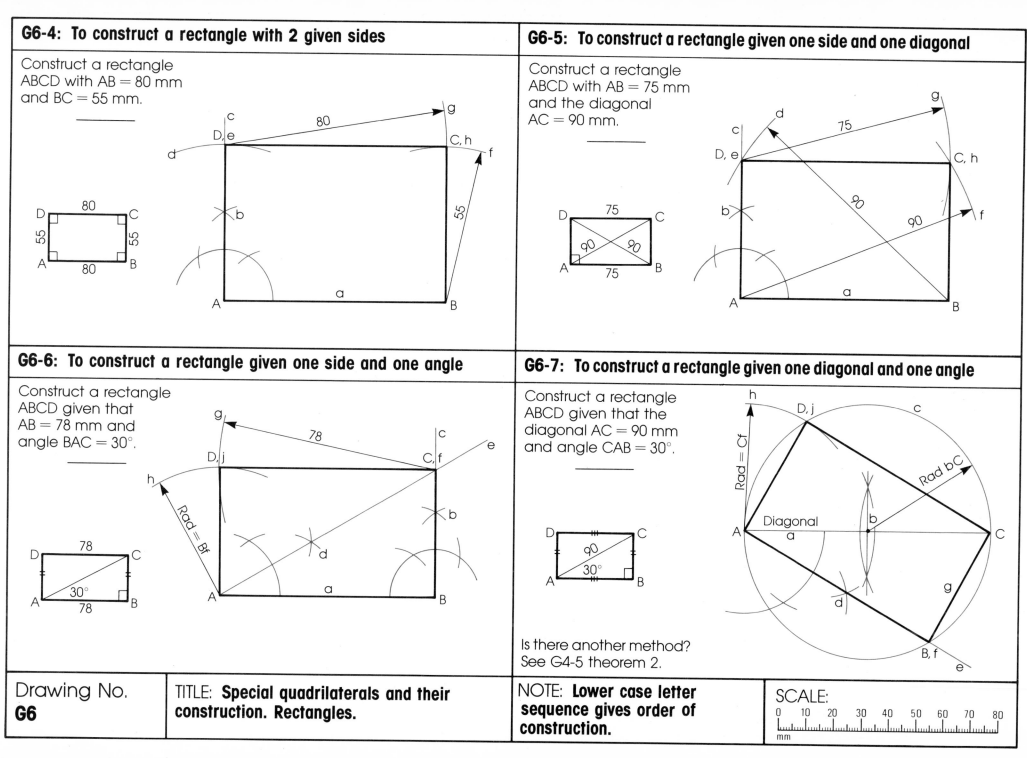

G6-4: To construct a rectangle with 2 given sides

Construct a rectangle
ABCD with AB = 80 mm
and BC = 55 mm.

G6-5: To construct a rectangle given one side and one diagonal

Construct a rectangle
ABCD with AB = 75 mm
and the diagonal
AC = 90 mm.

G6-6: To construct a rectangle given one side and one angle

Construct a rectangle
ABCD given that
AB = 78 mm and
angle BAC = 30°.

G6-7: To construct a rectangle given one diagonal and one angle

Construct a rectangle
ABCD given that the
diagonal AC = 90 mm
and angle CAB = 30°.

Is there another method?
See G4-5 theorem 2.

Drawing No.
G6

TITLE: **Special quadrilaterals and their construction. Rectangles.**

NOTE: **Lower case letter sequence gives order of construction.**

SCALE:
0   10   20   30   40   50   60   70   80
mm

21

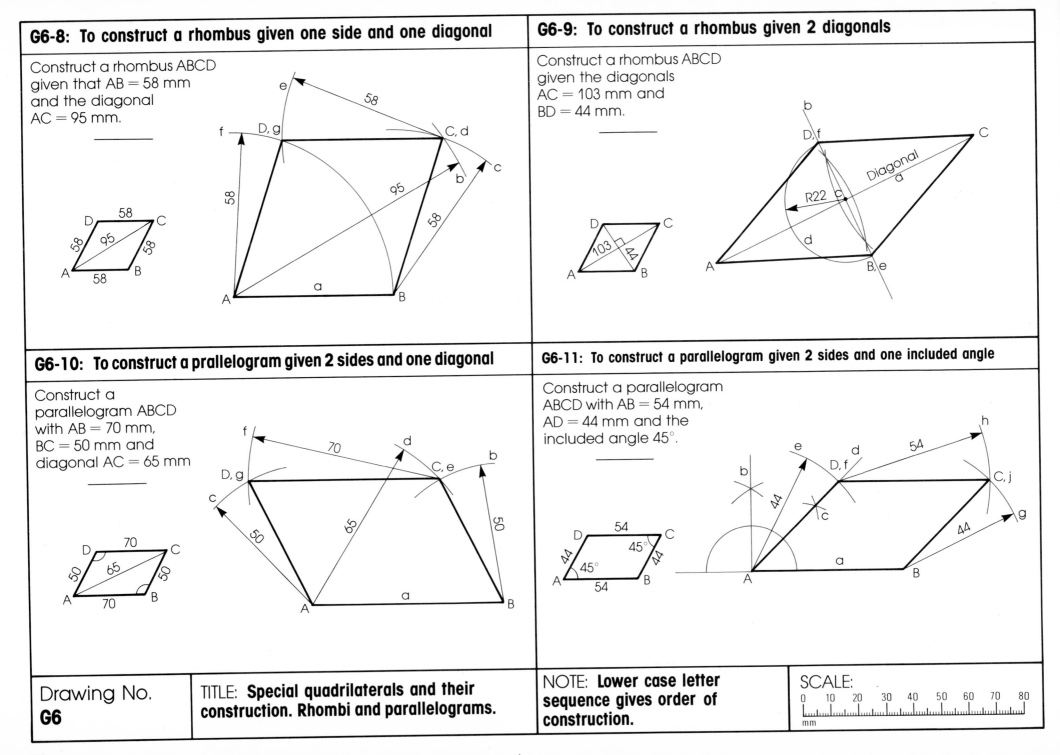

G6-8: To construct a rhombus given one side and one diagonal

Construct a rhombus ABCD given that AB = 58 mm and the diagonal AC = 95 mm.

G6-9: To construct a rhombus given 2 diagonals

Construct a rhombus ABCD given the diagonals AC = 103 mm and BD = 44 mm.

G6-10: To construct a prallelogram given 2 sides and one diagonal

Construct a parallelogram ABCD with AB = 70 mm, BC = 50 mm and diagonal AC = 65 mm

G6-11: To construct a parallelogram given 2 sides and one included angle

Construct a parallelogram ABCD with AB = 54 mm, AD = 44 mm and the included angle 45°.

Drawing No. **G6**

TITLE: **Special quadrilaterals and their construction. Rhombi and parallelograms.**

NOTE: **Lower case letter sequence gives order of construction.**

SCALE:
0 10 20 30 40 50 60 70 80
mm

22

G7-1: To construct a parallelogram given the diagonals and one side

Construct a parallelogram ABCD given the diagonals
AC = 110 mm
and BD = 76 mm
and side
AB = 60 mm.

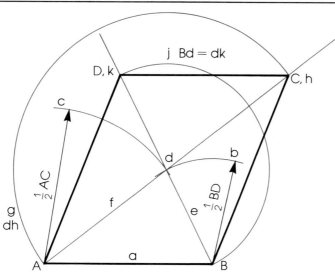
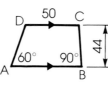

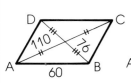

G7-2: To construct a trapezium given 2 angles and 2 sides

Construct a trapezium ABCD given that AB is parallel to CD and they are 44 mm apart.
CD = 50 mm with angle BAD = 60° and angle ABC = 90°.

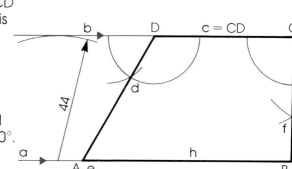

G7-3: To construct a trapezoid

Construct a trapezoid ABCD given AB = 72 mm,
BC = 50 mm,
AC = 60 mm and
AD = 32 mm. Angle ACD = 30° and angle BAD is obtuse.

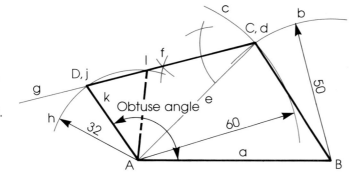

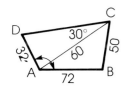

The description of the angle BAD as "obtuse" defines the position of D as "j" and not the possible alternative position of "l", i.e. it uniquely defines the position of D.

G7-4: To construct a trapezoid

Construct a trapezoid ABCD given AB = 60 mm,
BC = 80 mm, CD = 34 mm and diagonal BD = 89 mm
Angle ABC = 60°.

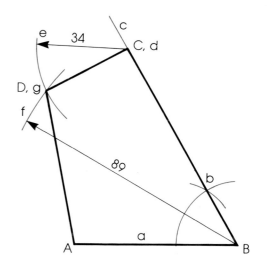

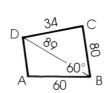

| Drawing No. **G7** | TITLE: **Construction of quadrilaterals.** | NOTE: **Lower case letter sequence gives order of construction.** | SCALE: 0 10 20 30 40 50 60 70 80 mm |

23

G7-5: To construct a triangle given one side and one angle

Construct a triangle having a base of 52 mm and base angle of 30° which also has the same area as a triangle ABC with AB = 52 mm, BC = 60 mm and AC = 54 mm.

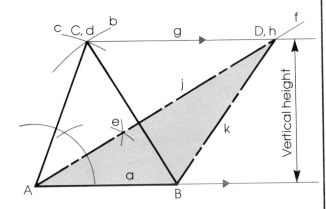

Area of given triangle = $\frac{1}{2}$(base AB × vertical height)

Area of triangle ABD = $\frac{1}{2}$(base AB × vertical height)

△ABC has the same base and vertical height as △ABD, therefore the same area.

G7-6: To construct a triangle given one side and one angle

Construct a triangle having an altitude of 68 mm and one side of 100 mm, equal in area to a triangle ABC with AB = 60 mm, AC = 50 mm and BC = 67 mm.

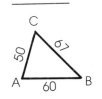

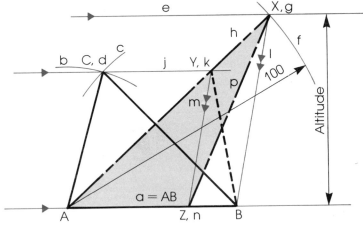

Triangle AXZ has the same area as triangle ABC and also fulfils the altitude and length of side conditions. See G7-7 for proof.

G7-7: To construct a triangle given altitude and base angle

Construct a triangle having an altitude of 70 mm and a base angle of 60°, equal in area to a triangle ABC with AB = 55 mm, AC = 45 mm and BC = 65 mm.

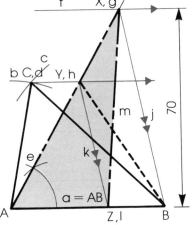

By area, △AYB = △ABC as they have the same base and vertical height. Similarly, △ZYX = △ZYB have same base ZY and the same vertical height, i.e. both triangles are between the parallel lines j and k.

△AYZ + △ZYX = △AYZ + △ZYB

Now △AZX = △AYZ + △ZYX

and △AYB = △AYZ + △ZYB.

*Then △AZX = △AYB.

Hence △AZX = △ABC since △ABC = △AYB (above).

Note: triangle AYZ is common to both △AZX and △AYB and △ZYX = △ZYB.

G7-8: To construct a triangle given base and base angle

Construct a triangle with a base of 40 mm and base angle of 60°, equal in area to a triangle ABC with AB = 65 mm, BC = 75 mm and AC = 45 mm.

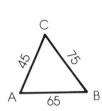

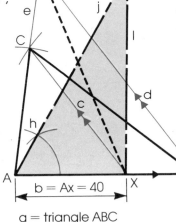

a = triangle ABC

By area, △YCX = △BCX, i.e. both have the same base CX and the same vertical height (both the triangles are between the parallel lines CX and YB).

△AYX = △ACB since △ACX is common to both and △YCX = △BCX. Now △ZAX = △YAX with the same base and vertical height.

∴ △ZAX = △ABC since △AYX = △ABC.

| Drawing No. **G7** | TITLE: **Equivalent areas of triangles.** | NOTE: **Lower case letter sequence gives order of construction.** | SCALE: |

G7-9: To construct a triangle of equal area to a given polygon

Construct any triangle ABC which is equal in area to a polygon PQRST with PQ = 45 mm, SQ = 70 mm, SP = 52 mm, PR = 48 mm, RQ = 33 mm and PT = ST = 30 mm.

△PQS is common to both the triangle ABC and polygon PQRST. △APS = △PTS and △BQS = △QRS, i.e. same bases and vertical heights. Then △PQS + △APS + △BQS = △PQS + △PTS + △QRS ∴ △ABC = polygon PQRST (see G7-5).

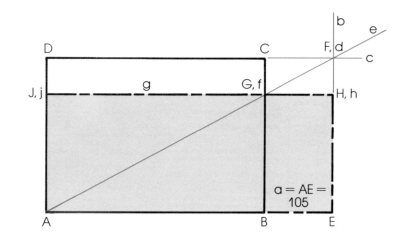

G7-10: To construct a rectangle of equal area to a given triangle

Redraw the triangle ABC which was determined in G7-9 and reduce it to a rectangle of the same area.

f = bisector of Ce

See G2-7 for perpendicular from point C.

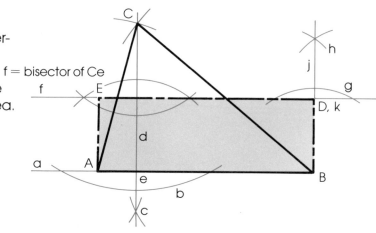

Area of rectangle ABDE = area of triangle ABC

AB × AE = AB × ½ vertical height

G7-11: To construct a rectangle of equal area to another given rectangle

Construct a rectangle which has one side of 105 mm and the same area as a rectangle ABCD with sides AB = 80 mm and BC = 55 mm.

Area of △GCF = area of △GHF (½ rectangle GHFC).

Area of △GJA = area of △GBA (½ rectangle GJAB).

△ADF − (△GCF + △GJA) = △AEF − (△GHF + △GBA), ∴ area JGCD = area HGBE.

Rectangle ABGJ is common to both the given rectangle ABCD and the derived rectangle AEHJ. Since rectangle JGCD = rectangle HGBE (proof given above) then ABGJ + JGCD = ABGT + HGBE, ∴ rectangle ABCD = AEHJ, i.e. given rectangle = derived rectangle AEHJ.

a = AE = 105

| Drawing No. G7 | TITLE: Equivalent areas of rectangles and polygons. | NOTE: Lower case letter sequence gives order of construction. | SCALE: |

G8-1: Definition of Pythagoras' Theorem

Analyse the information and reproduce the figure shown.

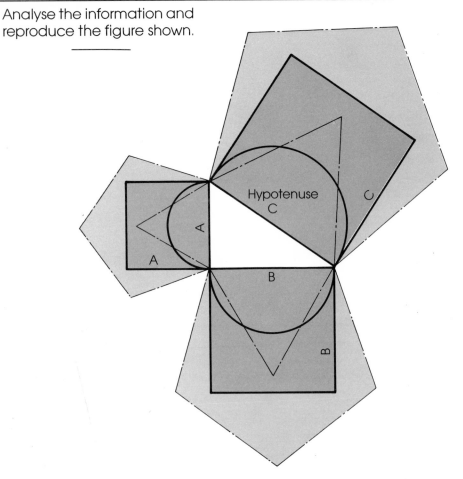

Pythagoras' Theorem: The area of the square on the hypotenuse of a right-angled triangle is equal to the combined areas of the squares on the other 2 sides, i.e. $C^2 = A^2 + B^2$ or by taking roots of both sides $C = \sqrt{A^2 + B^2}$.

Pythagoras also works for areas of any regular figures on the sides of a right-angled triangle, e.g. semicircles, equilateral triangles, pentagons, hexagons, etc.

G8-2: To determine cross-sectional area using Pythagoras' Theorem

Two pipes A and B form a tee junction as shown below. Determine the diameter of pipe C which is required to have the same cross-sectional area (C.S.A.) as both A and B combined.

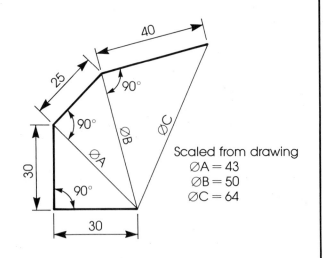

Pipe C from construction of triangle = Ø56

Pipe A Ø25

Pipe B Ø50

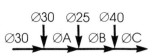

A Ø25

B Ø50

C Ø?

Area of C = area A + area B

Area of a circle = πr^2 or $\dfrac{\pi d^2}{4}$

$$\therefore \ \pi\left(\frac{\emptyset C}{4}\right)^2 = \pi\left(\frac{\emptyset A}{4}\right)^2 + \pi\left(\frac{\emptyset B}{4}\right)^2$$

$$\emptyset C^2 = \emptyset A^2 + \emptyset B^2$$

$$\emptyset C = \sqrt{25^2 + 50^2}$$

$$\emptyset C = 55.90$$

by calculation

Scale: 1:1

G8-3: To determine pipe diameters using Pythagoras' Theorem

Shown below are several pipes feeding together at varying intervals. Determine the diameters of the intermediate pipes A, B and C if the velocity of the fluid in the pipes is to remain constant.

Ø30   Ø25   Ø40

Ø30   ØA   ØB   ØC

Scaled from drawing
ØA = 43
ØB = 50
ØC = 64

Drawing No. **G8**

TITLE: **Pythagoras' Theorem.**

G8-4: To determine pipe diameter using Pythagoras

Pipe A is split into 2 pipes B and C which have a combined surface area equal to pipe A, as shown below. Determine the diameter of pipe C.

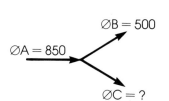

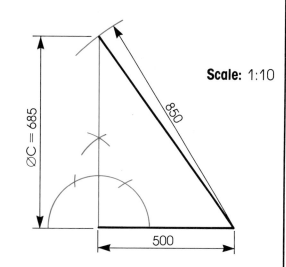

Scale: 1:10

G8-5: Graphical determination of roots using Pythagoras

Analyse and reproduce the figures shown.

Examples shown: $\sqrt{2}$, $\sqrt{3}$, $\sqrt{4}$, $\sqrt{5}$, $\sqrt{8}$, $\sqrt{10}$, $\sqrt{13}$, $\sqrt{20}$.

Scale: 1 unit = 10 mm.

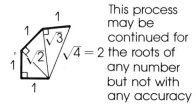

$$C = \sqrt{1^2 + 1^2}$$
$$C = 1.41, \text{ i.e.}$$
on drawing; see scale

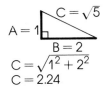

$$C = \sqrt{2}$$
$$(\sqrt{2})^2 = 2$$
$$E = \sqrt{C^2 + D^2}$$
$$E = \sqrt{2 + 1}$$
$$E = \sqrt{3} = 1.73$$

This process may be continued for the roots of any number but not with any accuracy

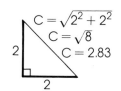

$$C = \sqrt{2^2 + 2^2}$$
$$C = \sqrt{8}$$
$$C = 2.83$$

$$C = \sqrt{5}$$
$$C = \sqrt{1^2 + 2^2}$$
$$C = 2.24$$

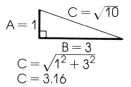

$$C = \sqrt{10}$$
$$C = \sqrt{1^2 + 3^2}$$
$$C = 3.16$$

G8-6: To determine $\sqrt{54}$

By construction determine the square root of 54, i.e. $\sqrt{54}$.

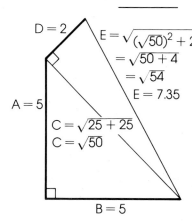

$$E = \sqrt{(\sqrt{50})^2 + 2^2}$$
$$= \sqrt{50 + 4}$$
$$= \sqrt{54}$$
$$E = 7.35$$

$$C = \sqrt{25 + 25}$$
$$C = \sqrt{50}$$

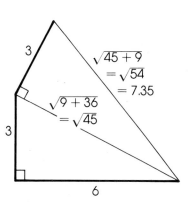

$$\sqrt{45 + 9} = \sqrt{54} = 7.35$$
$$\sqrt{9 + 36} = \sqrt{45}$$

Two of the many possible solutions for $\sqrt{54}$.

Scale: 1 unit = 10 mm.

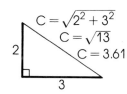

$$C = \sqrt{2^2 + 3^2}$$
$$C = \sqrt{13}$$
$$C = 3.61$$

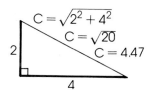

$$C = \sqrt{2^2 + 4^2}$$
$$C = \sqrt{20}$$
$$C = 4.47$$

| Drawing No. **G8** | TITLE: **Pythagoras' Theorem used to determine roots.** | | SCALE: |

G8-7: To determine $\sqrt{155}$

By construction determine $\sqrt{155}$.

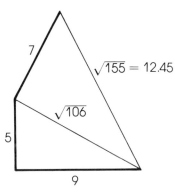

Scale: 1 unit = 5 mm.

G8-8: To determine the equivalent area of a rectangle using Pythagoras

Draw a rectangle 65 mm × 28 mm and
by construction reduce it to a square
of equivalent area.

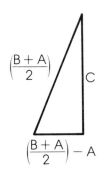

$$\left(\frac{B+A}{2}\right)^2 = C^2 + \left(\left(\frac{B+A}{2}\right) - A\right)^2$$

$$C^2 = \left(\tfrac{1}{4}B^2 + \tfrac{1}{2}AB + \tfrac{1}{4}A^2\right) - \left(\tfrac{1}{4}B^2 - \tfrac{1}{2}AB + \tfrac{1}{4}A^2\right)$$

$$C^2 = A \times B \text{ construction proved}$$

By Pythagoras

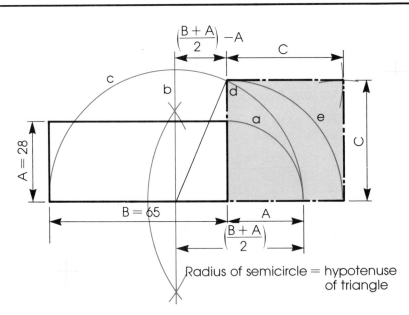

Radius of semicircle = hypotenuse
of triangle

Drawing No. **G8**	TITLE: **Pythagoras' Theorem used to determine roots and areas.**	NOTE: **Lower case letter sequence gives order of construction.**	SCALE:

G8-9: To determine the equivalent area of a triangle using Pythagoras

Draw a triangle ABC, AB = 70 mm, BC = 112 mm and AC = 66 mm. Reduce it to a square of equal area.

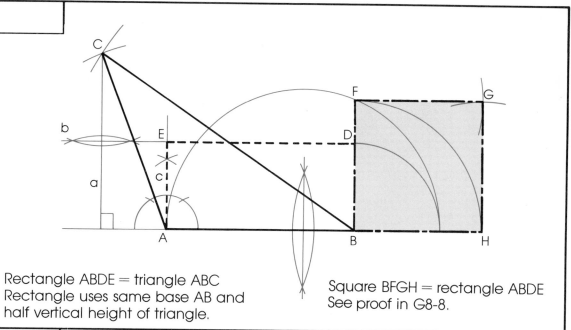

Rectangle ABDE = triangle ABC
Rectangle uses same base AB and half vertical height of triangle.

Square BFGH = rectangle ABDE
See proof in G8-8.

G8-10: To determine the equivalent area of a hexagon using Pythagoras

Reduce the irregular hexagon shown below to a square of equal area.

AB = 37	BC = 38	AC = 65
AF = 37	BF = 62	FE = 34
BE = 70	ED = 45	CD = 25

See G7-9 for reduction of a polygon to a triangle then see G8-9 and G8-8.

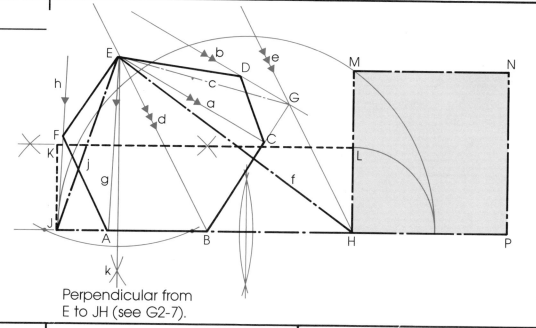

Perpendicular from E to JH (see G2-7).

Drawing No. **G8**	TITLE: **Pythagoras' Theorem used to determine areas.**	NOTE: **Lower case letter sequence gives order of construction.**	SCALE: 0 10 20 30 40 50 60 70 80 mm

29

Worksheets for G9 to G13

G9 INCREASE AND REDUCTION BY LINEAR AND AREA PROPORTION.

G9-1 Construct the quadrilateral shown in Fig 1 and produce a similar figure with the sides increased in length by the ratio of 5:3 over the given quadrilateral ABCD.

G9-2 Draw the polygon shown in Fig 2 using set square combinations and ruler only. Construct a similar polygon to the one given but having its sides 1.4 times longer than the polygon ABCDEFG.

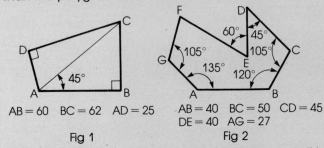

AB = 60 BC = 62 AD = 25

Fig 1

AB = 40 BC = 50 CD = 45
DE = 40 AG = 27

Fig 2

G9-3 Draw the shape illustrated in Fig 3 and reduce it to a similar figure having linear proportions $\frac{2}{3}$ that of the original shape.

G9-4 Draw Fig 4 full size and construct a similar polygon with its sides reduced in length by the ratio of 3:5.

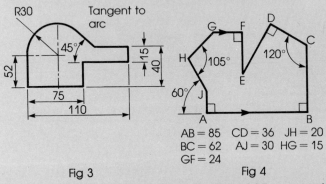

Fig 3

AB = 85 CD = 36 JH = 20
BC = 62 AJ = 30 HG = 15
GF = 24

Fig 4

G9-5 Draw a rectangle having sides of 35 mm and 60 mm and by construction produce a rectangle having the same proportions but double the area.

G9-6 Draw Fig 5 full size and construct a similar polygon which has its area increased in the ratio of 3:2 compared with the given figure.

G9-7 Draw a regular hexagon having a side of 50 mm and by construction reduce it to a similar figure having half the area.

G9-8 Produce the polygon given in Fig 6 full size and reduce it to a similar figure with its area in the ratio of 4:11.

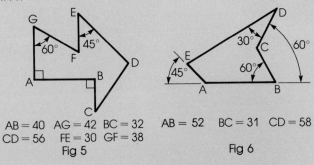

AB = 40 AG = 42 BC = 32
CD = 56 FE = 30 GF = 38

Fig 5

AB = 52 BC = 31 CD = 58

Fig 6

G10 CONSTRUCTION OF REGULAR POLYGONS.

G10-1 Construct a regular hexagon resting on a flat given: that the hexagon has a side of 35 mm, or its distance across corners (A/C) = 70 mm, or that it is circumscribed by a circle ⌀70 mm.

G10-2 Construct a regular hexagon resting on a flat given either that the hexagon has a distance across flats (A/F) = 60 mm or that it is inscribed by a circle ⌀60 mm.

G10-3 Construct a regular octagon given either that it has a distance A/C = 80 mm or that its circumscribing circle has a ⌀ = 80 mm.

G10-4 Construct a regular octagon given either that its distance A/F = 70 mm or that it lies in a square which has a side of 70 mm or is inscribed by a circle ⌀70 mm.

G10-5 Construct a regular pentagon which is circumscribed by a circle ⌀ 70 mm.

G10-6 Construct a regular pentagon which has a side of 50 mm.

G10-7 Construct a regular heptagon in a circle ⌀110, i.e. the circumscribing circle.

G10-8 Construct a regular heptagon given that it has a side of 60 mm.

G10-9 Construct a nonagon which is circumscribed by a circle ⌀120 mm.

G10-10 Construct a regular nonagon given that it has a side of 44 mm.

G11 PLAIN AND DIAGONAL SCALES.

G11-1 Draw lines to represent the following lengths to the scales stated.
(a) 120 mm at a scale of 1:2,
(b) 2.350 m at 1:50,
(c) 355 mm at 1:10,
(d) 1.57 m at 1:20,
(e) 29.5 mm at 2:1,
(g) 2 km at 1:25 000.

G11-2 Draw a plain scale to measure up to 8 m at a scale of 1:50 with increments of 1 m and 100 mm.

G11-3 Produce a plain scale which allows measurement by direct transfer with an accuracy to the nearest 100 m when reading from a map which is drawn to a scale of 1:25 000. The scale must have a range of 4 km.

G11-4 Draw a plain scale of 1:4 with a range of 600 mm and having increments of 100 mm, 25 mm and 5 mm.

G11-5 Produce a diagonal scale as an alternative to the plain scale described in G11-4 and illustrate measurements of 230 mm, 365 mm and 495 mm.

G11-6 Produce a diagonal scale of 2:1 with a range of 80 mm and increments of 10 mm, 2 mm and 0.5 mm. Illustrate lengths of 23.5 mm and 38.5 mm.

G11-7 Draw a diagonal scale of 1:1 having a range of 200 mm and increments of 10 mm, 5 mm and 0.5 mm. Illustrate lengths of 43.5 mm, 46.5 mm and 47.5 mm.

G11-8 It is required that the distances on a map drawn to a scale of 6 inches to the mile are to be read directly in metric from a diagonal scale. The scale is required to have increments of 1 km, 100 m and 10 m and a range of 2 km. 6 inches to 1 mile = 1:10 560, 1.61 km = 1 mile, 25.4 mm = 1 inch.

G12 TANGENTS AND CIRCLES IN CONTACT.

G12-1 Reproduce the shape given in Fig 1 full size. Show the construction used to determine the centre of arc, R40.

G12-2 Determine the radius of the circle which passes through the 3 points P_1, P_2 and P_3, shown in Fig 2.

G12-3 Revision of G3-5.

G12-4 Revision of G4-5.

G12-5 Construct a tangent to the circle shown in Fig 3. Point P which is also shown is on the tangent.

G12-6 Construct the common tangent to the circles shown in Fig 4.

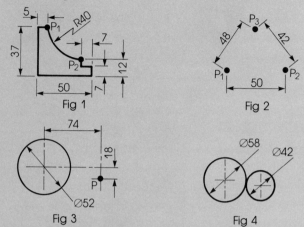

Fig 1

Fig 2

Fig 3

Fig 4

G12-7 Construct the common tangent to the circles shown in Fig 5.

G12-8 Construct the common tangent to the circles shown in Fig. 6.

G12-9 Construct the transverse common tangent to the circles shown in Fig 7.

G12-10 Construct the common tangent to the circles shown in Fig 8.

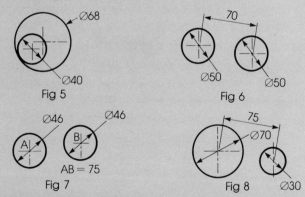

Fig 5

Fig 6

Fig 7

Fig 8

G12-11 Construct the transverse tangent to the circles shown in Fig 9.

G12-12 Determine the escribed circle of the triangle shown in Fig 10. The circle touches AB and AC produced, and BC.

G12-13 Construct the centre of the arc R22 to join the lines shown in Fig 11. Determine points of tangency.

G12-14 Join the line and circle in Fig 12 by an arc of radius 20 mm.

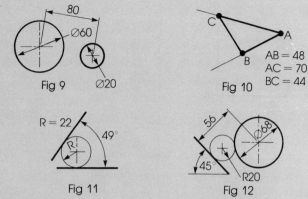

Fig 9

Fig 10
AB = 48
AC = 70
BC = 44

Fig 11

Fig 12

G12-15 Join point P to the circle in Fig 13 by an arc of radius 20 mm.

G12-16 Join the 2 circles in Fig 14 by an arc of radius 35 mm.

G12-17 Join the 2 circles in Fig 15 by an arc of radius 60 mm.

G12-18 Join the 2 circles in Fig 16 by an arc of radius 50 mm.

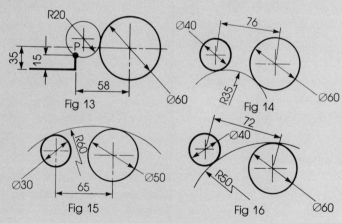

Fig 13

Fig 14

Fig 15

Fig 16

G13 PROBLEMS ON TANGENTS

G13-1 A point P is 100 mm from the centre, O, of a circle Ø60 mm. Construct: (a) both of the tangents from the circle to pass through point P, (b) the 2 circles which have both the tangents to circle O in common and also touch circle O, and (c) the tangential points of the 2

tangents with the larger of the 2 circles constructed in part (b).

G13-2 Fig 1 shows the layout for a paper feed mechanism. The paper is fed over the pressure pad A, round the guide roll B and onto the winding drum C. Construct the layout to a scale of 1:2 with drum C initially empty. Show all the tangential points where the paper comes into contact with, and leaves, the curved surfaces.

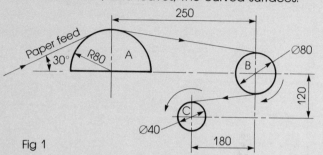

Fig 1

G13-3 Fig 2 shows 2 pulleys A and B, which rotate clockwise. They are connected by a belt; pulley A drives pulley B and the jockey pulley C keeps the belt tight as shown. Determine the points of contact between the belt and the 3 pulleys and also draw the belt which is tangential to the 3 pulleys. Show all tangential points.

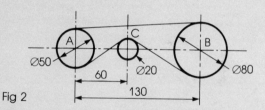

Fig 2

G13-4 Draw circles A and B as shown in Fig 3. Construct: (a) the tangents X and Y by first determining the tangential points P_1, P_2, P_3 and P_4, and (b) construct the centre of, and draw, the circle which is tangential to circle B and the 2 tangents constructed in (a).

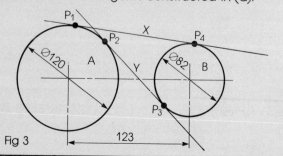

Fig 3

G9-1: To increase the linear proportions of a quadrilateral

Construct the quadrilateral shown (right) and produce a similar figure with the sides increased in length by the ratio of 5:3 over the given quadrilateral ABCD.

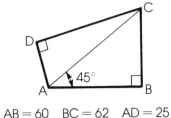

AB = 60   BC = 62   AD = 25

See G4-5 for construction of triangle ADC

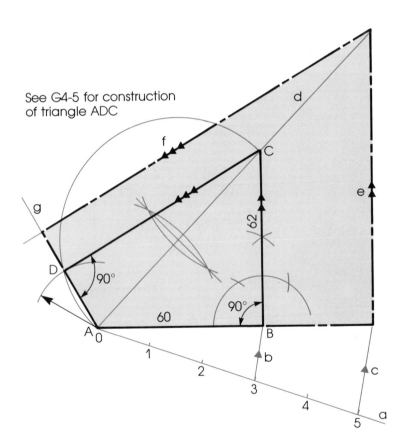

G9-2: To increase the linear proportions of a polygon

Draw the polygon shown (right) using set square combinations and ruler only. Construct a similar polygon but having its sides 1.4 times longer than the polygon ABCDEFG.

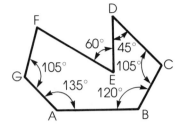

AB = 40   BC = 50   CD = 45
DE = 40   AG = 27

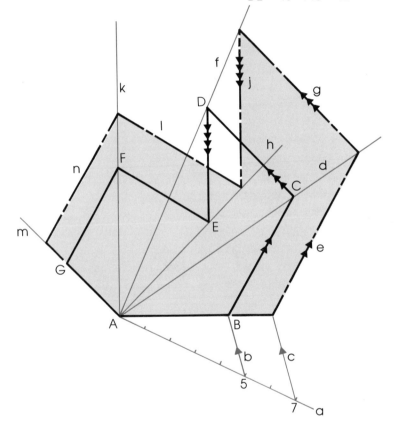

| Drawing No. **G9** | TITLE: **Increasing by linear proportions.** | NOTE: **Lower case letter sequence gives order of construction.** | SCALE: |

0 10 20 30 40 50 60 70 80
mm

32

G9-3: To reduce the linear proportions of a given shape

Draw the shape illustrated (right) and reduce it to a similar figure having linear proportions $\frac{2}{3}$ that of the original shape.

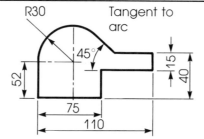

R30   Tangent to arc

45°
52
75
110
15
40

Centre U, of reduced arc, is obtained by intersection of line S with t

See G2-7 to determine the normal and hence tangential point T₁

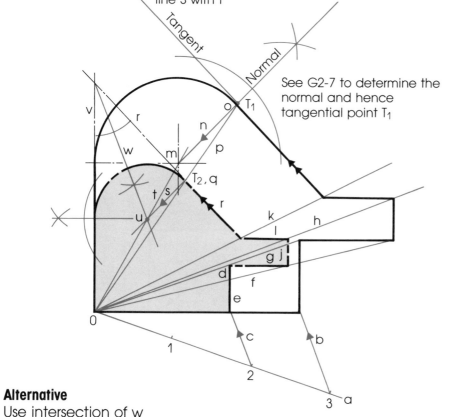

Alternative
Use intersection of w with s or t to get u.

G9-4: To reduce the linear proportions of a polygon

Draw the figure (right) full size and construct a similar polygon with its sides reduced in length by the ratio of 3:5.

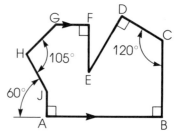

105°   120°   60°

AB = 85   CD = 36   JH = 20
BC = 62   AJ = 30   HG = 15
GF = 24

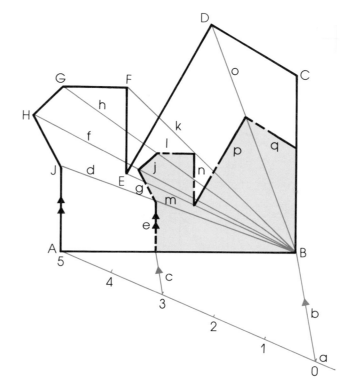

Drawing No.
G9

TITLE: **Reducing by linear proportions.**

NOTE: **Lower case letter sequence gives order of construction.**

SCALE:
0 10 20 30 40 50 60 70 80
mm

G9-5: To increase the area proportion of a rectangle

Draw a rectangle having sides of 35 mm and 60 mm and by construction produce a rectangle of the same proportions but double the area.

_____

See G8-8 for origins of the construction method.

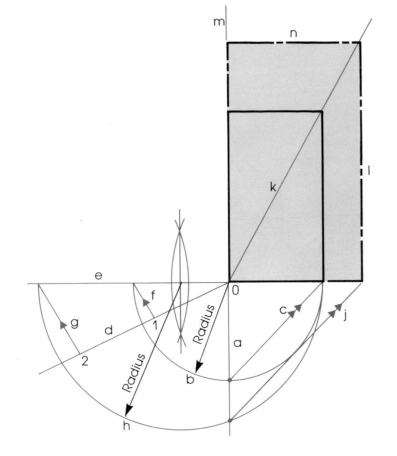

G9-6: To increase the area proportion of a polygon

Draw the figure (right) full size.
Construct a similar polygon which
has its area increased in the ratio of 3:2.

_____

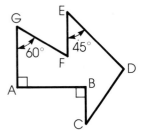

AB = 40   AG = 42   BC = 32
CD = 56   FE = 30   GF = 38

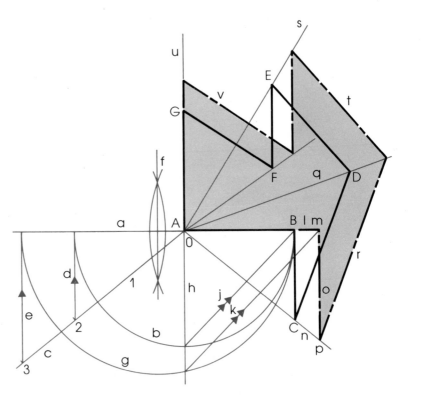

Drawing No.	TITLE: **Increasing by area proportion.**
G9	

NOTE: **Lower case letter sequence gives order of construction.**

SCALE:

0 10 20 30 40 50 60 70 80

mm

G9-7: To reduce the area proportion of a hexagon

Draw a regular hexagon having a side of 50 mm and by construction reduce it to a similar figure of half the area.

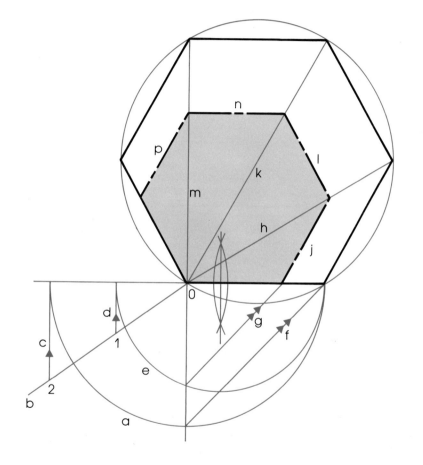

G9-8: To reduce the area proportion of a polygon

Produce the polygon (right) full size. Then reduce it to a similar figure with its area in the ratio of 4:11.

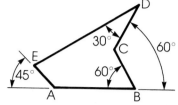

AB = 52   BC = 31   CD = 58

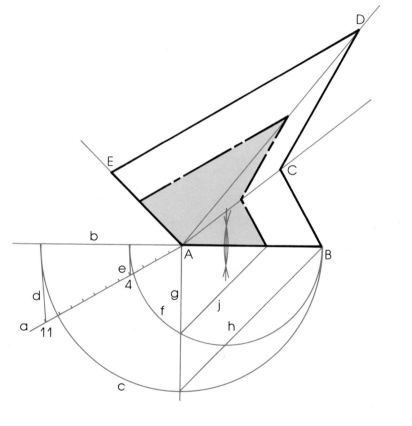

Drawing No.	TITLE: **Reducing by area proportion.**	NOTE: **Lower case letter sequence gives order of construction.**	SCALE:
G9			0 10 20 30 40 50 60 70 80 mm

G10-1: To construct a regular hexagon

Construct a regular hexagon resting on a flat given: that the hexagon has a side of 35 mm, or its distance across corners, A/C = 70 mm, or it is circumscribed by a circle of diameter 70 mm.

———

A hexagon has 6 sides.

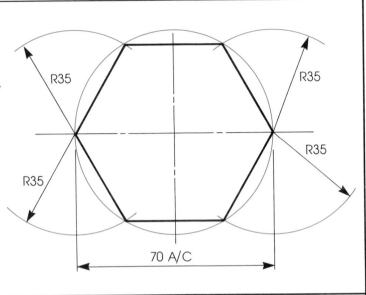

R35
R35
R35
R35
70 A/C

G10-2: To construct a regular hexagon

Construct a regular hexagon resting on a flat given either that the hexagon has a distance across flats, A/F = 60 mm, or that it is inscribed by a circle having a diameter of 60 mm.

———

The 60° angle gives tangential point C from B and the intersection of the tangent gives points E and D. CD is the side of the hexagon. 60° = 360°/number of sides.

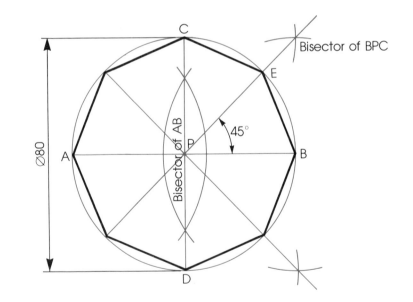

Alternative use of DE from P
DE
R = 60 A/F
DE
B D
60°
C
Bisector of AB
P
E
90°
A
R = 60 A/F
DE

G10-3: To construct a regular octagon

Construct a regular octagon given either that it has a distance A/C = 80 mm or that its circumscribing circle has a diameter of 80 mm.

———

An octagon has 8 sides.

$$\text{Angle EPB} = \frac{360°}{\text{number of corners}} = \frac{360°}{8} = 45°$$

C
Bisector of BPC
E
⌀80
Bisector of AB
A P 45° B
D

| Drawing No. **G10** | TITLE: **Construction of regular polygons. Hexagons and octagons.** | NOTE: **Letter sequence gives order of construction.** | SCALE: 0 10 20 30 40 50 60 70 80 mm |

G10-4: To construct a regular octagon

Construct a regular octagon given either that its distance A/F = 70 mm or that it lies in a square which has a side of 70 mm or is inscribed by a circle of diameter 70 mm.

$R = \frac{1}{2}AC$

□70 A/F

G10-5: To construct a regular pentagon

Construct a regular pentagon which is circumscribed by a circle of diameter 70 mm.

A pentagon has 5 sides

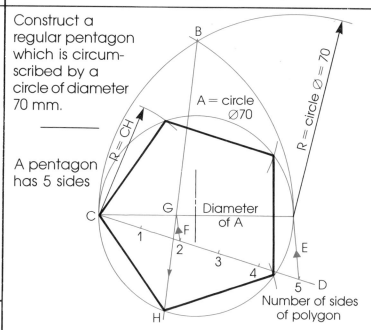

A = circle Ø70

R = CH

R = circle Ø = 70

Diameter of A

Number of sides of polygon

Intersection of BG produced with circle A gives point H.
Step off CH round circle.
H determines length of side CH.

Always use point 2 to get point G regardless of number of sides of polygon.

G10-6: To construct a regular pentagon

Construct a regular pentagon which has a side of 50 mm.

Point E4 is the centre of a square (4 sides)
Point F6 is the centre of a hexagon (6 sides)
Point G5 is the centre of circle H, i.e. centre of the pentagon (5 sides).

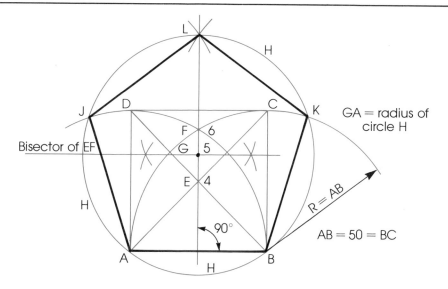

Bisector of EF

GA = radius of circle H

R = AB

AB = 50 = BC

90°

| Drawing No. G10 | TITLE: **Construction of regular polygons. Octagons and pentagons.** | NOTE: **Constructions G10-5 and G10-6 are only approximate. Letter sequence gives order of construction.** | SCALE: 0 10 20 30 40 50 60 70 80 mm |

G10-7: To construct a regular heptagon

Construct a regular heptagon in a circle of diameter 110 mm, i.e. the circumscribing circle.

———

A heptagon or septagon has 7 sides.

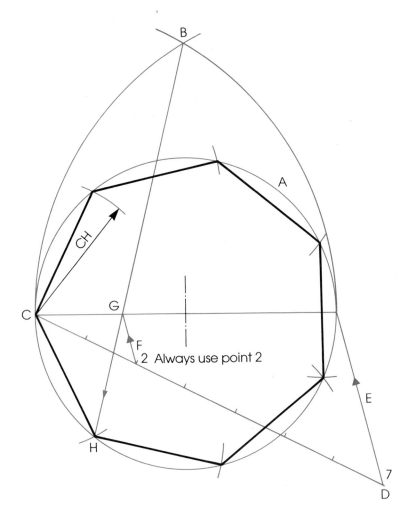

G10-8: To construct a regular heptagon

Construct a regular heptagon given that it has a side of 60 mm.

———

Point H7 is the centre of the heptagon and is obtained by extrapolation using the distance E4 to F6 stepped off from G5.

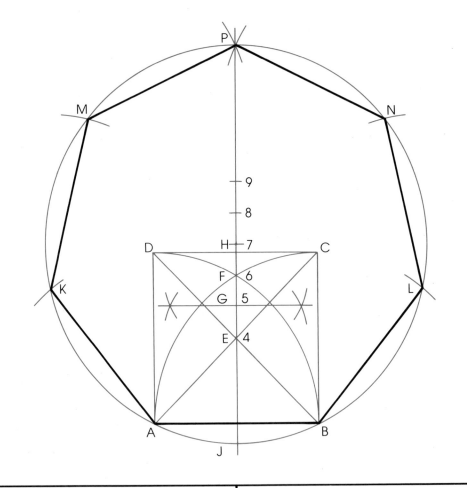

Drawing No. **G10**	TITLE: **Construction of regular polygons.** **Heptagons.**	NOTE: **Constructions G10-7 and G10-8 are only approximate.** **Letter sequence gives order of construction.**	SCALE:

SCALE:
0 10 20 30 40 50 60 70 80
mm

G10-9: To construct a regular nonagon

Construct a regular nonagon which is circumscribed by a circle of diameter 120 mm.

A nonagon has 9 sides.

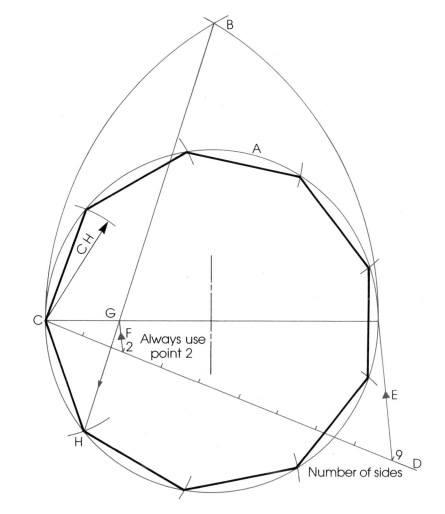

G10-10: To construct a regular nonagon

Construct a regular nonagon given that it has a side of 44 mm.

Point F9 is the centre of the nonagon determined as in G10-6 or by the intersection of the bisectors E of AB and D of BC. The exterior angle

$$\theta = \frac{360}{\text{number of sides of polygon}}$$

and is produced using a protractor.

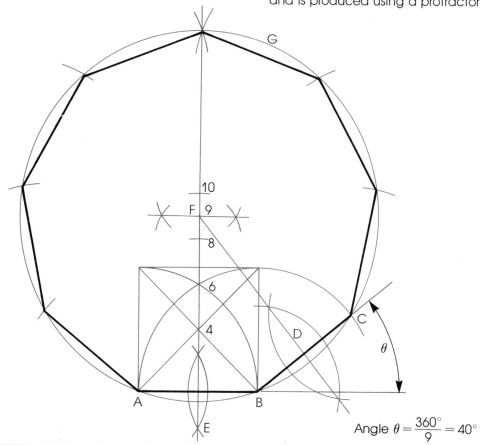

Angle $\theta = \frac{360°}{9} = 40°$

Drawing No. **G10**	TITLE: **Construction of regular polygons. Nonagons.**	NOTE: **Constructions G10-9 and G10-10 are only approximate. Letter sequence gives order of construction.**	SCALE:

SCALE:
0 10 20 30 40 50 60 70 80
mm

G11-1: To represent lengths to given scales

Draw lines to represent the following lengths to the scales stated.

(a) 120 mm at a scale of 1:2,
(b) 2.350 m at 1:50,
(c) 355 mm at 1:10,
(d) 1.57 m at 1:20,
(e) 29.5 mm at 2:1,
(f) 2 km at 1:25 000.

(a) Scale length $= 120\ mm \times \dfrac{1}{2} = 60\ mm$ The line shown represents 120 mm drawn to a scale of 1:2, i.e. $\frac{1}{2}$ size

|←——————— 120 ———————→|

Scale: 1:2

(b) Scale length $= 2.35 \times 1000 \times \dfrac{1}{50} = 47\ mm$ Multiply by 1000 to change metres to millimetres

|←——————— 2.35 m ———————→|

Scale: 1:50

(c) Scale length $= 355 \times \dfrac{1}{10} = 35.5\ mm$

|←——————— 355 ———————→|

Scale: 1:10

(d) Scale length $= 1.57 \times 1000 \times \dfrac{1}{20} = 78.5\ mm$

|←——————————— 1.57 m ———————————→|

Scale: 1:20

(e) Scale length $= 29.5 \times \dfrac{2}{1} = 59\ mm$, i.e. twice full size

|←——————— 29.5 ———————→|

Scale: 2:1

(f) Scale length $= 2 \times 1000 \times 1000 \times \dfrac{1}{25\ 000} = 80\ mm$

|←——————————— 2 km ———————————→|

Scale: 1:25 000

Note: 1000 millimetres = 1 metre and 1000 metres = 1 kilometre

G11-2: To construct a plain scale

Draw a plain scale to measure up to 8 m at a scale of 1:50 with increments of 1 m and 100 mm.

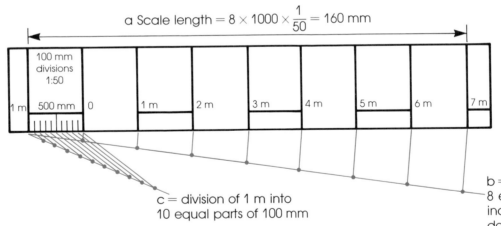

a Scale length $= 8 \times 1000 \times \dfrac{1}{50} = 160\ mm$

100 mm divisions 1:50

1 m | 500 mm | 0 | 1 m | 2 m | 3 m | 4 m | 5 m | 6 m | 7 m

b = division of scale length into 8 equal parts, i.e. 8 by 1 m scale increments. This can be done by direct transfer

c = division of 1 m into 10 equal parts of 100 mm

Plain scale: Given, scale 1:50, range 8 m, increments 1 m and 100 mm.

| Drawing No. **G11** | TITLE: **Plain scales.** | NOTE: **Recommended scales to B.S. 308 and B.S. 1347** 1000:1, 500:1, 200:1, 50:1, 20:1, 10:1, 5:1, 2:1, 1:1, 1:2, 1:10, 1:20, 1:50, 1:100 etc. | SCALE: 0 10 20 30 40 50 60 70 80 mm |

40

G11-3: To construct a plain scale

Produce a plain scale which allows measurement by direct transfer with an accuracy to the nearest 100 m when reading from a map which is drawn to a scale of 1:25 000. The scale must have a range of 4 km.

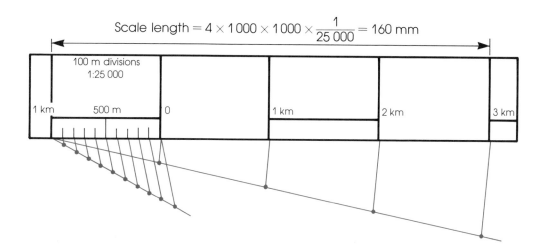

Scale length $= 4 \times 1\,000 \times 1\,000 \times \dfrac{1}{25\,000} = 160$ mm

100 m divisions 1:25 000

1 km   500 m   0   1 km   2 km   3 km

Plain scale: Given, scale = 1:25000, range = 4 km, increments 1 km and 100 m.

G11-4: To construct a plain scale

Draw a plain scale of 1:4 with a range of 600 mm and having increments of 100 mm, 25 mm and 5 mm.

Note: the small increments are difficult to focus on and construct. See G11-5 for better alternative.

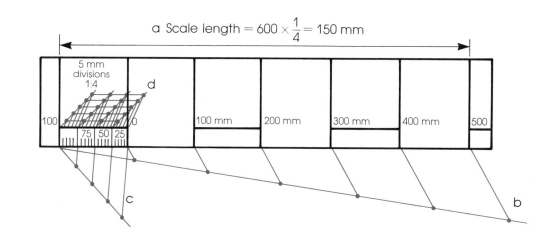

a Scale length $= 600 \times \dfrac{1}{4} = 150$ mm

5 mm divisions 1:4

d

100   0   100 mm   200 mm   300 mm   400 mm   500

75 50 25

c   b

Plain scale: Given, scale = 1:4, range = 600 mm, increments 100 mm, 25 mm and 5 mm.

Drawing No. **G11**	TITLE: **Plain scales.**	NOTE: **Lower case letter sequence gives order of construction.**	SCALE: 0 10 20 30 40 50 60 70 80 mm

G11-5: To construct a diagonal scale

Produce a diagonal scale as an alternative to the plain scale described in G11-4. Illustrate measurements of 230 mm, 365 mm and 495 mm.

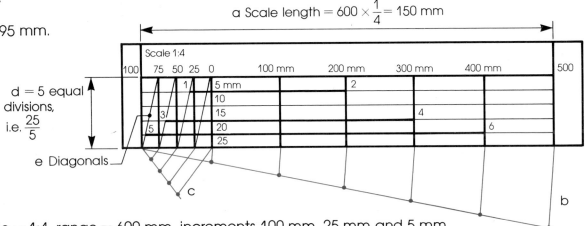

a Scale length $= 600 \times \frac{1}{4} = 150$ mm

d = 5 equal divisions, i.e. $\frac{25}{5}$

e Diagonals

1 to 2 = 200 + 25 + 5 = 230 mm

3 to 4 = 300 + 50 + 15 = 365 mm
5 to 6 = 400 + 75 + 20 = 495 mm
Lengths illustrated on scale

Diagonal scale: Given, scale = 1:4, range = 600 mm, increments 100 mm, 25 mm and 5 mm.

G11-6: To construct a diagonal scale

Produce a diagonal scale of 2:1 with a range of 80 mm and increments of 10 mm, 2 mm and 0.5 mm. Illustrate lengths of 23.5 mm and 38.5 mm.

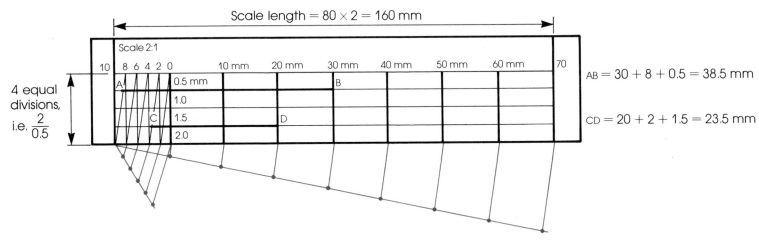

Scale length $= 80 \times 2 = 160$ mm

4 equal divisions, i.e. $\frac{2}{0.5}$

AB = 30 + 8 + 0.5 = 38.5 mm

CD = 20 + 2 + 1.5 = 23.5 mm

Diagonal scale: Given, scale = 2:1, range = 80 mm, increments 10 mm, 2 mm and 0.5 mm.

| Drawing No. G11 | TITLE: **Diagonal scales.** | NOTE: **Lower case letter sequence gives order of construction.** | SCALE: |

42

G11-7: To construct a diagonal scale

Draw a diagonal scale with the range and increments specified.
Illustrate lengths of 43.5 mm, 46.5 mm and 47.5 mm.
Given, scale = 1:1, range 200 mm, increments 10 mm, 5 mm, 0.5 mm.

Scale length = 200 × 1 = 200 mm

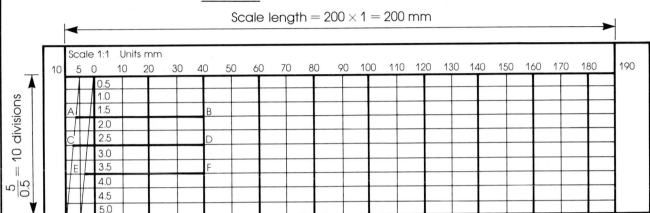

Alternative: Increments 20 mm, 4 mm, 0.5 mm.

$$AB = 40 + 5 + 1.5 = 46.5 \text{ mm}$$

$$CD = 40 + 5 + 2.5 = 47.5 \text{ mm}$$

$$EF = 40 + 0 + 3.5 = 43.5 \text{ mm}$$

GH = 46.5
JK = 43.5

G11-8: To construct a map scale

The distances on a map drawn to a scale of 6 inches to the mile are to be read directly in metric from a diagonal scale. Construct a suitable diagonal scale having a range of 2 km and increments of 1 km, 100 m and 10 m. You may find the following information useful:
 6 inches = 1 mile, i.e. 1:10560
 25.4 mm = 1 inch
 1.61 km = 1 mile.

Scale length by proportional construction 152.4 mm = 1 mile = 1.61 km e.g. $\frac{a}{b} = \frac{d}{c} = \frac{f}{e}$

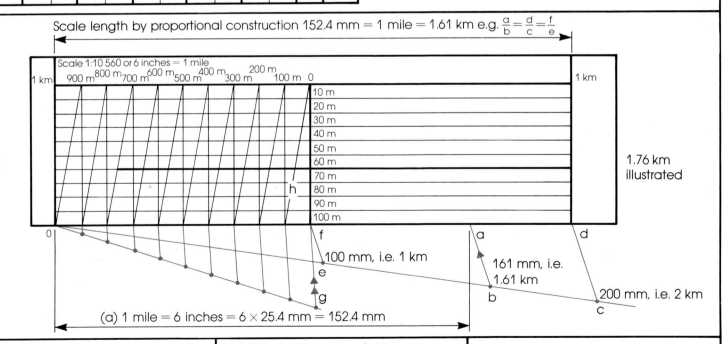

1.76 km illustrated

100 mm, i.e. 1 km

161 mm, i.e. 1.61 km

200 mm, i.e. 2 km

(a) 1 mile = 6 inches = 6 × 25.4 mm = 152.4 mm

| Drawing No. **G11** | TITLE: **Diagonal scales.** | NOTE: **Lower case letter sequence gives order of construction.** | SCALE: |

43

G12-1: To join 2 points by an arc using triangulation

Reproduce the shape given below full size. Show the construction used to determine the centre of arc, R40.

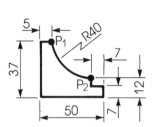

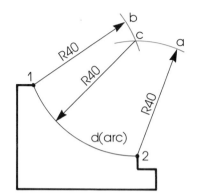

This is a revision of G3-3 and G4-7.

G12-2: To determine the radius of a circle touching 3 points

Determine the radius of the circle which passes through the 3 points P₁, P₂ and P₃ shown below.

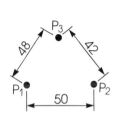

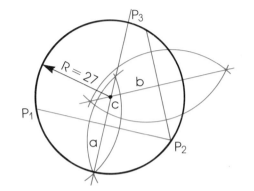

See G3-6.

G12-3: To construct a tangent — revision of G3-5

Construct a tangent to a point P on a circle of diameter 48 mm.

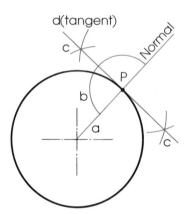

G12-4: Revision of G4-5

Any angle at the vertex of a triangle in a semicircle is 90°.

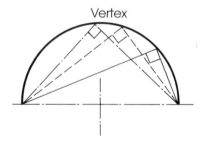

Vertex

| Drawing No. **G12** | TITLE: **Tangents and circles in contact.** |

NOTE: **Lower case letter sequence gives order of construction.**

SCALE:
0 10 20 30 40 50 60 70 80
mm

G12-5: To construct a tangent to a circle

Construct a tangent to the circle shown below. The tangent passes through point P which is outside the circle.

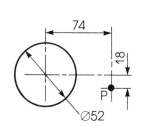

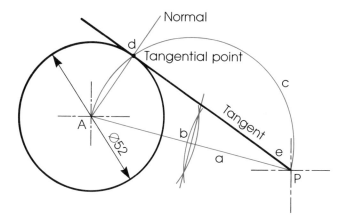

Construction uses the proposition in G12-4, d is the vertex of triangle AdP

G12-6: To construct a common tangent to 2 touching circles

Construct the common tangent to the circles shown below.

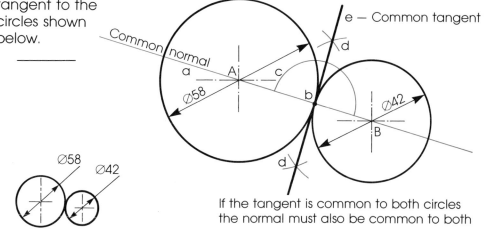

If the tangent is common to both circles the normal must also be common to both

G12-7: To construct a common tangent to 2 touching circles

Construct the common tangent to the circles (one inside the other) shown below.

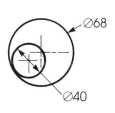

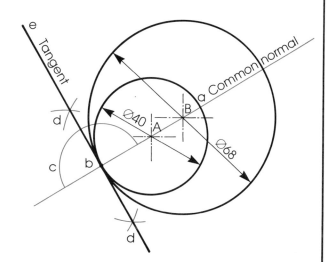

G12-8: To construct the common tangent to 2 equal circles

Construct the common tangent to the circles shown below.

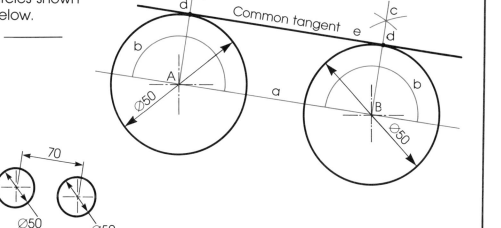

Drawing No.
G12

TITLE: **Tangents and circles in contact.**

NOTE: **Lower case letter sequence gives order of construction.**

SCALE:

0　10　20　30　40　50　60　70　80

mm

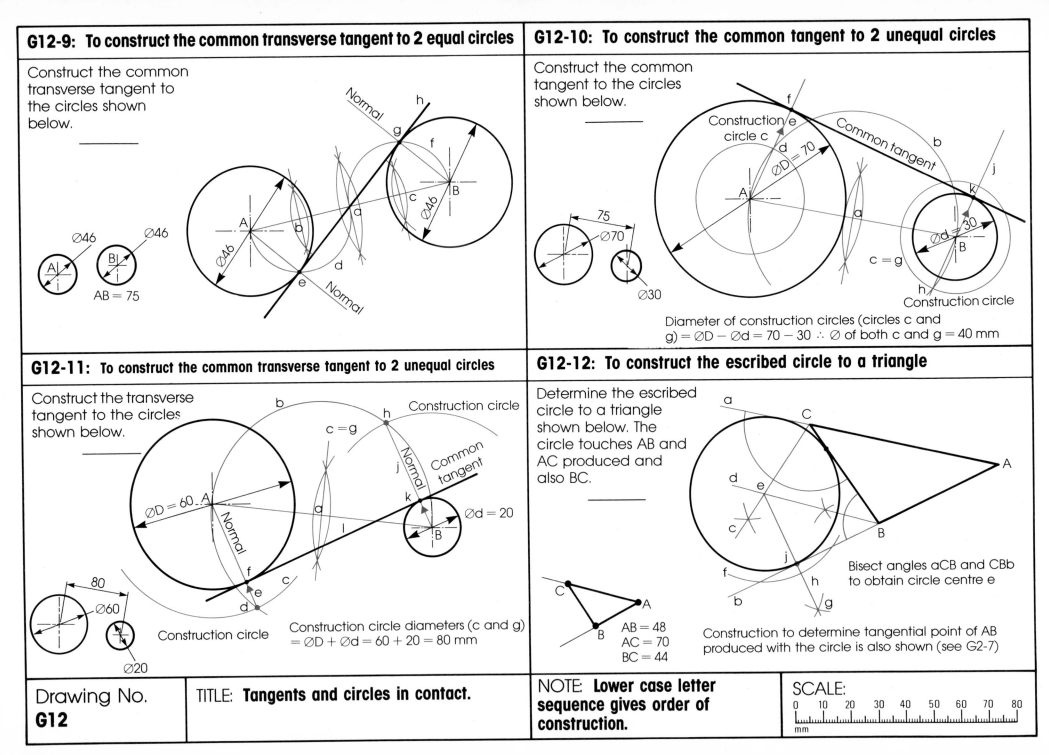

G12-9: To construct the common transverse tangent to 2 equal circles

Construct the common transverse tangent to the circles shown below.

Normal
h
g
f
A
B
Ø46
c
b
a
d
e
Normal
Ø46
Ø46
A
B
Ø46
Ø46
A
B
AB = 75

G12-10: To construct the common tangent to 2 unequal circles

Construct the common tangent to the circles shown below.

Construction circle c
f
e
d
ØD = 70
Common tangent
b
j
A
k
a
Ød = 30
B
c = g
h
Construction circle
75
Ø70
Ø30

Diameter of construction circles (circles c and g) = ØD − Ød = 70 − 30 ∴ Ø of both c and g = 40 mm

G12-11: To construct the common transverse tangent to 2 unequal circles

Construct the transverse tangent to the circles shown below.

b
h
Construction circle
c = g
Normal
Common tangent
j
ØD = 60
A
a
k
Normal
l
B
Ød = 20
f
e
c
d
Construction circle
80
Ø60
Ø20

Construction circle diameters (c and g) = ØD + Ød = 60 + 20 = 80 mm

G12-12: To construct the escribed circle to a triangle

Determine the escribed circle to a triangle shown below. The circle touches AB and AC produced and also BC.

a
C
A
d
e
c
B
j
f
h
b
g

Bisect angles aCB and CBb to obtain circle centre e

C
A
B
AB = 48
AC = 70
BC = 44

Construction to determine tangential point of AB produced with the circle is also shown (see G2-7)

Drawing No.
G12

TITLE: **Tangents and circles in contact.**

NOTE: **Lower case letter sequence gives order of construction.**

SCALE:
0 10 20 30 40 50 60 70 80
mm

46

G12-13: To join 2 intersecting lines with an arc of known radius

Construct the centre of the arc R22 to join the lines shown below. Determine the points of tangency.

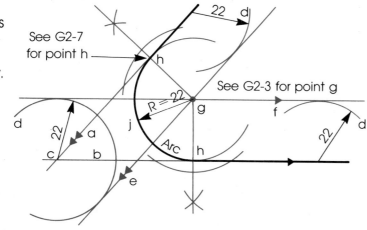

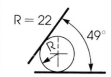

R = 22

49°

For point g to be equal in distance (22 mm) to lines a and b it must lie on lines e and f simultaneously.

G12-14: To join a line to a circle with an arc of known radius

Join the line and circle shown by an arc of radius 20 mm.

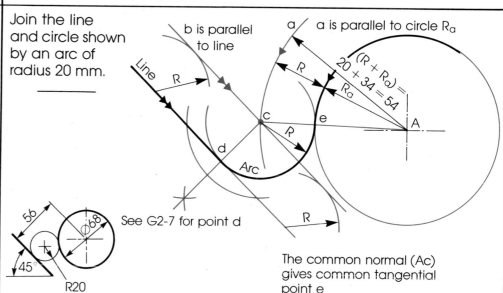

b is parallel to line

a is parallel to circle R_a

$(R + R_a) = 20 + 34 = 54$

See G2-7 for point d

56

⌀68

45°

R20

The common normal (Ac) gives common tangential point e

G12-15: To join a point to a circle by an arc of known radius

Join point P to the circle shown below by an arc of radius 20 mm.

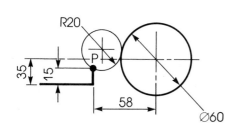

R20

35

15

58

⌀60

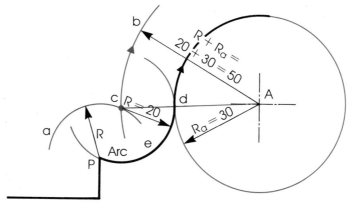

b

$R + R_a = 20 + 30 = 50$

c $R = 20$ d

A

a

R

$R_a = 30$

Arc

e

P

Common tangential point is d

| Drawing No. **G12** | TITLE: **Circles in contact.** | NOTE: **Lower case letter sequence gives order of construction.** | SCALE: |

G12-16: To join 2 circles by an arc of given radius

Join the 2 circles shown below by an arc of radius 35 mm.

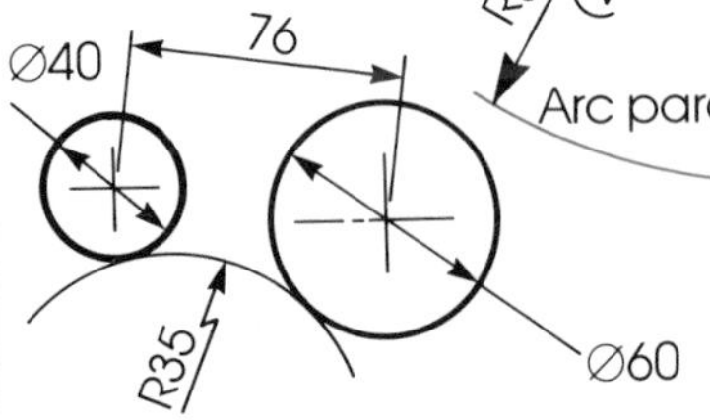

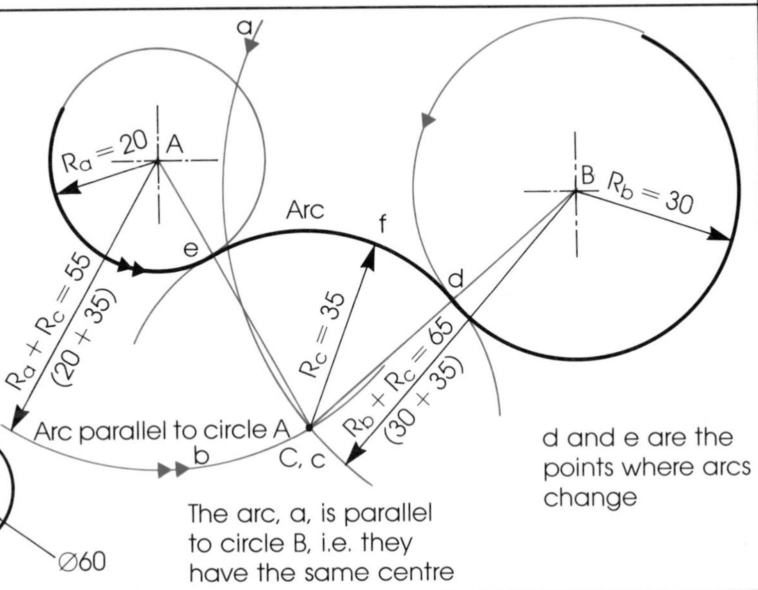

$R_a = 20$ A

B $R_b = 30$

a

Arc f

e

$R_a + R_c = 55$ $(20 + 35)$

$R_c = 35$

d

$R_b + R_c = 65$ $(30 + 35)$

Arc parallel to circle A

b

C, c

The arc, a, is parallel to circle B, i.e. they have the same centre

d and e are the points where arcs change

⌀40

76

R35

⌀60

G12-17: To join 2 circles by an arc of given radius

Join the 2 circles shown below by an arc of radius 60 mm.

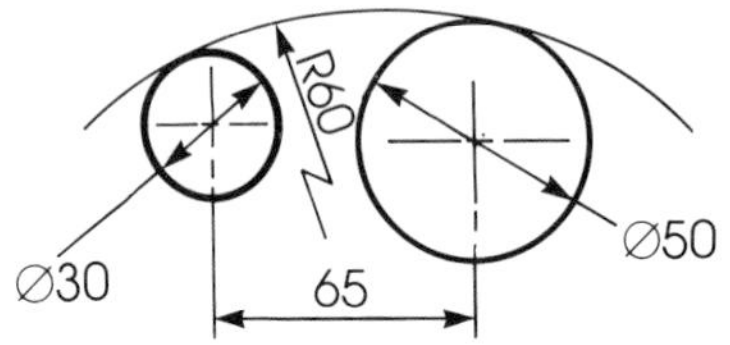

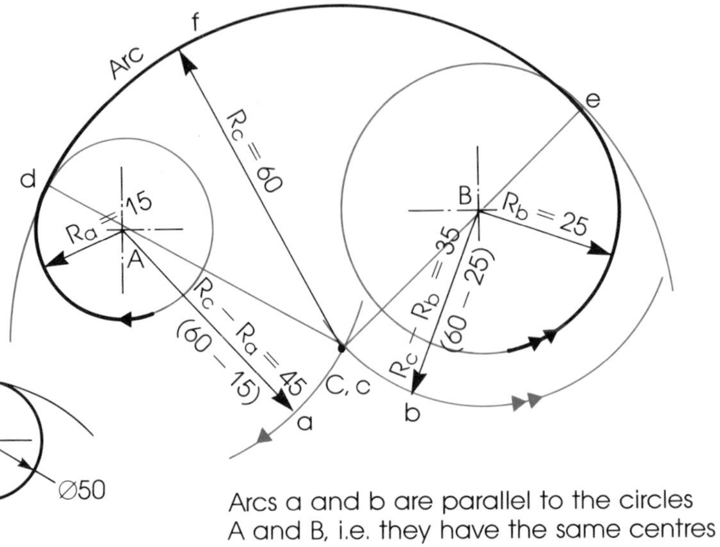

f

Arc

d

$R_a = 15$

A

$R_c = 60$

B $R_b = 25$

$R_c - R_a = 45$ $(60 - 15)$

$R_c - R_b = 35$ $(60 - 25)$

C, c

a

b

⌀30

R60

65

⌀50

Arcs a and b are parallel to the circles A and B, i.e. they have the same centres

G12:18: To join 2 circles by an arc of given radius

Join the 2 circles shown below by an arc of radius 50 mm.

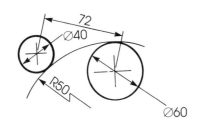

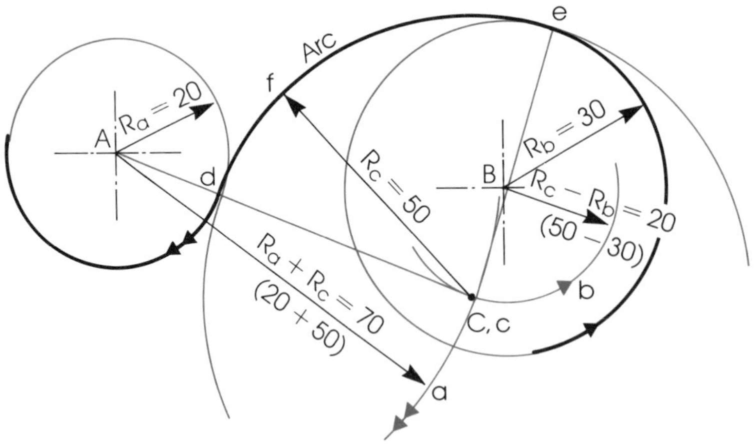

72

⌀40

R50

⌀60

e

f

Arc

A $R_a = 20$

$R_c = 50$

B

$R_b = 30$

$R_c - R_b = 20$ $(50 - 30)$

d

$R_a + R_c = 70$ $(20 + 50)$

b

C, c

a

Drawing No.
G12

TITLE: **Circles in contact.**

NOTE: **Lower case letter sequence gives order of construction.**

SCALE:
0 10 20 30 40 50 60 70 80
mm

G13-1: To construct tangents and circles in contact

A point P is 100 mm from the centre, O, of a circle which is 60 mm diameter. Construct:

(a) both of the tangents from the circle to pass through point P,

(b) the 2 circles having both the tangents to circle O in common and which also touch circle O,

(c) the tangential points of the 2 tangents with the largest of the 2 circles constructed in part (b).

———

Assemble information into a sketch of what is required. See Fig below.

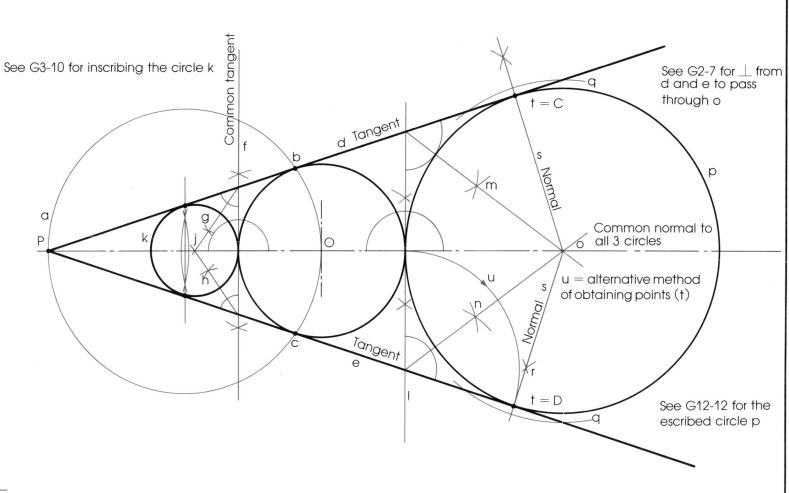

See G3-10 for inscribing the circle k

See G2-7 for ⊥ from d and e to pass through o

Common normal to all 3 circles

u = alternative method of obtaining points (t)

See G12-12 for the escribed circle p

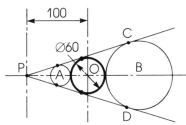

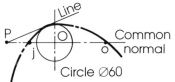

The centres j and o can be determined using loci principles, see G17, G56-11, G56-13, and the diagram given.

Locus of a point, which is equal in distance to the line and the circle ∅60, intersects common normal to give points j and o.

| Drawing No. **G13** | TITLE: **Problems involving tangent constructions.** | NOTE: **Lower case letter sequence gives order of construction.** | SCALE: |

G13-2: To construct the layout for a paper feed mechanism

The figure below shows the layout for a paper feed mechanism. The paper is fed over the pressure pad A, round the guide roll B and on to the winding drum C. Construct the layout to a scale of 1:2 with the drum C initially empty. Show all the tangential points where the paper comes into contact with, and leaves, the curved surfaces.

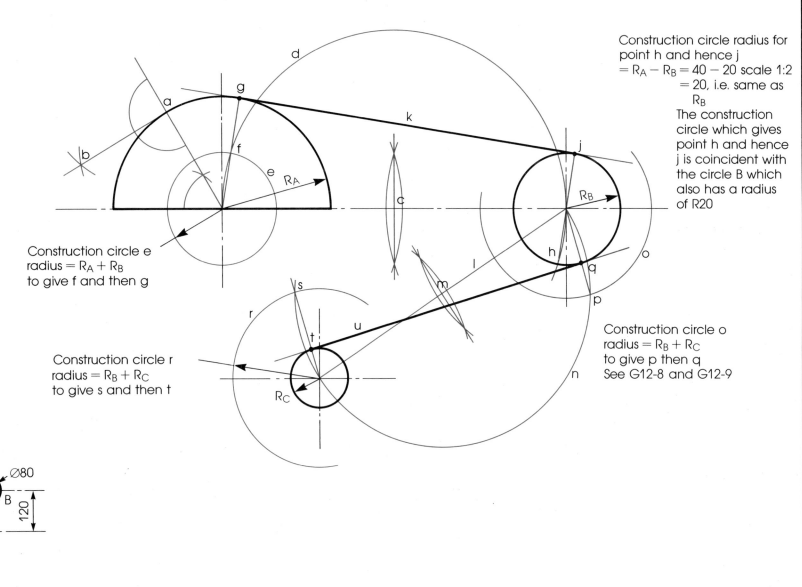

Construction circle e
radius = $R_A + R_B$
to give f and then g

Construction circle r
radius = $R_B + R_C$
to give s and then t

Construction circle radius for point h and hence j
= $R_A - R_B = 40 - 20$ scale 1:2
= 20, i.e. same as R_B
The construction circle which gives point h and hence j is coincident with the circle B which also has a radius of R20

Construction circle o
radius = $R_B + R_C$
to give p then q
See G12-8 and G12-9

Drawing No.	TITLE: **Problems involving tangent constructions.**	NOTE: **Lower case letter sequence gives order of construction.**	SCALE:
G13			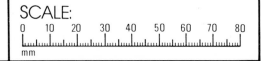

G13-3: To determine the points of contact between a belt and 3 pulleys

The figure below shows 2 pulleys A and B, which rotate clockwise. They are connected by a belt; pulley B drives pulley A and the jockey pulley C keeps the belt tight as shown. Determine the points of contact between the belt and the 3 pulleys and also draw the belt which is tangential to the 3 pulleys. Show all tangential points.

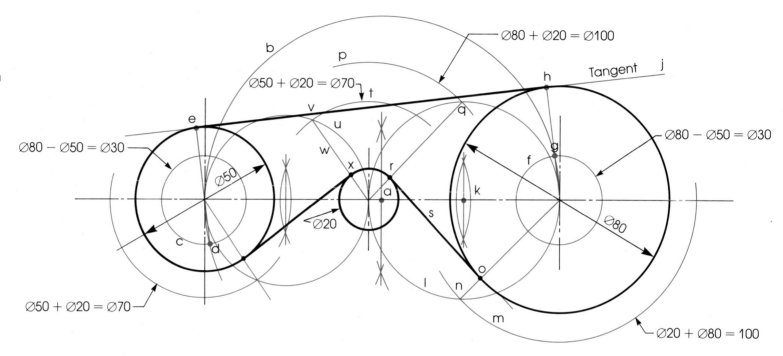

Ø80 + Ø20 = Ø100

Ø50 + Ø20 = Ø70

Ø80 − Ø50 = Ø30

Tangent

Ø80 − Ø50 = Ø30

Ø80

Ø50

Ø20

Ø50 + Ø20 = Ø70

Ø20 + Ø80 = 100

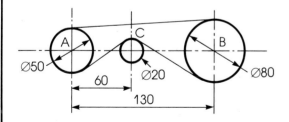

Ø50

60

Ø20

130

Ø80

| Drawing No. **G13** | TITLE: **Problems involving tangent constructions.** | NOTE: **Lower case letter sequence gives order of construction.** | SCALE: 0 10 20 30 40 50 60 70 80 mm |

G13-4: To construct tangents and circles given tangential points

Draw circles A and B as
shown below.
Construct:

(a) the tangents X and Y
by first determining the
tangential points P_1, P_2,
P_3 and P_4;

(b) the centre of, and draw,
the circle which is tangential
to circle B and the 2
tangents constructed in (a).

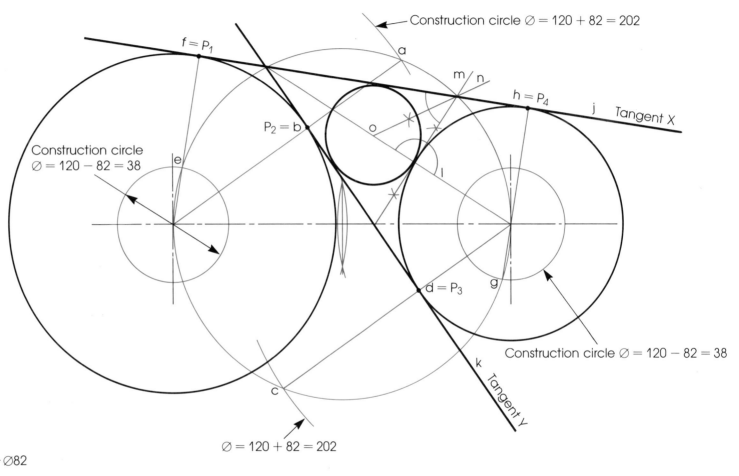

Construction circle $\emptyset = 120 + 82 = 202$

$f = P_1$

a

m n

$h = P_4$

j Tangent X

$P_2 = b$

o

Construction circle
$\emptyset = 120 - 82 = 38$

e

l

$d = P_3$

g

Construction circle $\emptyset = 120 - 82 = 38$

c

k Tangent Y

$\emptyset = 120 + 82 = 202$

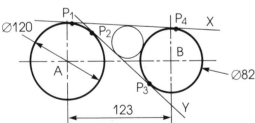

P_1

$\emptyset 120$

P_2

P_4 X

B

A

$\emptyset 82$

P_3

123

Y

Drawing No. **G13**	TITLE: **Problems involving tangent constructions.**	NOTE: **Lower case letter sequence gives order of construction.**	SCALE:

SCALE:
0 10 20 30 40 50 60 70 80
mm

Worksheets for G14 to G19

G14 PROBLEMS INVOLVING CIRCLES IN CONTACT, COMMON NORMALS AND TANGENTS.

G14-1 Construct the profile of the light bulb shown in Fig 1. The construction to determine the unknown centres of arcs must be evident, together with the exact point where one arc changes to another.

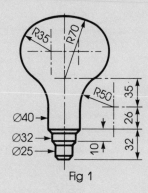

Fig 1

G14-2 Construct the profile of the plier leg shown in Fig 2. Determine the centres of arcs but only draw the tangent involved.

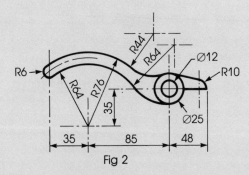

Fig 2

G14-3 Construct the spanner shown in Fig 3. The method of determining the centres of arcs and the exact points where one arc joins the next must be evident.

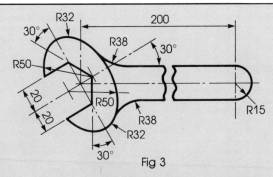

Fig 3

G14-4 Construct the radial arm shown in Fig 4. The construction to determine the unknown centres of arcs and the common tangential points must be shown.

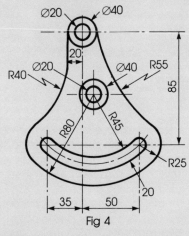

Fig 4

G14-5 Fig 5 shows part of the decoration for a wrought iron gate. Construct the scroll shown, by determining the unknown centres and the radii R_a, R_b, R_c, R_d. The given points A, B, C, D and E are common tangential points.

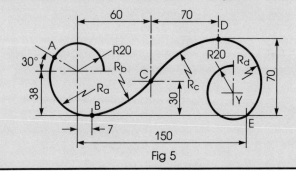

Fig 5

G15 LOCI. PROBLEMS INVOLVING MECHANISMS.

G15-1 Fig 1 shows the line diagram of a slider crank mechanism (similar to a piston, connecting rod, crankshaft and cylinder in a car engine). Plot the locus of the point P on the link AB as A rotates about O and B is constrained to slide along the line X-Y. A and B are pin joints.

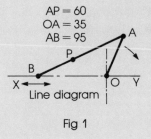

AP = 60
OA = 35
AB = 95

Line diagram

Fig 1

G15-2 Fig 2 shows a mechanism where A rotates about O, and B is constrained to follow the line X-Y. Plot the locus of the point P (which is fixed on the link AB), as A rotates about O. The link OA is pin jointed to AB at A and the link AB is pin jointed at B to the slider which follows the line X-Y.

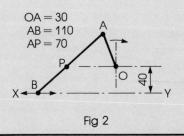

OA = 30
AB = 110
AP = 70

Fig 2

G15-3 Fig 3 shows a mechanism where link OA rotates about O, and end B of the link PAB is constrained to slide along X-Y. Link PAB is pin jointed to OA at A. Plot the locus of P as A rotates.

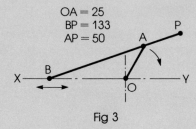

OA = 25
BP = 133
AP = 50

Fig 3

G15-4 Fig 4 shows a mechanism where the link OA rotates about O. The link AP slides through the pin X which can pivot about its axis. OA is pin jointed to AP at A. Plot the locus of P as A rotates.

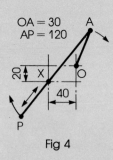

OA = 30
AP = 120

Fig 4

G15-5 Fig 5 shows a mechanism where A rotates about O and B pivots about X. A and B are pin joints pinning link AP to OA at A and XB at B. Plot the locus of point P for one revolution of OA.

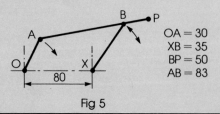

OA = 30
XB = 35
BP = 50
AB = 83

Fig 5

G15-6 Fig 6 shows a mechanism where B pivots about X and A rotates about O. The link AB is pin jointed to links OA and BX at A and B respectively. P is fixed on AB. Plot the locus of point P during one revolution of OA.

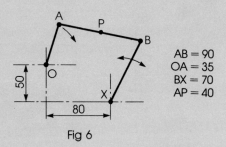

AB = 90
OA = 35
BX = 70
AP = 40

Fig 6

G16 THE ELLIPSE.

G16-1 Construct an ellipse given that an ellipse is the locus of a point having the sum of its distances to 2 fixed points (F_1 and F_2) constant. The constant is equal to the major axis which is 140 mm long. The distance between the fixed points F_1 and F_2 is 90 mm.

G16-2 Construct an ellipse by the concentric circles method given that the major axis = 157 mm and the minor axis = 120 mm.

G16-3 Construct an ellipse by the rectangle method given that the major axis = 140 mm and the minor axis = 100 mm.

G16-4 Construct an ellipse having an eccentricity of $\frac{2}{3}$ and given that the distance from the directrix to the nearest focal point is 50 mm.

G16-5 Construct an ellipse given that the major axis = 150 mm and the minor axis = 110 mm. Determine the focal points F_1 and F_2 and construct the normal and tangent to a point P located on the ellipse 108 mm from focal point F_1. Determine the distance from point P on the ellipse to the focal point F_2.

G16-6 Construct an ellipse given that the major axis = 120 mm and the distance between the focal points F_1 and F_2 is 90 mm.

G17 THE PARABOLA AND HYPERBOLA.

G17-1 Construct a parabola given that the distance between the directrix and the focal point is 50 mm. Note eccentricity for a parabola is always $\frac{1}{1} = 1$. See G16-4 for similar principles.

G17-2 Construct a parabolic curve given that the nearest point of the curve (the vertex) to the directrix is at a distance of 18 mm. Construct the tangent to a point on the curve, the point being 45 mm from the transverse axis.
If the parabola formed the profile of a car headlamp reflector where would the light-emitting element be positioned to give a parallel beam of light?

G17-3 Construct a parabola given the coordinates of 3 points which lie on the curve, P_1 (−60, −110), P_2 (+60, −110) and the vertex P_3 (0, 0).

G17-4 Construct a parabola to fit a rectangle 160 mm × 100 mm. The open ends of the parabola are 160 mm apart with the vertex located at the centre of the opposite side of the rectangle. Determine the focal point of the parabola.

G17-5 Construct a hyperbola given that the distance between the directrix and the focal point is 45 mm and that the eccentricity is $\frac{5}{4}$.

G17-6 Construct a hyperbola given that it has an eccentricity of $\frac{9}{7}$ and the distance from a focal point to the directrix is 30 mm.
Alternative: Plot the locus of a point, the ratio of its distances to a fixed point and a line being 9:7. The distance from line to point = 30 mm.

G18 ARCHIMEDIAN SPIRAL; INVOLUTE; HELIX.

G18-1 Determine the locus of a point which travels 60 mm from a fixed point with uniform velocity, whilst completing one clockwise revolution of the fixed point with constant angular velocity.

G18-2 Construct an Archimedian spiral by plotting the locus of a point which moves 70 mm away from a fixed point during one complete anticlockwise revolution. Both the linear and angular velocity are constant (i.e. directly related) during the cycle.

G18-3   Determine the locus of the free end of a piece of string as it unwraps $\frac{3}{4}$ of a revolution in a clockwise direction from a reel of ⌀45 mm. The string is kept tight all the time.

G18-4   A piece of string is unwrapped from a drum ⌀34 mm in an anticlockwise direction for one complete revolution. Construct an anticlockwise involute for one revolution with the involute having a base circle diameter of 34 mm. The free end of the string is kept tight whilst it unwraps.

G18-5   Construct a left-hand helix having a pitch of 25 mm and a pitch diameter of 35 mm. Produce 2 complete turns (revolutions) of the helix and find its true length.

G18-6   Plot the locus of a point which describes a right-hand helix with a pitch of 30 mm and lies on the cylinder shown below. Produce the locus for 4 revolutions around the cylinder starting at A.

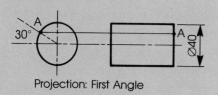

Projection: First Angle

G19   ENGINEERING FORMS OF THE HELIX.

G19-1   Draw the crests of a 2-start right-hand vee thread for 4 complete turns of both helices. The screw thread has a major diameter of 54 mm and a lead of 24 mm, i.e. a pitch of 12 mm.

G19-2   Draw the thread crests of a 3-start right-hand vee thread for a thread length of 60 mm. The thread has a major diameter of 40 mm and a lead of 30 mm.

G19-3   A thin ribbon (0.5 mm thick by 10 mm wide) of phosphor bronze is wound in helical form on to a cylinder of ⌀60 mm to form a spring with a pitch of 36 mm. Draw the spring having 3 complete turns.

G19-4   Produce a drawing of a single-start right-hand square screw thread having a major diameter of 100 mm, a minor diameter of 60 mm and a pitch of 40 mm. Show the full thread form for a length of 100 mm.

G19-5   Construct a 2-start right-hand square screw thread having a pitch of 20 mm, a major diameter of 70 mm and a thread length of 80 mm.

G19-6   A bar, 12 mm square, is wound into a spring of helical form with an outside diameter of 60 mm. The spring has a length of 144 mm between its flat ground ends and consists of a centre portion having 2 complete turns with a pitch of 48 mm; the remainder equally spaced at each end having a pitch of 24 mm. Draw the spring.

G19-7   A right-hand helical spring, formed by winding a bar ⌀12 mm on a mandril ⌀58 mm is 135 mm long over ground ends. 3 coils have a pitch of 36 mm, the remainder a pitch of 18 mm equally distributed at each end. Draw the spring.

G14-1: To construct the profile of a light bulb

Construct the profile of the light bulb
shown below. The construction to determine
the unknown centres of arcs must be
evident, together with the exact point
where one arc changes to another.

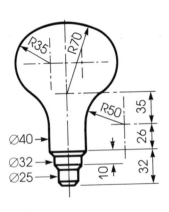

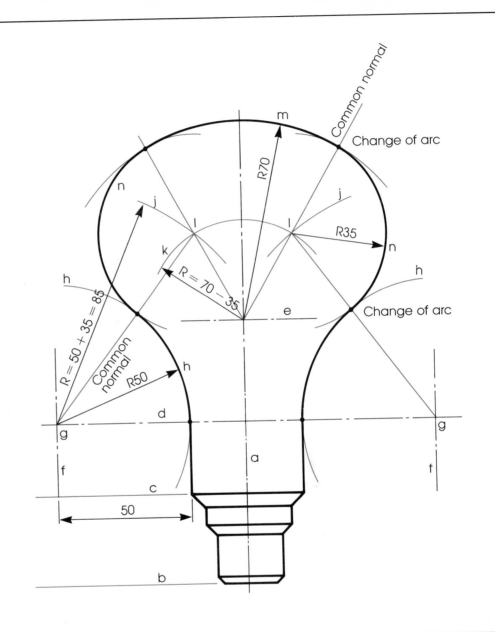

| Drawing No.
G14 | TITLE: **Problems involving circles in contact,
normals and tangents.** | NOTE: **Lower case letter sequence
gives order of construction.** | SCALE:
0 10 20 30 40 50 60 70 80
mm |

Construct the profile of the plier leg shown below. Determine the centres of arcs but only draw the tangent involved.

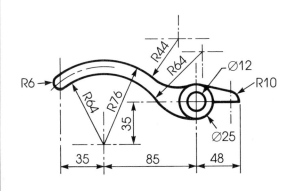

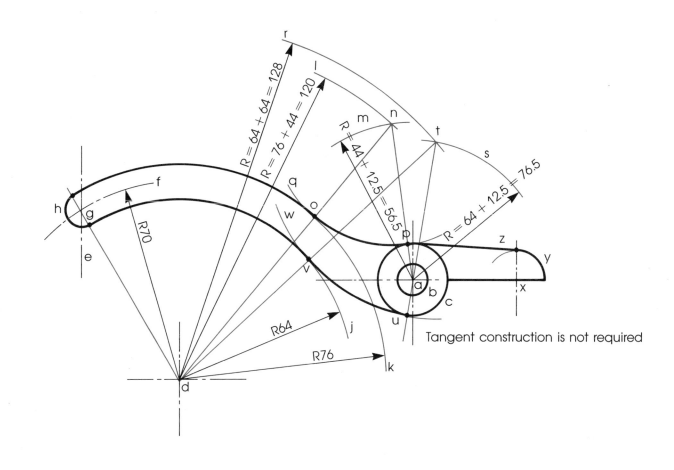

Tangent construction is not required

Drawing No. **G14**	TITLE: **Problems involving circles in contact, normals and tangents.**	NOTE: **Lower case letter sequence gives order of construction.**	SCALE: 0 10 20 30 40 50 60 70 80 mm

G14-3: To construct an open-ended spanner

Construct the spanner shown below.
The method of determining the
centres of arcs and the exact
points where one arc joins the
next must be evident.

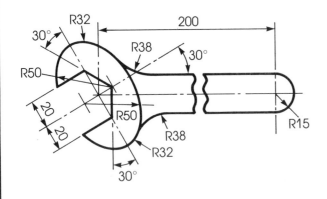

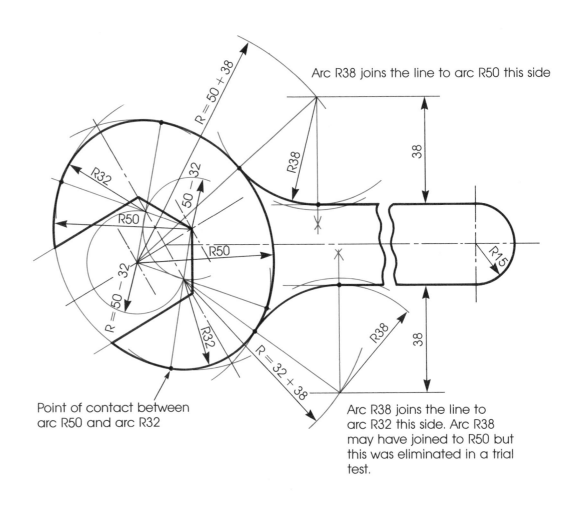

Arc R38 joins the line to arc R50 this side

Point of contact between
arc R50 and arc R32

Arc R38 joins the line to
arc R32 this side. Arc R38
may have joined to R50 but
this was eliminated in a trial
test.

Drawing No. **G14**	TITLE: **Problems involving circles in contact,** **normals and tangents.**		SCALE:

G14-4: To construct a radial arm

Construct the radial arm shown below.
The construction to determine the
unknown centres of arcs and the common
tangential points must be shown.

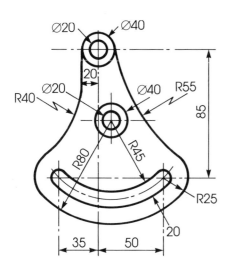

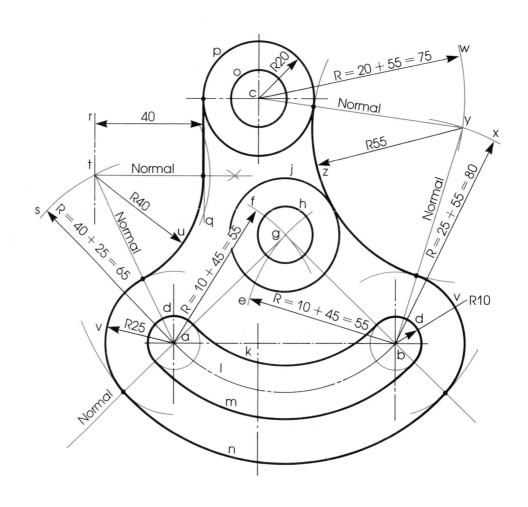

Drawing No. **G14**	**TITLE: Problems involving circles in contact, normals and tangents.**	NOTE: **Lower case letter sequence gives order of construction.**	SCALE:

G14-5: To construct the decoration for a wrought iron gate

The figure below shows part of the decoration for a wrought iron gate. Construct the scroll shown, by determining the unknown centres and the radii R_a, R_b, R_c and R_d. The given points A, B, C, D and E are common tangential points.

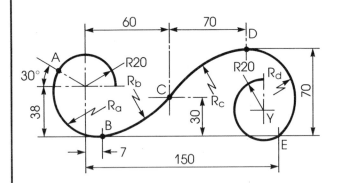

Scaled from drawing $R_a = 32$ $R_b = 51$
$R_c = 70$ $R_d = 39$

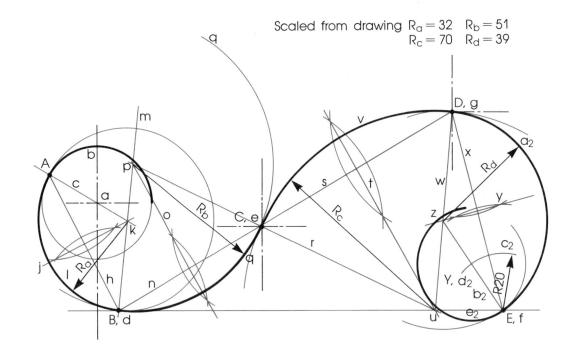

Method: Locate all known points and use common normals and chord bisectors to determine the centres of arcs. See G3-6 and G12.

| Drawing No. **G14** | TITLE: **Problems involving circles of contact, normals and tangents.** | NOTE: **Lower case letter sequence gives order of construction, i.e. a-to-z then a₂, b₂, c₂ etc.** | SCALE: |

G15-1: To construct the locus of a point on a slider crank mechanism

The line diagram shows a slider crank mechanism (similar to a piston, connecting rod, crankshaft and cylinder in a car engine). Plot the locus of the point P on the link AB as A rotates about O and B is constrained to slide along the line X–Y. A and B are pin joints.

Slider crank mechanism: uses include petrol and diesel engines and compressors.

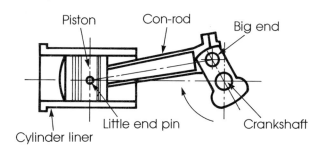

Piston   Con-rod   Big end

Little end pin   Crankshaft

Cylinder liner

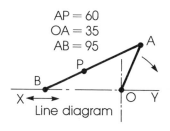

AP = 60
OA = 35
AB = 95

A
P
B
X ← → O Y
Line diagram

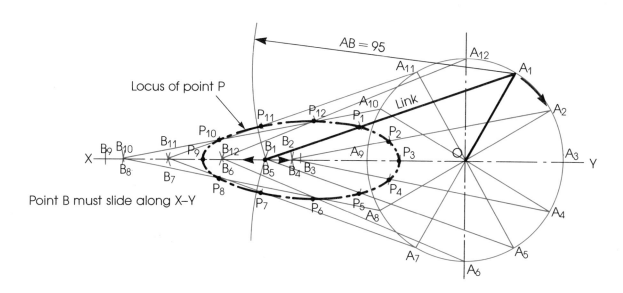

AB = 95

Locus of point P

Link

Point B must slide along X–Y

Point A is constrained to follow a circular path. A can be anywhere 35 mm from O, e.g. position A_1. B must be 95 mm from A and on X–Y, i.e. at B_1. When A rotates to position A_2 the link AB pulls B along X–Y to a new position B_2, which is 95 mm from position A_2.

| Drawing No. **G15** | TITLE: **Loci (mechanisms).** | NOTE: **The locus of a point is the path it is allowed to follow when constrained by a set of rules or axioms. The restraint provided by the mechanism linkage determines the rules in the above example.** | SCALE: 0 10 20 30 40 50 60 70 80 mm |

61

G15-2: To construct the locus of a point on an offset slider crank mechanism

The line diagram shows a mechanism in which A rotates about O, and B is constrained to follow the line X–Y. Plot the locus of the point P (which is fixed on the link AB), as A rotates about O. The link OA is pin jointed to AB at A and the link AB is pin jointed at B to the slider which follows the line X–Y.

$OA = 30$
$AB = 110$
$AP = 70$

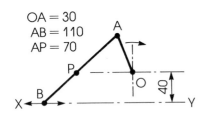

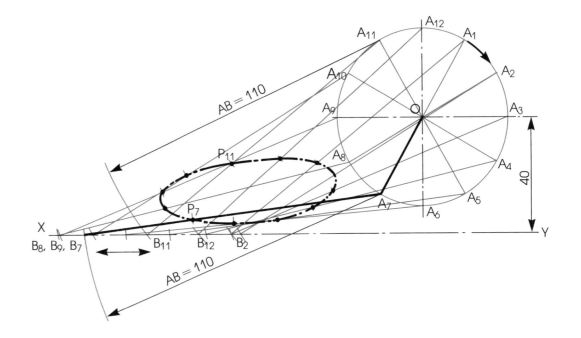

Drawing No.	TITLE: **Loci (mechanisms).**	NOTE: **The locus of a point is the path it is allowed to follow when constrained by a set of rules or axioms. The restraint provided by the mechanism linkage determines the rules in the above example.**	SCALE:
G15			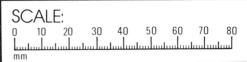

G15-3: To construct the locus of a point on a slider crank extension

The figure shows a mechanism in which link OA rotates about O, and end B of the link PAB is constrained to slide along X–Y. Link PAB is pin jointed to OA at A. Plot the locus of P as A rotates.

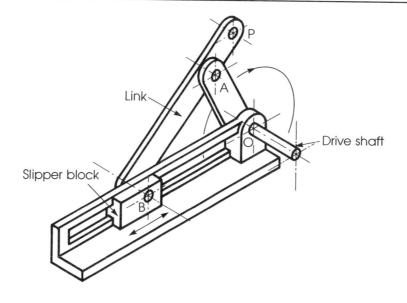

Link

Drive shaft

Slipper block

B

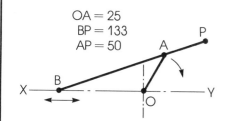

OA = 25
BP = 133
AP = 50

P
A
X —— B ———— O ———— Y

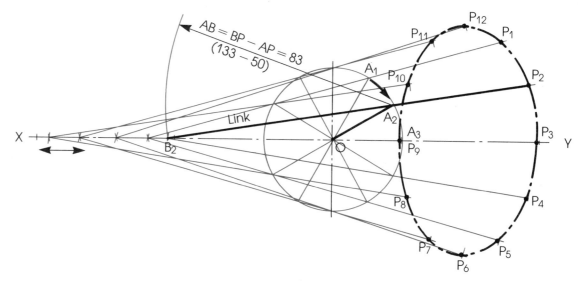

$AB = BP - AP = 83$
$(133 - 50)$

Link

Drawing No.	TITLE: **Loci (mechanisms).**	NOTE: **The locus of a point is the path it is allowed to follow when constrained by a set of rules or axioms. The restraint provided by the mechanism linkage determines the rules in the above example.**	SCALE:
G15			0 10 20 30 40 50 60 70 80 mm

G15-4: To construct the locus of a point on a mechanism

The line diagram shows a mechanism in which the link OA rotates about O. The link AP slides through the pin X which can pivot about its axis. OA is pin jointed to AP at A. Plot the locus of P as A rotates.

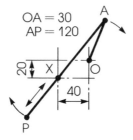

OA = 30
AP = 120

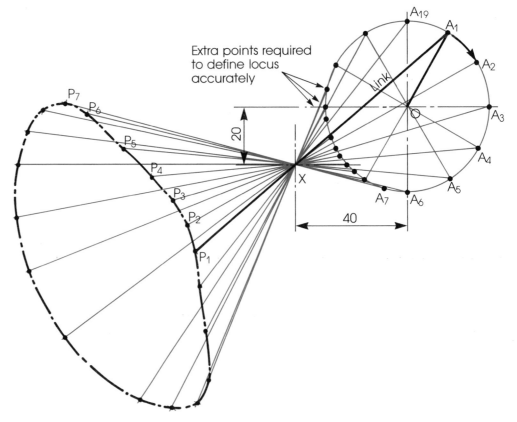

Extra points required to define locus accurately

Link

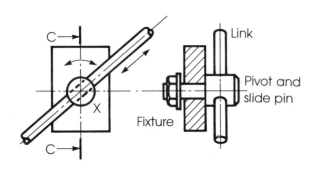

Link

Pivot and slide pin

Fixture

Section C–C: The pin is free to pivot in the fixture and the link is free to slide through the pin. The diagram shows detail of point X (pivot).

| Drawing No. **G15** | TITLE: **Loci (mechanisms).** | NOTE: **The locus of a point is the path it is allowed to follow when constrained by a set of rules or axioms. The restraint provided by the mechanism linkage determines the rules in the above example.** | SCALE: |

G15-5: To construct the locus of a point on a mechanism

Shown below is a mechanism in which
A rotates about O and B pivots
about X. A and B are pin joints
pinning link AP to OA at A, and
XB at B. Plot the locus of point
P for one revolution of OA.

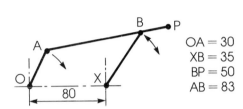

OA = 30
XB = 35
BP = 50
AB = 83

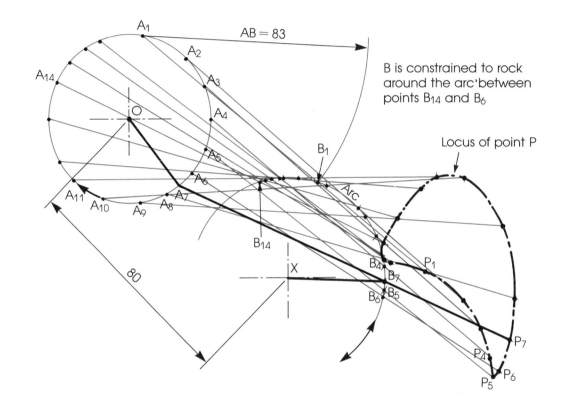

AB = 83

B is constrained to rock
around the arc'between
points B_{14} and B_6

Locus of point P

80

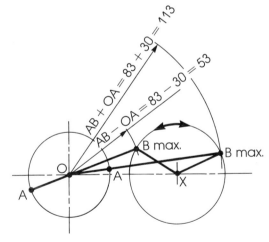

To obtain the limits of movement of
point B as it rocks in an arc about X.
See G12-18 for theory.
SCALE: 1:2

Drawing No.	TITLE: **Loci (mechanisms).**	NOTE: **The locus of a point is the path it is allowed to follow when constrained by a set of rules or axioms. The restraint provided by the mechanism linkage determines the rules in the above example.**	SCALE:
G15			

G15-6: To construct the locus of a point on a mechanism

The line drawing below shows a mechanism in which B pivots about X and A rotates about O. The link AB is pin jointed to links OA and BX at A and B respectively. P is fixed on AB. Plot the locus of point P during one revolution of OA.

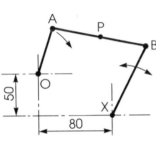

AB = 90   BX = 70
OA = 35   AP = 40

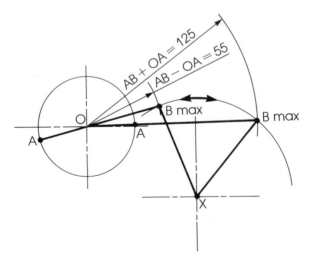

To obtain the limits of movement of point B as it rocks in an arc about X.
SCALE: 1:2

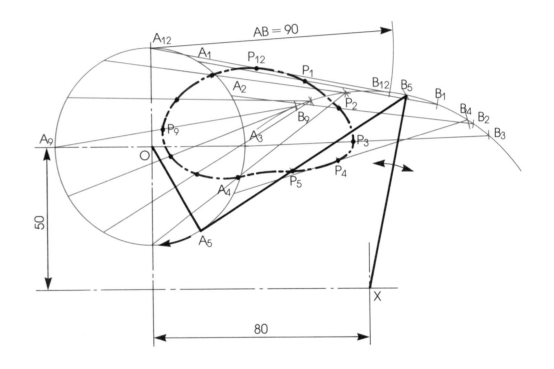

Drawing No.	TITLE: **Loci (mechanisms).**	NOTE: **The locus of a point is the path it is allowed to follow when constrained by a set of rules or axioms. The restraint provided by the mechanism linkage determines the rules in the above example.**	SCALE:
G15			

66

G16-1: To construct an ellipse

Construct an ellipse given that an
ellipse is the locus of a point which
moves such that the sum of its distances
$(X + Y)$ to 2 fixed points $(F_1$ and $F_2)$
is constant, i.e. equal to the major axis.
In this example the major axis is 140 mm
long and the distance between the fixed
points F_1 and F_2 is 90 mm.

_____

The fixed points F_1 and F_2 are referred to
as the focal points

$\quad X + Y = $ major axis $=$ constant (C)

$\quad C = X_1 + Y_1 = X_2 + Y_2 = X_3 + Y_3 = X_5 + Y_5$ etc.

$\quad (X_5 = Y_5 = \frac{1}{2}$ major axis).

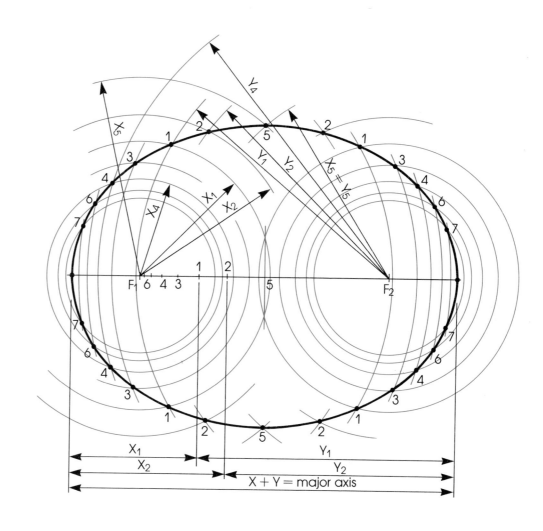

| Drawing No.
G16 | TITLE: **Construction of the ellipse.** | | SCALE: |

G16-2: To construct an ellipse by the concentric circles method

Construct an ellipse by the concentric circles method given that the major axis = 157 mm and the minor axis = 120 mm.

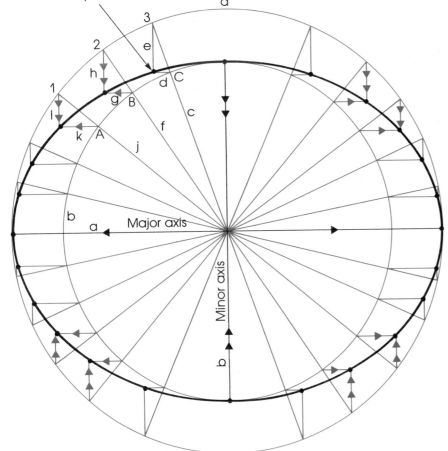

Intersection of the horizontal parallel d from C and the vertical parallel e from 3 gives a point on the ellipse

G16-3: To construct an ellipse by the rectangle method

Construct an ellipse by the rectangle method given that the major axis = 140 mm and the minor axis = 100 mm.

Note: Both sides of the rectangle are divided in an equal number of parts.

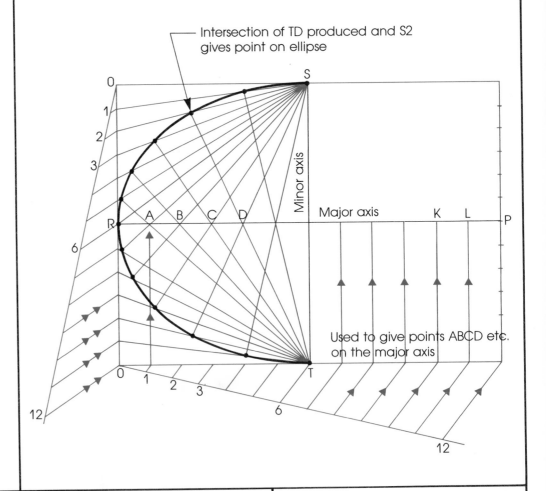

Intersection of TD produced and S2 gives point on ellipse

Used to give points ABCD etc. on the major axis

Drawing No. **G16**	TITLE: **Construction of the ellipse.**	NOTE: **In G16-2 lower case letter sequence gives order of construction.**	SCALE:

SCALE:
0 10 20 30 40 50 60 70 80
mm

G16-4: To construct an ellipse of given eccentricity

Construct an ellipse with an eccentricity of $\frac{2}{3}$ and given that the distance from the directrix to the nearest focal point is 50 mm.

_____

Where S is the distance to the locus from the focal point and T is the distance to the locus from the line or directrix.

Equation 1: $S = \frac{2}{3}T$ (from eccentricity)

then $T_3 = 50 + X + 20$ (see line diagram below)
and $S_3 = X + 20$

Substituting T_3 and S_3 in Equation 1

$$X + 20 = \frac{2}{3}(50 + X + 20)$$

therefore $X = 80$, i.e. F_1 to F_2.

Major axis $= (S_1 + S_3) = S_1 + (X + 20) = 20 + 80 + 20 = 120$.

Having determined the major axis and F_1 to F_2 the ellipse could be constructed by the easier concentric circles method!

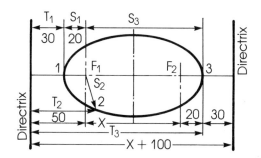

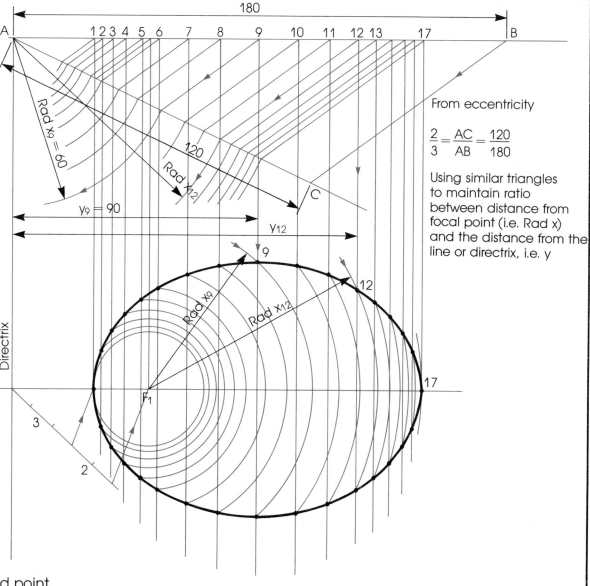

From eccentricity

$$\frac{2}{3} = \frac{AC}{AB} = \frac{120}{180}$$

Using similar triangles to maintain ratio between distance from focal point (i.e. Rad x) and the distance from the line or directrix, i.e. y

Alternative definition of ellipse to that given on G16-1:
The ellipse is the locus of a point whose distance from a fixed point, F_1 and a line is always in a constant ratio which is less than unity, > 1:1.

Drawing No.	TITLE: **Construction of the ellipse.**		SCALE:

G16

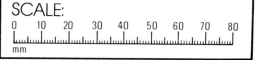

G16-5: To construct the tangent to an ellipse of given axes

Construct an ellipse given that the major axis = 150 mm and the minor axis = 110 mm. Determine the focal points F_1 and F_2 and construct the normal and tangent to a point P located on the ellipse 108 mm from focal point F_1. Determine the distance from point P on the ellipse to the focal point F_2.

———

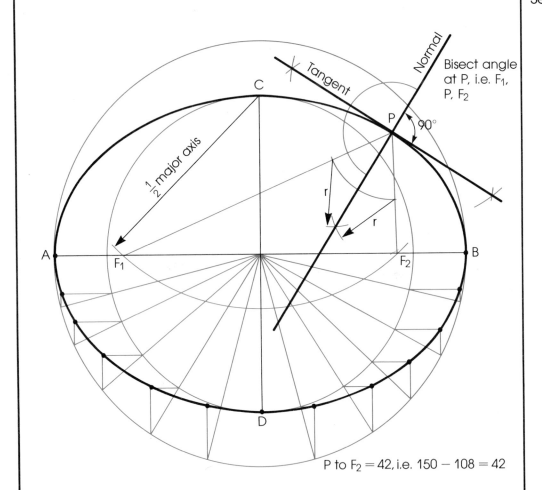

Bisect angle at P, i.e. F_1, P, F_2

P to F_2 = 42, i.e. 150 − 108 = 42

G16-6: To construct an ellipse of given axis and focal points

Construct an ellipse given that the major axis = 120 mm and the distance between the focal points F_1 and F_2 is 90 mm.

———

Draw major axis AB and locate F_1 and F_2 which are spaced symmetrically on AB. Now F_1 to C = F_2 to C = $\frac{1}{2}$ major axis.

See G16-1.

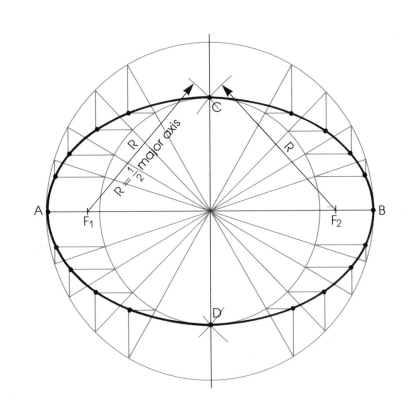

Drawing No.	TITLE: **Construction of the ellipse.**		SCALE:
G16			0 10 20 30 40 50 60 70 80 mm

70

G17-1: To construct a parabola

Construct a parabola given that the distance between the directrix and the focal point is 50 mm.

___

In a parabola the ratio or eccentricity of the point (P) from a fixed point (FP) and a line (directrix) is always unity, i.e. $1:1 = \dfrac{A}{A} = \dfrac{B}{B} = \dfrac{C}{C} = \dfrac{25}{25} = \dfrac{1}{1} = 1$.

The parabola is the locus of a point whose distances to both a fixed point (the focal point) and a line are equal, i.e. point P_c is a distance "c" from both the line and fixed point.

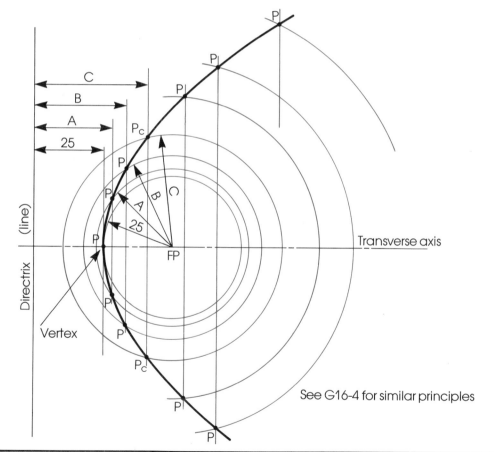

See G16-4 for similar principles

G17:2: To construct a parabola and a tangent to a point on it

Construct a parabolic curve given that the nearest point of the curve (the vertex) to the directrix is at a distance of 18 mm. Construct the tangent to a point on the curve, the point being 45 mm from the transverse axis.

___

If the parabola formed the profile of a car headlamp reflector where would the light-emitting element be positioned to give a parallel beam of light?

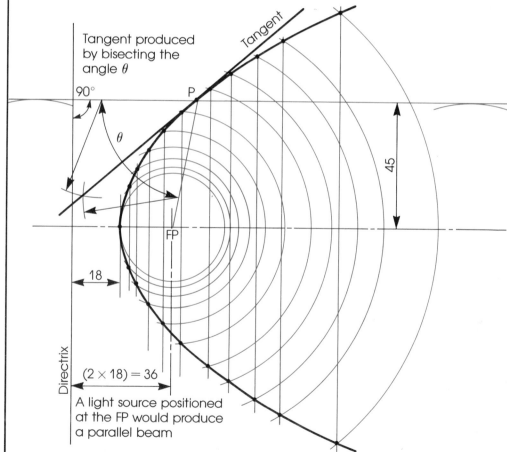

Tangent produced by bisecting the angle θ

$(2 \times 18) = 36$

A light source positioned at the FP would produce a parallel beam

Drawing No.	TITLE: **Loci. The parabola.**		SCALE:
G17			

G17-3: To construct a parabola given the coordinates of 3 points

Construct a parabola given the coordinates
of 3 points which lie on the curve,
P₁ (−60, −110), P₂ (+60, −110) and the vertex
P₃ (0, 0), i.e. the parabola will be
constructed within a rectangle 120 mm × 110 mm
with its transverse axis parallel to the
rectangle's shorter side.

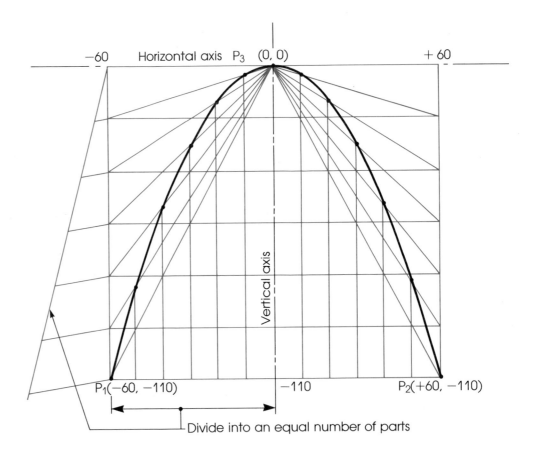

−60   Horizontal axis   P₃   (0, 0)   + 60

Vertical axis

P₁(−60, −110)   −110   P₂(+60, −110)

Divide into an equal number of parts

Drawing No. **G17**	TITLE: **Loci. The parabola.**		SCALE:

SCALE:
0 10 20 30 40 50 60 70 80
mm

72

G17-4: To construct a parabola within a rectangle

Construct a parabola to fit a rectangle
160 mm × 100 mm. The open ends of the
parabola are 160 mm apart with the
vertex located at the centre of the
opposite side of the rectangle. Determine
the focal point of the parabola.

_____

To determine the focal point of a
parabola:

$$AC = AB = 2(AV)$$

AV may be any length.

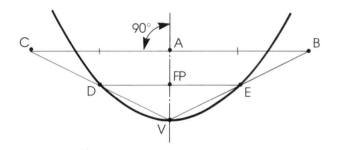

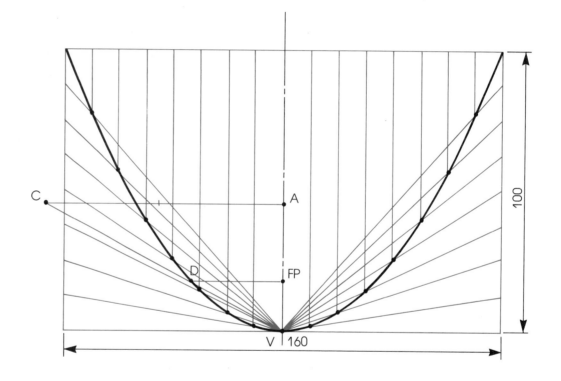

Drawing No.	TITLE: **Loci. The parabola.**		SCALE:
G17			0 10 20 30 40 50 60 70 80

G17-5: To construct a hyperbola

Construct a hyperbola given that the distance between the directrix and the focal point is 45 mm and the eccentricity is $\frac{5}{4}$.

___

The hyperbola is the locus of a point which moves so that its distances to a fixed point and a line are in a constant ratio which is greater than 1.

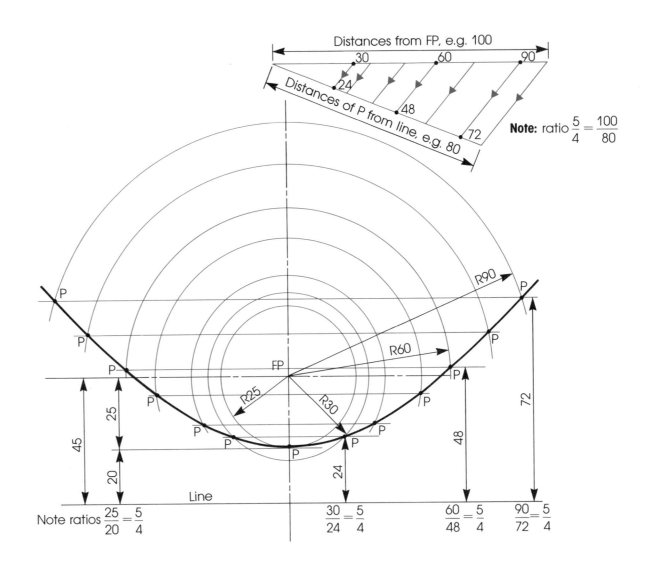

Distances from FP, e.g. 100

Distances of P from line, e.g. 80

Note: ratio $\frac{5}{4} = \frac{100}{80}$

Note ratios $\frac{25}{20} = \frac{5}{4}$ $\frac{30}{24} = \frac{5}{4}$ $\frac{60}{48} = \frac{5}{4}$ $\frac{90}{72} = \frac{5}{4}$

Drawing No.	TITLE: **Loci. The hyperbola.**		SCALE:
G17			0 10 20 30 40 50 60 70 80 mm

G17-6: To construct a hyperbola

Construct a hyperbola given that it has an eccentricity of $\frac{9}{7}$ and the distance from a focal point to the directrix is 30 mm.

Alternative: Plot the locus of a point, the ratio of its distances to a fixed point and a line being 9:7. The distance from line to point = 30 mm.

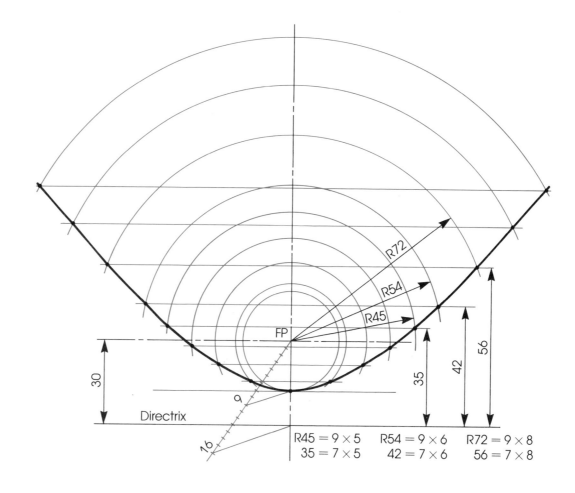

Directrix

FP

R45 = 9 × 5	R54 = 9 × 6	R72 = 9 × 8
35 = 7 × 5	42 = 7 × 6	56 = 7 × 8

Drawing No.	TITLE: **Loci. The hyperbola.**		SCALE:
G17			

G18-1: To construct an Archimedian spiral

Determine the locus of a point which travels 60 mm from a fixed point with uniform velocity, whilst completing one clockwise revolution of the fixed point with constant angular velocity.

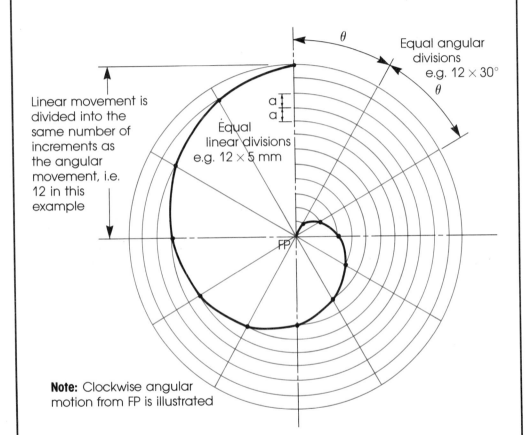

Linear movement is divided into the same number of increments as the angular movement, i.e. 12 in this example

Equal linear divisions e.g. 12 × 5 mm

θ

Equal angular divisions e.g. 12 × 30°

θ

a
a

FP

Note: Clockwise angular motion from FP is illustrated

The Archimedian spiral can be considered as the locus of a point which moves around a fixed point with constant angular velocity and from it with constant linear velocity, i.e. a compound motion.

G18-2: To construct an Archimedian spiral

Construct an Archimedian spiral by plotting the locus of a point which moves 70 mm away from a fixed point during one complete anticlockwise revolution. Both the linear and angular velocity are constant (i.e. directly related) during the cycle.

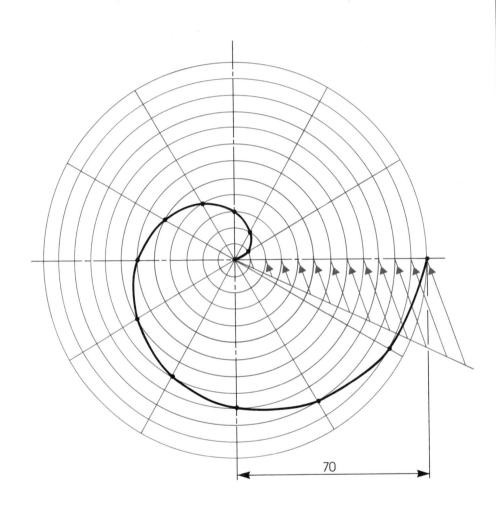

70

| Drawing No. G18 | TITLE: **Archimedian spiral.** | | SCALE: |

SCALE:
0 10 20 30 40 50 60 70 80
mm

G18-3: To construct the involute from a circle

Determine the locus of the free end
of a piece of string as it unwraps
$\frac{3}{4}$ of a revolution in a clockwise
direction from a reel of 45 mm diameter.
The string is kept tight all the time.

The figure below shows the tangent
to the <u>involute</u>. Note that the
normal is tangential to the base
circle at C (see G12-5).

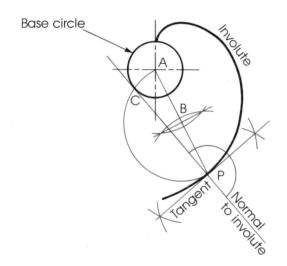

Base circle

Involute

A

C

B

P

Tangent

Normal
to involute

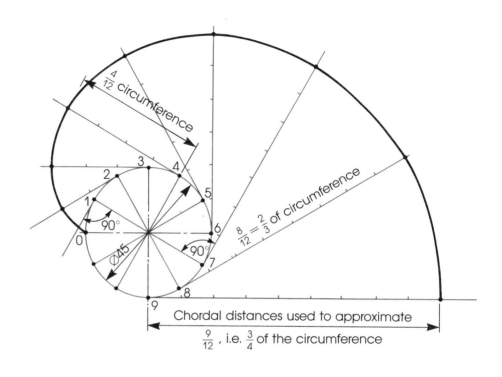

$\frac{4}{12}$ circumference

3
4
2
5
1
90°
0
6
Ø45
90°
7
8
9

$\frac{8}{12} = \frac{2}{3}$ of circumference

Chordal distances used to approximate

$\frac{9}{12}$, i.e. $\frac{3}{4}$ of the circumference

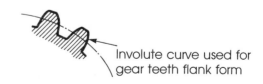

Involute curve used for
gear teeth flank form

The involute can be considered as
the locus of the end of a piece
of string which is unwrapped from
a cylinder with the string kept tight.

Drawing No.	TITLE: **The involute.**		SCALE:
G18			0 10 20 30 40 50 60 70 80
			mm

G18-4 To construct an anticlockwise involute

A piece of string is unwrapped from a drum of diameter 34 mm in an anticlockwise direction for one complete revolution. Construct an anticlockwise involute for one revolution with the involute having a base circle of diameter 34 mm. The free end of the string is kept tight whilst it unwraps.

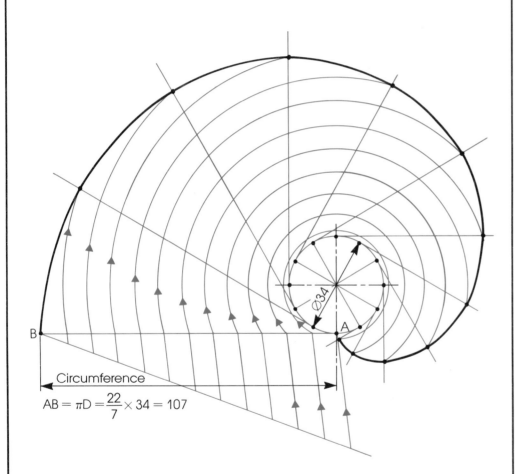

B

Circumference

$$AB = \pi D = \frac{22}{7} \times 34 = 107$$

G18-5: To construct a left-hand helix

Construct a left-hand helix having a pitch of 25 mm and a pitch diameter of 35 mm. Produce 2 complete turns (revolutions) of the helix and find its true length.

The helix is the locus of a point which moves along a cylinder with constant velocity whilst rotating around the cylinder with a corresponding angular velocity.

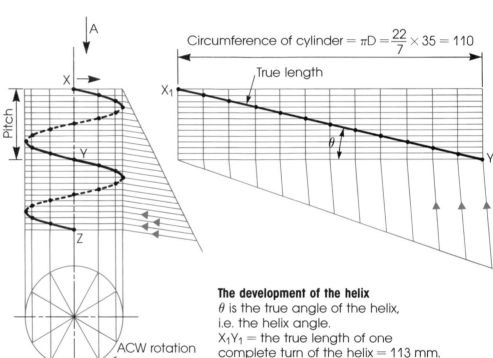

Circumference of cylinder $= \pi D = \frac{22}{7} \times 35 = 110$

True length

ACW rotation

Start X

View on arrow A
Note that anticlockwise (ACW) rotation produces a left-hand helix

The development of the helix
θ is the true angle of the helix, i.e. the helix angle.
$X_1Y_1 =$ the true length of one complete turn of the helix = 113 mm.
True length of X to Z = $2 \times 113 = 226$ mm.

The <u>pitch</u> is the distance travelled along the cylinder during one complete revolution of the helix.

Drawing No. **G18**	TITLE: **The involute and the helix.**	NOTE: **First Angle projection used for helix.**	SCALE: 0 10 20 30 40 50 60 70 80 mm

G18-6: To construct a right-hand helix

Plot the locus of a point which describes a right-hand helix with a pitch of 30 mm and lying on a cylinder of diameter 40 mm. Produce the locus for 4 revolutions around the cylinder as shown below, starting at A.

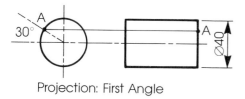

Projection: First Angle

The finish E is in line with the start A when complete revolutions are used

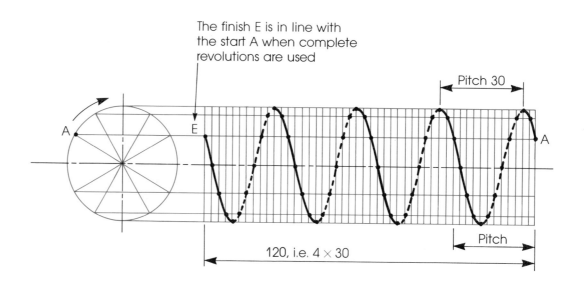

Pitch 30

120, i.e. 4 × 30

Pitch

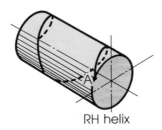

RH helix

The locus moves clockwise and away from the viewing position for a right-hand helix.

Drawing No. **G18**	TITLE: **The helix.**	NOTE: **First Angle projection used for helix.**	SCALE:

0 10 20 30 40 50 60 70 80
mm

G19-1: To construct the crests of a 2-start right-hand vee thread

Draw the crests of a 2-start right-hand vee thread for four complete turns of both helices. The screw thread has a major diameter of 54 mm and a lead of 24 mm, i.e. a pitch of 12 mm.

G19-2: To construct the crests of a 3-start right-hand vee thread

Draw the thread crests of a 3-start right-hand vee thread for a thread length of 60 mm. The thread has a major diameter of 40 mm and a lead of 30 mm.

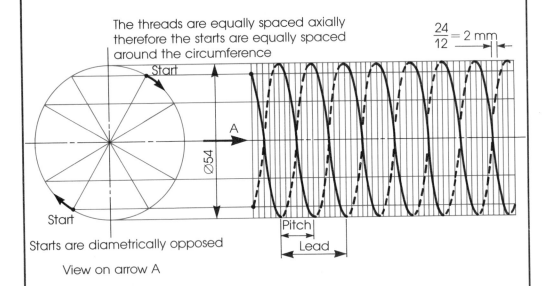

The threads are equally spaced axially therefore the starts are equally spaced around the circumference

$\frac{24}{12} = 2$ mm

Start

A

Ø54

Start

Starts are diametrically opposed

View on arrow A

Pitch

Lead

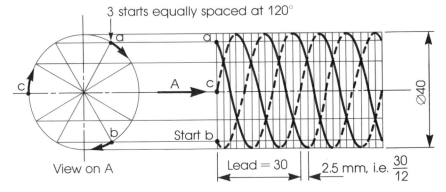

3 starts equally spaced at 120°

a   a

c   A   c

b   Start b

Ø40

View on A

Lead = 30   2.5 mm, i.e. $\frac{30}{12}$

$$\text{Pitch} = \frac{\text{lead}}{\text{no. of starts}}$$

Lead is the pitch of a single helix measured axially.

| Drawing No. **G19** | TITLE: **Engineering forms of the helix.** | NOTE: **Third Angle projection used.** | SCALE: |

SCALE:
0 10 20 30 40 50 60 70 80
mm

G19-3: To construct a spring

A thin ribbon (0.5 mm thick by 10 mm wide) of phosphor bronze is wound in helical form on to a cylinder of diameter 60 mm, to form a spring with a pitch of 36 mm. Draw the spring having 3 complete turns.

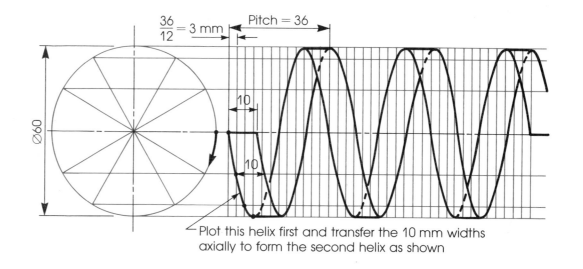

$\frac{36}{12} = 3$ mm

Pitch = 36

Ø60

10

10

Plot this helix first and transfer the 10 mm widths axially to form the second helix as shown

G19-4: To construct a single-start right-hand square screw thread

Produce a drawing of a single-start right-hand square screw thread which has a major diameter of 100 mm, a minor diameter of 60 mm and a pitch of 40 mm. Show the full thread form for a length of 100 mm.

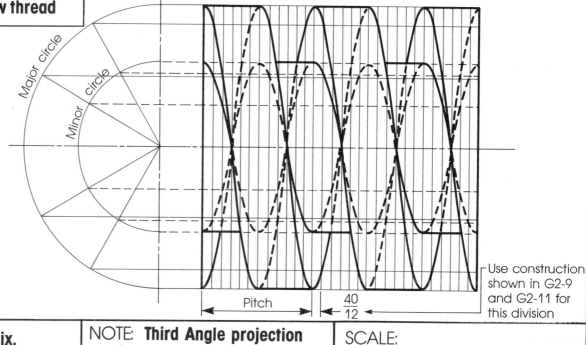

Major circle

Minor circle

Pitch

$\frac{40}{12}$

Use construction shown in G2-9 and G2-11 for this division

Drawing No. G19	TITLE: **Engineering forms of the helix.**	NOTE: **Third Angle projection used.**	SCALE:

0 10 20 30 40 50 60 70 80
mm

G19-5: To construct a 2-start right-hand square screw thread

Construct a 2-start right-hand square screw thread with a pitch of 20 mm, a major diameter of 70 mm and a thread length of 80 mm.

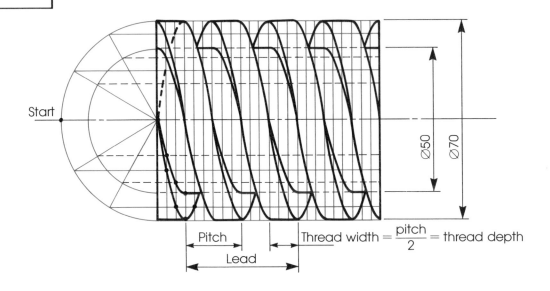

Start

Ø50
Ø70

Pitch

Lead

Thread width $= \dfrac{\text{pitch}}{2} =$ thread depth

G19-6: To construct a spring of helical form

A bar, 12 mm square, is wound into a spring of helical form with an outside diameter of 60 mm. The spring has a length of 144 mm between its flat ground ends and consists of a centre portion having 2 complete turns with a pitch of 48 mm; the remainder, equally spaced at each end, has a pitch of 24 mm. Draw the spring.

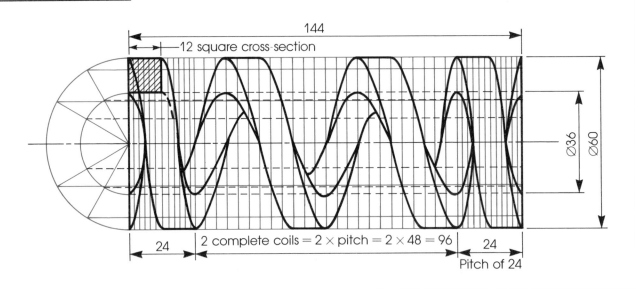

144

12 square cross-section

Ø36
Ø60

24

2 complete coils $= 2 \times$ pitch $= 2 \times 48 = 96$

24

Pitch of 24

| Drawing No. **G19** | TITLE: **Engineering forms of the helix.** | NOTE: **Third Angle projection used.** | SCALE: |

0 10 20 30 40 50 60 70 80
mm

G19-7: To construct a right-hand helical spring

A right-hand helical spring, formed by winding a bar of diameter 12 mm on a mandril of diameter 58 mm is 135 mm long over its ground ends. 3 central coils have a pitch of 36 mm and the remainder a pitch of 18 mm equally distributed at each end. Draw the spring.

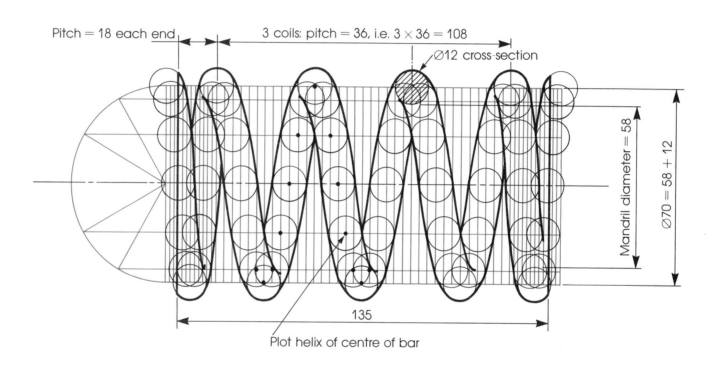

Pitch = 18 each end

3 coils: pitch = 36, i.e. 3 × 36 = 108

Ø12 cross-section

Mandril diameter = 58

Ø70 = 58 + 12

135

Plot helix of centre of bar

| Drawing No. **G19** | TITLE: **Engineering forms of the helix.** | NOTE: **Third Angle projection used.** | SCALE: |

0 10 20 30 40 50 60 70 80
mm

Worksheets for G20 and G21

G20 THE CYCLOID, HYPOCYCLOID AND EPICYCLOID.

G20-1 Fig 1 illustrates a disc ⌀60 mm which rolls without slip along the plane surface. Construct the locus of point P which lies on the periphery of the disc as the disc completes one clockwise revolution along the plane surface. Start with point P coincident with the plane when constructing the locus and construct a tangent to the cycloid when point P attains the position P_X shown.

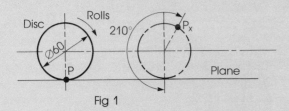

Fig 1

G20-2 Construct the locus of a point P located on the periphery of a disc of ⌀70 mm as shown in Fig 2. Starting with the point coincident with the circle the disc rolls for one complete anticlockwise revolution around the inside of the circle. Name the curve produced by the locus.

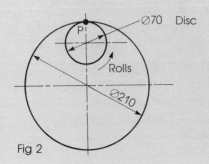

Fig 2

G20-3 Trace the locus of the point P located on the periphery of a disc of ⌀80 mm as shown in Fig 3. Starting with the point P coincident with the circle, the disc rolls for one complete clockwise revolution without slip around the outside of the circle.
Construct the tangent to the epicycloid produced at point P when P attains the position P_X.

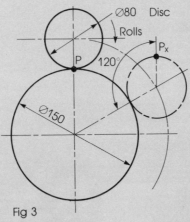

Fig 3

G21 LOCI PROBLEMS.

G21-1 Construct the locus produced by point P on the periphery of the disc shown in Fig 1 as the disc rotates one revolution clockwise. It rolls, without slip, along the plane starting with the point P as illustrated. Show the disc in position when P attains the position P_X.

G21-2 Construct the locus of point P which lies on the periphery of the disc shown in Fig 2 as it rolls $\frac{1}{2}$ revolution down the incline and $\frac{1}{2}$ revolution around the curve. Start with P coincident with the plane.

G21-3 Plot the locus of point M on the pantograph shown in Fig 3, as T on the link AD traces the shape of the triangle 1, 2, 3. O is a fixed pivot and A, B, C and D pin joints.

G21-4 Fig 4 shows the profile of a writing bureau lid and tie strap. Plot locus of B as the lid closes. A is a pin joint, D a hinge and E a fixed pin located in a slot.

G21-5 Construct the locus of point P on the link XY shown in Fig 5. End X is constrained to follow AB and end Y, CO.

G21-6 Fig 6 shows a mechanism where B is constrained to slide along X-Y with D pivoting about K. Construct the locus of P as A rotates about O. A, B, C and D are pin joints.

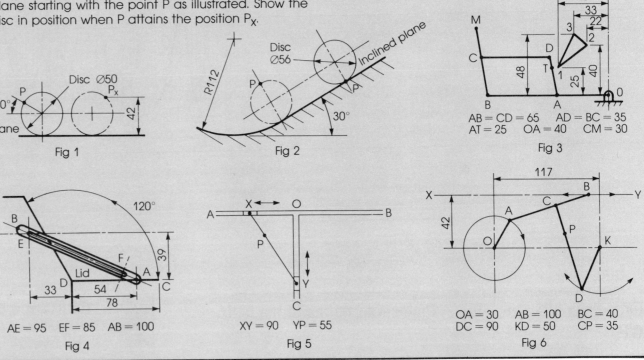

Fig 1

Fig 2

AB = CD = 65   AD = BC = 35
AT = 25   OA = 40   CM = 30
Fig 3

AE = 95   EF = 85   AB = 100
Fig 4

XY = 90   YP = 55
Fig 5

OA = 30   AB = 100   BC = 40
DC = 90   KD = 50   CP = 35
Fig 6

84

G20-1: To construct a cycloid

The figure (right) illustrates a disc of diameter 60 mm which rolls without slip along the plane surface. Construct the locus of point P which lies on the periphery of the disc as the disc completes one clockwise revolution along the plane surface (the locus produced is called the cycloid). Start with point P coincident with the plane when constructing the locus, and construct a tangent to the cycloid when point P attains the position P_x shown.

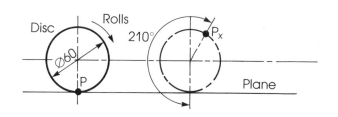

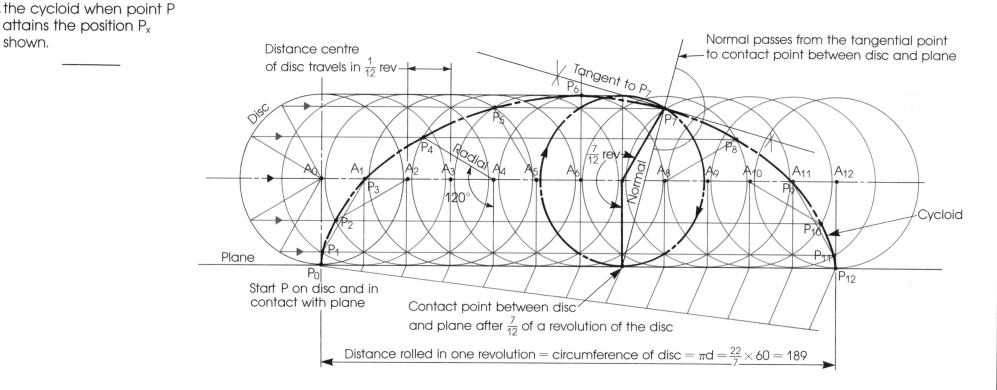

Distance centre of disc travels in $\frac{1}{12}$ rev

Normal passes from the tangential point to contact point between disc and plane

Tangent to P_7

$\frac{7}{12}$ rev

Radial

120°

Cycloid

Plane

Start P on disc and in contact with plane

Contact point between disc and plane after $\frac{7}{12}$ of a revolution of the disc

Distance rolled in one revolution = circumference of disc = $\pi d = \frac{22}{7} \times 60 = 189$

Cycloid: the locus of a point on the periphery of a disc which rolls without slip along a plane.

| Drawing No.
G20 | TITLE: **The cycloid.** | NOTE: **A Spirograph set provides a useful model.** | SCALE: |

G20-2: To construct a hypocycloid

Construct the locus of a point P located on the periphery of a disc having a diameter of 70 mm as shown below. Starting with the point coincident with the circle the disc rolls for one complete anticlockwise revolution around the inside of the circle.

Hypocycloid: the locus of a point on the periphery of a disc which rolls without slip around the inside of a circle.

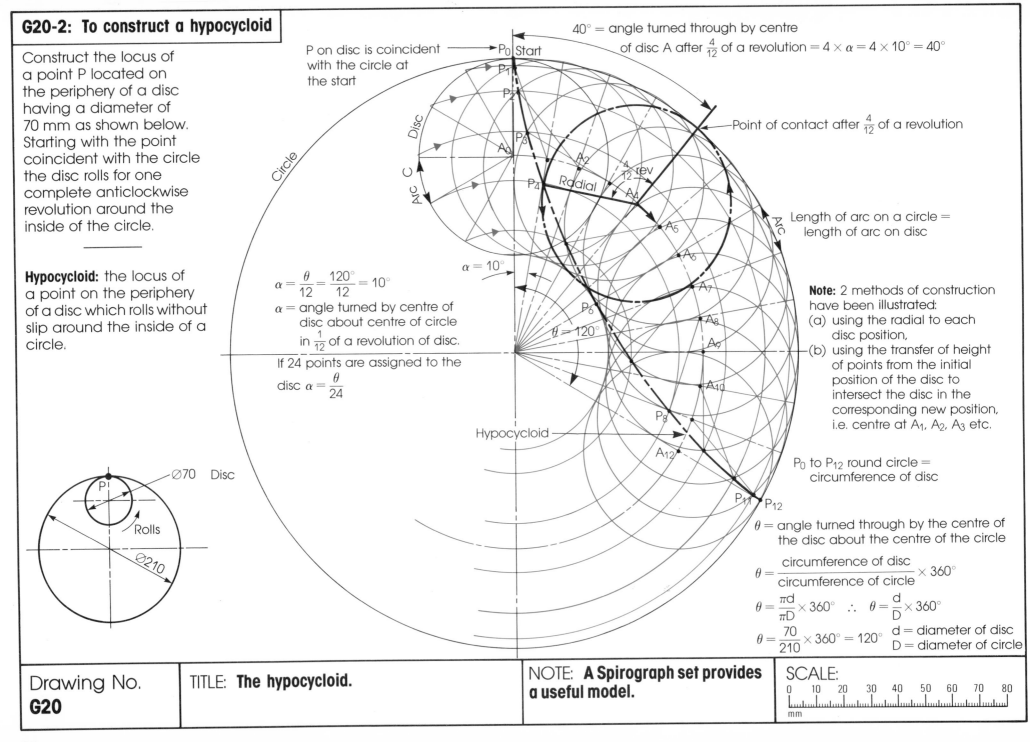

P on disc is coincident with the circle at the start

P_0 Start

40° = angle turned through by centre of disc A after $\frac{4}{12}$ of a revolution = $4 \times \alpha = 4 \times 10° = 40°$

Point of contact after $\frac{4}{12}$ of a revolution

$\frac{4}{12}$ rev

Radial

Length of arc on a circle = length of arc on disc

$\alpha = \dfrac{\theta}{12} = \dfrac{120°}{12} = 10°$

α = angle turned by centre of disc about centre of circle in $\frac{1}{12}$ of a revolution of disc.

If 24 points are assigned to the disc $\alpha = \dfrac{\theta}{24}$

$\alpha = 10°$

$\theta = 120°$

Note: 2 methods of construction have been illustrated:
(a) using the radial to each disc position,
(b) using the transfer of height of points from the initial position of the disc to intersect the disc in the corresponding new position, i.e. centre at A_1, A_2, A_3 etc.

Hypocycloid

P_0 to P_{12} round circle = circumference of disc

θ = angle turned through by the centre of the disc about the centre of the circle

$\theta = \dfrac{\text{circumference of disc}}{\text{circumference of circle}} \times 360°$

$\theta = \dfrac{\pi d}{\pi D} \times 360° \quad \therefore \quad \theta = \dfrac{d}{D} \times 360°$

$\theta = \dfrac{70}{210} \times 360° = 120°$

d = diameter of disc
D = diameter of circle

⌀70 Disc

P

Rolls

⌀210

| Drawing No. **G20** | TITLE: **The hypocycloid.** | NOTE: **A Spirograph set provides a useful model.** | SCALE: |

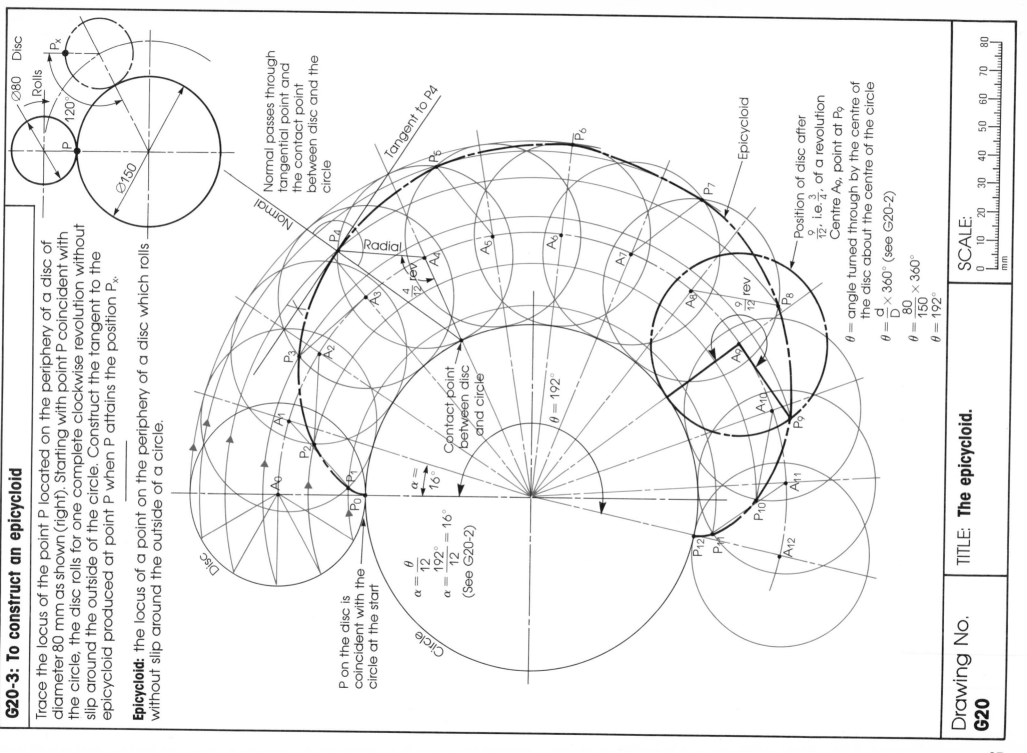

G20-3: To construct an epicycloid

Trace the locus of the point P located on the periphery of a disc of diameter 80 mm as shown (right). Starting with point P coincident with the circle, the disc rolls for one complete clockwise revolution without slip around the outside of the circle. Construct the tangent to the epicycloid produced at point P when P attains the position P_x.

Epicycloid: the locus of a point on the periphery of a disc which rolls without slip around the outside of a circle.

Ø80   Disc
Rolls
120°
P
Ø150

Normal passes through tangential point and the contact point between disc and the circle

Tangent to P4

Radial

Normal

$\frac{4}{12}$ rev

Epicycloid

Position of disc after $\frac{9}{12}$, i.e. $\frac{3}{4}$, of a revolution
Centre A_9, point at P_9

θ = angle turned through by the centre of the disc about the centre of the circle

$$\theta = \frac{d}{D} \times 360° \text{ (see G20-2)}$$

$$\theta = \frac{80}{150} \times 360°$$

$$\theta = 192°$$

$\frac{9}{12}$ rev

Contact point between disc and circle

$\theta = 192°$

$\alpha = 16°$

$$\alpha = \frac{\theta}{12}$$

$$\alpha = \frac{192°}{12} = 16°$$

(See G20-2)

P on the disc is coincident with the circle at the start

Disc

Circle

Epicycloid

Drawing No. **G20**   TITLE: **The epicycloid.**   SCALE:

mm

G21-1: To construct the locus of a point on the periphery of a rolling disc

Construct the locus produced by point P on the periphery of the disc shown in the line diagram as the disc rotates one revolution clockwise. It rolls, without slip, along the plane starting with the point P as illustrated. Show the disc in position when P reaches the position P_x.

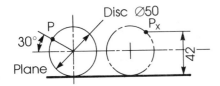

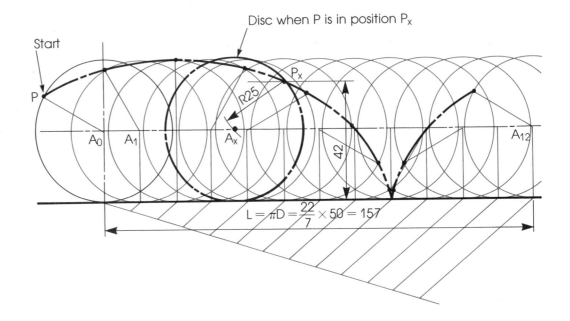

Disc when P is in position P_x

Start

$L = \pi D = \dfrac{22}{7} \times 50 = 157$

Drawing No.	TITLE: **General problems involving loci.**	SCALE:
G21		0 10 20 30 40 50 60 70 80 mm

G21-2: To construct the locus of a point on the periphery of a disc rolling down a plane and curved surface

Construct the locus of point P which lies on the periphery of the disc shown below as it rolls $\frac{1}{2}$ revolution down the incline and $\frac{1}{2}$ revolution around the curve. Start with P coincident with the plane as illustrated below.

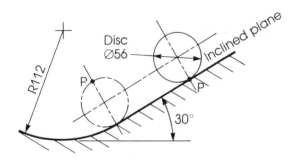

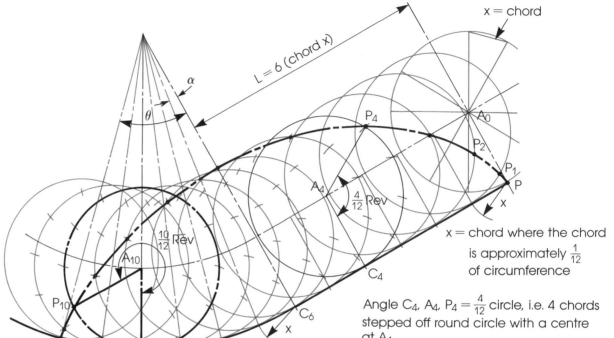

Angle C_{10}, A_{10}, P_{10} is $\frac{10}{12}$ of circle

Step off 10 chords (x) round circle from C_{10}

x = chord where the chord is approximately $\frac{1}{12}$ of circumference

Angle C_4, A_4, $P_4 = \frac{4}{12}$ circle, i.e. 4 chords stepped off round circle with a centre at A_4

x is used to determine angle α, angle θ and length L (approx.)

By calculation $\theta = \frac{6}{12} \times \frac{56}{224} \times 360° = 45°$

$$\alpha = \frac{45°}{6} = 7\frac{1}{2}°$$

$L = \frac{1}{2}$ circumference of disc

$L = \frac{1}{2} \pi \times 56 = 88$ mm

Drawing No.	TITLE: **General problems involving loci.**		SCALE:
G21			0 10 20 30 40 50 60 70 80 mm

G21-3: To draw a figure similar to one given using the principles of the pantograph

A pantograph is shown in the line diagram below. Plot the locus of point M on the pantograph as T on the link A-D traces the shape of the triangle 1, 2, 3. O is a fixed pivot and A, B, C and D are pin joints.

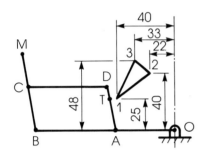

$AB = CD = 65$ $AD = BC = 35$
$AT = 25$ $OA = 40$ $CM = 30$

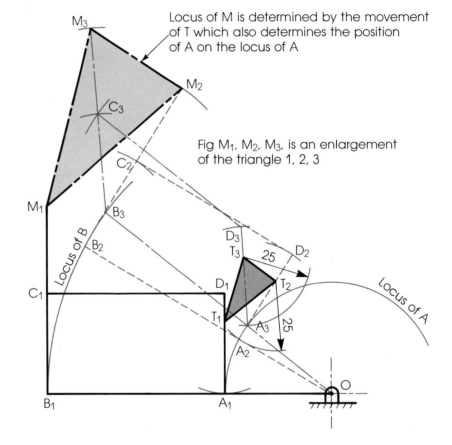

Locus of M is determined by the movement of T which also determines the position of A on the locus of A

Fig M_1, M_2, M_3, is an enlargement of the triangle 1, 2, 3

The ratio of the enlargement is given by the pantograph dimensions OA and OB which in the case illustrated gives

an englargement of $\dfrac{OB}{OA}$:1 which equals

$\dfrac{65 + 40}{40} = 2.625{:}1.$

| **Drawing No.** **G21** | TITLE: **General problems involving loci.** | | SCALE:  |

G21-4: To construct the locus of a point on a slotted link

The line diagram shows the profile of a writing bureau lid and tie strap. Plot the locus of B as the lid closes. A is a pin joint, D a hinge and E a fixed pin located in a slot.

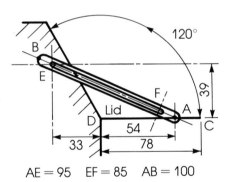

120°

39

AE = 95   EF = 85   AB = 100

54

33   78

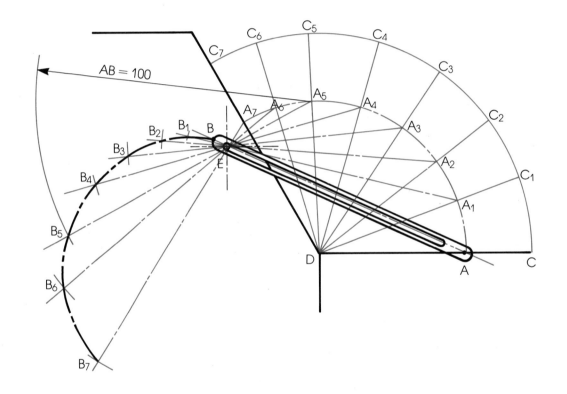

AB = 100

G21-5: To construct the locus of a point on a sliding link

Construct the locus of point P
on the link X–Y shown below.
End X is constrained to
follow AB and end Y follows
CO.

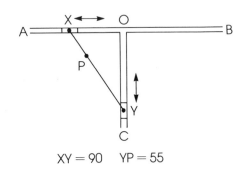

XY = 90   YP = 55

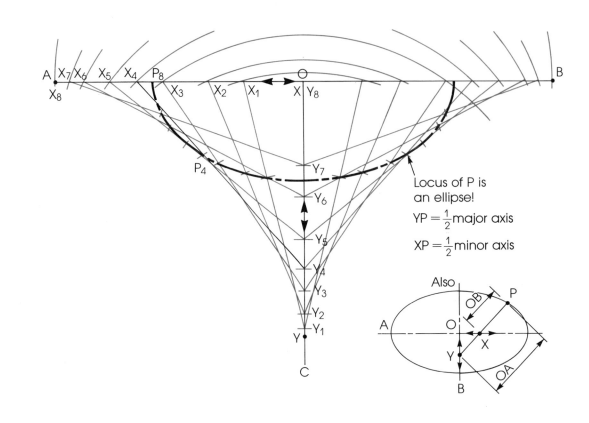

Locus of P is
an ellipse!

$YP = \frac{1}{2}$major axis

$XP = \frac{1}{2}$minor axis

Drawing No.	TITLE: **General problems involving loci.**		SCALE:
G21			0 10 20 30 40 50 60 70 80
			mm

G21-6: To construct the locus of a point on a mechanism

The line diagram shows a mechanism where B is constrained to slide along X–Y with D pivoting about K. Construct the locus of P as A rotates about O. A, B, C and D are pin joints.

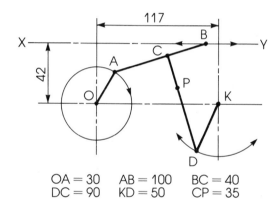

OA = 30   AB = 100   BC = 40
DC = 90   KD = 50   CP = 35

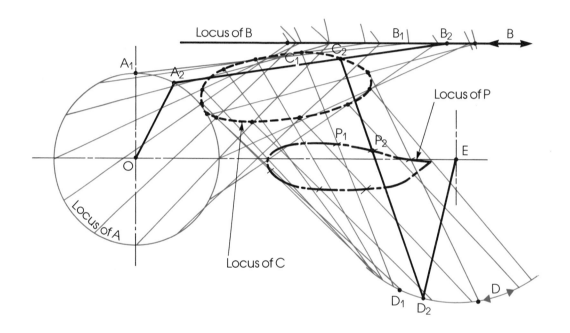

Drawing No.	TITLE: **General problems involving loci.**		SCALE:

G21

SOLID GEOMETRY

Stage 1
The solid in a
defined space.

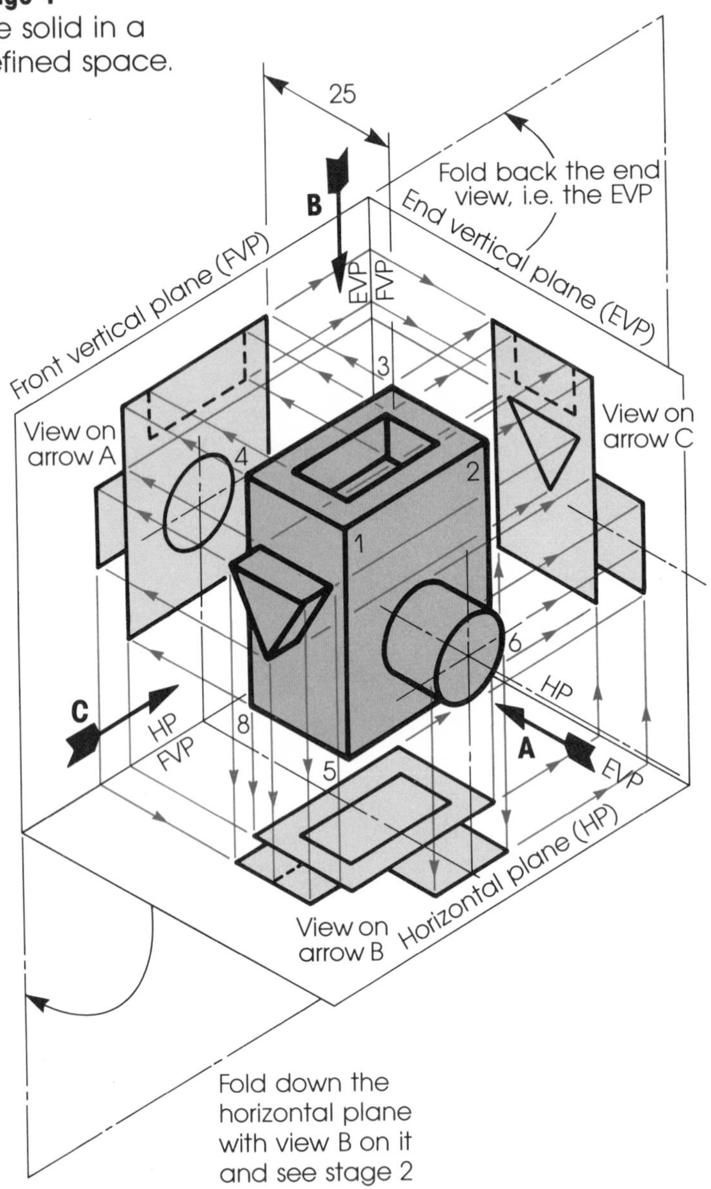

Stage 2
The solid has been removed
and the views folded back
to form a single flat plane.

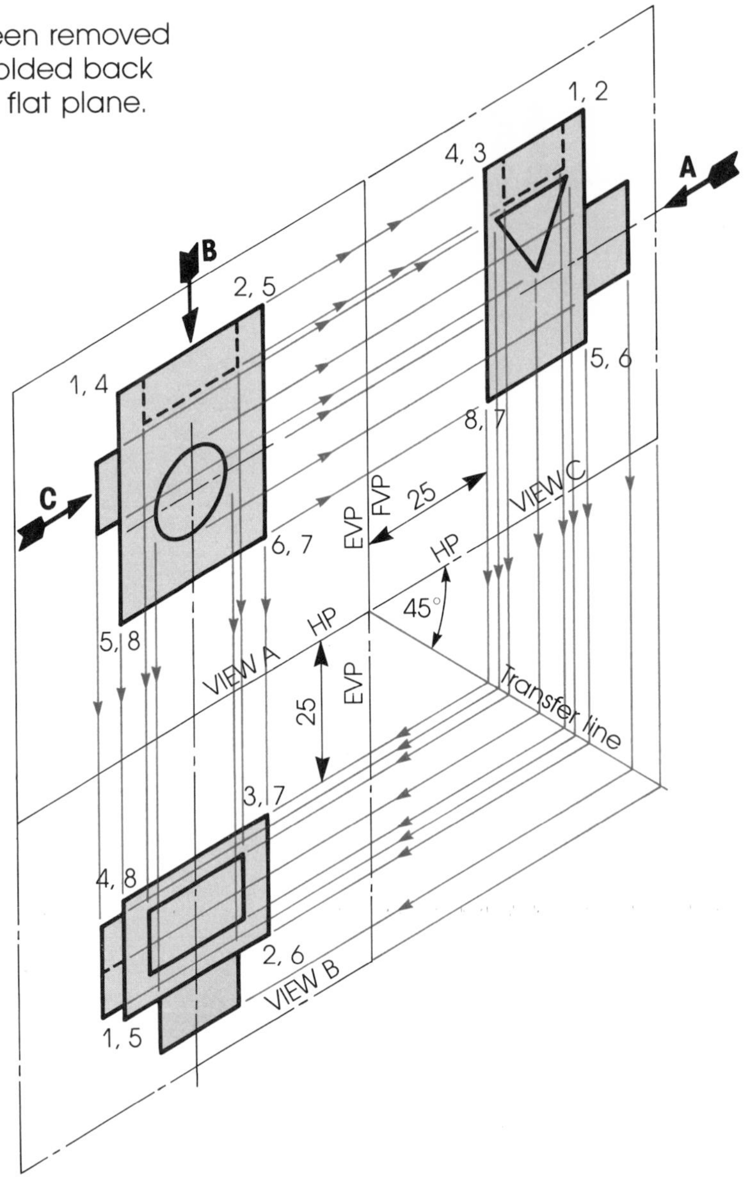

25

B

Fold back the end
view, i.e. the EVP

Front vertical plane (FVP)

End vertical plane (EVP)

View on
arrow A

View on
arrow C

3

4

2

1

6

HP
FVP

C

8

5

A

EVP

HP

View on
arrow B   Horizontal plane (HP)

Fold down the
horizontal plane
with view B on it
and see stage 2

1, 2

4, 3

A

B

2, 5

1, 4

5, 6

C

8, 7

6, 7

EVP FVP   25

HP

45°

5, 8

VIEW A   HP

25

EVP

VIEW C

Transfer line

3, 7

4, 8

2, 6

1, 5   VIEW B

Drawing No.
G22

TITLE: **Introduction to solid geometry.**
First Angle projection (English).

NOTE: **Types of line used:** _____ **Centre lines/**
moved planes.
——— **Visible outlines.**
——→ **Projection/ construction.** ----- **Hidden edges.**

SCALE:
0 10 20 30 40 50 60 70 80
mm

G22-2: Orthographic representation of an adjoining solid. First Angle projection

Stage 3
Produce the true shape of each feature as it appears in each view.

Note convention: When points or corners are numbered (e.g. 1,4) it means two points are in line, with point 1 being in front of point 4, that is, nearest the viewing position.

Stage 4
Project from the true shapes the apparent shapes in each view, i.e. stage 2 viewed direct.

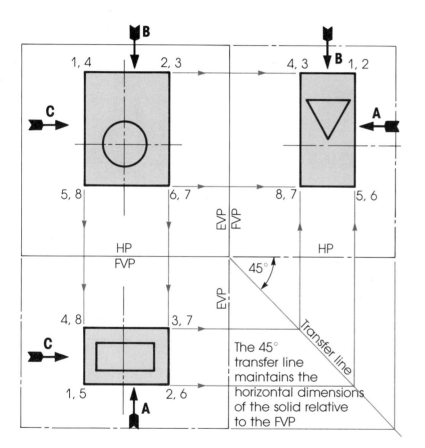

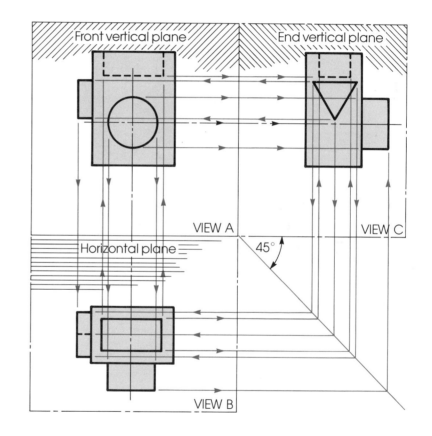

| Drawing No. G22 | TITLE: **Introduction to solid geometry. First Angle projection (English).** | NOTE: **Types of line used:** _ _ _ _ _ _ **Centre lines/ moved planes.** —— **Visible outlines.** → **Projection/construction.** - - - - **Hidden edges.** | SCALE: 0 10 20 30 40 50 60 70 80 mm |

Stage 1
Solid defined.

Stage 2
Projected views folded
back to a single plane.

Fold the HP up
to extend
the FVP

Horizontal
plane

Front vertical
plane

End
vertical
plane

Fold EVP
forward
to extend the FVP

Transfer line

Horizontal
plane

Front vertical
plane

End vertical
plane

45°

VIEW Y

VIEW X

VIEW Z

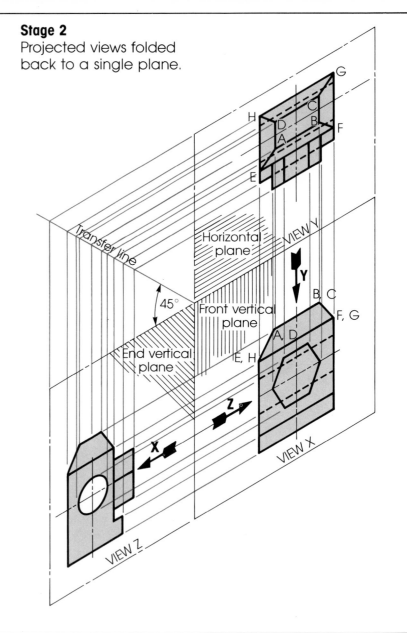

| Drawing No. **G22** | TITLE: **Introduction to solid geometry. Third Angle projection. (American and ISO recommended).** | NOTE: **Types of line used:** ──── **Centre lines/ moved planes.** ──── **Visible outlines.** ──→ **Projection/ construction.** ----- **Hidden edges.** | SCALE: 0 10 20 30 40 50 60 70 80 mm |

G22-4: Orthographic representation of an adjoining solid. Third Angle Projection

Stage 3

Work in all 3 views simultaneously and produce the shape of each feature which appears as a true shape.

Note: The true shape of a surface can only be seen when the viewing position is normal to the surface, i.e. at 90° to the surface.

Stage 4

Direct view on stage 2. Join A to E, B to F, C to G and D to H to obtain oblique bevelled faces.

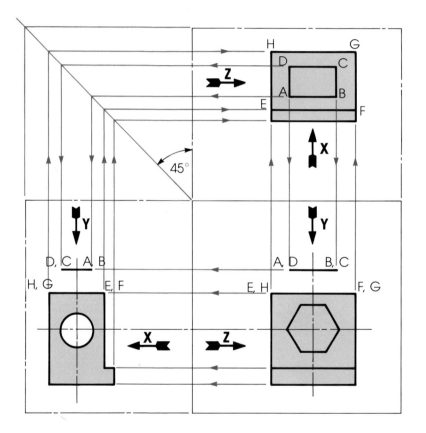

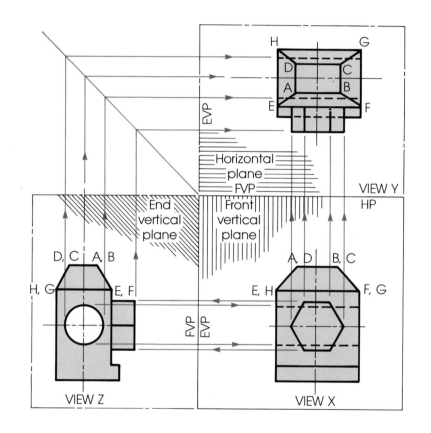

Drawing No.	TITLE: **Introduction to solid geometry.**	NOTE: **Types of line used:** _ _ _ _	**Centre lines/**	SCALE:
G22	**Third Angle projection.**	—— **Visible outlines.**	**moved planes.**	0 10 20 30 40 50 60 70 80
	(American and ISO recommended).	——► **Projection/construction.** - - - - - **Hidden edges.**		mm

Worksheets for G23 to G26

G23 THE RECTANGULAR PRISM (FIRST ANGLE PROJECTION).

G23-1 Draw views A, B and C of the prism to First Angle projection.

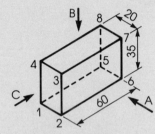

G23-2 Draw the given front elevation of a rectangular prism 60 mm × 35 mm × 20 mm and project, to First Angle, views B and C.

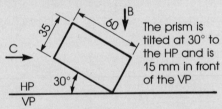

The prism is tilted at 30° to the HP and is 15 mm in front of the VP

G23-3 Draw the given plan view of a rectangular prism 60 mm × 35 mm × 20 mm. Project, to First Angle, a view A and a view C projected from view A.

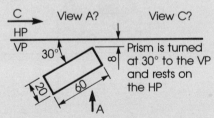

View A?   View C?

Prism is turned at 30° to the VP and rests on the HP

G23-4 Draw the given end elevation of a rectangular prism 60 mm × 35 mm × 20 mm. Project, to First Angle, a view A and a view B projected from view A.

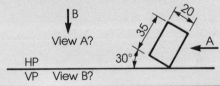

View A?

View B?

G23-5 Draw the given elevation cut by the plane A-A. Project views B and C and the auxiliary elevation to show the true shape of section.

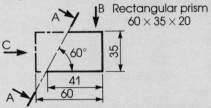

Rectangular prism 60 × 35 × 20

G23-6 Draw the given plan cut by the plane B-B. Project view A direct and a view C from view A. Project an auxiliary elevation on plane B-B.

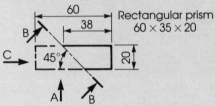

Rectangular prism 60 × 35 × 20

G23-7 Draw the given views of a prism cut by the plane C-C. Project view B and an auxiliary elevation on the plane C-C to show the true shape of the section.

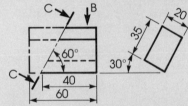

G23-8 Draw the given elevation and complete the plan view B of the prism cut by the plane D-D. Project a view C and auxiliary elevation on D-D.

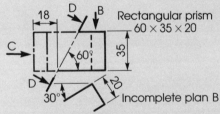

Rectangular prism 60 × 35 × 20

Incomplete plan B

G23-9 Draw the plan view and complete elevation A of the prism cut by the plane E-E. Project a view C and an auxiliary view on the plane E-E to show the true shape of the section.

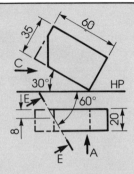

G24 THE TRIANGULAR PRISM (FIRST ANGLE PROJECTION).

G24-1 Draw the 2 given views of a triangular prism and project a view B direct from the position illustrated.

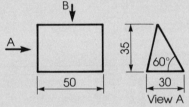

View A

G24-2 Draw an auxiliary view on D and produce the given view. Produce views B and C projected direct from the given view to First Angle.

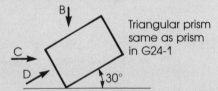

Triangular prism same as prism in G24-1

G24-3 Draw an auxiliary view on D and produce the given view. Project a view A direct from the given view and project view C from view A.

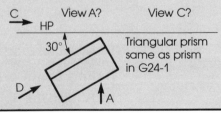

View A?   View C?

Triangular prism same as prism in G24-1

100

G24-4 Draw the given view of a triangular prism and project views A and B as illustrated to First Angle.

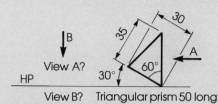

View A?
View B? Triangular prism 50 long

G24-5 Draw the given elevation cut by the plane C-C. Project views A and B and an auxiliary elevation looking on C-C to show the true shape of the section.

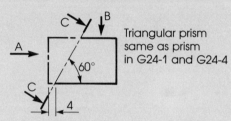

Triangular prism same as prism in G24-1 and G24-4

G24-6 Draw the given plan cut by the plane D-D. Project view A direct and a view C from view A. Project an auxiliary elevation on the plane D-D.

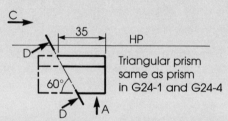

Triangular prism same as prism in G24-1 and G24-4

G24-7 Draw the given views of a prism cut by the plane E-E. Project view B and an auxiliary elevation on the plane E-E to show the true shape of the section.

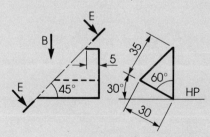

G24-8 Draw the given plan of the prism. Project view A and a view to show the true shape of section F-F.

G24-9 Draw the plan view and complete elevation A of the prism cut by the plane G-G. Project a view C and an auxiliary view on the plane E-E to show the true shape of the section.

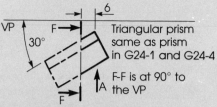

Triangular prism same as prism in G24-1 and G24-4

F-F is at 90° to the VP

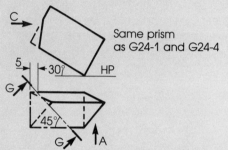

Same prism as G24-1 and G24-4

G25 THE HEXAGONAL PRISM (FIRST ANGLE PROJECTION).

G25-1 Draw the 2 given views of the prism and project a plan view B.

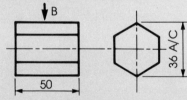

G25-2 Draw an auxiliary view on D and produce the given view. Produce views B and C projected direct from the given view to First Angle.

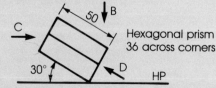

Hexagonal prism 36 across corners

G25-3 Draw an auxiliary view on D and produce the given view. Project a view A direct from the given view and project view C from view A.

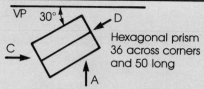

Hexagonal prism 36 across corners and 50 long

G25-4 Draw and complete the 2 given views of the prism cut by the plane C-C. Project a plan view B direct from the given view A.

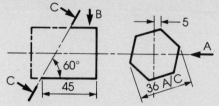

G25-5 Draw the given elevation cut by the plane D-D. Project views A and B and an auxiliary elevation looking on D-D to show the true shape of the section.

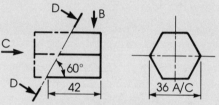

G26-6 Draw the given view of the prism cut by the plane E-E. Project views B and C and an auxiliary elevation on E-E direct from the given view.

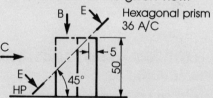

Hexagonal prism 36 A/C

G25-7 Draw the given plan cut by the plane F-F. Project a view A direct and a view C from view A. Project an auxiliary elevation on the plane F-F.

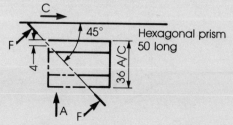

Hexagonal prism 50 long

G25-8 Draw the 2 given views of the prism cut by the plane G-G. Project a view C and an auxiliary view on the section plane G-G to show the true shape of the cut section.

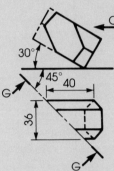

G25-9 Draw the given elevation and complete the plan view B of the prism cut by the plane H-H. Project a view C direct and an auxiliary elevation on the plane H-H to show the true shape of the section.

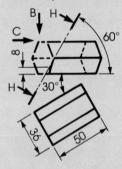

G26 THE CYLINDER AND THE SPHERE (FIRST ANGLE PROJECTION).

G26-1 Draw views A, B and C of the cylinder to First Angle projection.

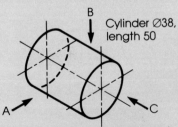

Cylinder Ø38, length 50

G26-2 Draw the given plan and a view B. Project a view C from view B and an auxiliary view on the plane A-A.

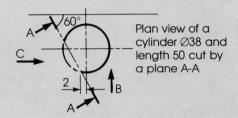

Plan view of a cylinder Ø38 and length 50 cut by a plane A-A

G26-3 Draw an auxiliary view on D and produce the given view. Project views B and C direct from the given view to First Angle.

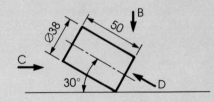

G26-4 Draw the given view of a cylinder cut by a plane B-B. Project a view C and an auxiliary view on the plane B-B.

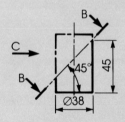

G26-5 Draw the given view of a cylinder cut by a plane C-C. Project a view on B and an auxiliary elevation on the plane C-C.

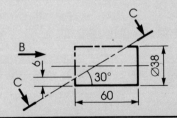

G26-6 Draw the given view of a cylinder cut by the plane D-D. Project view A direct and a view C from view A. Draw an auxiliary elevation on D-D.

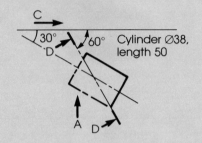

Cylinder Ø38, length 50

G26-7 The sphere shown is cut by the planes E-E and F-F. Draw the views on E-E and F-F to show the true shape of the sections.

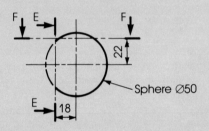

Sphere Ø50

G26-8 Draw the given view of a sphere cut by the plane G-G. Project an auxiliary elevation on G-G, a view A and a view C from view A.

View A

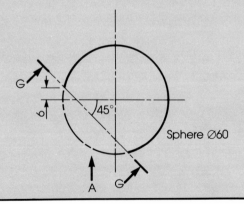

Sphere Ø60

G23-1

Draw views A, B and C of the prism to First Angle projection.

Note: By convention, looking on arrow A, corner 7 is in front of 8. Therefore in view A corner 7 is noted first, i.e. 7, 8.

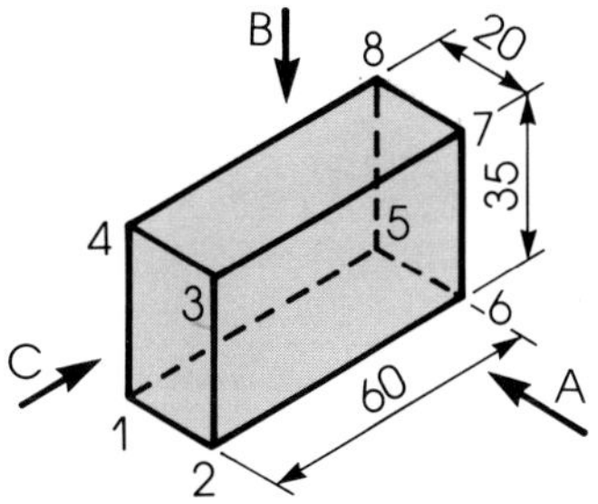

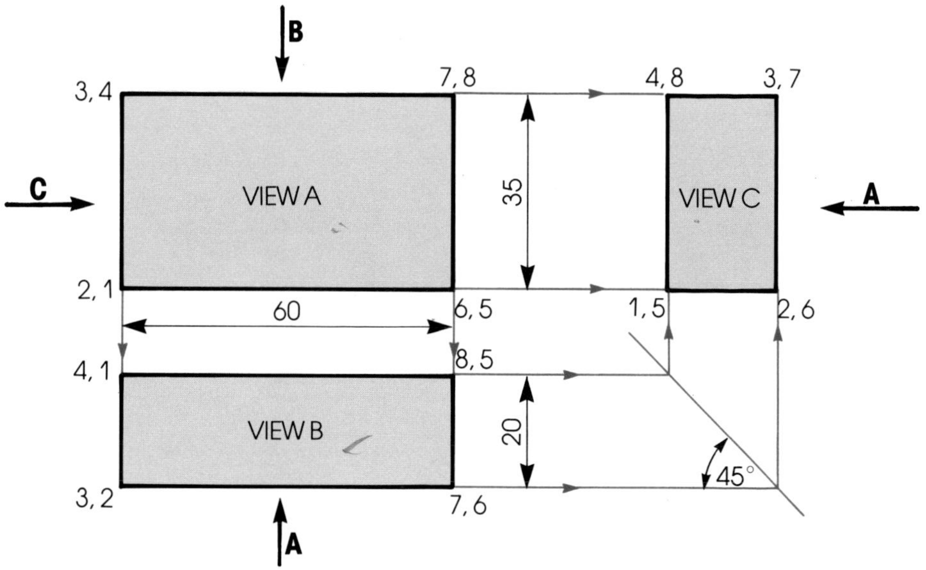

G23-2

Draw the front elevation of a rectangular prism 60 mm × 35 mm × 20 mm and project, to First Angle, views B and C.

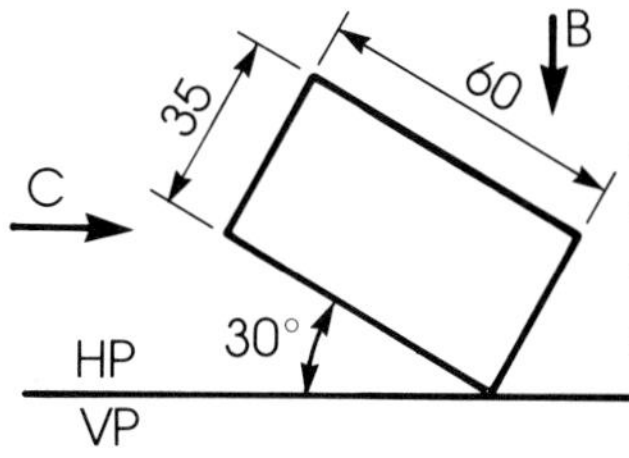

The prism is tilted at 30° to the HP and is 15 mm in front of the VP

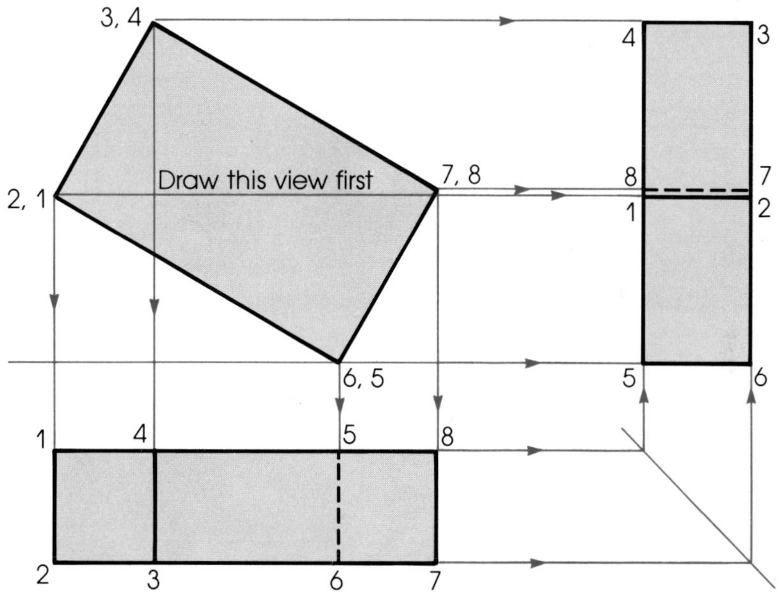

Drawing No. **G23**	TITLE: **The rectangular prism.**	NOTE: **First Angle projection used.**	SCALE: 

103

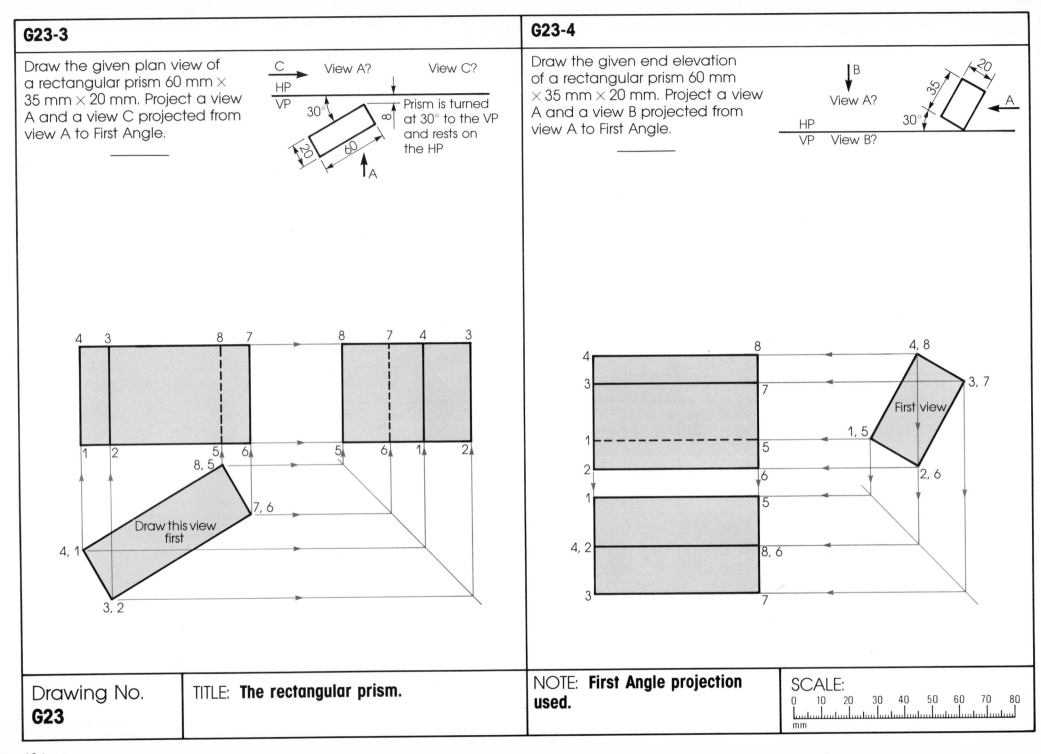

G23-3

Draw the given plan view of a rectangular prism 60 mm × 35 mm × 20 mm. Project a view A and a view C projected from view A to First Angle.

C → View A?   View C?

HP
VP   30°   8   Prism is turned at 30° to the VP and rests on the HP

20   60

↑A

4 3   8 7   8 7 4 3

1 2   5 6   5 6 1 2

8, 5

7, 6

Draw this view first

4, 1

3, 2

G23-4

Draw the given end elevation of a rectangular prism 60 mm × 35 mm × 20 mm. Project a view A and a view B projected from view A to First Angle.

↓B

View A?

20
35

← A

HP
VP   View B?   30°

4   8   4, 8
3   7   3, 7
                  First view
1   5   1, 5
2   6   2, 6

1   5
4, 2   8, 6
3   7

Drawing No. **G23**   TITLE: **The rectangular prism.**

NOTE: **First Angle projection used.**

SCALE:
0 10 20 30 40 50 60 70 80
mm

104

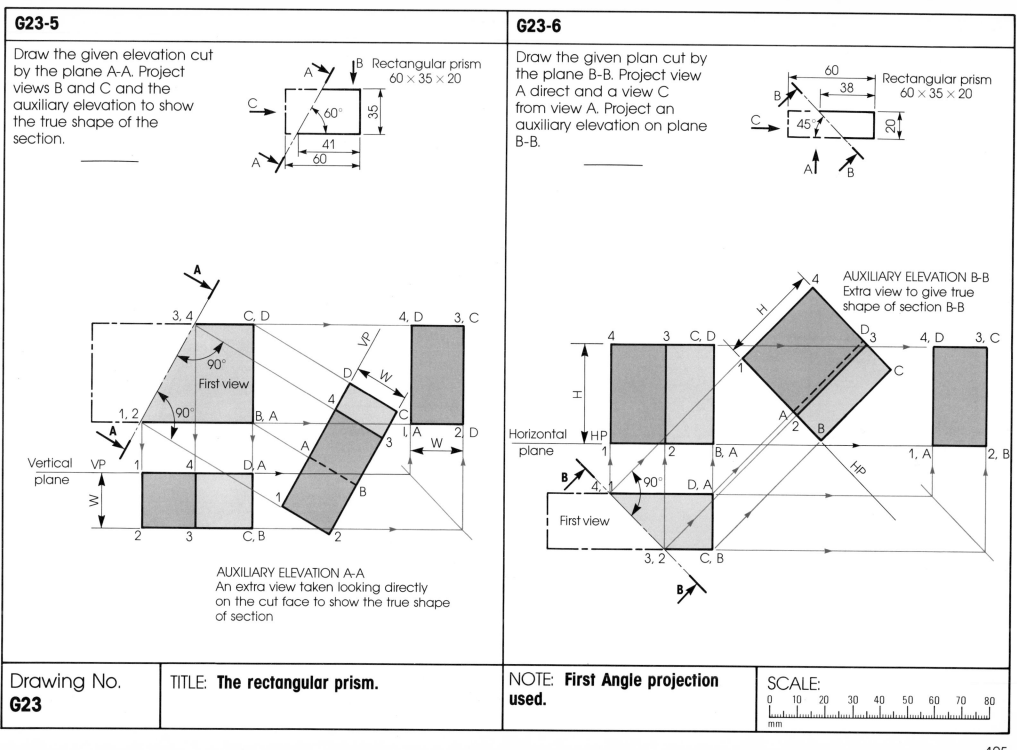

G23-5

Draw the given elevation cut by the plane A-A. Project views B and C and the auxiliary elevation to show the true shape of the section.

B Rectangular prism
60 × 35 × 20

60°
35
41
60

A

3, 4   C, D   4, D   3, C

90°
First view

VP

90°

1, 2   B, A

D   W
4   C
A   3
1   I, A   2, D
B   W

Vertical plane   VP   1   4   D, A

W

2   3   C, B   2

AUXILIARY ELEVATION A-A
An extra view taken looking directly on the cut face to show the true shape of section

G23-6

Draw the given plan cut by the plane B-B. Project view A direct and a view C from view A. Project an auxiliary elevation on plane B-B.

60
38
Rectangular prism
60 × 35 × 20

B
C   45°   20
A   B

AUXILIARY ELEVATION B-B
Extra view to give true shape of section B-B

4   3   C, D   4, D   3, C
H   D3
1   C
H   A   2   B
Horizontal plane   HP   1   2   B, A   1, A   2, B
B   4, 1   90°   D, A   HP
First view
3, 2   C, B
B

Drawing No.
G23

TITLE: **The rectangular prism.**

NOTE: **First Angle projection used.**

SCALE:
0 10 20 30 40 50 60 70 80
mm

105

G23-7

Draw the given views of a prism cut by the plane C-C. Project view B and an auxiliary elevation on the plane C-C to show the true shape of the section.

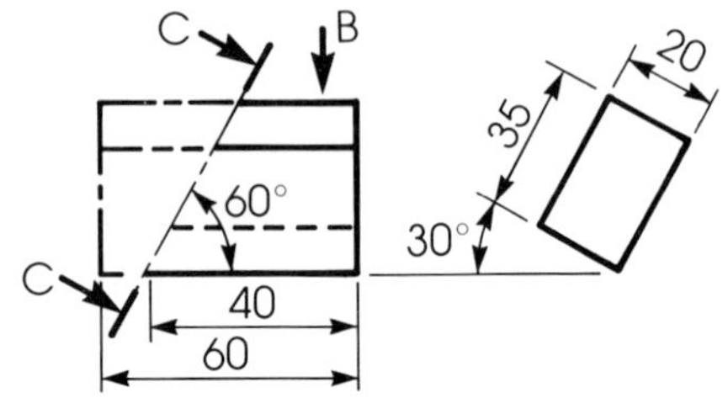

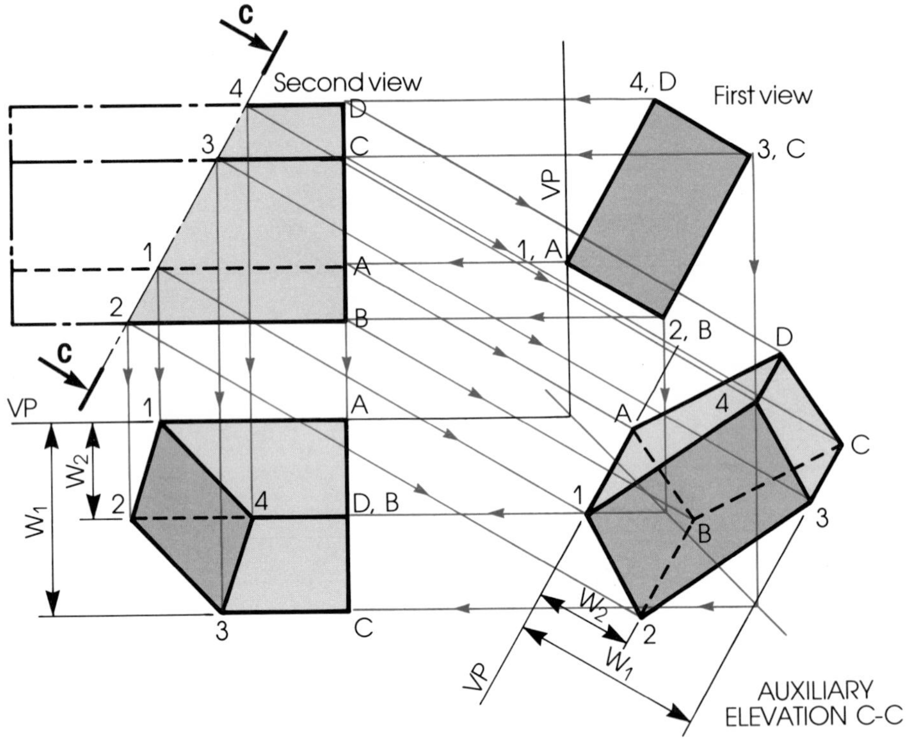

———

C   B
60°
30°
35
20
40
60

G23-8

Draw the given elevation and complete the plan view B of the prism cut by plane D-D. Project a view C and the auxiliary elevation on D-D.

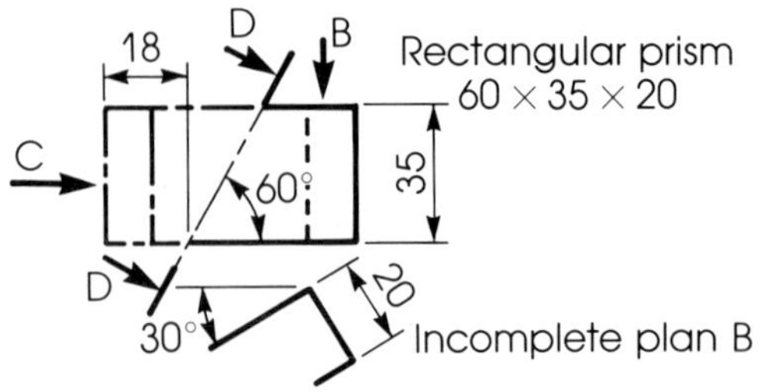

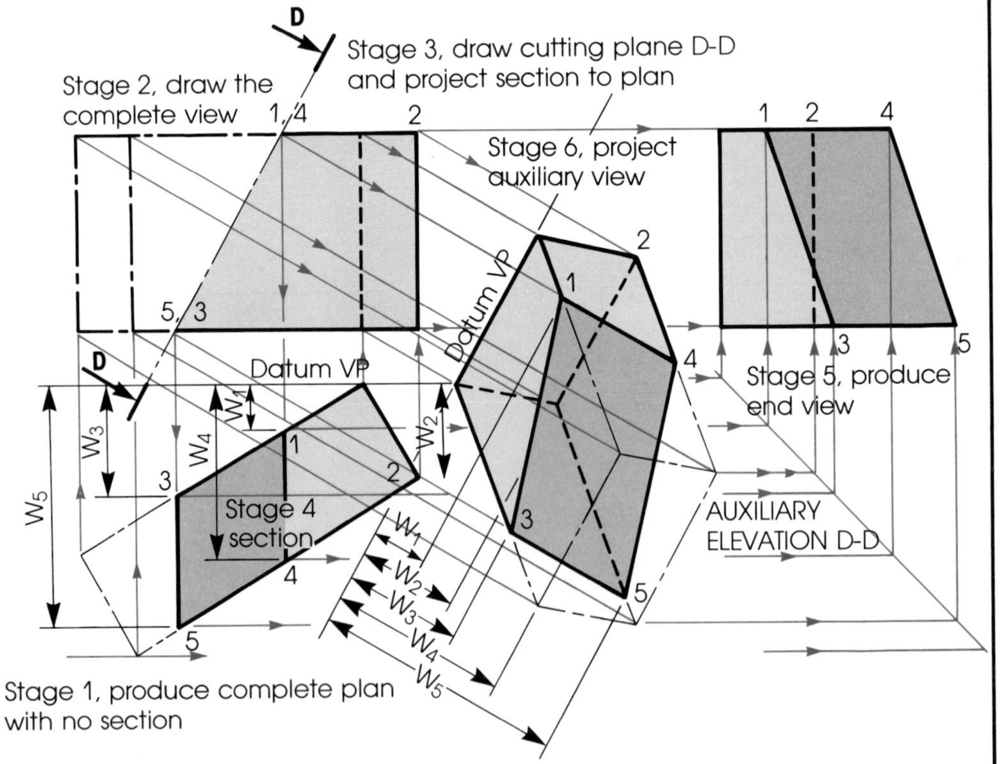

———

18   D   B
Rectangular prism
60 × 35 × 20
C
60°
35
D
30°
20
Incomplete plan B

Second view   4, D   First view
Stage 2, draw the complete view
Stage 3, draw cutting plane D-D and project section to plan
Stage 6, project auxiliary view
Stage 5, produce end view
Stage 4 section
Datum VP
Stage 1, produce complete plan with no section
AUXILIARY ELEVATION C-C
AUXILIARY ELEVATION D-D

| Drawing No. **G23** | TITLE: **The rectangular prism.** | NOTE: **First Angle projection used.** | SCALE: |

0 10 20 30 40 50 60 70 80
mm

Draw the plan view and complete elevation A of the prism cut by the plane E-E. Project a view C and an auxiliary view on the plane E-E to show the true shape of the section.

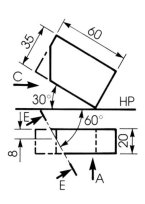

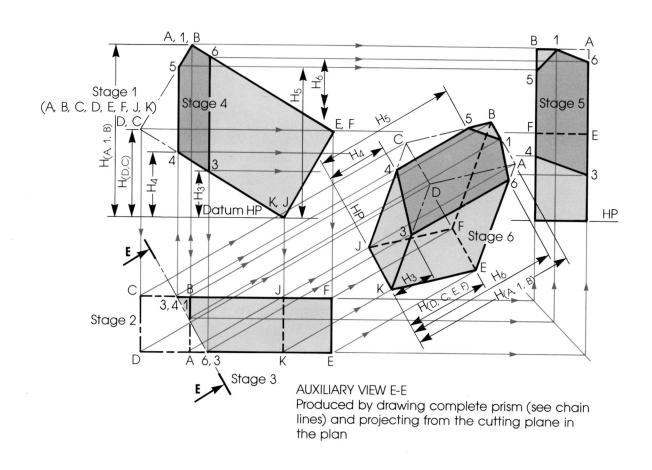

AUXILIARY VIEW E-E
Produced by drawing complete prism (see chain lines) and projecting from the cutting plane in the plan

Drawing No.	TITLE: **The rectangular prism.**	NOTE: **First Angle projection used.**	SCALE:
G23			0 10 20 30 40 50 60 70 80 mm

G24-1

Draw the 2 given views of a triangular prism and project a view B direct from the position illustrated.

G24-2

Draw an auxiliary view on D and produce the given view. Produce views B and C projected direct from the given view to First Angle.

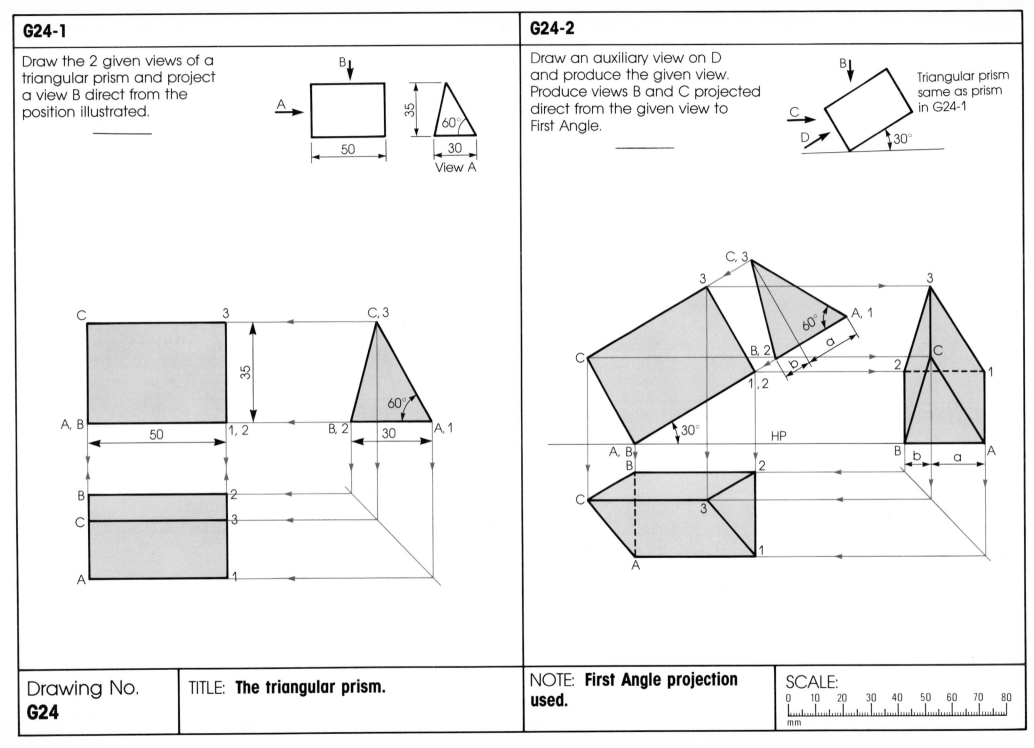

| Drawing No. **G24** | TITLE: **The triangular prism.** | NOTE: **First Angle projection used.** | SCALE: |

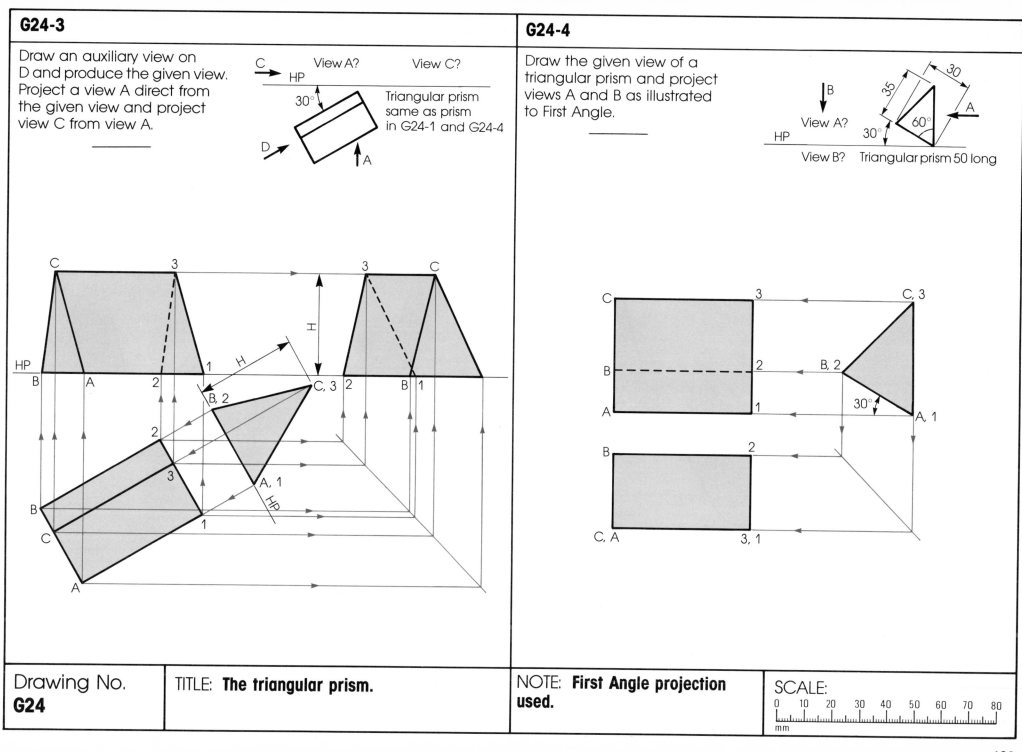

G24-3

Draw an auxiliary view on D and produce the given view. Project a view A direct from the given view and project view C from view A.

C → View A?   View C?
HP
30°   Triangular prism same as prism in G24-1 and G24-4
D →   ↑A

G24-4

Draw the given view of a triangular prism and project views A and B as illustrated to First Angle.

↓B
30   35   30
View A?   60°
HP   30°   ↑A
View B?   Triangular prism 50 long

Drawing No.
G24

TITLE: **The triangular prism.**

NOTE: **First Angle projection used.**

SCALE:
0 10 20 30 40 50 60 70 80
mm

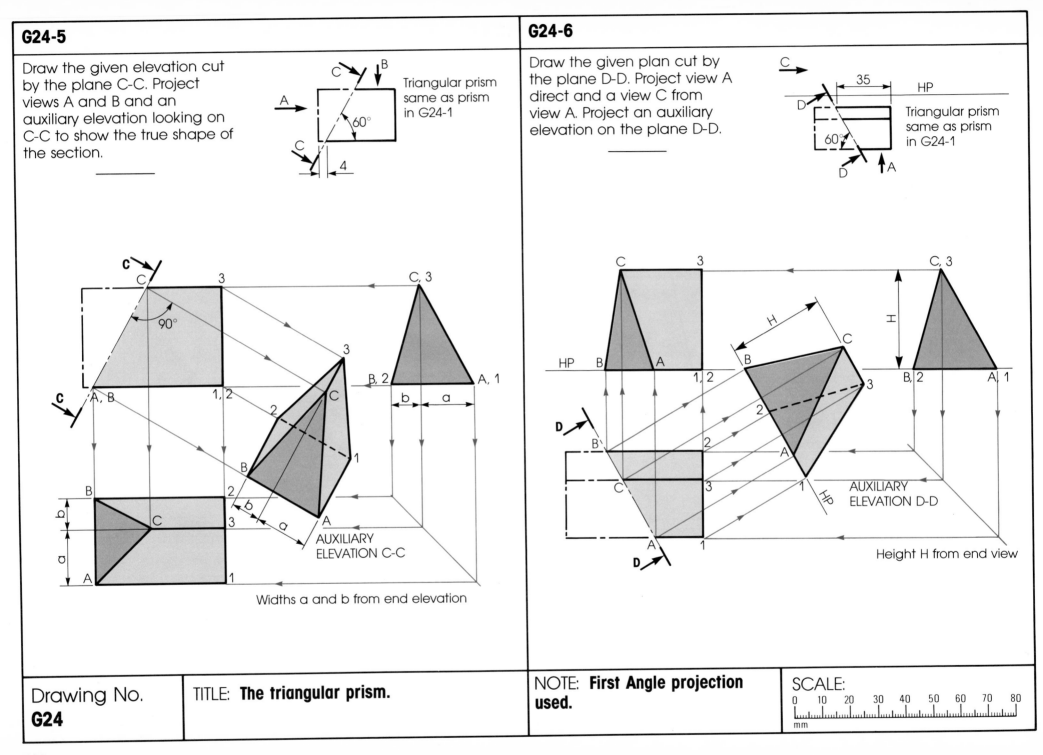

G24-5

Draw the given elevation cut by the plane C-C. Project views A and B and an auxiliary elevation looking on C-C to show the true shape of the section.

Triangular prism same as prism in G24-1

60°

4

90°

C

A, B

1, 2

B, 2

A, 1

b   a

B

b

C

a

A

1

AUXILIARY ELEVATION C-C

Widths a and b from end elevation

G24-6

Draw the given plan cut by the plane D-D. Project view A direct and a view C from view A. Project an auxiliary elevation on the plane D-D.

Triangular prism same as prism in G24-1

35   HP

60°

A

HP   B   A   1, 2

C, 3

H

H

B, 2   A, 1

D

AUXILIARY ELEVATION D-D

Height H from end view

| Drawing No. G24 | TITLE: **The triangular prism.** | NOTE: **First Angle projection used.** | SCALE: |

0 10 20 30 40 50 60 70 80
mm

110

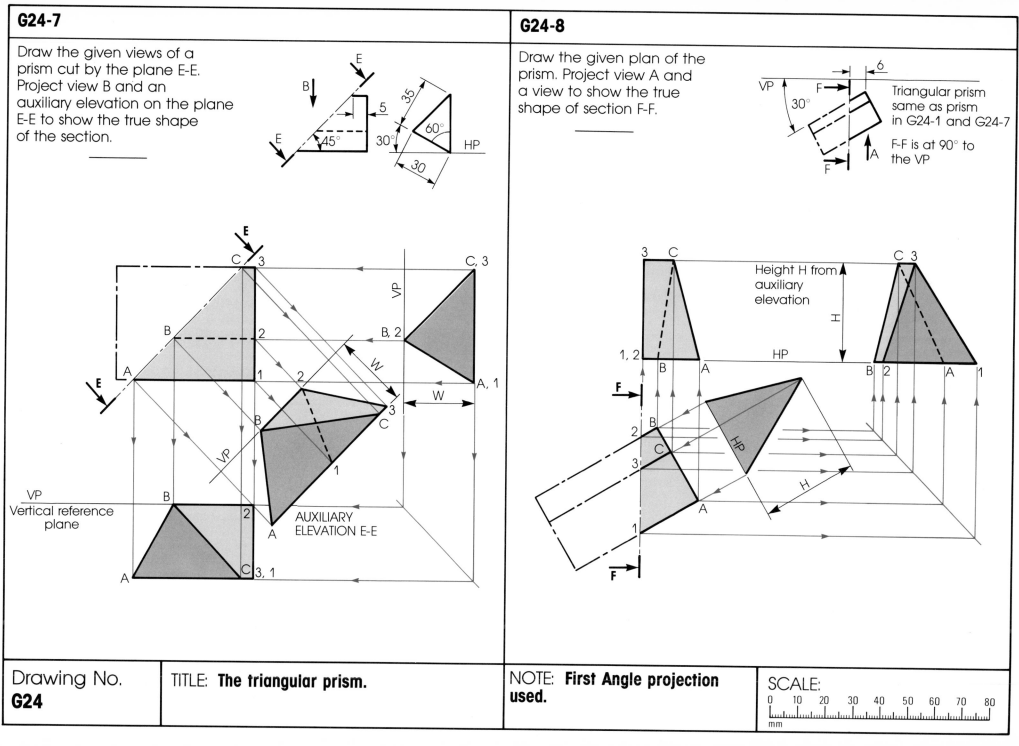

G24-7

Draw the given views of a prism cut by the plane E-E. Project view B and an auxiliary elevation on the plane E-E to show the true shape of the section.

35
5
45°
30°
60°
30
HP

E
B
E
E

VP
Vertical reference plane

AUXILIARY ELEVATION E-E

W
W

G24-8

Draw the given plan of the prism. Project view A and a view to show the true shape of section F-F.

Triangular prism same as prism in G24-1 and G24-7

F-F is at 90° to the VP

VP
30°
6
F
A
F

Height H from auxiliary elevation
H
HP
HP
H

Drawing No. **G24**

TITLE: **The triangular prism.**

NOTE: **First Angle projection used.**

SCALE:
0 10 20 30 40 50 60 70 80
mm

111

Draw the plan view and complete
elevation A of the prism cut
by the plane G-G. Project a
view C and an auxiliary view
on the plane E-E to show the
true shape of the section.

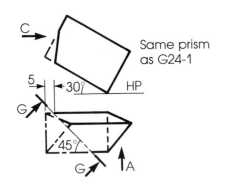

Same prism
as G24-1

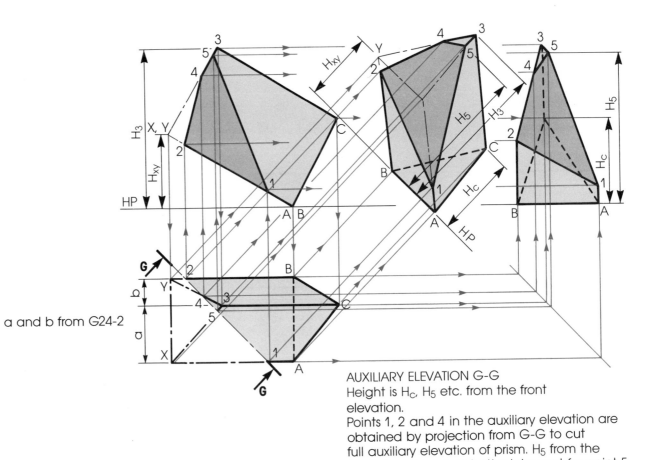

a and b from G24-2

AUXILIARY ELEVATION G-G
Height is H_C, H_5 etc. from the front
elevation.
Points 1, 2 and 4 in the auxiliary elevation are
obtained by projection from G-G to cut
full auxiliary elevation of prism. H_5 from the
front elevation gives better intercept for point 5

| Drawing No. G24 | TITLE: **The triangular prism.** | NOTE: **First Angle projection used.** | SCALE: |

G25-1

Draw the 2 given views of the prism and project a plan view B.

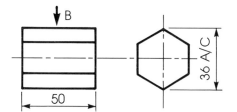

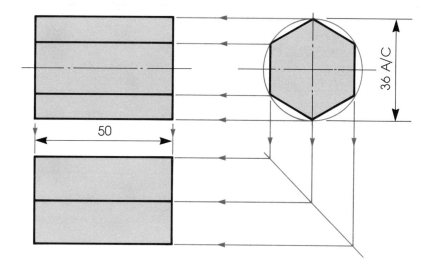

G25-2

Draw an auxiliary view on D and produce the given view. Produce views B and C projected direct from the given view to First Angle.

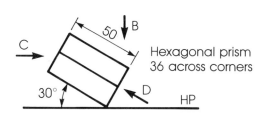

Hexagonal prism 36 across corners

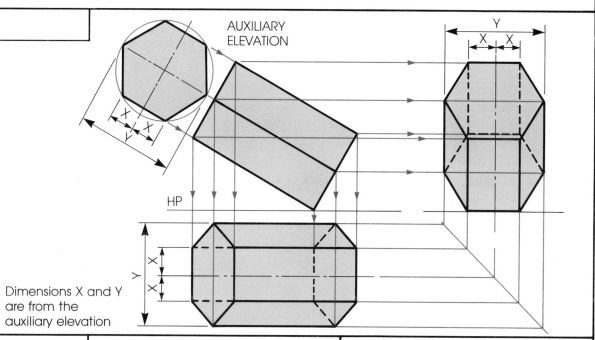

AUXILIARY ELEVATION

HP

Dimensions X and Y are from the auxiliary elevation

Drawing No. **G25**	TITLE: **The hexagonal prism.**	NOTE: **First Angle projection used.**	SCALE:

0 10 20 30 40 50 60 70 80
mm

113

G25-3

Draw an auxiliary view on D and produce the given view. Project a view A direct from the given view and project view C from view A.

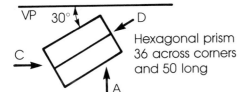

VP 30°   D

Hexagonal prism 36 across corners and 50 long

C

A

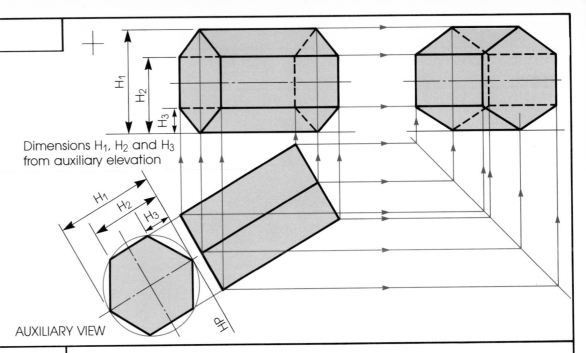

Dimensions H_1, H_2 and H_3 from auxiliary elevation

H_1 H_2 H_3

H_1 H_2 H_3

AUXILIARY VIEW

HP

G25-4

Draw the 2 given views of the prism cut by the plane C-C. Project a plan view B direct from the given view A.

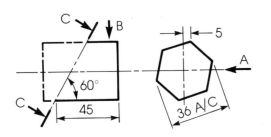

C   B

5

60°

45

36 A/C

C

A

C

| Drawing No. **G25** | TITLE: **The hexagonal prism.** | NOTE: **First Angle projection used.** | SCALE: |

0 10 20 30 40 50 60 70 80
mm

114

G25-5

Draw the given elevation cut by the plane D-D. Project views A and B and an auxiliary elevation looking on D-D to show the true shape of the section.

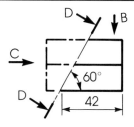

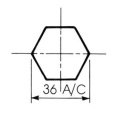

60°

42

36 A/C

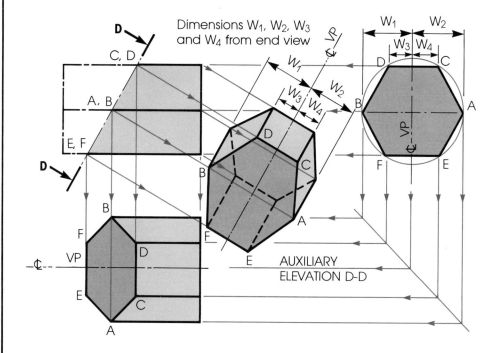

Dimensions W₁, W₂, W₃ and W₄ from end view

W_1 W_2 W_3 W_4

AUXILIARY ELEVATION D-D

G25-6

Draw the given view of the prism cut by the plane E-E. Project views B and C and an auxiliary elevation on E-E direct from the given view.

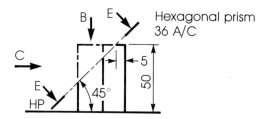

Hexagonal prism 36 A/C

45°

HP

5

50

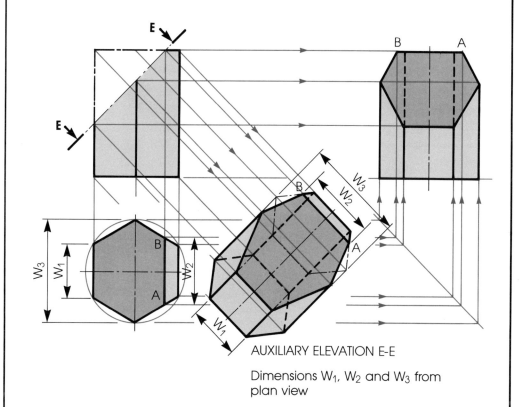

AUXILIARY ELEVATION E-E

Dimensions W₁, W₂ and W₃ from plan view

Drawing No. **G25**	TITLE: **The hexagonal prism.**	NOTE: **First Angle projection used.**	SCALE:

0 10 20 30 40 50 60 70 80
mm

Draw the given plan cut by the plane
F-F. Project a view A direct and
a view C from view A. Project
an auxiliary elevation on the plane
F-F.

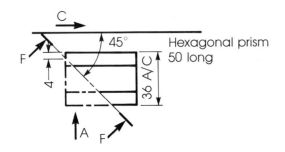

45°

F

4

36 A/C

C

A   F

Hexagonal prism
50 long

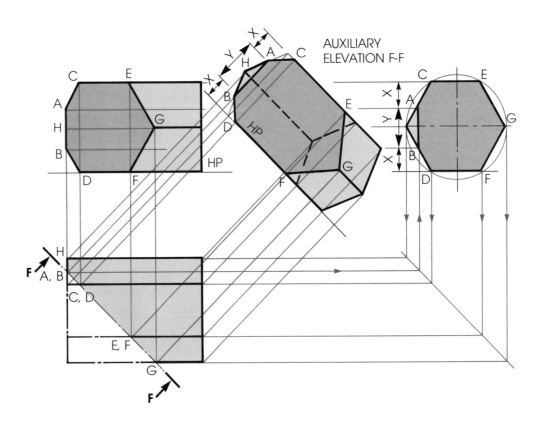

AUXILIARY
ELEVATION F-F

Drawing No.
G25

TITLE: **The hexagonal prism.**

NOTE: **First Angle projection
used.**

SCALE:
0   10   20   30   40   50   60   70   80
mm

116

Draw the 2 given views of the prism cut by the plane G-G. Project a view C and an auxiliary view on the section plane G-G to show the true shape of the cut section.

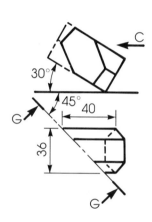

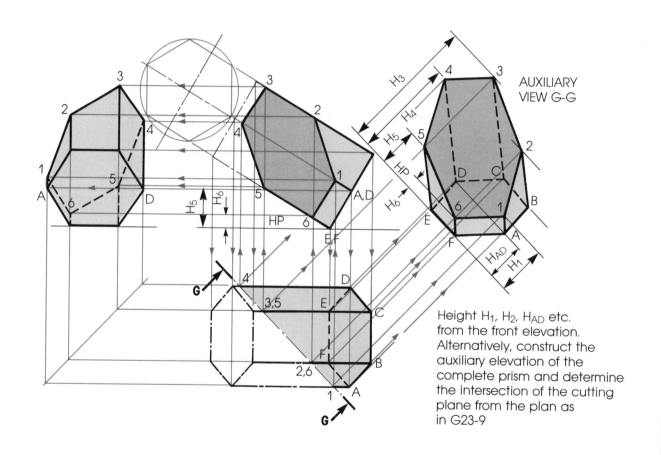

AUXILIARY
VIEW G-G

Height H_1, H_2, H_{AD} etc. from the front elevation. Alternatively, construct the auxiliary elevation of the complete prism and determine the intersection of the cutting plane from the plan as in G23-9

Drawing No. **G25**	TITLE: **The hexagonal prism.**	NOTE: **First Angle projection used.**	SCALE:

0 10 20 30 40 50 60 70 80
mm

Draw the given elevation and complete
the plan view B of the prism cut
by the plane H-H. Project a view C
direct and an auxiliary elevation
on the plane H-H to show the
true shape of the section.

Corner 9 is used to determine
the direction of the line 8 to 2
more accurately

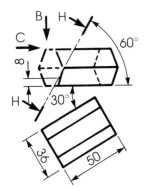

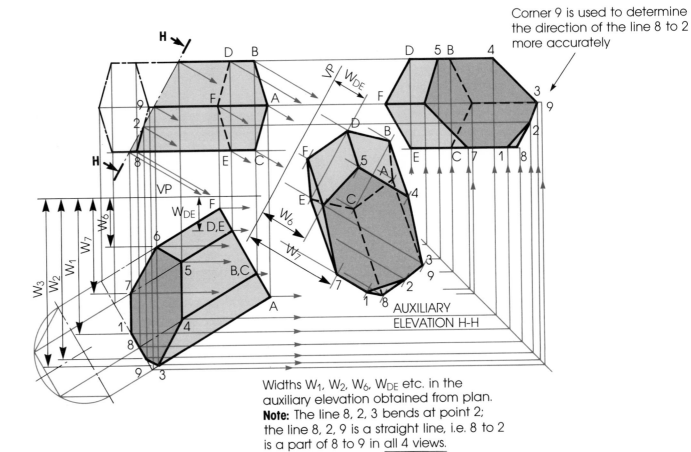

AUXILIARY
ELEVATION H-H

Widths W₁, W₂, W₆, W_DE etc. in the
auxiliary elevation obtained from plan.
Note: The line 8, 2, 3 bends at point 2;
the line 8, 2, 9 is a straight line, i.e. 8 to 2
is a part of 8 to 9 in <u>all 4 views</u>.

Drawing No.	TITLE: **The hexagonal prism.**	NOTE: **First Angle projection used.**	SCALE:
G25			0 10 20 30 40 50 60 70 80 mm

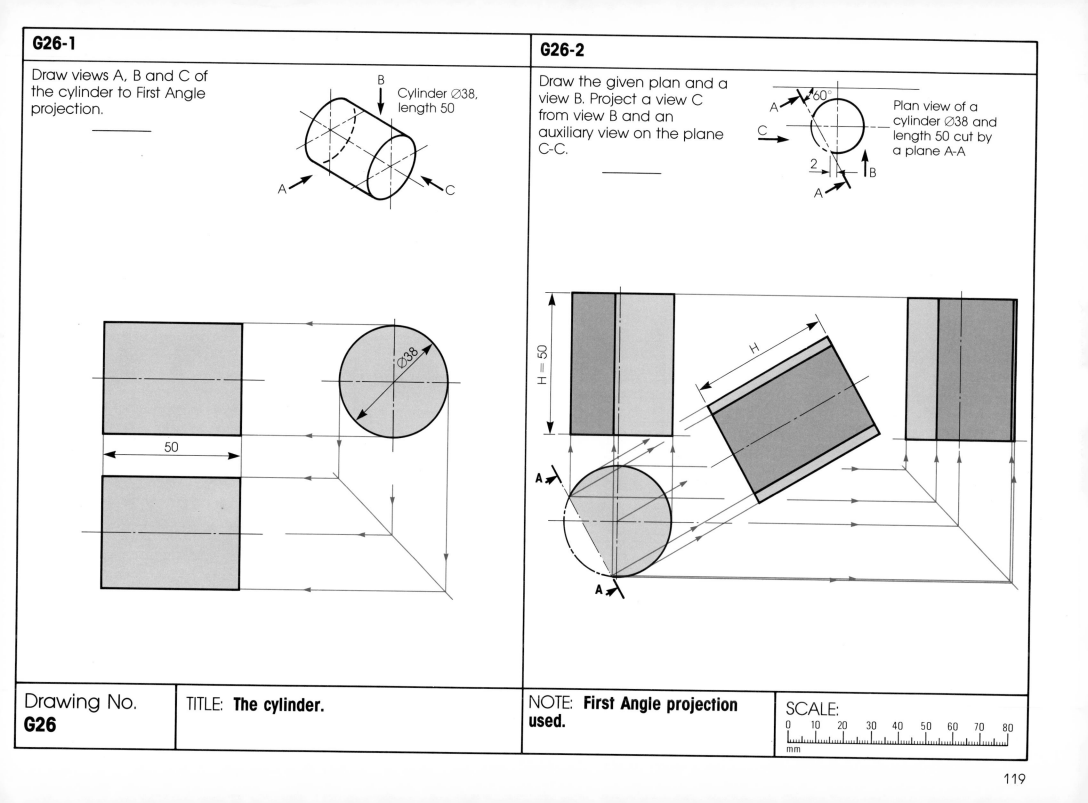

G26-1

Draw views A, B and C of the cylinder to First Angle projection.

Cylinder ⌀38, length 50

B

A

C

⌀38

50

G26-2

Draw the given plan and a view B. Project a view C from view B and an auxiliary view on the plane C-C.

60°

A

C

2

B

A

Plan view of a cylinder ⌀38 and length 50 cut by a plane A-A

H = 50

H

A

A

| Drawing No. **G26** | TITLE: **The cylinder.** | NOTE: **First Angle projection used.** | SCALE: |

0 10 20 30 40 50 60 70 80
mm

119

G26-3

Draw an auxiliary view on D and produce the given view. Project views B and C direct from the given view to First Angle.

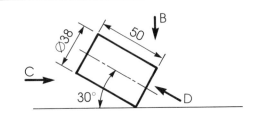

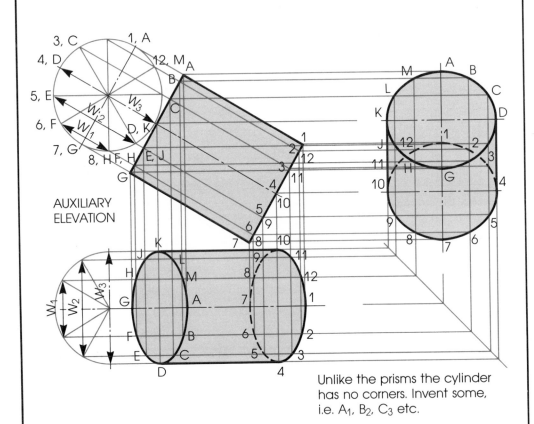

AUXILIARY ELEVATION

Unlike the prisms the cylinder has no corners. Invent some, i.e. A_1, B_2, C_3 etc.

G26-4

Draw the given view of a cylinder cut by a plane B-B. Project a view C and an auxiliary elevation on the plane B-B.

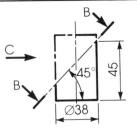

Note: The section "appears" as a circle in the end elevation when the cylinder is cut by a 45° plane as shown. Why is this so?

In auxiliary elevation, obtain W_1, W_2 etc. from the plan

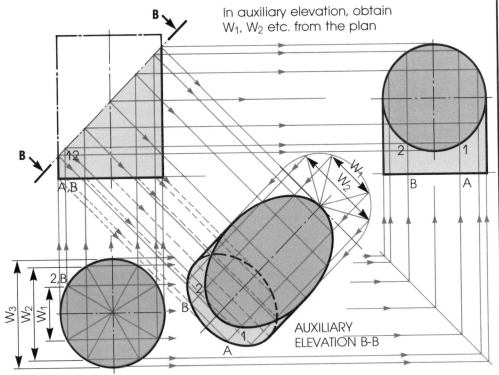

AUXILIARY ELEVATION B-B

Drawing No.
G26

TITLE: **The cylinder.**

NOTE: **First Angle projection used.**

SCALE:
0 10 20 30 40 50 60 70 80
mm

G26-5

Draw the given view of a cylinder cut by a plane C-C. Project a view on B and an auxiliary elevation on the plane C-C.

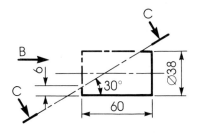

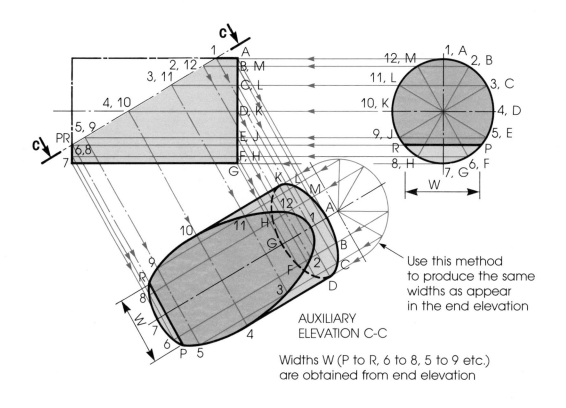

Use this method to produce the same widths as appear in the end elevation

AUXILIARY ELEVATION C-C

Widths W (P to R, 6 to 8, 5 to 9 etc.) are obtained from end elevation

Drawing No. **G26**	TITLE: **The cylinder.**	NOTE: **First Angle projection used.**	SCALE:

SCALE: 0 10 20 30 40 50 60 70 80 mm

G26-6

Draw the given view of a cylinder cut by the plane D-D. Project view A direct and a view C from view A. Draw an auxiliary elevation on D-D.

Note: The cut section "appears" as the major segment of a circle in the front elevation when the cylinder and cutting plane are related as shown. Why is this so?

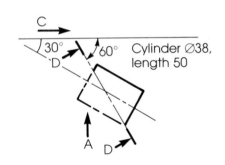

Cylinder ∅38, length 50

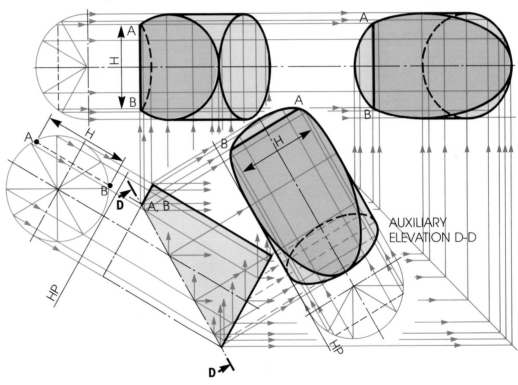

AUXILIARY ELEVATION D-D

Drawing No. **G26**	TITLE: **The cylinder and the sphere.**	NOTE: **First Angle projection used.**	SCALE:

0 10 20 30 40 50 60 70 80
mm

Shown below is a sphere cut by
the planes E-E and F-F. Draw
the views on E-E and F-F to
show the true shapes of the sections.

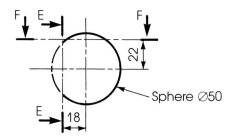

Sphere ⌀50

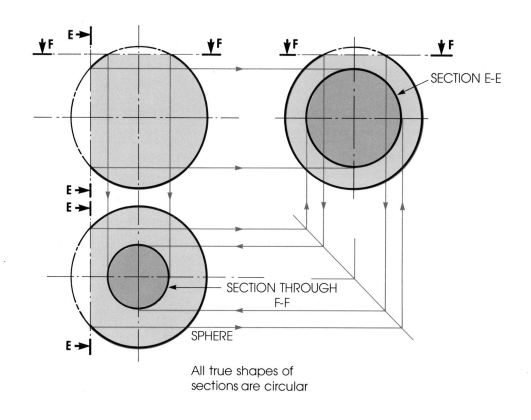

SECTION E-E

SECTION THROUGH
F-F

SPHERE

All true shapes of
sections are circular

Drawing No.	TITLE: **The sphere.**	NOTE: **First Angle projection used.**	SCALE:
G26			0 10 20 30 40 50 60 70 80 mm

Draw the given view of a sphere cut
by the plane G-G. Project an auxiliary
elevation on G-G, a view A and a
view C from view A.

C ➔ View A

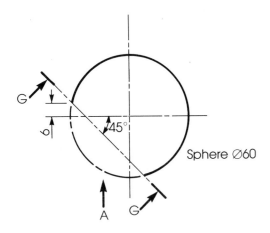

G

6

45°

A   G

Sphere ∅60

Curve of sphere
outline intersects
curve of section
somewhere between
point 5 and point 6

Alternative half circle method for producing
heights H₁, H₂ etc., semicircle diameter from auxilary elevation

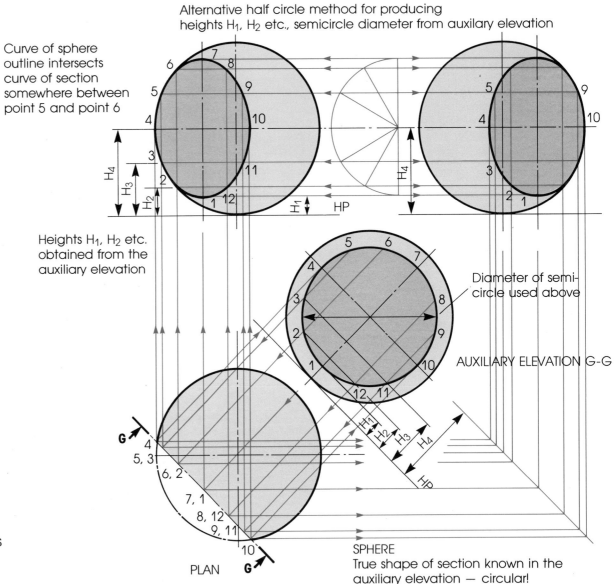

Heights H₁, H₂ etc.
obtained from the
auxiliary elevation

Diameter of semi-
circle used above

HP

AUXILIARY ELEVATION G-G

PLAN

SPHERE
True shape of section known in the
auxiliary elevation — circular!

Draw the plan cut by plane G-G, project
the auxiliary elevation and using H₄ etc.
from the auxiliary elevation, project all the points
on the circular section to the plan and
on to the other views from the cutting plane.

Drawing No. **G26**	TITLE: **The sphere.**	NOTE: **First Angle projection used.**	SCALE: 0 10 20 30 40 50 60 70 80 mm

Worksheets for G27 to G30

G27 THE RIGHT SQUARE PYRAMID (FIRST ANGLE PROJECTION).

G27-1 Draw the given elevation of a square pyramid and project views B and C to First Angle.

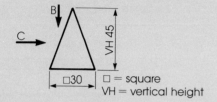

□ = square
VH = vertical height

G27-2 Draw the given elevation of a pyramid and project views B and C to First Angle.

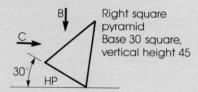

Right square pyramid
Base 30 square,
vertical height 45

G27-3 Draw the given view of the pyramid and project views B and C to First Angle.

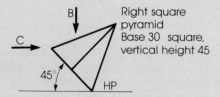

Right square pyramid
Base 30 square,
vertical height 45

G27-4 Draw the given view of a pyramid cut by the plane T-T. Project views B and C and an auxiliary view on T-T to show the true shape of the section.

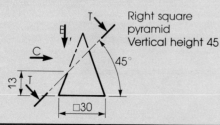

Right square pyramid
Vertical height 45

G27-5 Draw the given view of a pyramid cut by plane V-V. Project views B and C of the frustum and an auxiliary view on the plane V-V.

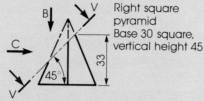

Right square pyramid
Base 30 square,
vertical height 45

G27-6 Draw the given view cut by the plane W-W. Project view A direct and a view C from view A. Project an auxiliary elevation on the plane W-W.

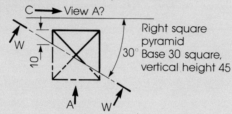

Right square pyramid
Base 30 square,
vertical height 45

G27-7 Draw the given view cut by the plane X-X. Project views A and B and the auxiliary elevation to show the true shape of the cut section.

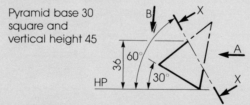

Pyramid base 30 square and vertical height 45

G27-8 Draw the given front elevation cut by the plane Y-Y and complete the plan of the frustum below the plane. Draw a view C and an auxiliary view on Y-Y to show the true shape of the section.

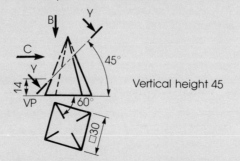

Vertical height 45

G27-9 Draw the given view of a square pyramid cut by a plane Z-Z. Project views A and B and an auxiliary view on Z-Z to show the true shape of the section.

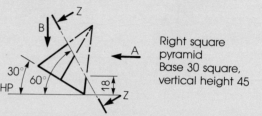

Right square pyramid
Base 30 square,
vertical height 45

G28 THE RIGHT HEXAGONAL PYRAMID (FIRST ANGLE PROJECTION).

G28-1 Draw the given elevation of a hexagonal pyramid and project the views B and C to First Angle.

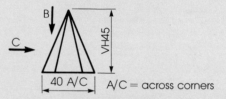

A/C = across corners

G28-2 Draw the given elevation of the hexagonal pyramid and project the views B and C to First Angle.

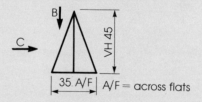

A/F = across flats

G28-3 Draw the given elevation of a pyramid and project the views B and C to First Angle.

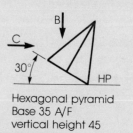

Hexagonal pyramid
Base 35 A/F
vertical height 45

G28-4 Draw the given view of a pyramid cut by the plane D-D. Project views B and C of the frustum and an auxiliary view on the plane D-D.

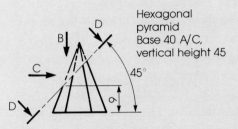

Hexagonal pyramid
Base 40 A/C,
vertical height 45

45°

G28-5 Draw the given view of a pyramid cut by the plane E-E. Project views B and C of the frustum and an auxiliary view to show the true shape of the section.

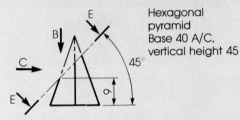

Hexagonal pyramid
Base 40 A/C,
vertical height 45

45°

G28-6 Draw the given view of a pyramid cut by the plane F-F. Project view A direct and view C from view A. Project an auxiliary view on the plane F-F.

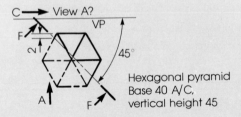

View A?
VP
45°

Hexagonal pyramid
Base 40 A/C,
vertical height 45

G28-7 Draw the given view of a pyramid cut by a plane G-G. Project view A direct and view C from view A. Project an auxiliary elevation on the plane G-G.

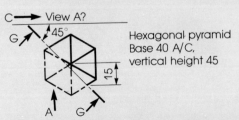

View A?
45°

Hexagonal pyramid
Base 40 A/C,
vertical height 45

15

G28-8 Complete the given elevations of the hexagonal pyramid cut by the plane H-H. Draw the view C and project an auxiliary elevation on the plane to show the frustum with the true shape of the section.

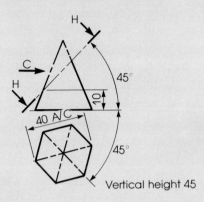

45°
10
40 A/C
45°

Vertical height 45

G28-9 Draw the given view of a pyramid and project a view B of the frustum on the left of the cutting plane. Draw a view to show the true shape of the cut face.

Hexagonal pyramid
vertical height 45

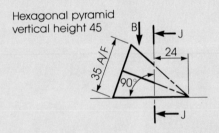

24
35 A/F
90°

G29 THE RIGHT CONE (FIRST ANGLE PROJECTION).

G29-1 Draw the given view of a right cone cut by the plane A-A. Project a view C and a view on A-A to show the true shape of the section.

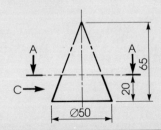

65
20
Ø50

G29-2 Draw the given view of a right cone. Project a view C and a view B direct from the given view.

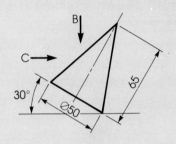

B
C
30°
Ø50
65

G29-3 Draw the given view of a right cone cut by the plane B-B and project views A and C direct from it. Project an auxiliary view of the cut section only, to show its true shape.

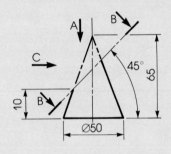

A
B
C
45°
65
10
B
Ø50

G29-4 Using an alternative method to that shown in G29-3 draw the given view of the cone cut by the plane C-C and project the views A and B direct. Draw a full auxiliary elevation on C-C to show the true shape of the section.

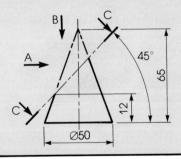

B
C
A
45°
65
12
Ø50

G29-5 Draw the given view of the cone cut by the plane D-D which is parallel to the outline edge. Project views B and C and an auxiliary elevation on D-D to show the true shape of the section.

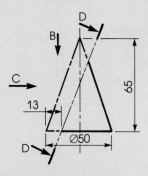

G29-6 Draw the given plan view of a cone cut by the plane E-E. Project view A direct and a view C from view A. Project an auxiliary elevation on E-E to show the true shape of the section.

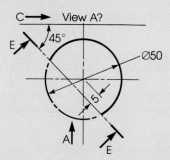

G30 COMBINED SOLIDS: TRUE SHAPES OF SECTION (FIRST ANGLE PROJECTION).

G30-1 Draw the given views of the solid cut by the plane A-A. Project a plan view C and an auxiliary view on the plane A-A to show the true shape of the section.

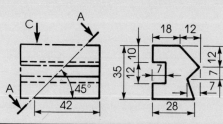

G30-2 Draw the given views of the solid cut by the plane B-B. Project a plan view C and an auxiliary view on the plane B-B to show the true shape of the section.

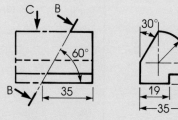

G30-3 Draw the given views of the solid cut by the plane C-C. Project a view A direct and a view B from view A. Draw an auxiliary view to show the true shape of the cut section.

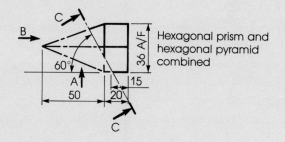

Hexagonal prism and hexagonal pyramid combined

G30-4 Draw the given view of the circular sectioned solid cut by the plane D-D. Project views B and C and an auxiliary view on D-D to show the true shape of the section.

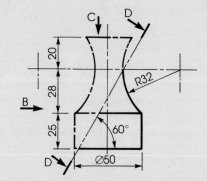

G30-5 Draw the given view and project a view C and an auxiliary elevation on the plane E-E to show the true shape of the cut section.

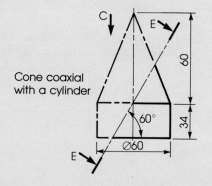

Cone coaxial with a cylinder

G30-6 Draw the given view of the cylinder and sphere segment cut by the plane F-F. Project a view C and an auxiliary elevation to show the true shape of the cut section F-F only.

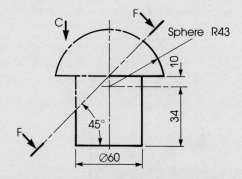

Sphere R43

G30-7 Draw the given view of the solid cut by the plane G-G which is tangential to the centre line axis. Project a view B and an auxiliary elevation on the plane G-G to show the true shape of the cut section.

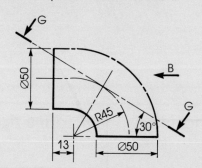

127

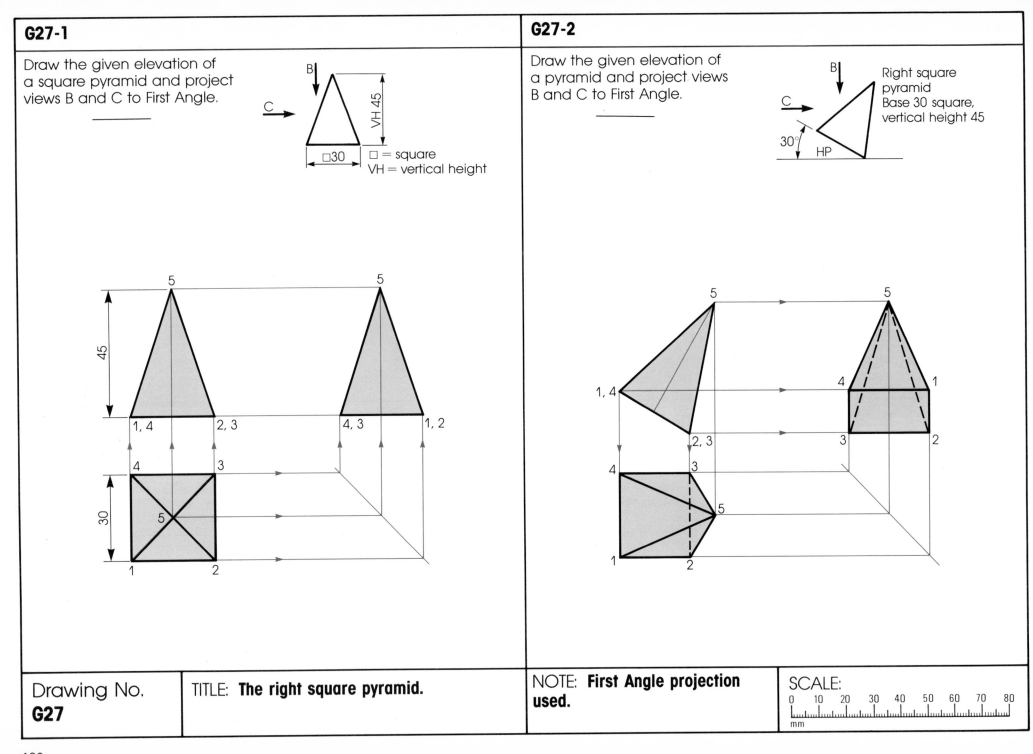

G27-1

Draw the given elevation of a square pyramid and project views B and C to First Angle.

B

C

VH 45

□30   □ = square
       VH = vertical height

5   5

45

1, 4   2, 3   4, 3   1, 2

4   3

30

5

1   2

G27-2

Draw the given elevation of a pyramid and project views B and C to First Angle.

B

C

30°   HP

Right square pyramid
Base 30 square,
vertical height 45

5   5

1, 4   4   1

2, 3   3   2

4   3

5

1   2

Drawing No.
G27

TITLE: **The right square pyramid.**

NOTE: **First Angle projection used.**

SCALE:
0   10   20   30   40   50   60   70   80
mm

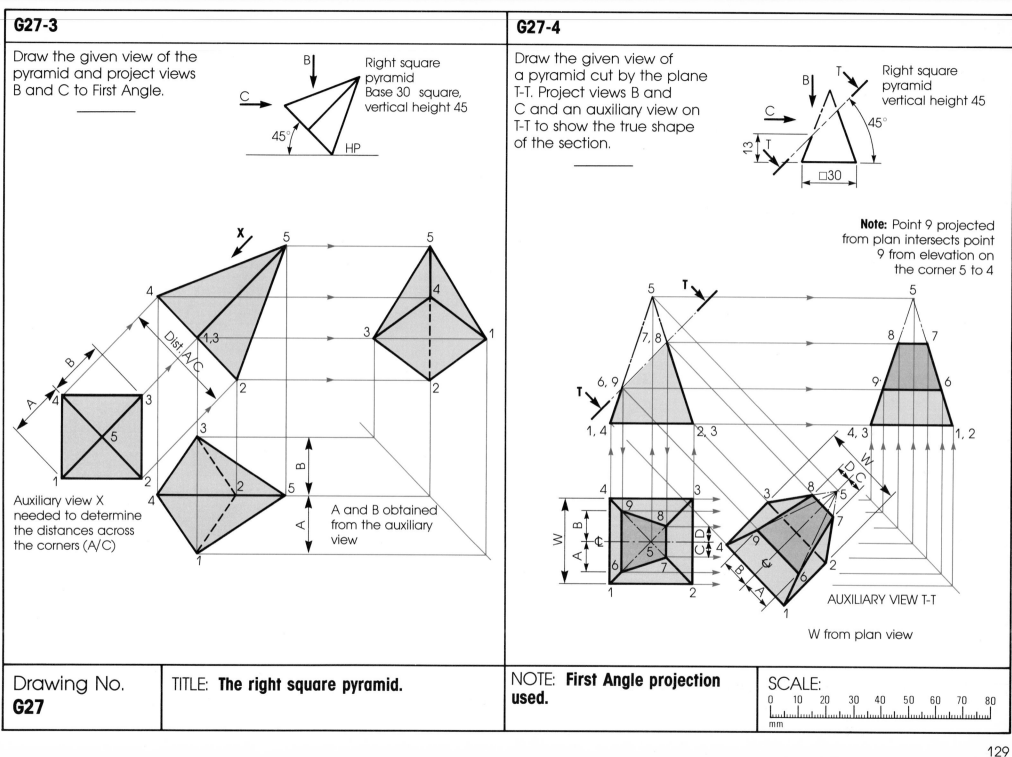

G27-3

Draw the given view of the pyramid and project views B and C to First Angle.

B
C
45°
HP

Right square pyramid
Base 30 square, vertical height 45

X

5
4
Dist. A/C
1,3
B
2
A
4   3
5
1   2
3
2   5
B
4
A
1

5
3   4   1
2

A and B obtained from the auxiliary view

Auxiliary view X needed to determine the distances across the corners (A/C)

G27-4

Draw the given view of a pyramid cut by the plane T-T. Project views B and C and an auxiliary view on T-T to show the true shape of the section.

B   T
C
45°
13
T
□30

Right square pyramid vertical height 45

Note: Point 9 projected from plan intersects point 9 from elevation on the corner 5 to 4

5   T
7,8
6,9
T
1,4   2,3

5
8   7
9   6
4,3   1,2

4   9   3
W   B   8
A   ℄   5
6   7   D
1   2

3   8   5
9   7
℄   6
B   A   2
1

AUXILIARY VIEW T-T

W from plan view

Drawing No.	TITLE: **The right square pyramid.**	NOTE: **First Angle projection used.**	SCALE:
G27			0 10 20 30 40 50 60 70 80 mm

129

Draw the given view of a pyramid
cut by plane V-V. Project views
B and C of the frustum and
an auxiliary view on the plane
V-V.

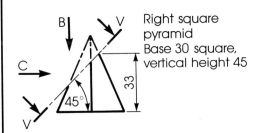

Right square
pyramid
Base 30 square,
vertical height 45

Note: Use of end elevation
to determine width W_b in plan

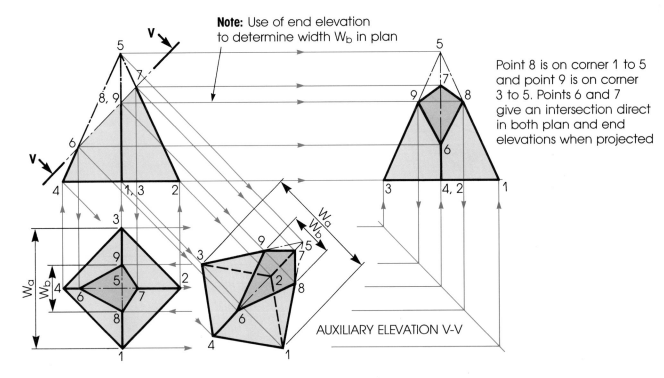

Point 8 is on corner 1 to 5
and point 9 is on corner
3 to 5. Points 6 and 7
give an intersection direct
in both plan and end
elevations when projected

AUXILIARY ELEVATION V-V

Complete pyramid is constructed in the auxiliary
elevation using W_a. Width W_b in auxiliary elevation
should coincide with W_b in other elevations

| Drawing No. **G27** | TITLE: **The right square pyramid.** | NOTE: **First Angle projection used.** | SCALE: |

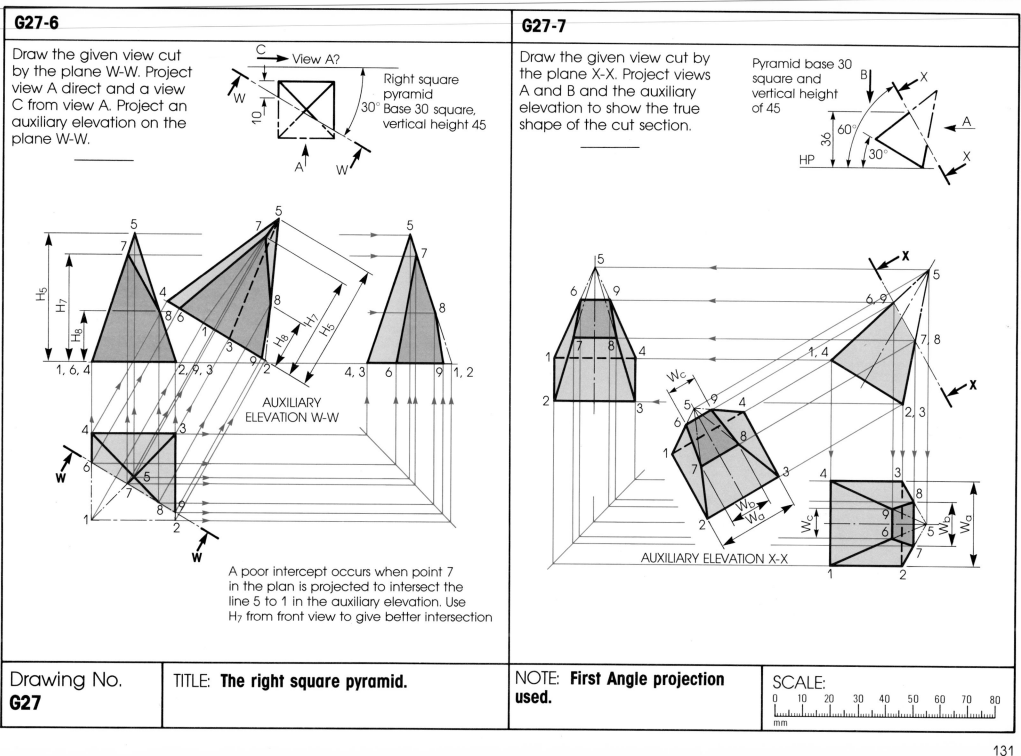

G27-6

Draw the given view cut by the plane W-W. Project view A direct and a view C from view A. Project an auxiliary elevation on the plane W-W.

View A?

Right square pyramid
30° Base 30 square, vertical height 45

10

AUXILIARY ELEVATION W-W

A poor intercept occurs when point 7 in the plan is projected to intersect the line 5 to 1 in the auxiliary elevation. Use H7 from front view to give better intersection

G27-7

Draw the given view cut by the plane X-X. Project views A and B and the auxiliary elevation to show the true shape of the cut section.

Pyramid base 30 square and vertical height of 45

36   60°   30°

HP

AUXILIARY ELEVATION X-X

Drawing No.
G27

TITLE: **The right square pyramid.**

NOTE: **First Angle projection used.**

SCALE:

0 10 20 30 40 50 60 70 80
mm

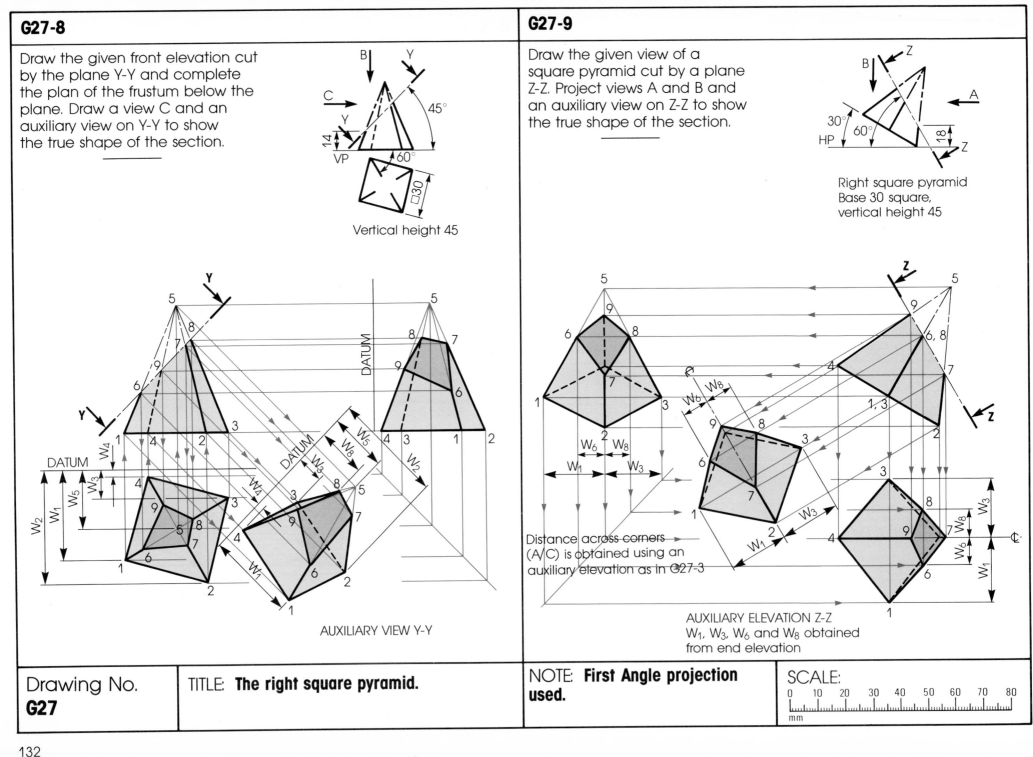

G27-8

Draw the given front elevation cut by the plane Y-Y and complete the plan of the frustum below the plane. Draw a view C and an auxiliary view on Y-Y to show the true shape of the section.

45°

60°

14

VP

□30

Vertical height 45

DATUM

AUXILIARY VIEW Y-Y

G27-9

Draw the given view of a square pyramid cut by a plane Z-Z. Project views A and B and an auxiliary view on Z-Z to show the true shape of the section.

30°

60°

HP

18

Right square pyramid
Base 30 square,
vertical height 45

Distance across corners (A/C) is obtained using an auxiliary elevation as in G27-3

AUXILIARY ELEVATION Z-Z
W1, W3, W6 and W8 obtained from end elevation

Drawing No.
G27

TITLE: **The right square pyramid.**

NOTE: **First Angle projection used.**

SCALE:

0 10 20 30 40 50 60 70 80

mm

132

G28-1

Draw the given elevation of a hexagonal pyramid and project the views B and C to First Angle.

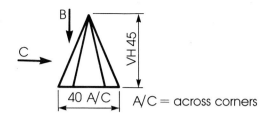

A/C = across corners

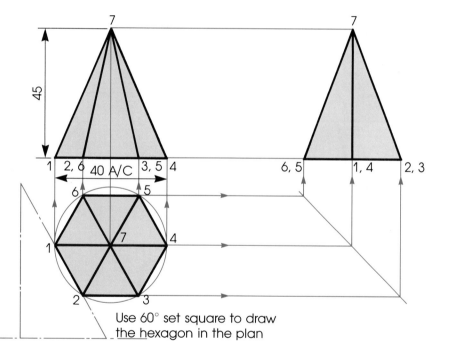

Use 60° set square to draw the hexagon in the plan

G28-2

Draw the given elevation of the hexagonal pyramid and project the views B and C to First Angle.

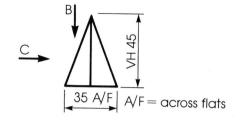

A/F = across flats

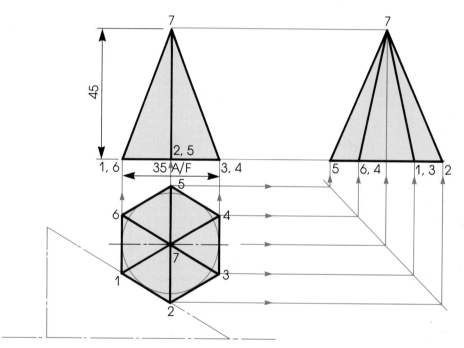

Use 30° set square to draw the hexagon in the plan

Drawing No.	TITLE: **The right hexagonal pyramid.**	NOTE: **First Angle projection used.**	SCALE:
G28			0 10 20 30 40 50 60 70 80 mm

133

G28-3

Draw the given elevation of a pyramid and project the views B and C to First Angle.

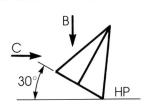

Hexagonal pyramid
Base 35 A/F,
vertical height 45

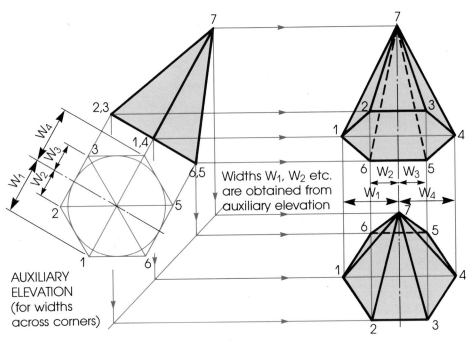

Widths W_1, W_2 etc. are obtained from auxiliary elevation

AUXILIARY
ELEVATION
(for widths
across corners)

G28-4

Draw the given view of a pyramid cut by the plane D-D. Project views B and C of the frustum and an auxiliary view on the plane D-D.

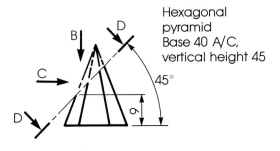

Hexagonal pyramid
Base 40 A/C,
vertical height 45

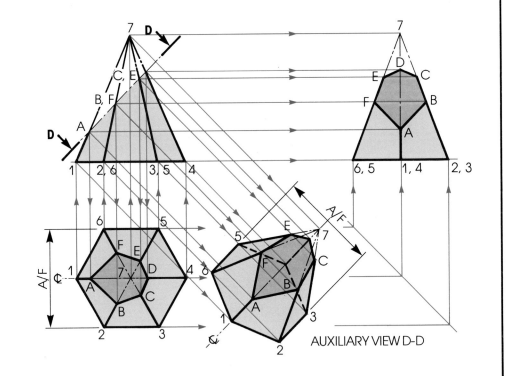

AUXILIARY VIEW D-D

Drawing No.
G28

TITLE: **The right hexagonal pyramid.**

NOTE: **First Angle projection used.**

G28-5

Draw a given view of a pyramid cut by the plane E-E. Project views B and C of the frustum and auxiliary view to show the true shape of the section.

———

E
B
C
45°
6

Hexagonal pyramid Base 40 A/C, vertical height 45

Determine the width B to E through end elevation and project to the plan via the 45° transfer line

7
C, D
B, E
A, F
E
1, 6   2, 5   3, 4

7
D C
E B
F A
5   6, 4   1, 3 2

W_5 W_2

Transfer line

5
6 F E
4
7 C
1 A B 3
2
W_5 W_6 W_1 W_2

4 E D
5 7 C
6 F B
A 1 2 3
W_6 W_1

AUXILIARY VIEW E-E

G28-6

Draw the given view of a pyramid cut by the plane F-F. Project view A direct and view C from A. Project an auxiliary view on the plane F-F.

———

C → View A?
VP
F
2
45°

A   F

Hexagonal pyramid Base 40 A/C, vertical height 45

7
C D
B
H_C H_D H_B
6 A 5   4   E 3

B C D
H_B 7
5 A 4
3 E
H_D H_C

7
C D
B
5, 4 A   E

AUXILIARY VIEW F-F

F
5 4
A
B C D
6 7
E
1   2
F

Drawing No.	TITLE: **The right hexagonal pyramid.**	NOTE: **First Angle projection used.**	SCALE:
G28			0 10 20 30 40 50 60 70 80 mm

135

G28-7

Draw the given view of a pyramid cut by a plane G-G. Project view A direct and a view C from view A. Project an auxiliary elevation on the plane G-G.

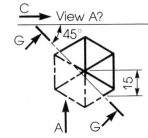

Hexagonal pyramid Base 40 A/C, vertical height 45

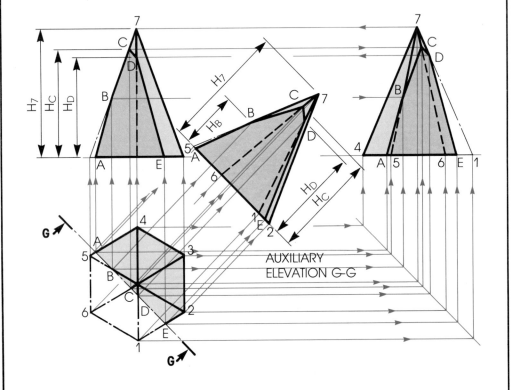

AUXILIARY ELEVATION G-G

G28-8

Complete the given elevations of the hexagonal pyramid cut by the plane H-H. Draw the view C and project an auxiliary elevation on the plane to show the frustum with the true shape of the section.

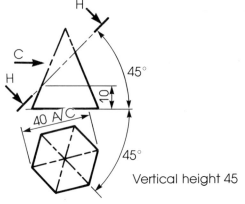

Vertical height 45

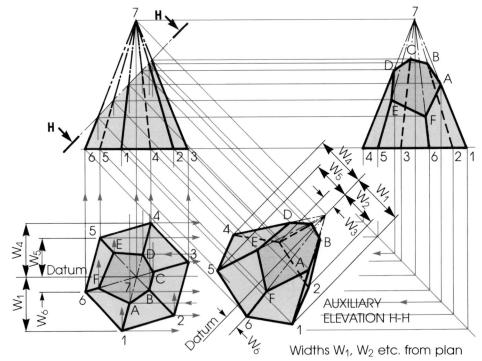

AUXILIARY ELEVATION H-H

Widths W_1, W_2 etc. from plan

Drawing No. **G28**	TITLE: **The right hexagonal pyramid.**	NOTE: **First Angle projection used.**	SCALE: 0 10 20 30 40 50 60 70 80 mm

G28-9

Draw the given view of a pyramid and project a view B of the frustum on the left of the cutting plane. Draw a view to show the true shape of the cut face.

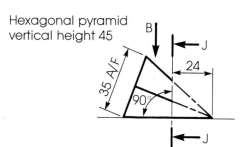

Hexagonal pyramid
vertical height 45
B
J
24
35 A/F
90°
J
Stage 1: Draw the pyramid in the vertical erect position with the hexagon base resting on the HP
3
4
2
5
1
7
6
3, 4
2, 5
1, 6
7 HP
R
J
J
Stage 2: Tip the pyramid over, i.e. rotate it about the base edge, 1, 6 until one of the triangular faces rests on the HP
5
6
4
7
1
3
2
Stage 3: Consider the cutting or section plane J-J and project the cut section to the end elevation

Drawing No. **G28**	TITLE: **The right hexagonal pyramid.**	NOTE: **First Angle projection used.**	SCALE: 0 10 20 30 40 50 60 70 80 mm

Draw the given view of a right cone cut by the plane A-A. Project a view C and a view on A-A to show the true shape of the section.

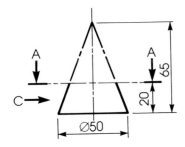

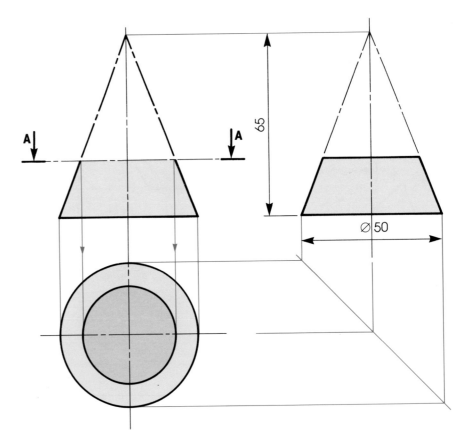

The plan illustrates that a section of circular form is produced when a section plane cuts a cone at right angles to its axis

Drawing No. G29	TITLE: **The right cone.**	NOTE: **First Angle projection used.**	SCALE: 0 10 20 30 40 50 60 70 80 mm

138

Draw the given view of a right
cone. Project a view C and
a view B direct from the
given view.

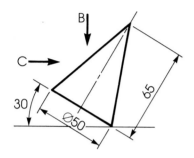

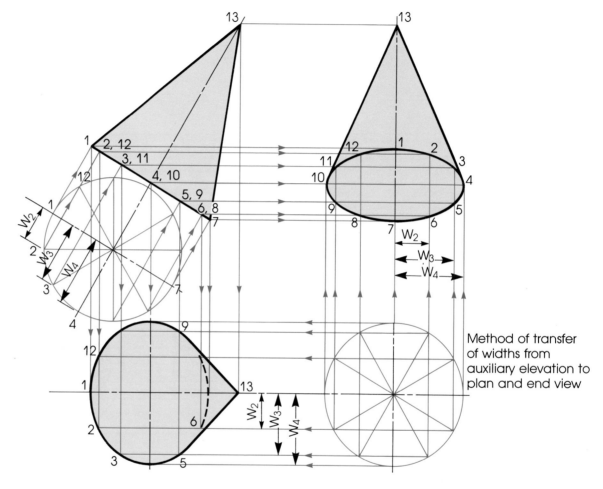

Method of transfer
of widths from
auxiliary elevation to
plan and end view

Note: The profile edge from the top point (13) to
the base is a line which is tangential to the base
curve

| Drawing No.
G29 | TITLE: **The right cone.** | NOTE: **First Angle projection used.** | SCALE:
0 10 20 30 40 50 60 70 80
mm |

G29-3

Draw the given view of a right cone cut by the plane B-B and project views A and C direct from it. Project an auxiliary view of the cut section only to show its true shape.

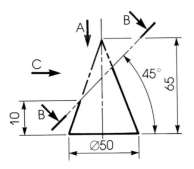

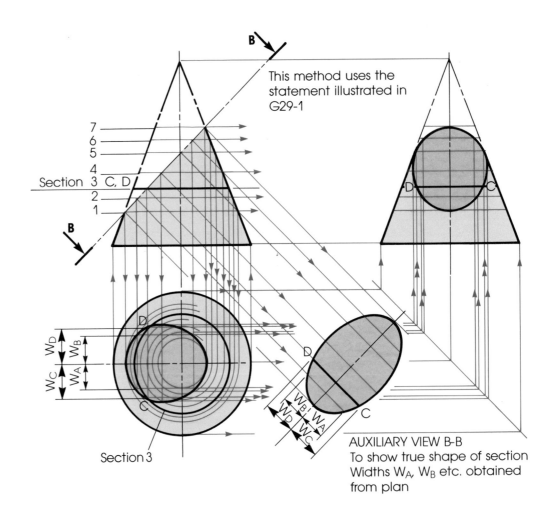

This method uses the statement illustrated in G29-1

7
6
5
4
Section 3 C, D
2
1

B

Section 3

AUXILIARY VIEW B-B
To show true shape of section
Widths W_A, W_B etc. obtained from plan

| Drawing No. **G29** | TITLE: **The right cone.** | NOTE: **First Angle projection used.** | SCALE: |

0 10 20 30 40 50 60 70 80
mm

Using an alternative method to that shown in G29-3 draw the given view of the cone cut by the plane C-C and project the views A and B direct. Draw a full auxiliary elevation on C-C to show the true shape of the section.

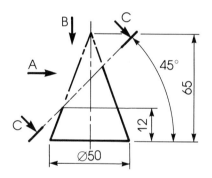

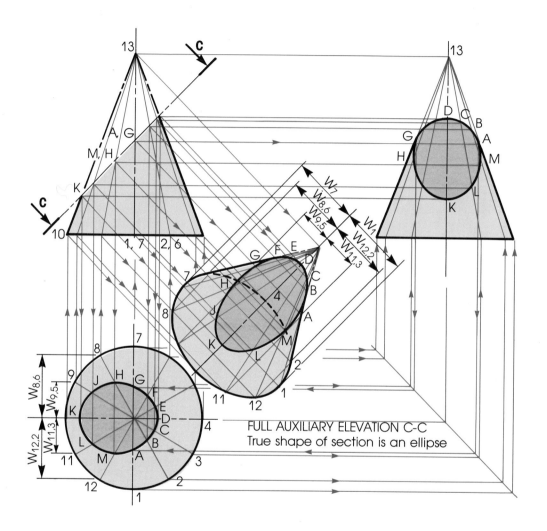

FULL AUXILIARY ELEVATION C-C
True shape of section is an ellipse

This method uses the same principles as used for the pyramids.
Since the cone has no corners some have been invented, i.e. 12 equally spaced around the cone e.g. (1, 13), (2, 13), (3, 13), (4, 13), etc.

Drawing No.	TITLE: **The right cone.**	NOTE: **First Angle projection used.**	SCALE:
G29			

G29-5

Draw the given view of the cone
cut by the plane D-D which is
parallel to the outline edge. Project
views B and C and an auxiliary
elevation on D-D to show the
true shape of the section.

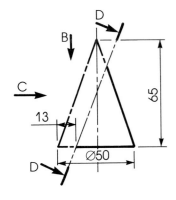

The construction method uses the principle
of circular sections (see G29-1) cut by
the section plane.

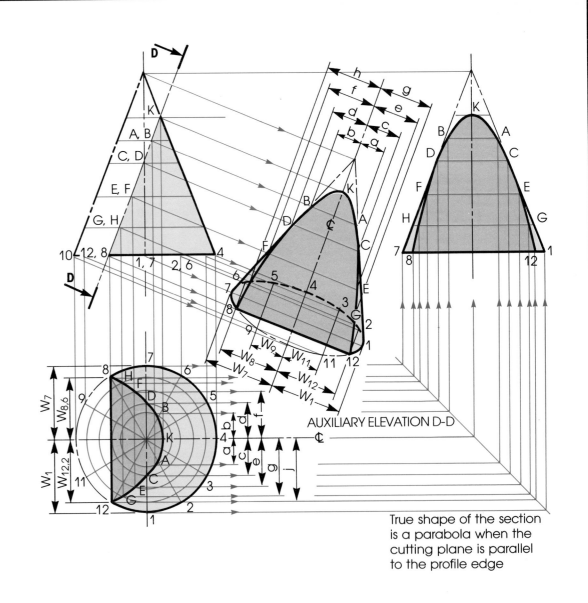

AUXILIARY ELEVATION D-D

True shape of the section
is a parabola when the
cutting plane is parallel
to the profile edge

Drawing No. **G29**	TITLE: **The right cone.**	NOTE: **First Angle projection used.**	SCALE: 0 10 20 30 40 50 60 70 80 mm

Draw the given plan view of a cone cut by the plane E-E. Project view A direct and a view C from view A. Project an auxiliary elevation on E-E to show the true shape of the section.

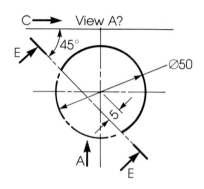

View A?

45°

∅50

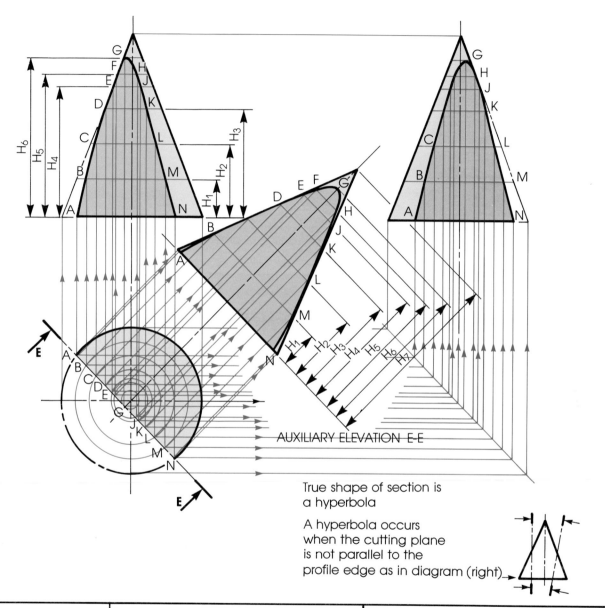

AUXILIARY ELEVATION E-E

True shape of section is a hyperbola

A hyperbola occurs when the cutting plane is not parallel to the profile edge as in diagram (right)

Drawing No. **G29**	TITLE: **The right cone.**	NOTE: **First Angle projection used.**	SCALE: 0 10 20 30 40 50 60 70 80 mm

G30-1

Draw the given views of the solid cut by the plane A-A. Project a plan view C and an auxiliary view on the plane A-A to show the true shape of the section.

18 12
35 12 10 12
7
7
7
42
28

A
4, 5
7, 6
3
2
8, 9
1, 10
A

5 4
6
7
8
9
10
3
2
1

Datum
W_7 W_2 W_1 W_3
W_4

5
6
7
4
9
8
2 3

Datum
10 9 6 5
W_7
8 7
10
W_3 W_1 W_2 W_4
1 2
4
3

AUXILIARY ELEVATION A-A

G30-2

Draw the given views of the solid cut by the plane B-B. Project a plan view C and an auxiliary view on the plane B-B to show the true shape fo the section.

30° R21
60°
18
19 7
35

Invent these corners to plot curve in other views

B
A, 1
B
C
D
6
2, 3
4, 5
B

Datum
$W_{2,D}$ W_C W_B W_A W_1
6
5
A B
3 4
D
2
$W_{4,3}$
$W_{2,D}$

Datum 5 6
4 3
1
A
B
C
2 D

AUXILIARY ELEVATION B-B

1 A
B
C
6 D
3 2
4
5
W_1
$W_{4,3}$
W_A
W_B
W_C
$W_{2,D}$

Drawing No. **G30**

TITLE: **Combined solids.**

NOTE: **First Angle projection used.**

SCALE:
0 10 20 30 40 50 60 70 80
mm

144

Draw the given views of the solid
cut by the plane C-C. Project a view
A direct and a view B from view
A. Draw an auxiliary view to show
the true shape of the cut section.

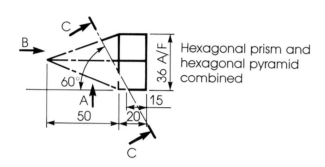

Hexagonal prism and
hexagonal pyramid
combined

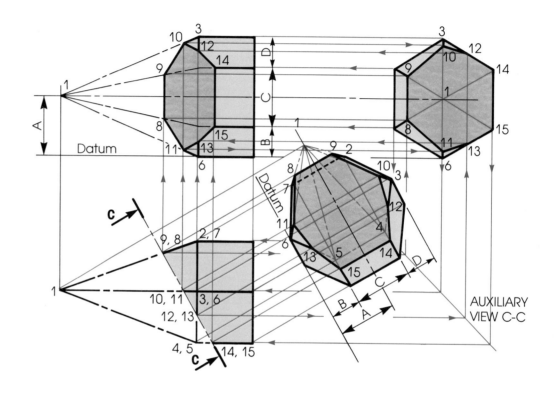

AUXILIARY
VIEW C-C

Drawing No. **G30**	TITLE: **Combined solids.**	NOTE: **First Angle projection used.**	SCALE: 

145

Draw the given view of the
circular sectioned solid cut
by the plane D-D. Project
views B and C and an
auxiliary view on D-D to
show the true shape of the
section.

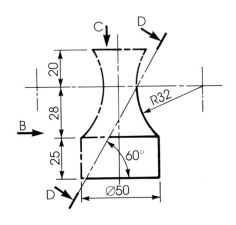

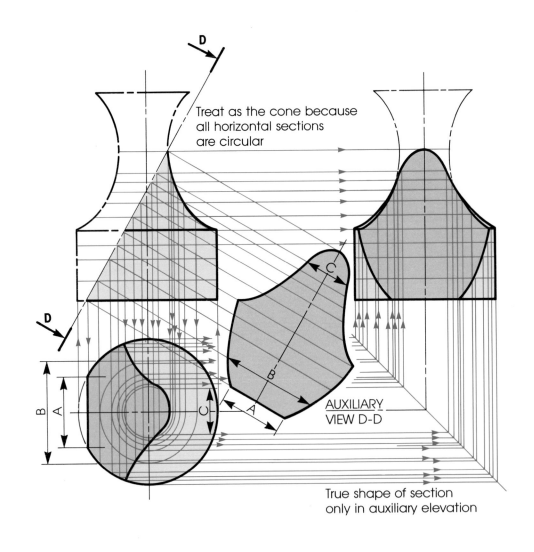

Treat as the cone because
all horizontal sections
are circular

AUXILIARY
VIEW D-D

True shape of section
only in auxiliary elevation

Drawing No.	TITLE: **Combined solids.**	NOTE: **First Angle projection used.**	SCALE:
G30			

Draw the given view and project a view C and an auxiliary elevation on the plane E-E to show the true shape of the cut section.

Note: The widths (P to R, N to S etc.) in the auxiliary elevation can be obtained by projecting from the cutting plane to cut the relevant line in the auxiliary elevation, i.e. AH and AF: or AJ and AE etc. that is by direct projection.

An alternative is to transfer the widths from the plan.

Cone coaxial with a cylinder

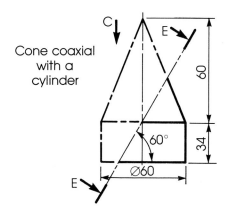

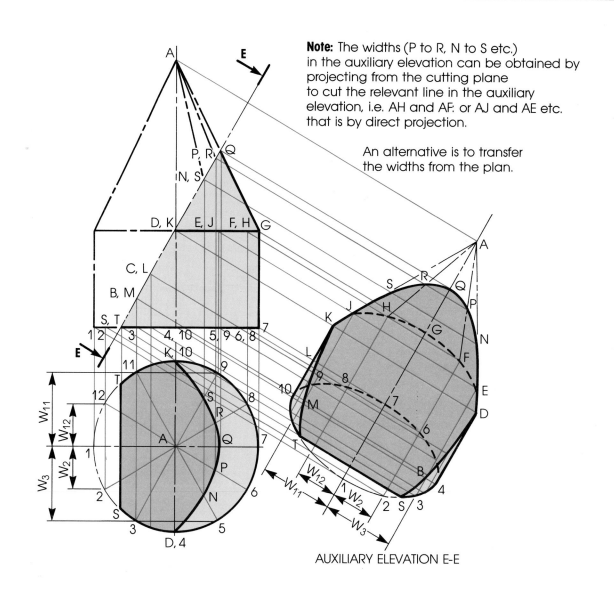

AUXILIARY ELEVATION E-E

| Drawing No. **G30** | TITLE: **Combined solids.** | NOTE: **First Angle projection used.** | SCALE: |

0 10 20 30 40 50 60 70 80
mm

Draw the given view of the cylinder and sphere segment cut by the plane F-F. Project a view C and an auxiliary elevation to show the true shape of the cut section F-F only.

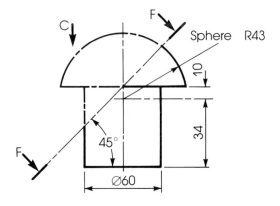

The widths W_1 to W_4 of the section through the spherical part are known in the auxiliary elevation and can be transferred to the plan when constructing the projected shape of the section there. The converse occurs when the cylinder is considered since the widths of the cylindrical part are known in the plan and can be used to construct the section in the auxiliary elevation

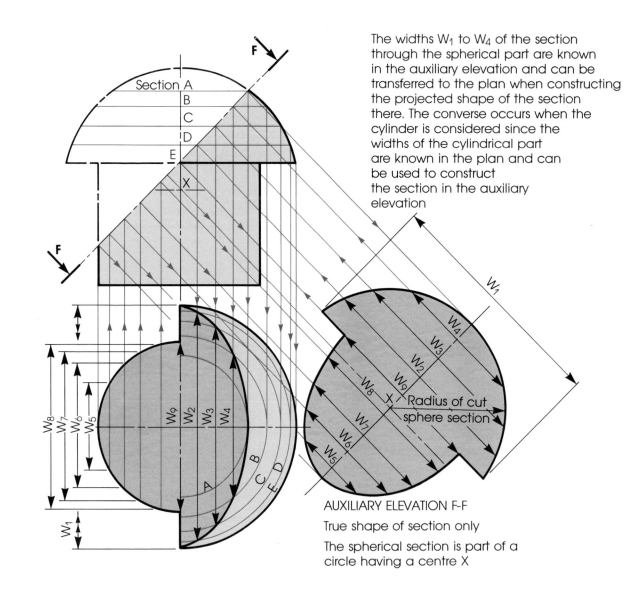

AUXILIARY ELEVATION F-F

True shape of section only

The spherical section is part of a circle having a centre X

Drawing No.	TITLE: **Combined solids.**	NOTE: **First Angle projection used.**	SCALE:
G30			0 10 20 30 40 50 60 70 80 mm

Draw the given view of the solid
cut by the plane G-G which is
tangential to the centre line axis.
Project a view B and an auxiliary
elevation on the plane G-G to show
the true shape of the cut section.

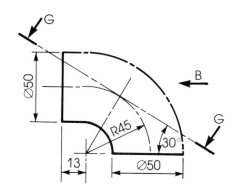

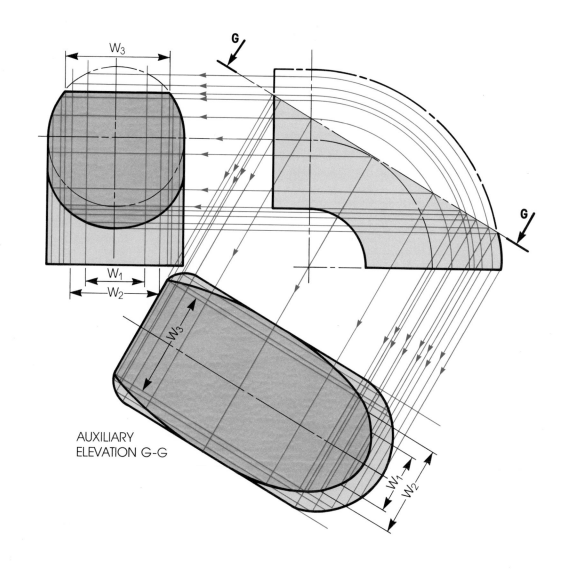

AUXILIARY
ELEVATION G-G

Drawing No.	TITLE: **Combined solids.**	NOTE: **First Angle projection used.**	SCALE:
G30			0 10 20 30 40 50 60 70 80 mm

Worksheets for G31 to G33

G31 INTRODUCTION TO LINES IN SPACE (FIRST ANGLE PROJECTION).

G31-1 A line AB is positioned so that A is 10 mm above the horizontal plane (HP) and 50 mm in front of the front vertical plane (FVP). End B is 55 mm above the horizontal plane and 22 mm in front of the front vertical plane. End A is 23 mm in front of the end vertical plane (EVP) and end B is 90 mm in front of the end vertical plane.
Represent the line AB described above by using First Angle orthographic projection. Determine: (a) the true length of the line AB, and (b) the true angle the line makes with the horizontal plane.

G31-2 The frustum of a pyramid is shown below. Determine the true lengths of any corner which does not appear as true in any of the 3 orthographic views given.

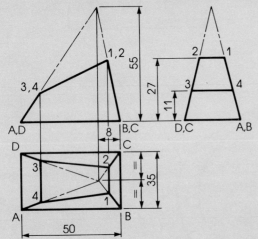

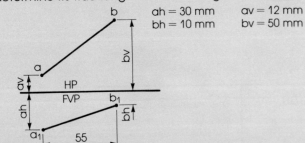

G31-3 Given the plan and elevation of a line AB determine its true length and true angle to the FVP.

ah = 30 mm   av = 12 mm
bh = 10 mm   bv = 50 mm

G31-4 Produce the plan and elevation of a line given the position of its ends relative to the principle planes. Vertical height of A above the HP, av = 41 mm; vertical height of B above the HP, bv = 11 mm. The horizontal distance of A in front of the VP, ah = 38 mm and the horizontal distance of B in front of the VP, bh = 15 mm. The end of the line A is to the left of end B and AB has a true length of 68 mm.

G31-5 Determine the plan view of the line AB given the front elevation and the position of end B in the plan as shown if the true length of AB is given as 94 mm, i.e. $a^1b^1 = 94$ mm.

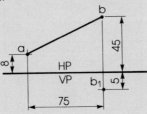

G32 LINES IN SPACE: PROBLEMS INTRODUCING TRACES (FIRST ANGLE PROJECTION).

G32-1 Determine the front elevation of a line AB given the plan, position of B in the front elevation as shown, and that the true length of AB is 80 mm.

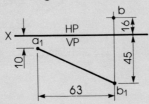

G32-2 Determine the front elevation of a line AB given its plan as shown and the position of B in the front elevation. The true angle of the line to the HP is 35°.

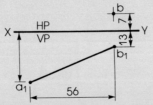

G32-3 A line AB has a true length of 46 mm and is inclined at 60° to the HP. End A is located 6 mm above the HP and the line disposed in the plan as shown. Draw the plan and elevation of the line and determine its vertical trace (VT) and its horizontal trace (HT).

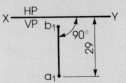

End A is lower than end B

G32-4 The plan and elevation given shows the position of the traces of a line AB. Draw the line AB in both views, given that end A is 40 mm above the HP and end B is 25 mm in front of the VP.

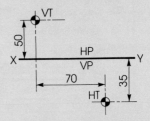

G32-5 The front elevation and plan of a line are given. Determine the horizontal trace and the vertical trace of the line AB.

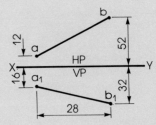

G32-6 The front elevation and plan of a line AB are given. Determine the vertical and horizontal traces.

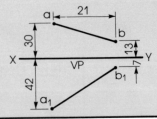

G32-7 The given plan shows the attitude of a line AB to the FVP. AB has a true length of 80 mm and its true angle to the HP is 30°. End A is 12 mm in front of the FVP and 45 mm above the HP. Draw the plan and elevation of AB, determine its traces and its true angle to the FVP.

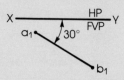

G32-8 The front elevation of 2 lines AB and CD is given. AB is parallel to, and 30 mm in front of, the FVP. CD has a true length of 71 mm, end D being 6 mm in front of the FVP. Draw the plan and elevation of the lines, show the true angle between the lines and the true length of AB.

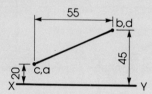

G33 PROBLEMS INVOLVING LINES IN SPACE (FIRST ANGLE PROJECTION).

G33-1 Two views of a lamina ABC which is triangular in shape are shown in orthographic projection. Determine the true shape of the lamina.

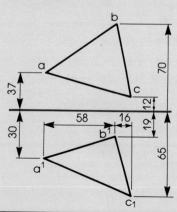

G33-2 The plan and elevation of a rotary clothes line frame is shown in orthographic projection.
Determine the lengths of the components used in the frame by drawing to a scale of 1:20 and finding the lengths of any which do not appear as true in either of the given views.
The arms are designated HA, HB and HC; the ties GD, GE and GF. Centre pole XY is 2 m high, GH is 0.7 m and HY is 1.22 m. Shortest distance of D, E and F to XY is 0.83 m.

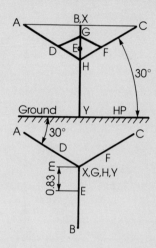

G33-3 The plan and elevation of an animal feed hopper is shown. Determine the lengths of any corners which do not appear as true lengths in either of the given orthographic views. Use a scale of 1:10 for the solution.

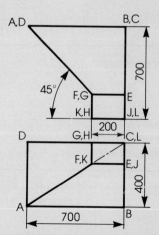

G33-4 The plan and elevation of a part of a roof structure is given. Determine: (a) the true length of the hip rafters AC and BC, and (b) the true angle between any pair of jack rafters which support the hip rafters AC and BC, i.e. the true angle of θ. Use a scale of 1:100 for the solution.

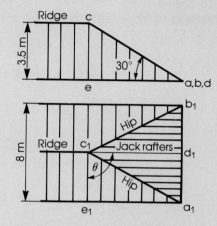

G31-1: Isometric and orthographic representations of a line in space

A line AB is positioned so that A is 10 mm above the horizontal plane and 50 mm in front of the front vertical plane. End B is 55 mm above the horizontal plane and 22 mm in front of the front vertical plane. End A is 23 mm in front of the end vertical plane and end B is 90 mm in front of the end vertical plane.
Represent the line AB described above by using First Angle orthographic projection. Determine: (a) the true length of the line AB and (b) the true angle the line makes with the horizontal plane.

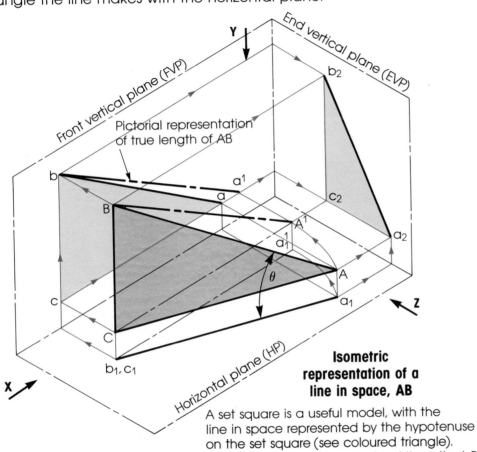

Isometric representation of a line in space, AB

A set square is a useful model, with the line in space represented by the hypotenuse on the set square (see coloured triangle).

To observe the true length of AB rotate the coloured triangle about its vertical, BC, until A attains the position A^1, i.e. the triangle A^1BC is normal (at 90°) to the viewing position Z. This operation, i.e. rotation, can be observed from arrow Y which gives the orthographic plan, a_1 moving to a_1^1. Corner A maintains its height from the HP with this being observed from Z. Front elevation shows a move to a^1.

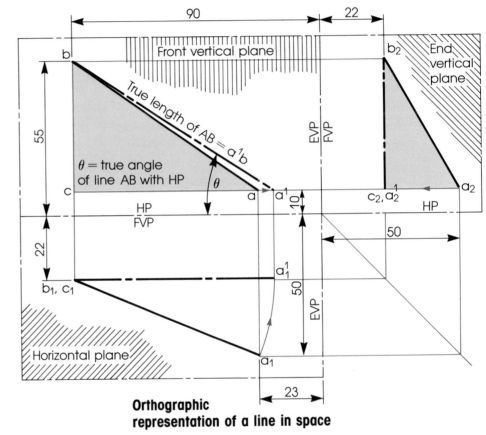

Orthographic representation of a line in space

a, b and c: position of A, B and C in front elevation
a_1, b_1 and c_1: position of A, B and C in plan
a_2, b_2 and c_2: position of A, B and C in end elevation
a_1^1: position of a_1 after rotation about b_1 c_1
a^1: position of a after rotation about bc

Drawing No. **G31**	TITLE: **Introduction to lines in space.**	NOTE: **First Angle projection used.**	SCALE: 

G31-2(a): To determine the true lengths of any corner of a cut pyramid

The frustum of a pyramid is shown below.
Determine the true lengths of any corner
which does not appear as true in any of
the 3 orthographic views given.

To observe the true length
of BGE when looking from
arrow Z, the triangle BEK
must be pivoted about
EK until it is normal to
the arrow Z, i.e. you are
looking straight on to it.

Note: B should have
rotated to position B¹
and G to position G¹
with the true length now
able to be observed
from Z. The rotation
can be observed looking
from Y, i.e. in the plan view.

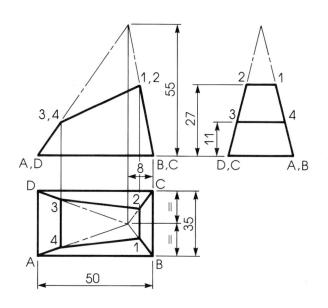

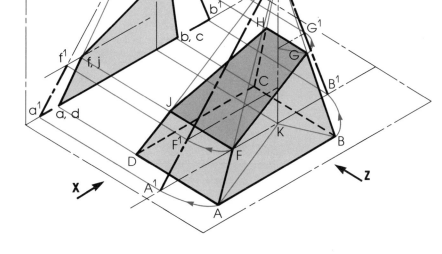

Drawing No. **G31**	TITLE: **Introduction to lines in space.**	NOTE: **First Angle projection used.**	SCALE:

G31-2(b): To determine the true lengths of any corner of a cut pyramid

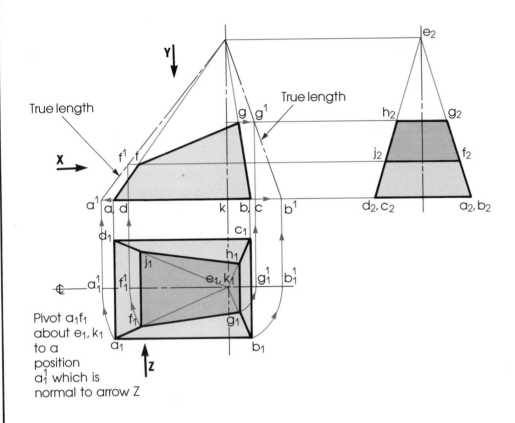

True length

Pivot a_1f_1 about e_1, k_1 to a position a_1^1 which is normal to arrow Z

Development

Shows the use of true lengths.
The pyramid is symmetrical about the ℄ in plan, therefore the true length of HC is equal to the true length of GB and JD = FA. True length of GB = g^1b^1 = HC. True length of FA = f^1a^1 = JD. True lengths of AB, BC and CD are normal to the viewing position Y and therefore true in the plan, i.e. $a_1 b_1$ and $b_1 c_1$ etc.

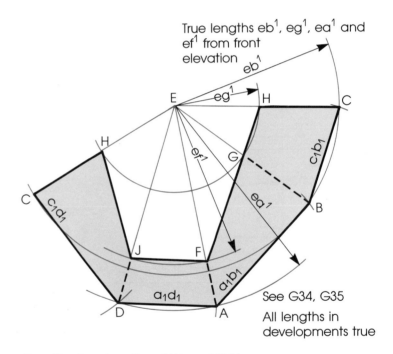

True lengths eb^1, eg^1, ea^1 and ef^1 from front elevation

See G34, G35

All lengths in developments true

Since the length of a line can only be observed as true when viewed from a position normal (i.e. at 90°) to the line, none of the orthographic views (X, Y and Z) shows the true length of the corners FA, GB, HC or DA.

Note: The true lengths of HJ and GJ have been determined in the development

Drawing No. **G31**	TITLE: **Introduction to lines in space.**	NOTE: **First Angle projection used.**	SCALE:

G31-3: To construct the true length and true angle of a line AB

Given the plan and elevation
of a line AB determine its
true length and true angle
to the front vertical plane.

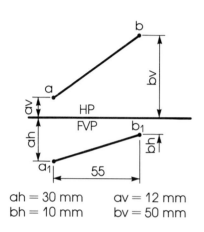

ah = 30 mm   av = 12 mm
bh = 10 mm   bv = 50 mm

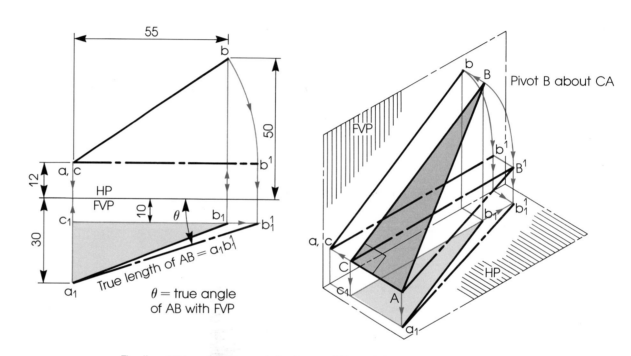

θ = true angle
of AB with FVP

The line AB has been modelled on a different right-angled triangle than in G31-1. The
edge BC of the triangle ABC is maintained parallel to the FVP whilst pivoting or
rebating the triangle about CA. When the triangle is parallel to the horizontal plane
(i.e. in the position CAB^1) its true shape can be seen in the plan view together with
the true angle of the line to the front vertical plane.

Drawing No. **G31**	TITLE: **Introduction to lines in space.**	NOTE: **First Angle projection used.**	SCALE:

G31-4: To construct the plan and elevation of a line

Produce the plan and elevation of a line given the position of its ends relative to the principle planes. Vertical height of A above the horizontal plane, $av = 41$ mm; vertical height of B above the horizontal plane, $bv = 11$ mm. The horizontal distance of A in front of the vertical plane, $ah = 38$ mm and the horizontal distance of B in front of the vertical plane, $bh = 15$ mm. The end of the line A is to the left of end B and AB has a true length of 68 mm.

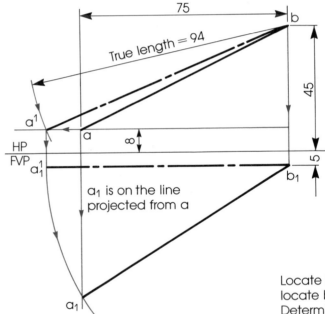

a¹ and a are on this line

True length = 68

HP
FVP

41

38

11

15

a₁ is on this line

Locate b and project and locate b_1 in plan.
Locate a^1 on line 41 above the HP by intersection with true length arc and project a_1 to the plan position a^1_1.
Pivot a^1_1 about b_1 until it coincides with the line which determines the distance of a_1 from the front vertical plane in the plan. Project position of a from a_1. Synthesis (putting together) of information given involves a reversal of the process illustrated in G31-1 to find the true length.

G31-5: To construct the plan view of a line

Determine the plan view of the line AB given the front elevation and the position of end B in the plan as shown if the true length of AB is given as 94 mm, i.e. $a^1b^1 = 94$ mm

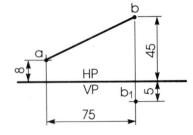

b

45

a

8

HP
VP

b₁

5

75

75

True length = 94

a¹

a

8

HP
FVP
a₁¹

b

45

b₁

5

a₁ is on the line projected from a

a₁

Locate b and project and locate b_1 in plan.
Determine position of a and use true length to locate a^1 and project its position to a^1_1 in plan.
Locate a_1 by pivoting a^1_1 about b_1 to intersect the projected position of a in the plan to give a_1.

Drawing No.
G31

TITLE: **Introduction to lines in space.**

NOTE: **First Angle projection used.**

SCALE:
0 10 20 30 40 50 60 70 80
mm

G32-1: To construct the front elevation of a line

Determine the front elevation of a line AB given the plan and position of B in the front elevation as shown. The true length of AB is 80 mm.

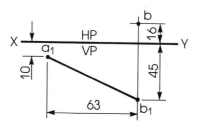

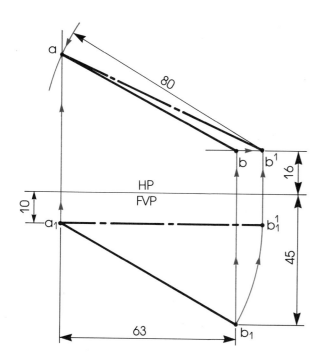

G32-2: To construct the front elevation of a line

Determine the front elevation of a line AB given its plan as shown and the position of B in the front elevation. The true angle of the line to the horizontal plane is 35°.

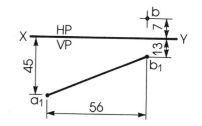

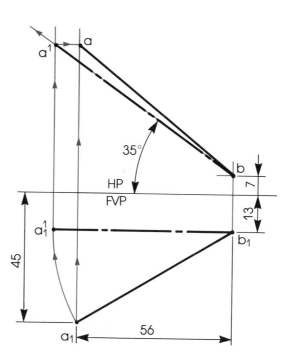

| Drawing No. G32 | TITLE: **Lines in space.** | NOTE: **First Angle projection used.** | SCALE: |

Horizontal and vertical traces

A trace is the point where a line in space, if produced or extended, would intersect a principal plane.

HT: The horizontal trace is the point where a line produced intersects the horizontal plane.

VT: The vertical trace is the point where a line produced intersects the vertical plane.

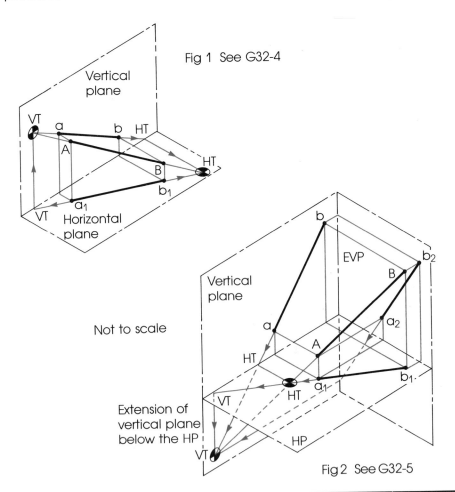

Fig 1 See G32-4

Vertical plane

Horizontal plane

Not to scale

Vertical plane

EVP

Extension of vertical plane below the HP

HP

Fig 2 See G32-5

G32-3: To construct the vertical and horizontal traces of a line

A line AB has a true length of 46 mm and is inclined at 60° to the horizontal plane. End A is located 6 mm above the horizontal plane and the line disposed in the plan as shown. Draw the plan and elevation of the line and determine its vertical and horizontal traces.

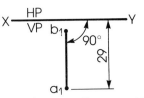

End A is lower than end B

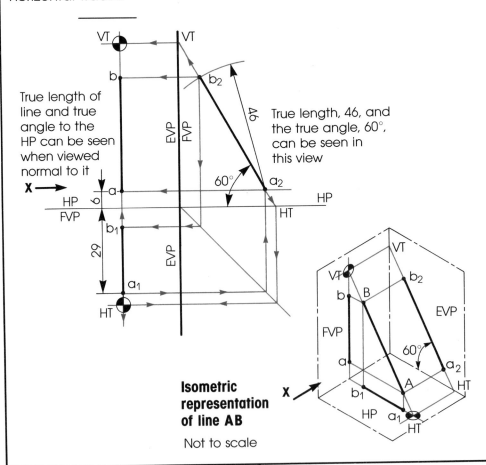

True length of line and true angle to the HP can be seen when viewed normal to it

True length, 46, and the true angle, 60°, can be seen in this view

Isometric representation of line AB

Not to scale

Drawing No.
G32

TITLE: **Lines in space and problems involving traces.**

NOTE: **First Angle projection used.**

SCALE:
0 10 20 30 40 50 60 70 80

mm

G32-4: To construct a line given the vertical and horizontal traces

The plan and elevation given shows the position of the traces of a line AB. Draw the line AB in both views, given that end A is 40 mm above the horizontal plane and end B is 25 mm in front of the vertical plane.

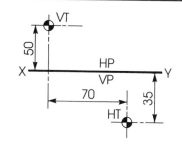

___

Refer to Fig 1, previous page

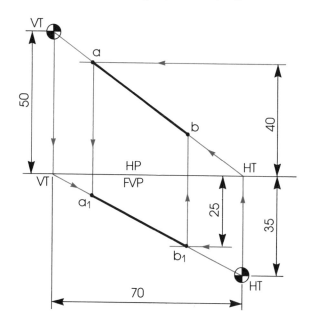

G32-5: To construct the horizontal and vertical traces of a line

The front elevation and plan of a line are given. Determine the horizontal trace and the vertical trace of the line AB.

___

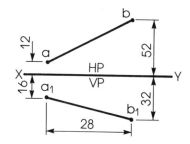

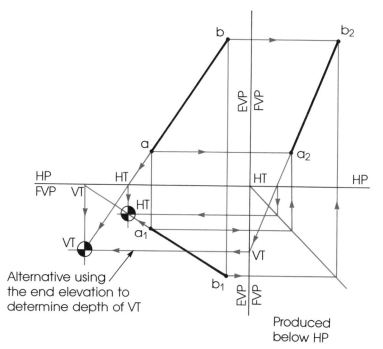

Alternative using the end elevation to determine depth of VT

Produced below HP

See Fig 2, previous page

Drawing No.	TITLE: **Lines in space and problems involving traces.**	NOTE: **First Angle projection used.**	SCALE:
G32			0 10 20 30 40 50 60 70 80 mm

G32-6: To construct the vertical and horizontal traces of a line

The front elevation and plan of a line AB are given. Determine the vertical and horizontal traces, i.e. the vertical trace and horizontal trace.

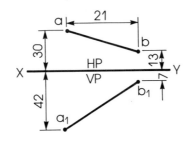

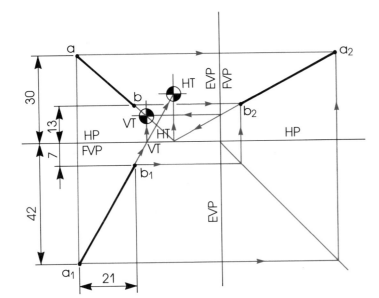

G32-7: To construct the plan, elevation and traces of a line

The given plan shows the attitude of a line AB to the front vertical plane. AB has a true length of 80 mm and its true angle to the horizontal plane is 30°. End A is 12 mm in front of the front vertical plane and 45 mm above the horizontal plane. Draw the plan and elevation of AB, determine its traces and its true angle to the front vertical plane.

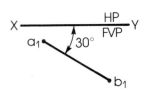

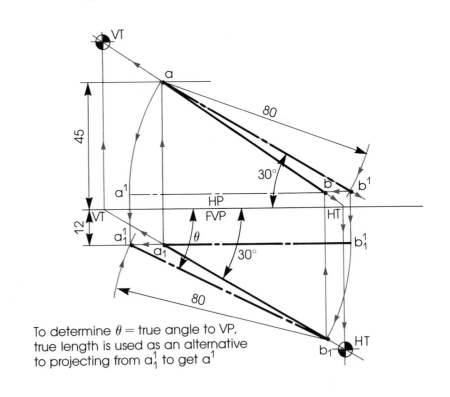

To determine θ = true angle to VP, true length is used as an alternative to projecting from a_1^1 to get a^1

| Drawing No. **G32** | TITLE: **Lines in space and problems involving traces.** | NOTE: **First Angle projection used.** | SCALE: 0 10 20 30 40 50 60 70 80 mm |

G32-8: To construct the plans and elevations of 2 lines, the true angle between them and the true length of one

The front elevation of 2 lines AB and CD is given. AB is parallel to, and 30 mm in front of, the front vertical plane. CD has a true length of 71 mm, end D being 6 mm in front of the front vertical plane. Draw the plan and elevation of the lines, show the true angle between the lines and true length of AB.

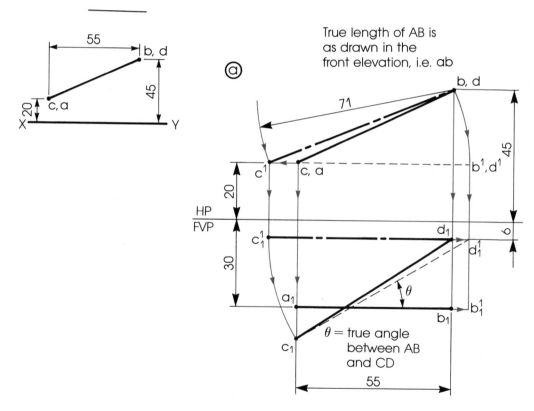

True length of AB is as drawn in the front elevation, i.e. ab

(a)

θ = true angle between AB and CD

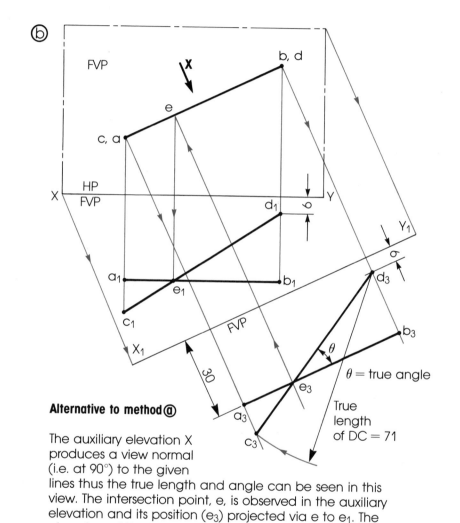

(b)

Alternative to method (a)

The auxiliary elevation X produces a view normal (i.e. at 90°) to the given lines thus the true length and angle can be seen in this view. The intersection point, e, is observed in the auxiliary elevation and its position (e₃) projected via e to e₁. The plan view of the line DC can be drawn by producing d₁ to e₁ to c₁.

θ = true angle

True length of DC = 71

Drawing No. G32	TITLE: **Lines in space and problems involving traces.**	NOTE: **First Angle projection used.**	SCALE:

161

G33-1(a): To construct the true shape of a triangular lamina. First method

2 views of a lamina ABC which is triangular in shape are shown in orthographic projection. Determine the true shape of the lamina.

This method considers each line (i.e. element) in turn, analyses them individually and synthesises the information, i.e. true lengths, to form the true shape.

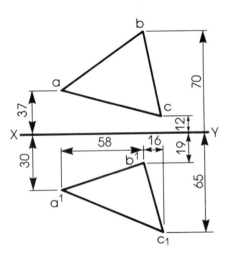

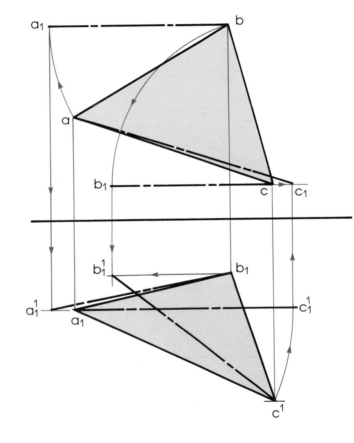

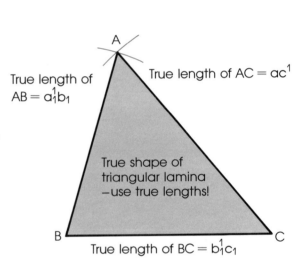

True length of AB = $a_1^1 b_1$

True length of AC = ac^1

True length of BC = $b_1^1 c_1$

True shape of triangular lamina —use true lengths!

Drawing No. **G33**	TITLE: **Practical applications of lines in space.**	NOTE: **First Angle projection used.**	SCALE:

162

G33-1(b): To construct the true shape of a triangular lamina. Second method

In this method the triangle is analysed as a whole and manipulated stage by stage into a position where it can be observed directly, i.e. normal to the viewing position. The front elevation shows the true shape designated by $a^1 b^3 c^1$. See table below for operations.

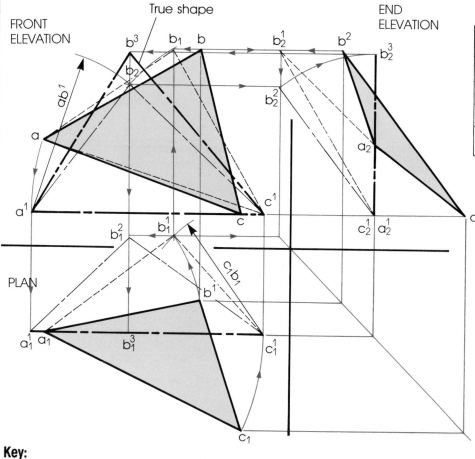

FRONT ELEVATION

True shape

END ELEVATION

PLAN

OPERATION	FRONT ELEVATION	PLAN	END ELEVATION
Start position	a b c	$a_1 b_1 c_1$	$a_2 b_2 c_2$
Pivot △ about a_1 in plan	$a b^1 c^1$	$a_1 b_1^1 c_1^1$	$a_2 b_2^1 c_2^1$
Pivot △ about c^1 in front elevation	$a^1 b^2 c^1$	$a_1^1 b_1^2 c_1^1$	$a_2^1 b_2^2 c_2$
Pivot △ about $c_2^1 a_2^1$ in end elevation	$a^1 b^3 c^1$ True shape	$a_1^1 b_1^3 c_1^1$	$a_2^1 b_2^3 c_2^1$

The method of tabulating the sequence of positional changes may arouse interest in the algebra of matrices, a topic which may be studied in mathematics. Matrix theory may provide a useful tool in computer graphics and analysis. The example uses a 3-dimensional matrix. Can you see a <u>useful</u> pattern?

Key:

b_2 ⟋

gives number of positional changes from start

gives elevation, i.e. ₁ for plan, ₂ for end elevation.

Drawing No. **G33**	TITLE: **Practical applications of lines in space.**	NOTE: **First Angle projection used.**	SCALE: 0 10 20 30 40 50 60 70 80 mm

G33-2: To construct the lengths of the components of a rotary clothes line frame

The plan and elevation of a rotary clothes line frame is shown in orthographic projection. Determine the lengths of the components used in the frame by drawing to a scale of 1:20 and finding the lengths of any which do not appear as true in either of the given views. The arms are designated HA, HB and HC; the ties GD, GE and GF. Centre pole XY is 2 m high, GH is 0.7 m and HY is 1.22 m. Shortest distance of D,E and F to XY is 0.83 m.

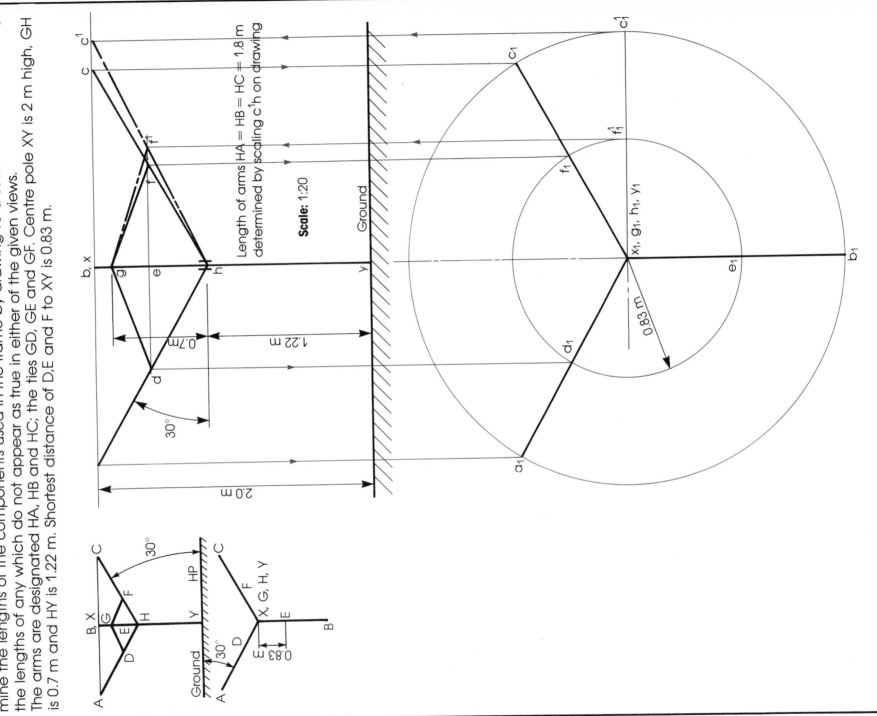

Length of arms HA = HB = HC = 1.8 m determined by scaling c¹h on drawing

Scale: 1:20

Drawing No.	TITLE: **Practical applications of lines in space.**	NOTE: **First Angle projection used.**
G33		

164

G33-3: To construct the lengths of corners of a feed hopper

The plan and elevation of an animal feed hopper is shown. Determine the lengths of any corners which do not appear as true lengths in either of the given orthographic views. Use a scale of 1:10 for the solution.

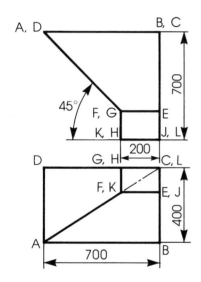

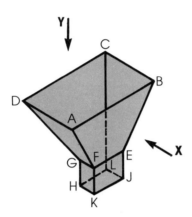

All lengths except AF and BE appear as true in either the plan or elevation

True length of AF = a^1f = 760 mm
True length of BE = b^1e = 580 mm

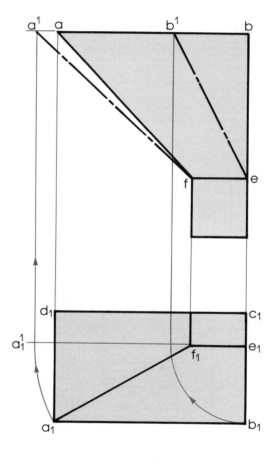

Scale: 1:10

Drawing No.	TITLE: **Practical applications of lines in space.**	NOTE: **First Angle projection used.**	SCALE:
G33			0 10 20 30 40 50 60 70 80

165

G33-4: To construct the true lengths of rafters in a roof and the true angles between them

The plan and elevation of a part of a roof structure is given. Determine:
(a) the true length of the hip rafters AC and BC, and
(b) the true angle between any pair of jack rafters which support the hip rafters AC and BC, i.e. the true angle of θ. Use a scale of 1:100 for the solution.

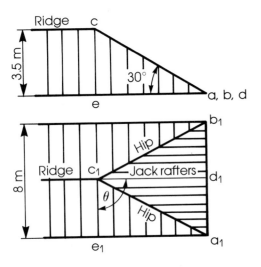

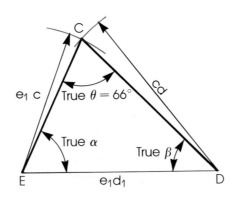

True lengths of $\triangle$ DCE are used to determine true angles

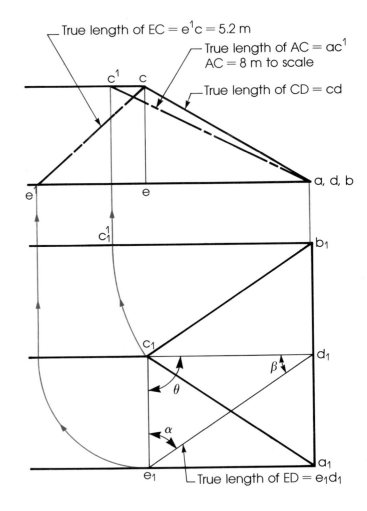

True length of EC = e^1c = 5.2 m

True length of AC = ac^1
AC = 8 m to scale

True length of CD = cd

True length of ED = e_1d_1

α, β and θ are not true angles

| Drawing No. G33 | TITLE: **Practical applications of lines in space.** | NOTE: **First Angle projection used.** | SCALE: 0 10 20 30 40 50 60 70 80 mm |

166

Worksheets for G34 to G37

G34 INTRODUCTION TO DEVELOPMENTS: PRISMS TO CYLINDERS (FIRST ANGLE PROJECTION).

G34-1 Produce the development of the open-topped box shown.

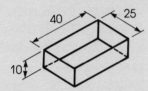

G34-2 Produce the development of the open-ended square duct or pipe cut at one end by a 30° plane.

G34-3 Produce the development of the open-ended square duct which is to fit to the angled wall as shown.

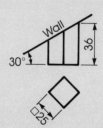

G34-4 Produce the development of the square tube shown complete with a top to close the angled face created by the 30° plane.

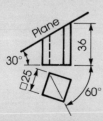

G34-5 A hollow hexagonal tube is shown cut at 45° at one end. Produce the development of the sheet metal prior to folding.

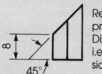

Regular hexagonal prism
Distance AC = 34, i.e. the hexagon's side is 17 mm

G34-6 A hollow hexagonal tube is shown cut by a 45° plane and viewed across corners. Produce the development.

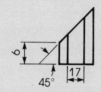

G34-7 Produce the development of the open-ended cylinder shown.

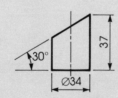

G34-8 The storage bin shown is to be produced from sheet metal. The bottom is to be sealed and the top left open. Produce the shape of the cut sheet prior to folding to shape and welding.

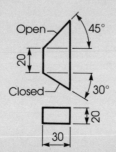

G34-9 The front elevation of a loading chute is given together with an auxiliary elevation showing its cross-sectional form. Produce a development of the chute to a scale 1:10.

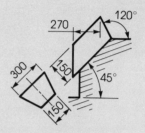

G34-10 The intermediate piece A has the same cross-sectional shape as the 2 pieces to which it is joined. Produce a development of the intermediate piece.

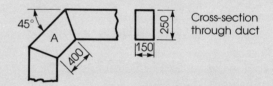

Cross-section through duct

G35 DEVELOPMENTS: CYLINDERS CUT BY PLANE AND CURVED SURFACES (FIRST ANGLE PROJECTION).

G35-1 Produce the development of the pipe A which forms a tee junction with the square tube.

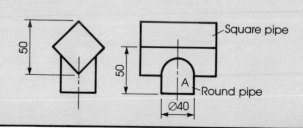

167

G35-2 Two pipes of equal diameter form a tee junction as shown. Produce the development of pipe A.

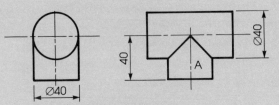

G35-3 The given elevation shows a ⌀35 mm feeder pipe to a fuel tank. The top of the pipe is parallel to the base of the fuel tank. Produce the development of the pipe.

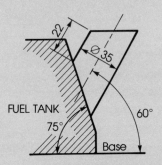

G35-4 The cylindrical duct mounted on the roof is used to expel dust and fumes from the roof space. Produce a development of the ⌀40 mm duct.

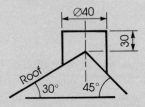

G35-5 Two pipes meet to form a tee junction. Pipe A is mounted vertically on pipe B but with its axis offset by 5 mm. Develop the pipe A.

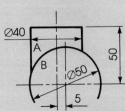

G35-6 Produce the development of the cylinder A, complete with hole to accept the ⌀44 mm cylinder.

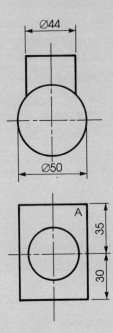

G36 DEVELOPMENTS: PYRAMIDS AND CONES (FIRST ANGLE PROJECTION).

G36-1 Produce the development of the pyramid with an open base.

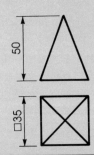

G36-2 Produce the development of the hexagonal pyramid with an open base.

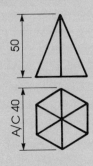

G36-3 Produce the development of the cone with an open base.

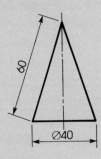

G36-4 Complete the plan view of the lower part of the hexagonal pyramid cut by the plane A-A and develop the portion below the plane, i.e. without the base.

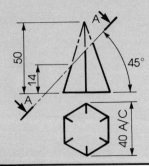

G36-5 Complete the plan view of the portion of the hexagonal pyramid below the plane B-B. Produce the shape of the development of the part of the pyramid which lies below the plane.

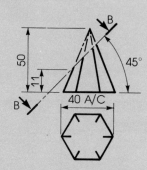

G37 DEVELOPMENTS: CONES, LEADING TO TRIANGULATION METHOD (FIRST ANGLE PROJECTION).

G37-1 A pipe which contains a feed screw is loaded through a conical hopper as shown. Develop the part of the cone which forms the hopper and sits astride the pipe.

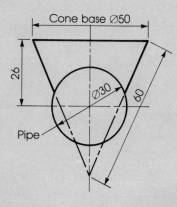

G37-3 Develop the frustum of the oblique cone which lies below the cutting plane A-A.

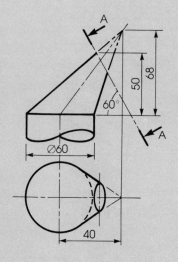

G36-6 Produce the development of the part of the cone which lies below the cutting plane C-C. The plane C-C is at 45° to the HP.

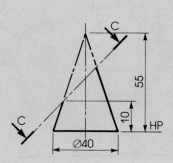

G37-2 Develop the conical shaped dust and fume ventilator which sits astride the roof ridge as shown. Use a scale of 1:10 for your solution.

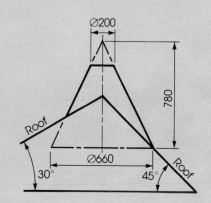

G37-4 A hood to extract fumes from a machine has a rectangular base but tapers to allow a circular pipe to be attached to the top. Produce the development of the transitional tapered hood to a scale of 1:20.

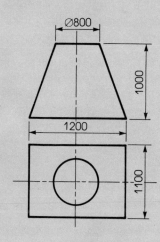

Produce the development of
the open-topped box shown.

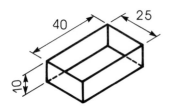

Developments

A development is the shape produced
when a 3-dimensional object which
is made from thin sheet material is
unfolded and laid flat on a plane
surface. This can often be achieved
in several ways as shown. Fig A
shows the most economical method of
development as this would create least
waste in multiple production, be folded
by a simpler design of folding tool
and be jointed by welding more quickly
due to shorter seams.

All the examples given have been
developed with respect to the shortest
seam but for various design reasons
this may not always be possible,
e.g. grain flow of material may affect
strength.

True lengths only must be used
for developments.

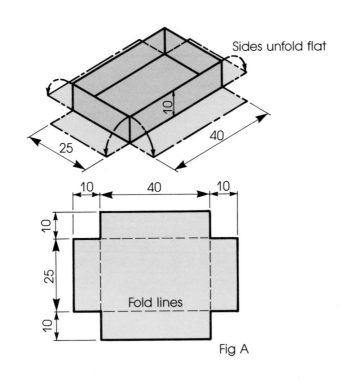

Sides unfold flat

Fig A

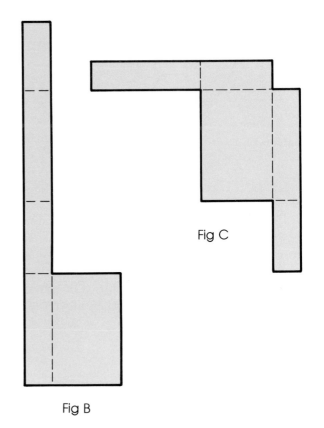

Fig C

Fig B

Drawing No.	TITLE: **Introduction to developments.**		SCALE:
G34			0 10 20 30 40 50 60 70 80 mm

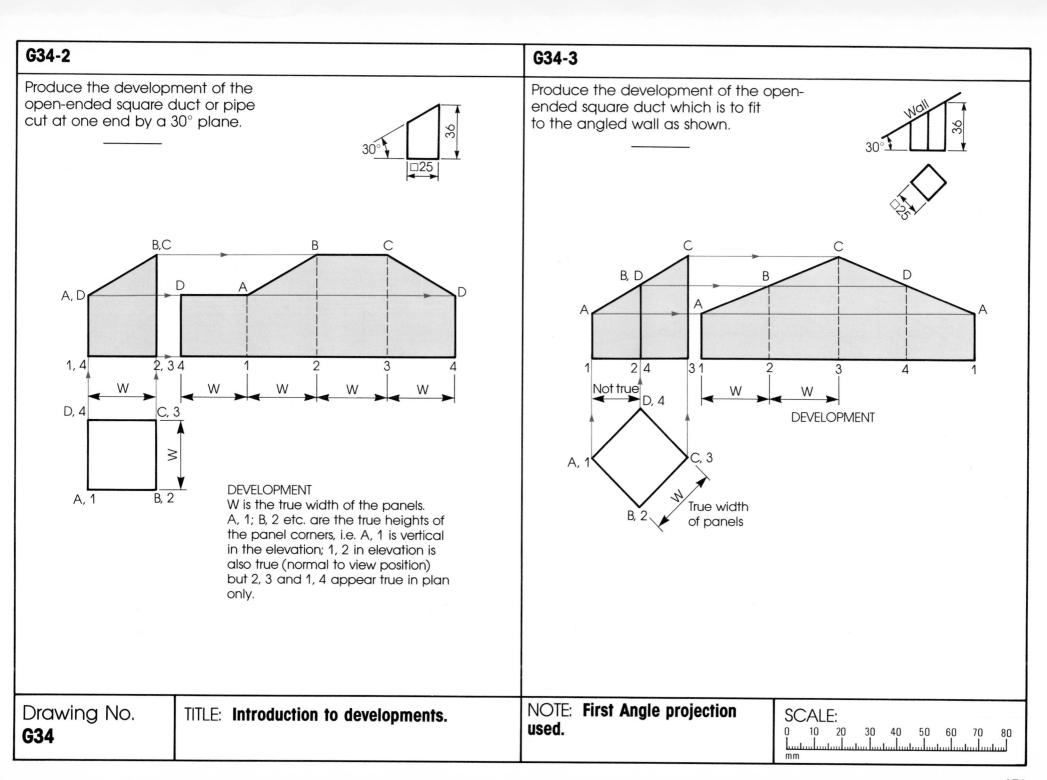

G34-2

Produce the development of the open-ended square duct or pipe cut at one end by a 30° plane.

36

30°

□25

B, C — B — C

A, D — D — A — D

1, 4 — 2, 3 — 4 — 1 — 2 — 3 — 4

W — W — W — W — W

D, 4 — C, 3

W

A, 1 — B, 2

DEVELOPMENT
W is the true width of the panels.
A, 1; B, 2 etc. are the true heights of the panel corners, i.e. A, 1 is vertical in the elevation; 1, 2 in elevation is also true (normal to view position) but 2, 3 and 1, 4 appear true in plan only.

G34-3

Produce the development of the open-ended square duct which is to fit to the angled wall as shown.

Wall

36

30°

□25

C — C

B, D — B — D

A — A — A

1 — 2 — 4 — 3 — 1 — 2 — 3 — 4 — 1

Not true

W — W

DEVELOPMENT

D, 4

A, 1 — C, 3

W — True width of panels

B, 2

Drawing No.
G34

TITLE: **Introduction to developments.**

NOTE: **First Angle projection used.**

SCALE:
0 10 20 30 40 50 60 70 80
mm

171

G34-4

Produce the development of the square tube shown complete with a top to close the angled face created by the 30° plane.

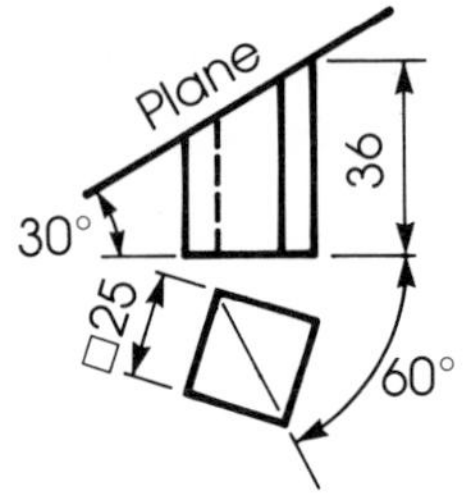

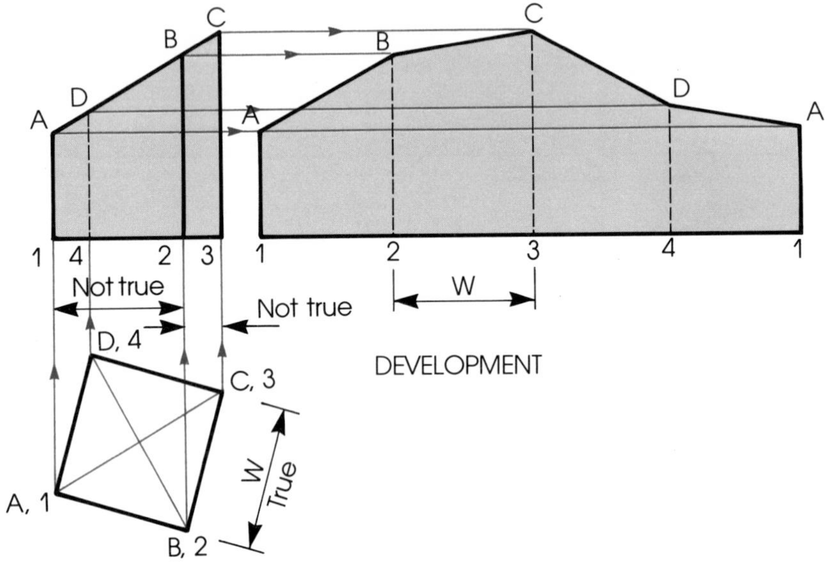

Plane

30°

36

□25

60°

1 4 2 3   1   2   3   4   1

Not true

Not true

W

DEVELOPMENT

D, 4

C, 3

A, 1

W
True

B, 2

G34-5

A hollow hexagonal tube is shown cut at 45° at one end. Produce the development of the sheet metal prior to folding.

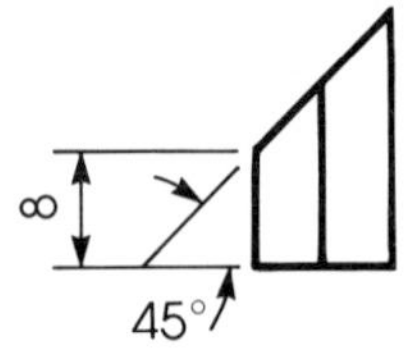

8

45°

Regular hexagonal prism
Distance AC = 34, i.e. the hexagon's side is 17 mm

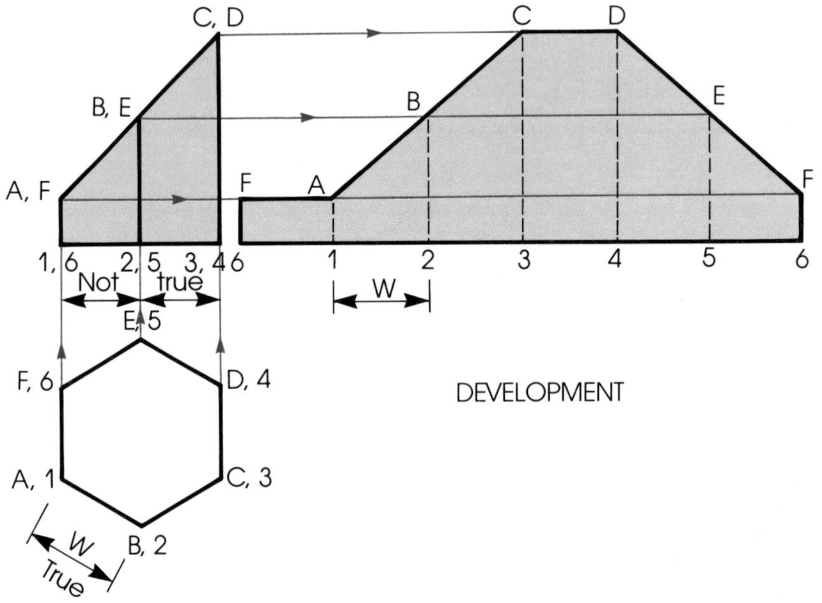

C, D   C   D

B, E   B   E

A, F   F   A   F

1, 6   2, 5 3, 4 6   1   2   3   4   5   6

Not   true

W

E, 5

F, 6   D, 4

A, 1   C, 3

W
True   B, 2

DEVELOPMENT

| Drawing No. **G34** | TITLE: **Introduction to developments. Prisms.** | NOTE: **First Angle projection used.** | SCALE: 0 10 20 30 40 50 60 70 80 mm |

G34-6

A hollow hexagonal tube is shown cut by a 45° plane and viewed across corners. Produce the development.

DEVELOPMENT

True

Not true

W

G34-7

Produce the development of the open-ended cylinder shown.

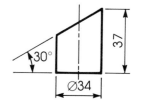

Note: points are joined by curves of good fit, i.e. interpolation. In plan, AB is curved.

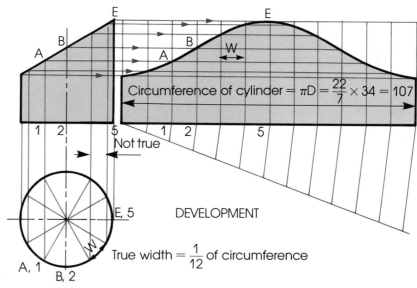

Circumference of cylinder = $\pi D = \dfrac{22}{7} \times 34 = 107$

DEVELOPMENT

Not true

True width = $\dfrac{1}{12}$ of circumference

Unfortunately the cylinder has no corners, so invent some e.g. A, 1 B, 2 etc.

Drawing No.
G34

TITLE: **Introduction to developments. Prisms and cylinders.**

NOTE: **First Angle projection used.**

SCALE:

0 10 20 30 40 50 60 70 80

mm

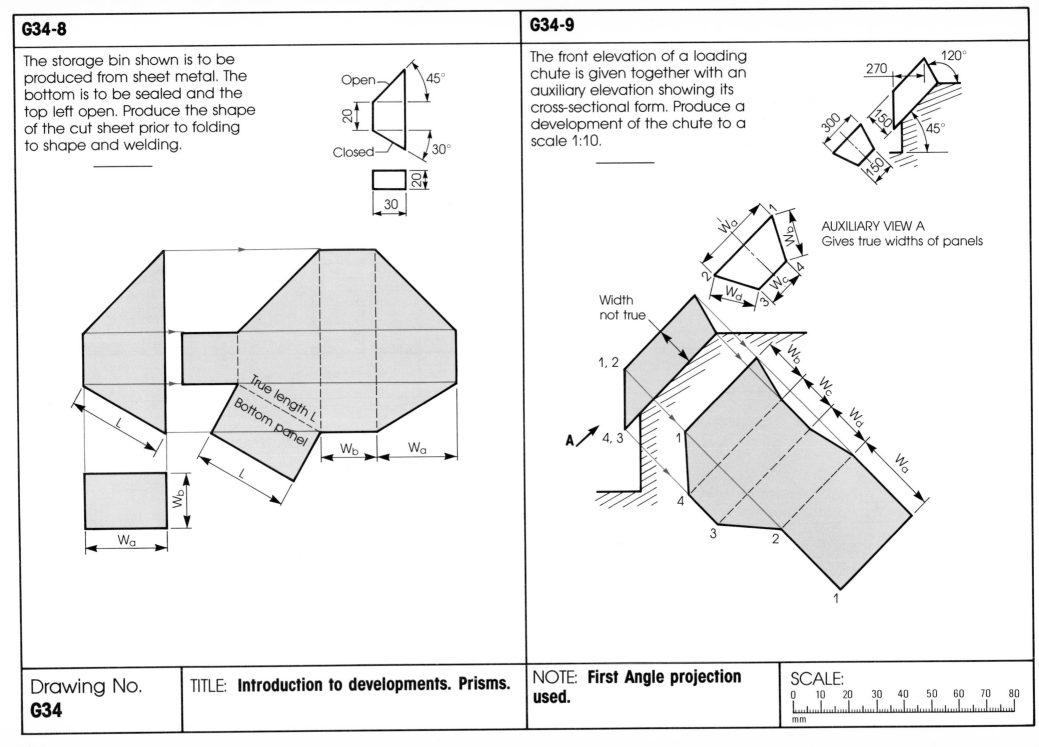

G34-8

The storage bin shown is to be produced from sheet metal. The bottom is to be sealed and the top left open. Produce the shape of the cut sheet prior to folding to shape and welding.

Open 45°
20
Closed 30°

20
30

L
L

True length L
Bottom panel

W$_b$ W$_a$

W$_b$

W$_a$

G34-9

The front elevation of a loading chute is given together with an auxiliary elevation showing its cross-sectional form. Produce a development of the chute to a scale 1:10.

120°
270
150
300
45°
150

AUXILIARY VIEW A
Gives true widths of panels

W$_a$ 1
W$_b$
2   4
W$_d$ W$_c$
3

Width not true

1, 2
A   4, 3   1
4
3   2

W$_b$
W$_c$
W$_d$
W$_a$

1

Drawing No.
G34

TITLE: **Introduction to developments. Prisms.**

NOTE: **First Angle projection used.**

SCALE:
0 10 20 30 40 50 60 70 80
mm

174

The intermediate piece, A, has the same cross-sectional shape as the 2 pieces to which it is joined. Produce a development of the intermediate piece.

45°

A

400

250

150

Cross-section through duct

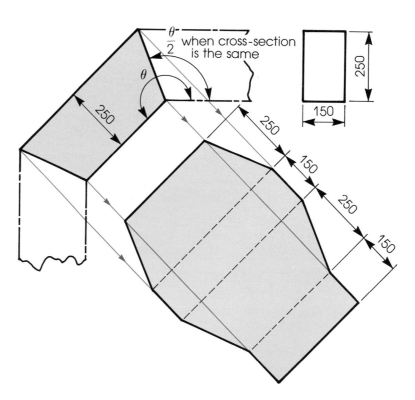

$\frac{\theta}{2}$ when cross-section is the same

θ

250

250

250

150

250

150

250

150

150

Drawing No. **G34**	TITLE: **Introduction to developments.**	NOTE: **First Angle projection used.**	SCALE:

SCALE:
0 10 20 30 40 50 60 70 80
mm

Produce the development of the pipe A which
forms a tee junction with the square tube.

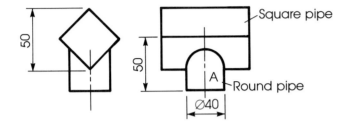

Square pipe

Round pipe

∅40

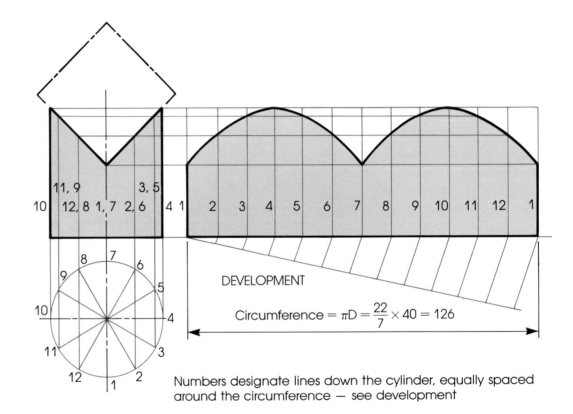

11, 9   3, 5
12, 8 1, 7 2, 6

DEVELOPMENT

$$\text{Circumference} = \pi D = \frac{22}{7} \times 40 = 126$$

Numbers designate lines down the cylinder, equally spaced
around the circumference — see development

Drawing No. **G35**	TITLE: **Developments of the cylinder.**	NOTE: **First Angle projection used.**	SCALE:

0 10 20 30 40 50 60 70 80
mm

Two pipes of equal diameter form a tee junction as shown. Produce the development of pipe A.

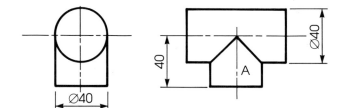

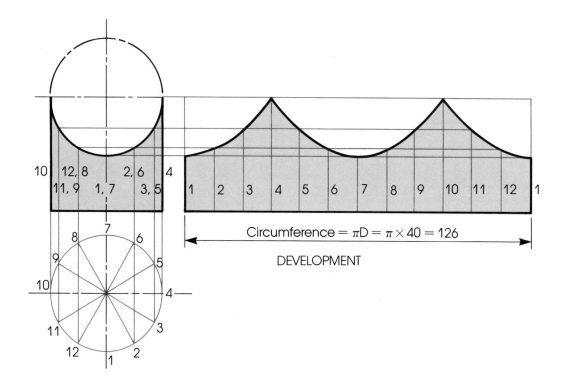

Circumference = $\pi D = \pi \times 40 = 126$

DEVELOPMENT

Drawing No. **G35**	TITLE: **Developments of the cylinder.**	NOTE: **First Angle projection used.**	SCALE: 0 10 20 30 40 50 60 70 80 mm

177

The given elevation shows a 35 mm
diameter feeder pipe to a fuel
tank. The top of the pipe is parallel
to the base of the fuel tank.
Produce the development of the pipe.

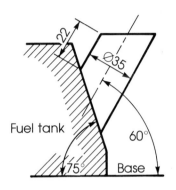

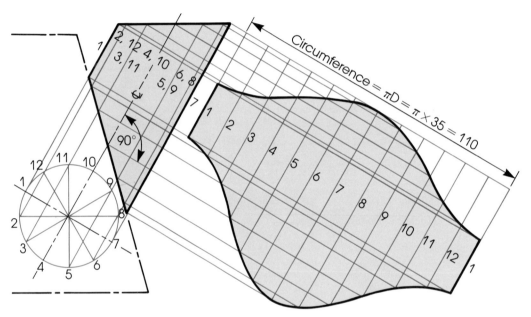

Develop at 90° to ₵ axis of cylinder, i.e. unwrap the cylinder

Drawing No. **G35**	TITLE: **Developments of the cylinder.**	NOTE: **First Angle projection used.**	SCALE:

The cylindrical duct mounted on the roof is used
to expel dust and fumes from the roof space.
Produce a development of the 40 mm diameter duct.

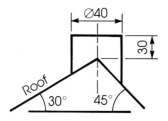

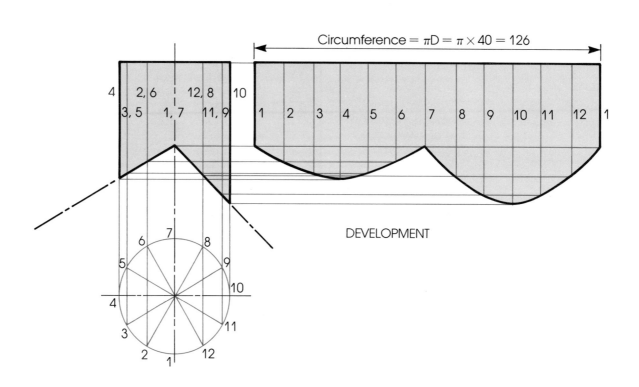

Circumference = πD = π × 40 = 126

DEVELOPMENT

Drawing No.	TITLE: **Developments of the cylinder.**	NOTE: **First Angle projection used.**	SCALE:
G35			0 10 20 30 40 50 60 70 80 mm

Two pipes meet to form a tee junction. Pipe A is
mounted vertically on pipe B but with its axis
offset by 5 mm. Develop the pipe A.

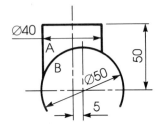

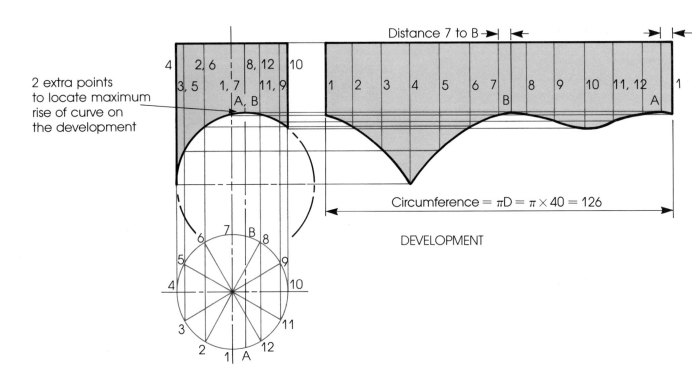

Distance 7 to B

Distance 1 to A
from plan view
to locate point
of highest rise
around the
circumference

2 extra points
to locate maximum
rise of curve on
the development

Circumference = $\pi D = \pi \times 40 = 126$

DEVELOPMENT

Drawing No.	TITLE: **Developments of the cylinder.**	NOTE: **First Angle projection used.**	SCALE:
G35			0 10 20 30 40 50 60 70 80 mm

Produce the development of the cylinder A, complete with hole to accept the 44 mm diameter cylinder.

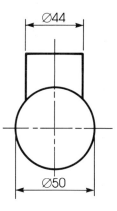

∅44

∅50

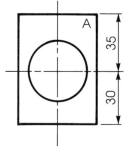

A

35

30

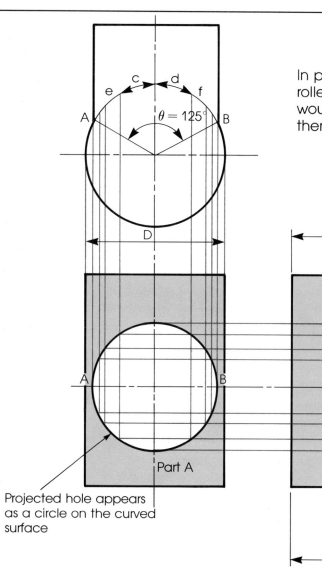

θ = 125°

A   B

D

A   B

Part A

Projected hole appears as a circle on the curved surface

In practice the upper cylinder would be developed, (see G35-2), rolled to a cylinder, welded, and mounted astride part A which would be in cylinder form. The shape of the seating would then be transferred to part A and the hole cut.

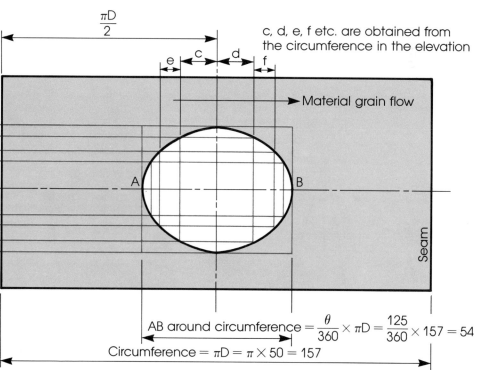

$\frac{\pi D}{2}$

c, d, e, f etc. are obtained from the circumference in the elevation

e   c   d   f

Material grain flow

A   B

Seam

AB around circumference $= \frac{\theta}{360} \times \pi D = \frac{125}{360} \times 157 = 54$

Circumference $= \pi D = \pi \times 50 = 157$

DEVELOPMENT
This development has been produced with the longer seam in order to utilise the inherent strength in the grain flow, strengthening the hole side.

Drawing No.	TITLE: **Developments of the cylinder.**	NOTE: **First Angle projection used.**	SCALE:
G35			0 10 20 30 40 50 60 70 80 mm

181

Produce the development of the pyramid with an open base.

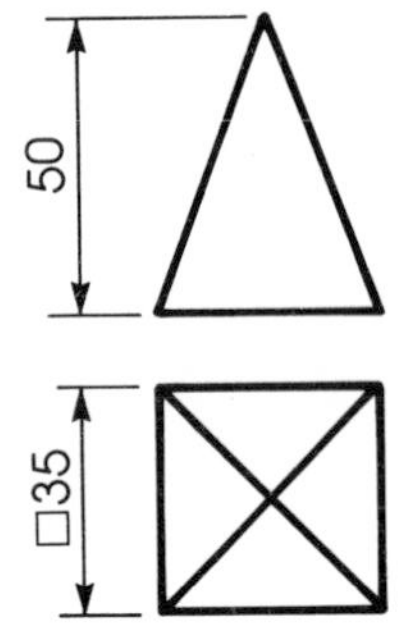

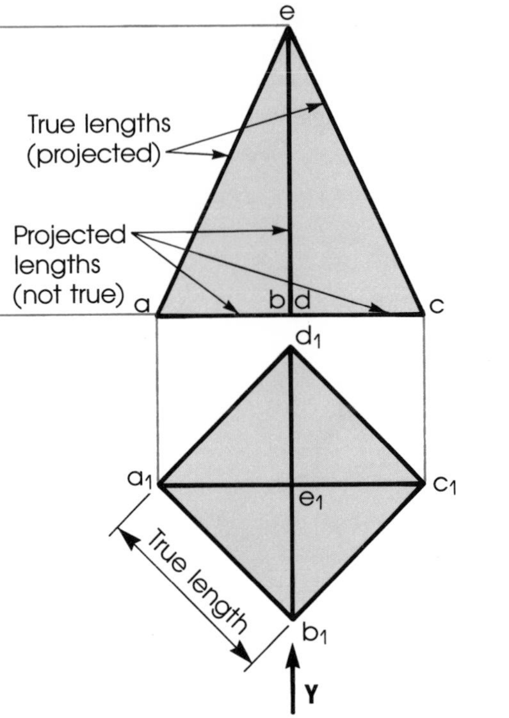

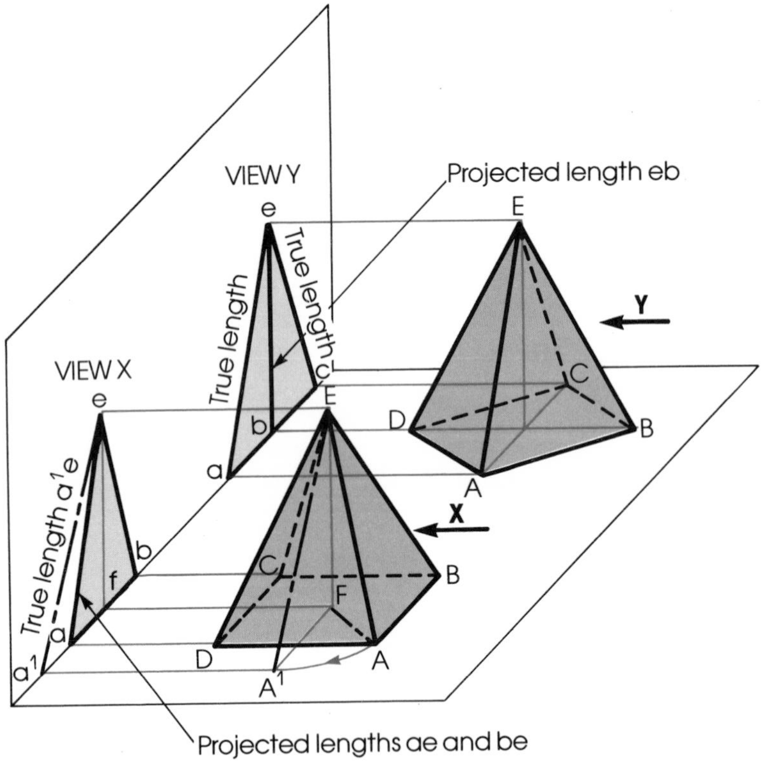

50

□35

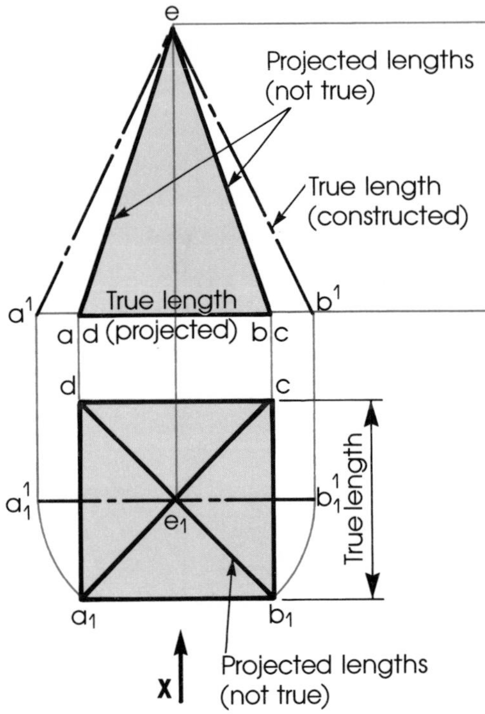

Projected lengths (not true)

True length (constructed)

True length

a^1 b^1

a d (projected) b c

True length (projected)

d

c

a^1_1 b^1_1

True length

e_1

a_1 b_1

X

Projected lengths (not true)

True lengths (projected)

a b d c

Projected lengths (not true)

d_1

a_1 c_1

e_1

True length

b_1

Y

Since the pyramid is a right square pyramid
$EA = EB = EC = ED = ea^1$

See G28 for more details on true lengths of lines

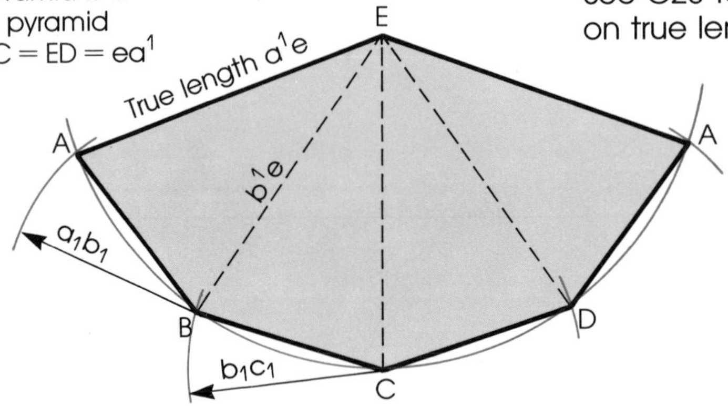

VIEW Y

Projected length eb

e

E

True length

True length

b

c

E

D

C

B

a

A

Y

VIEW X

e

E

True length a^1e

b

True length

f

C

F

B

a

a^1

D

A^1

A

X

Projected lengths ae and be

E

True length a^1e

A

A

b^1e

a_1b_1

B

D

b_1c_1

C

Developments must use true lengths, not projected ones, unless of course the projected lengths are also true as illustrated above.

| Drawing No. **G36** | TITLE: **Developments of pyramids.** | NOTE: **First Angle projection used.** | SCALE: 0 10 20 30 40 50 60 70 80 mm |

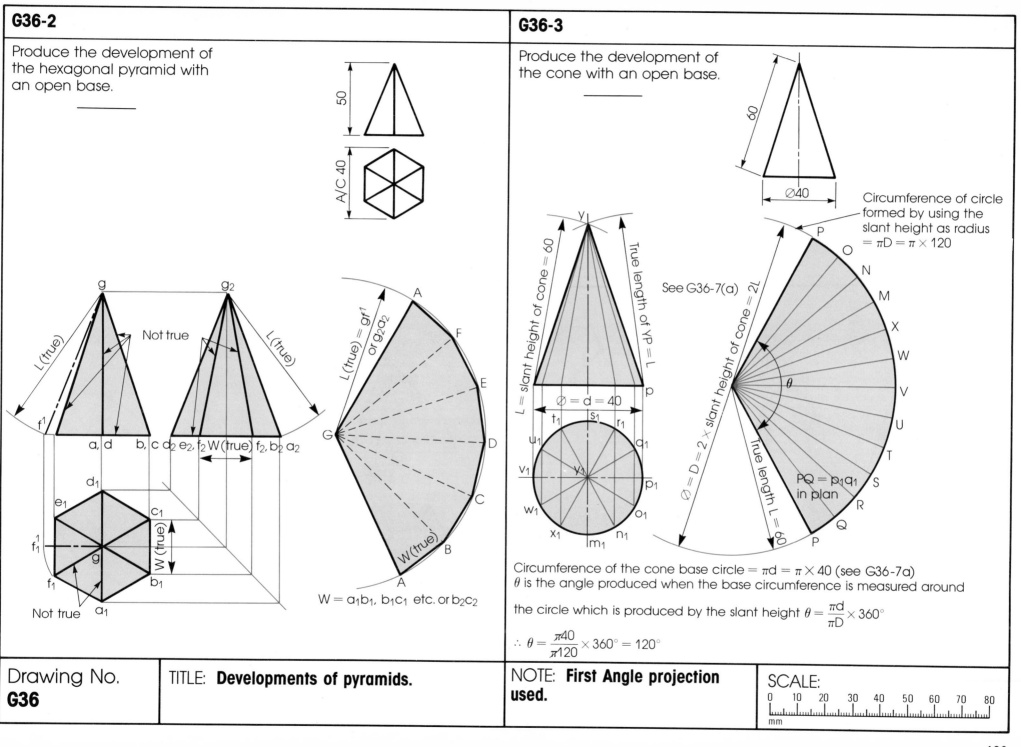

G36-2

Produce the development of the hexagonal pyramid with an open base.

50

A/C 40

g   g₂

Not true

L (true)   L (true)

L(true) = gf¹ or g₂a₂

a, d   b, c d₂ e₂, f₂ W(true) f₂, b₂ a₂

W (true)

d₁

e₁   c₁

W (true)

f₁¹

g

f₁   b₁

Not true   a₁

W = a₁b₁, b₁c₁ etc. or b₂c₂

A

F

E

G

D

C

W (true)   B

A

G36-3

Produce the development of the cone with an open base.

60

Ø40

Circumference of circle formed by using the slant height as radius $= \pi D = \pi \times 120$

See G36-7(a)

L = slant height of cone = 60

True length of YP = L

y

Ø = d = 40

t₁   s₁   r₁

u₁   q₁

v₁   y₁   p₁

w₁   o₁

x₁   n₁

m₁

P   O   N   M   X   W   V   U   T   S   R   Q   P

θ

Ø = D = 2 × slant height of cone

True length L = 60

PQ = p₁q₁ in plan

Circumference of the cone base circle $= \pi d = \pi \times 40$ (see G36-7a)
θ is the angle produced when the base circumference is measured around the circle which is produced by the slant height $\theta = \dfrac{\pi d}{\pi D} \times 360°$

$\therefore \theta = \dfrac{\pi 40}{\pi 120} \times 360° = 120°$

Drawing No.
G36

TITLE: **Developments of pyramids.**

NOTE: **First Angle projection used.**

SCALE:

0 10 20 30 40 50 60 70 80

mm

183

G36-4

Complete the plan view of the lower part of the hexagonal pyramid cut by the plane A-A and develop the portion below the plane, i.e without the base.

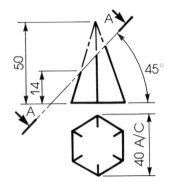

G36-5

Complete the plan view of the portion of the hexagonal pyramid below the plane B-B. Produce the shape of the development of the part of the pyramid lying below the plane.

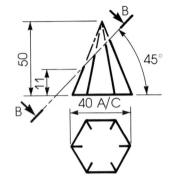

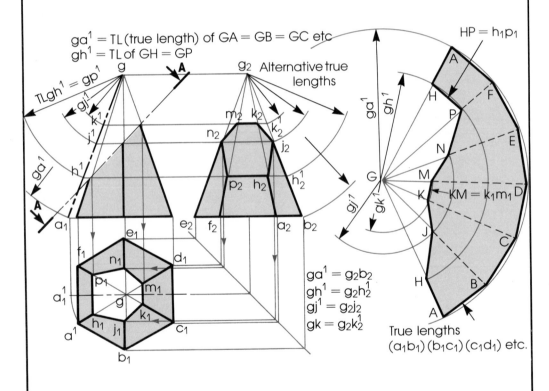

$ga^1 = TL$ (true length) of $GA = GB = GC$ etc
$gh^1 = TL$ of $GH = GP$

$HP = h_1p_1$

$ga^1 = g_2b_2$
$gh^1 = g_2h_2^1$
$gj^1 = g_2j_2$
$gk = g_2k_2^1$

Alternative true lengths

$KM = k_1m_1$

True lengths $(a_1b_1)(b_1c_1)(c_1d_1)$ etc.

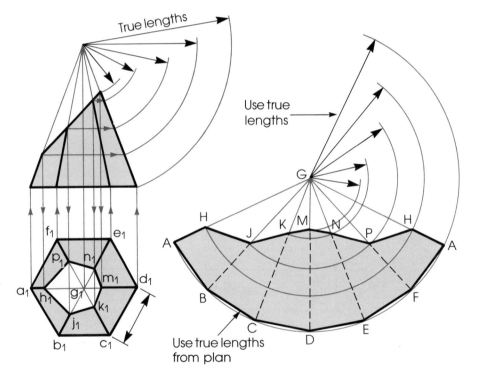

True lengths

Use true lengths

Use true lengths from plan

| Drawing No. G36 | TITLE: **Developments of pyramids.** | NOTE: **First Angle projection used.** | SCALE: |

SCALE: 0 10 20 30 40 50 60 70 80 mm

184

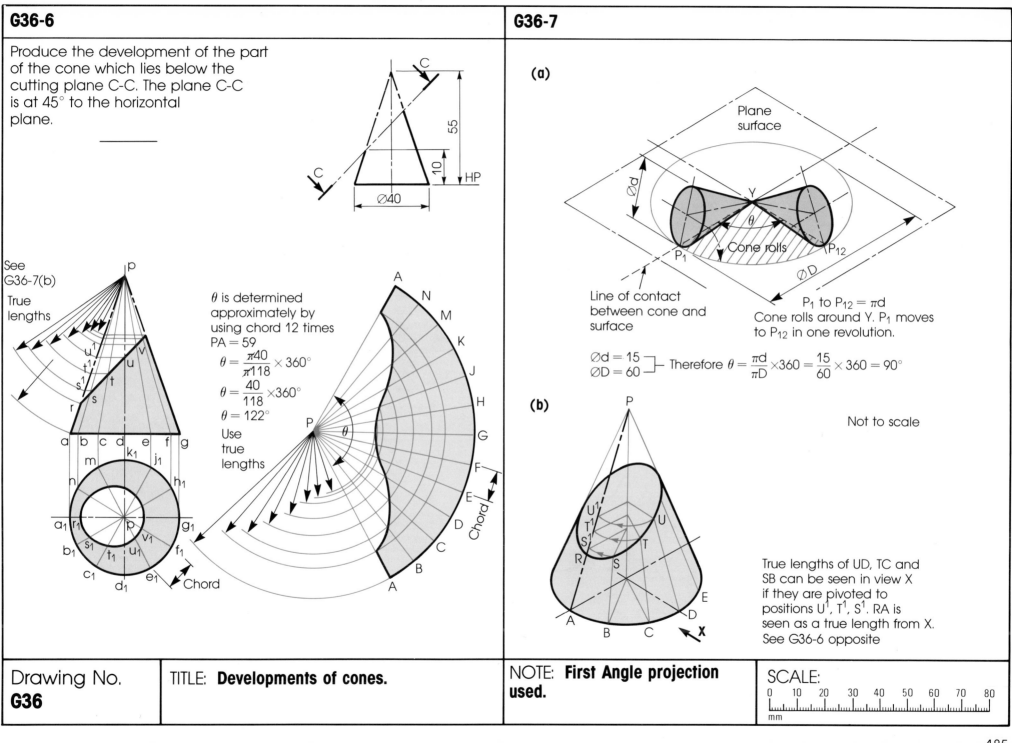

G36-6

Produce the development of the part of the cone which lies below the cutting plane C-C. The plane C-C is at 45° to the horizontal plane.

55

10

HP

∅40

See G36-7(b)

True lengths

θ is determined approximately by using chord 12 times
PA = 59

$$\theta = \frac{\pi 40}{\pi 118} \times 360°$$

$$\theta = \frac{40}{118} \times 360°$$

$$\theta = 122°$$

Use true lengths

Chord

G36-7

(a)

Plane surface

∅d

Y

θ

Cone rolls

P₁

P₁₂

∅D

Line of contact between cone and surface

P_1 to $P_{12} = \pi d$
Cone rolls around Y. P_1 moves to P_{12} in one revolution.

$$\left. \begin{array}{l} \varnothing d = 15 \\ \varnothing D = 60 \end{array} \right\} \text{Therefore } \theta = \frac{\pi d}{\pi D} \times 360 = \frac{15}{60} \times 360 = 90°$$

(b)

Not to scale

True lengths of UD, TC and SB can be seen in view X if they are pivoted to positions U^1, T^1, S^1. RA is seen as a true length from X. See G36-6 opposite

Drawing No. **G36**

TITLE: **Developments of cones.**

NOTE: **First Angle projection used.**

SCALE:
0 10 20 30 40 50 60 70 80
mm

185

A pipe which contains a feed screw is loaded through a conical hopper as shown. Develop the part of the cone which forms the hopper and sits astride the pipe.

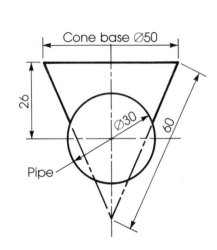

Cone base ⌀50

26

⌀30

60

Pipe

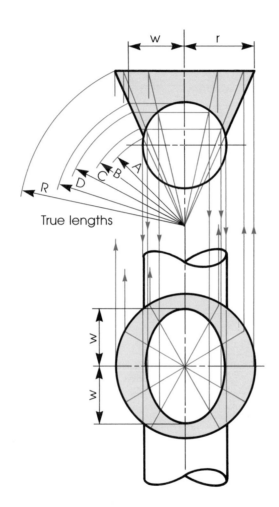

w   r

True lengths

R   D C B A

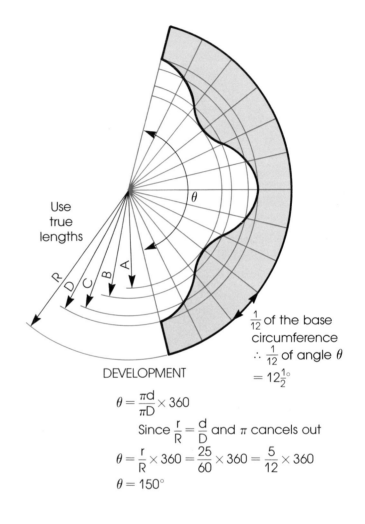

Use true lengths

R D C B A

θ

DEVELOPMENT

$\frac{1}{12}$ of the base circumference
∴ $\frac{1}{12}$ of angle θ
= $12\frac{1}{2}°$

$$\theta = \frac{\pi d}{\pi D} \times 360$$

Since $\frac{r}{R} = \frac{d}{D}$ and π cancels out

$$\theta = \frac{r}{R} \times 360 = \frac{25}{60} \times 360 = \frac{5}{12} \times 360$$

$$\theta = 150°$$

| Drawing No. **G37** | TITLE: **Developments of the cone and an introduction to triangulation.** | NOTE: **First Angle projection used.** | SCALE: |

0 10 20 30 40 50 60 70 80
mm

Develop the conical shaped dust
and fume ventilator which sits
astride the roof ridge as shown.
Use a scale of 1:10 for your
solution.

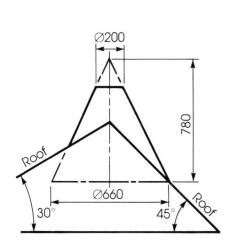

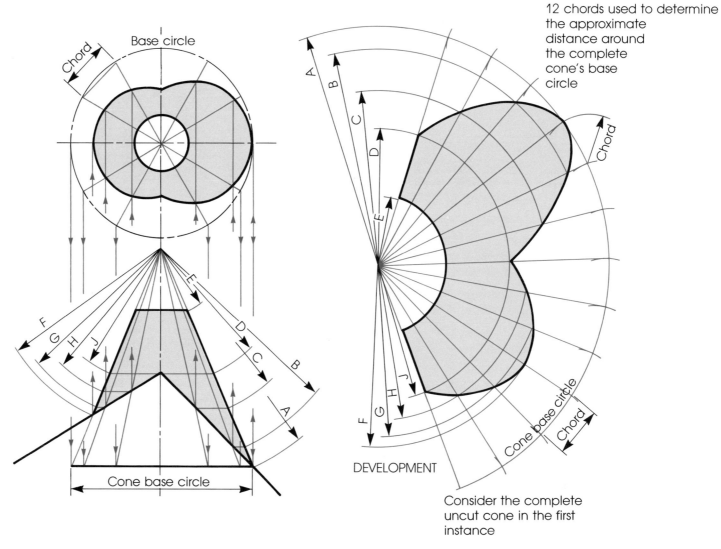

Base circle

Chord

12 chords used to determine
the approximate
distance around
the complete
cone's base
circle

Chord

DEVELOPMENT

Cone base circle

Chord

Consider the complete
uncut cone in the first
instance

Cone base circle

Ø200

780

Roof

Roof

30°   45°

Ø660

Drawing No. **G37**	TITLE: **Developments of the cone and an introduction to triangulation.**	NOTE: **First Angle projection used.**	SCALE:

SCALE:
0 10 20 30 40 50 60 70 80
mm

Develop the frustum of the oblique
cone which lies below the cutting
plane A-A.

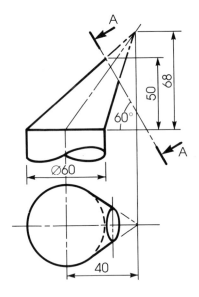

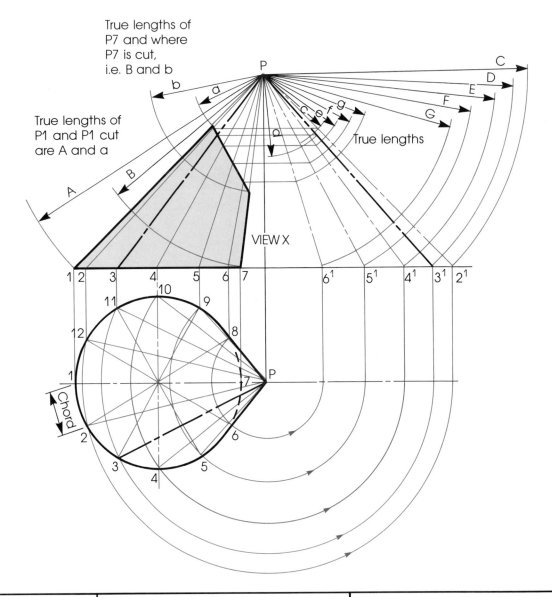

True lengths of
P7 and where
P7 is cut,
i.e. B and b

True lengths of
P1 and P1 cut
are A and a

True lengths

VIEW X

Chord

| Drawing No. **G37** | TITLE: **Developments of the cone and an introduction to triangulation.** | NOTE: **First Angle projection used.** | SCALE: 0 10 20 30 40 50 60 70 80 mm |

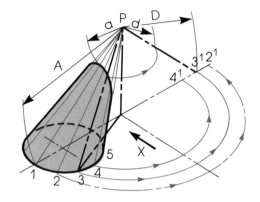

D is the true length of P to 3
when viewed on arrow X.
The true length from P to the
position where P3 is cut is
the length d.

Note: P3 = P11, P4 = P10, etc. Base
is not circular in the development
as P1 does not equal P2 or P3
etc., therefore triangulation using
chords for the base curve has
been illustrated.

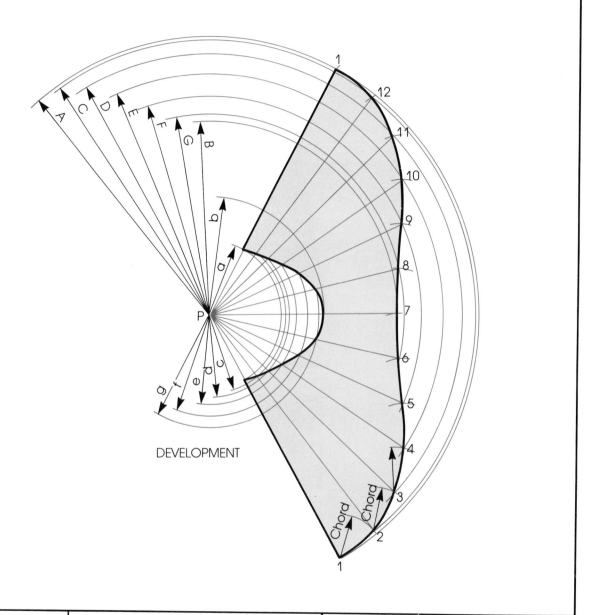

DEVELOPMENT

Drawing No.	TITLE: **Developments of the cone and an introduction to triangulation.**	NOTE: **First Angle projection used.**	SCALE:
G37			0 10 20 30 40 50 60 70 80 mm

A hood to extract fumes from a machine has a rectangular base but tapers to allow a circular pipe to be attached to the top. Produce the development of the transitional tapered hood to a scale of 1:20.

True length of EB = b^1e = EA and NC = ND = c^1n
True length of HB = b^1h = SA and HC = SD = c^1h
True length of GB = b^1g = TA and KC = RD = c^1k
True length of FB = b^1f = UA and MC = PD = c^1m

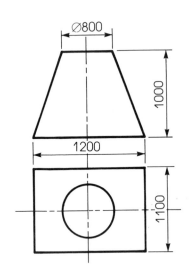

⌀800

1000

1200

1100

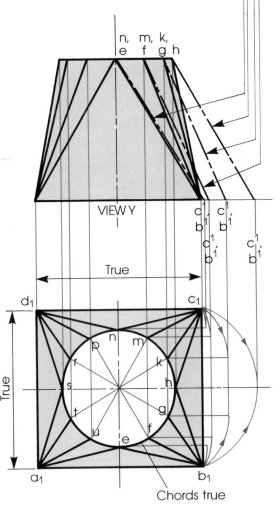

n, m, k,
e f g h

VIEW Y

True

True

d_1 c_1

c^1_1, c^1_1
b^1_1, b^1_1
c^1_1
b^1_1
c^1_1
b^1_1

p n m
r k
s h
t g
u e f

a_1 b_1

Chords true

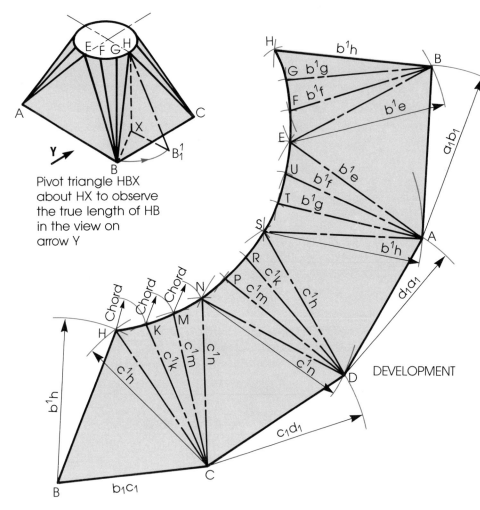

E F G H

A

X

Y

B B^1_1

C

Pivot triangle HBX about HX to observe the true length of HB in the view on arrow Y

DEVELOPMENT

Chord Chord Chord

H b^1h B
G b^1g
F b^1f b^1e
E
U b^1e
T b^1f
b^1g
S   A
b^1h
R c^1k
P c^1m c^1h
N
M c^1k
K c^1m c^1n
c^1h
H c^1h
b^1h
B b_1c_1 C

a_1b_1
d_1a_1
c_1d_1

Drawing No. **G37**	TITLE: **Developments of the cone and an introduction to triangulation.**	NOTE: **First Angle projection used.**	SCALE: 0 10 20 30 40 50 60 70 80 mm

Worksheets for G38 to G42

G38 LINES OF INTERSECTION OR INTERPENETRATION: SQUARE PRISMS (FIRST ANGLE PROJECTION).

G38-1 Draw and complete the elevations and plan of the right-angled tee junction between the square tubes. Produce the development of part A.

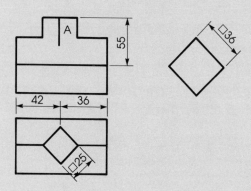

G38-2 Draw the given elevation and plan and produce a front elevation of the offset tee junction shown. Develop part A.

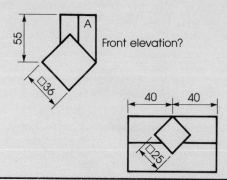

Front elevation?

G38-3 Draw and complete the 2 principle elevations of the angled tee piece which is to be produced for a ducting system. Develop part A and show the line of intersection in the elevation. Draw a plan.

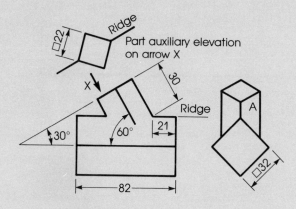

Part auxiliary elevation on arrow X

G38-4 The tee junction shown has the branch A both offset and with its entry to the larger tube angled at 60°. Complete the given elevations and produce a plan showing joint lines between the tubes. Develop part A.

Part A is a square tube, the square having a side of 22 mm

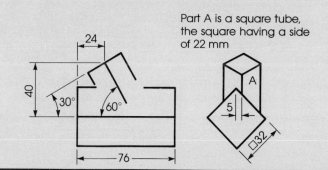

G39 LINES OF INTERSECTION: HEXAGONAL WITH SQUARE PRISMS (FIRST ANGLE PROJECTION)

G39-1 Draw the given plan and complete the 2 elevations showing the intersection between the hexagonal and square tubes. Develop part A.

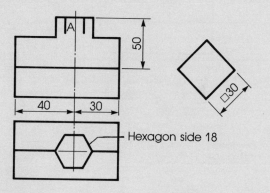

Hexagon side 18

G39-2 Draw the plan and complete both elevations of the offset hexagonal tube mounted at 90° to the square tube. Show the intersection and develop A.

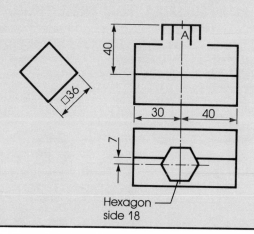

Hexagon side 18

191

G39-3 Draw and complete the 2 given principle views and produce a plan of the angled-entry hexagonal tube mounted astride the square tube. Produce a development of the hexagonal tube to suit.

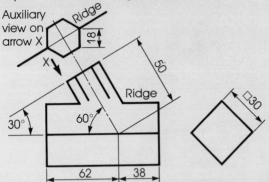

G39-4 Complete the given elevations of an angled-entry offset hexagonal tube fitted to the square tube. Show the intersection between the tubes and draw a plan. Develop the hexagonal tube to suit.

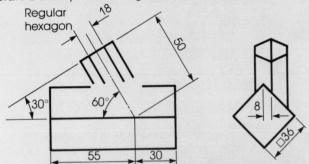

G40 CURVES OF INTERSECTION: CYLINDERS AND PLANE SURFACES (FIRST ANGLE PROJECTION).

G40-1 The drawing shows an incomplete front elevation of a cylinder sat astride 2 plane sloping surfaces inclined at 45° in the end elevation. Draw the plan and complete the front elevation determining the intersection.

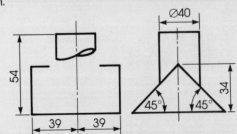

G40-2 A partial front elevation and a complete end elevation of a cylinder sat astride 2 plane sloping surfaces is shown with the centre of the cylinder coincident with the intersection of the planes. Draw the complete front elevation.

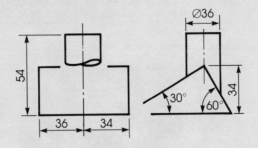

G40-3 Draw and complete the given elevations of the cylinder sat astride the 2 planes as shown by determining the curve of intersection between the cylinder and the plane surfaces. A plan is useful!

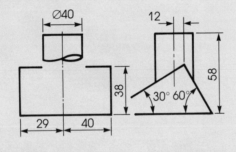

G40-4 The 2 elevations show a cylinder inclined and positioned centrally about the ridge formed by 2 plane surfaces.
(a) Draw and complete the given elevations showing the intersection curve, (b) draw a complete plan, and (c) develop the cylinder.

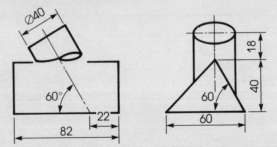

G40-5 The given elevations show a cylinder inclined at 60° to the ridge formed by the intersection of 2 plane surfaces with its axis offset behind the ridge by 13 mm.
(a) Complete the given views, (b) draw a plan, and (c) develop the cylinder to suit.

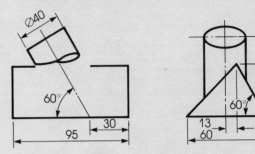

G41 CURVES OF INTERSECTION: CYLINDERS AND CURVED SURFACES (FIRST ANGLE PROJECTION).

G41-1 The drawing shows an end view and an incomplete front elevation of a right-angled tee junction between two Ø50 mm pipes. Complete the front elevation by determining the curve of intersection.

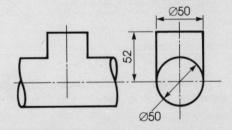

G41-2 A Ø40 mm pipe forms a right-angled tee junction with a Ø48 mm pipe as shown. Draw and complete the given elevations by determining the curve of intersection.

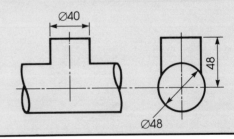

G41-3 The given elevations show 2 intersecting cylinders with the axis of cylinder A offset by 4 mm behind the axis of cylinder B, and at 90° to it, in the incomplete front elevation. Draw both elevations completed.

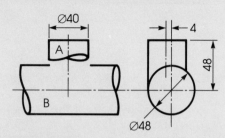

Ø40
4
48
A
B
Ø48

G41-4 The given end elevation shows a pipe A joining a Ø46 mm pipe. The incomplete front elevation shows the angle of entry of the pipe (Ø38 mm) with the Ø46 mm pipe.
(a) Complete the front elevation, (b) draw a plan, and
(c) develop pipe A to suit.

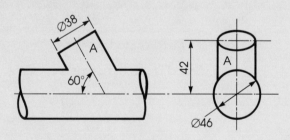

Ø38
A
60°
42
A
Ø46

G41-5 The given elevations show 2 intersecting cylinders with the axis of cylinder A offset by 4 mm in front of the axis of cylinder B. The angle of entry of cylinder A with cylinder B is shown as 60° in the incomplete elevation.
(a) Complete the given elevations, (b) draw a plan, and
(c) develop pipe A to suit.

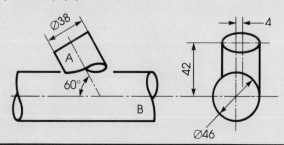

Ø38
4
A
60°
42
B
Ø46

G42   INTERSECTION OF SOLIDS: SQUARE PYRAMID WITH PRISMS AND CYLINDERS (FIRST ANGLE PROJECTION).

G42-1 Draw and complete the 2 given elevations by constructing the intersection between the prism and the pyramid. Project a plan from the incomplete elevation.

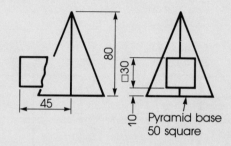

80
□30
45
10
Pyramid base
50 square

G42-2 Draw and complete the 2 given elevations by constructing the intersection between the prism and the pyramid. Project a plan from the incomplete elevation.

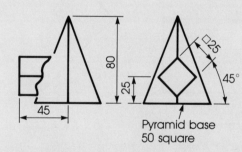

80
25
45
□25
45°
Pyramid base
50 square

G42-3 Draw and complete the 2 given elevations by constructing the intersection between the prism and the pyramid. Project a plan from the incomplete elevation.

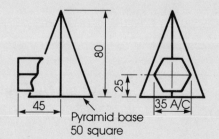

80
25
45
35 A/C
Pyramid base
50 square

G42-4 Draw and complete the 2 given elevations by constructing the intersection between the prism and the pyramid. Project a plan from the incomplete elevation.

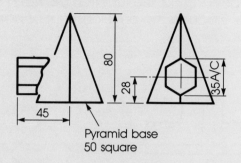

80
28
45
35 A/C
Pyramid base
50 square

G42-5 Draw and complete the 2 given elevations by constructing the intersection between the cylinder and the pyramid. Project a plan from the incomplete elevation.

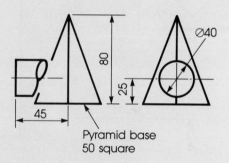

80
Ø40
25
45
Pyramid base
50 square

G42-6 Draw and complete the 2 given elevations by constructing the curve of intersection between the cylinder and the pyramid. Project a plan from the incomplete elevation.

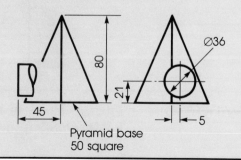

80
Ø36
21
45
5
Pyramid base
50 square

Draw and complete the elevations and plan of
the right-angled tee junction between the square
tubes. Produce the development of part A.

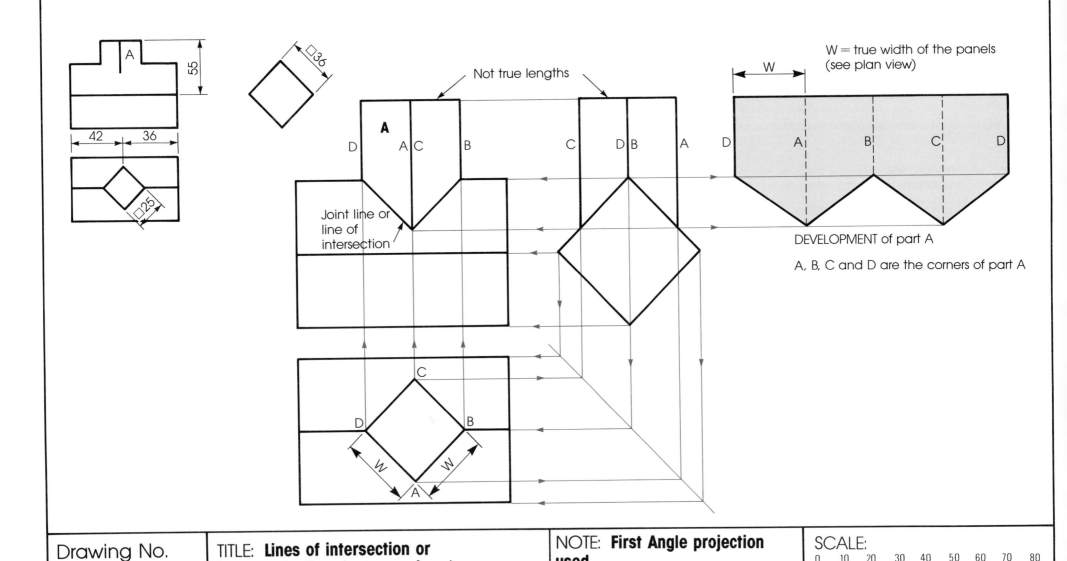

W = true width of the panels
(see plan view)

Not true lengths

Joint line or
line of
intersection

DEVELOPMENT of part A

A, B, C and D are the corners of part A

Drawing No.	TITLE: **Lines of intersection or**	NOTE: **First Angle projection**	SCALE:
G38	**interpenetration (square prisms).**	**used.**	0 10 20 30 40 50 60 70 80 mm

Draw the given elevation and plan and produce
a front elevation of the offset tee junction.
Develop part A.

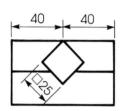

55

□36

Front elevation?

40   40

□25

W_e and W_f are the widths of imaginary lines drawn parallel to the corners A, B, C and
D down the panels. The position of these lines has been chosen to coincide with the
ridge line

W_e W_f

D   E   A   F   B   C   D

W   W

DEVELOPMENT of part A

W_e and W_f locate E and F with respect
to A and can be seen as true in the plan.
The points e and f are the points where
the ridge line intersects the panels DA
and AB respectively.

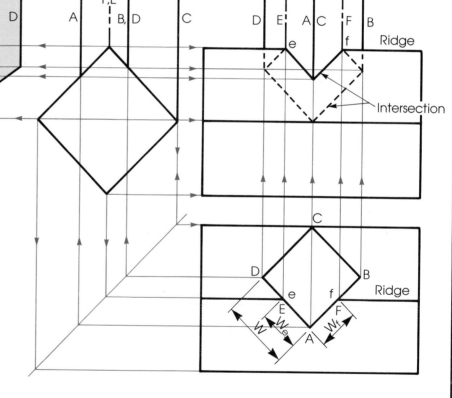

A

F,E

A   B,D   C

D   E   A   C   F   B

e   f   Ridge

Intersection

C

D   B

e   f   Ridge

E   F

W W_e A W_f

Drawing No. G38	TITLE: **Lines of intersection or interpenetration (square prisms).**	NOTE: **First Angle projection used.**	SCALE: 0 10 20 30 40 50 60 70 80 mm

195

G38-3

Draw and complete the 2 principal elevations of the angled tee piece which is to be produced for a ducting system. Develop part A and show the line of intersection in the elevation. Draw a plan.

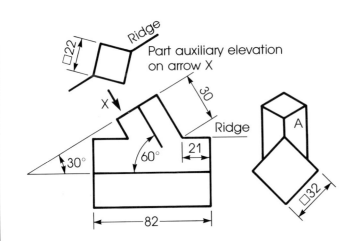

Part auxiliary elevation on arrow X

Ridge

Note: Mixed projection is not generally recommended. In this case the auxiliary view is a construction to help in producing the other views (it would not be retained on an original drawing). Since the auxiliary view relates more directly to the view with which it is concerned by using the Third Angle position, mixed projection is acceptable practice.
Drawing to First Angle would either require more space, or construction from the auxiliary would interfere with the plan view.

Auxiliary elevation on arrow X to Third Angle projection for convenience

From auxiliary elevation

DEVELOPMENT of part A

From auxiliary elevation

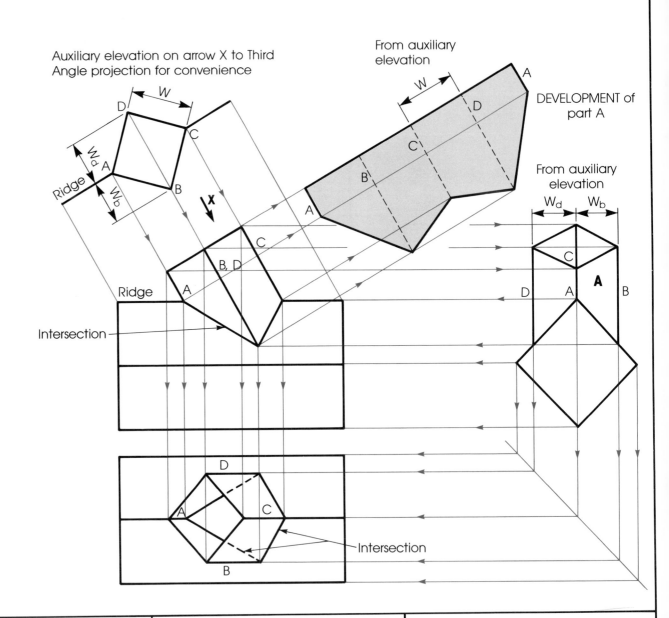

Intersection

Ridge

Intersection

Drawing No.	TITLE: **Lines of intersection or**	NOTE: **First Angle projection used**	SCALE:
G38	**interpenetration (square prisms).**	**as indicated.**	

196

G38-4

The tee junction shown has the branch A offset and with its entry to the larger tube angled at 60°. Complete the given elevations and produce a plan; show joint lines between the tubes. Develop part A.

Auxiliary elevation on arrow X to Third Angle projection for convenience

Widths W, W_{ab} and W_{cd} are obtained from the auxiliary elevation

DEVELOPMENT of part A

The corners have been defined by their ends, i.e. (1, 5), (2, 6), (3, 7), (4, 8)

$W_{3,7}$ and $W_{1,5}$ are obtained from the auxiliary elevation

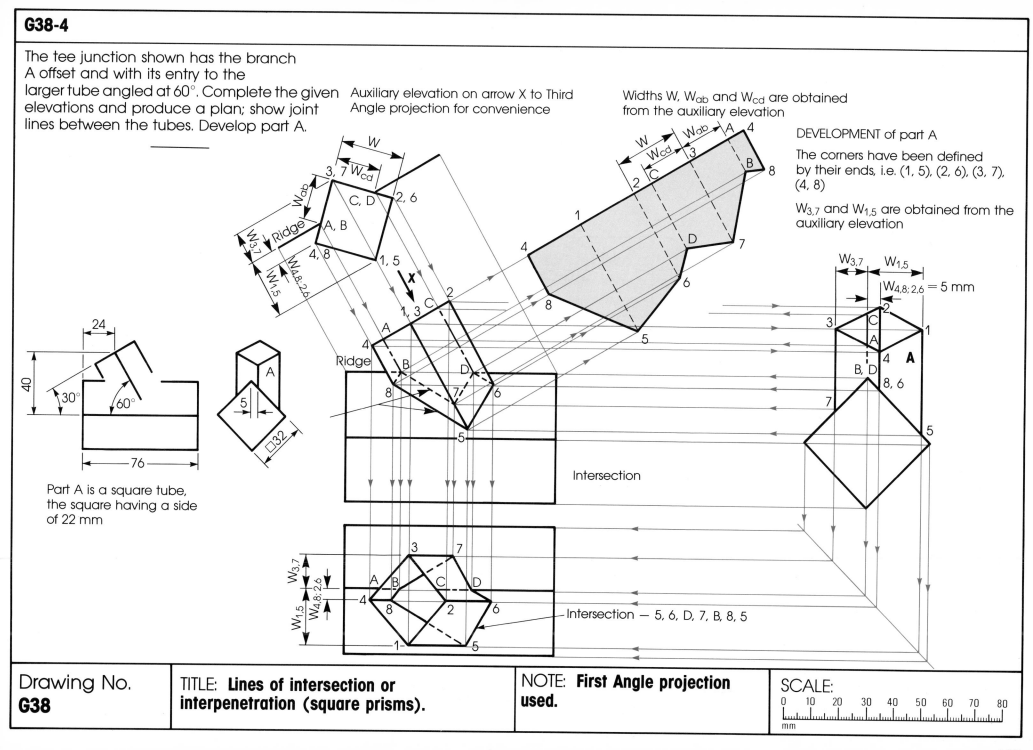

$W_{4,8;\ 2,6} = 5$ mm

Part A is a square tube, the square having a side of 22 mm

Intersection

Intersection — 5, 6, D, 7, B, 8, 5

Drawing No.	TITLE: **Lines of intersection or interpenetration (square prisms).**	NOTE: **First Angle projection used.**	SCALE:
G38			0 10 20 30 40 50 60 70 80 mm

197

Draw the given plan and complete the
elevations showing the intersection between the
hexagonal and square tubes. Develop part A.

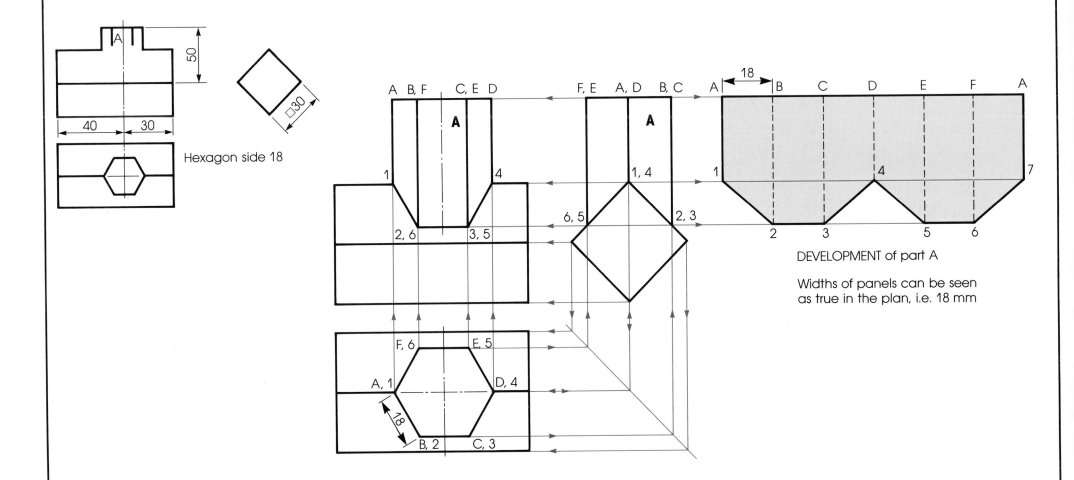

Hexagon side 18

DEVELOPMENT of part A

Widths of panels can be seen
as true in the plan, i.e. 18 mm

Drawing No. **G39**	TITLE: **Lines of intersection (hexagonal with square prisms).**	NOTE: **First Angle projection used.**	SCALE:

G39-2

Draw the plan and complete both elevations of the offset hexagonal tube mounted at 90° to the square tube. Show the intersection and develop A.

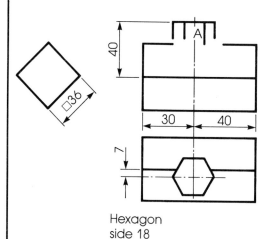

Hexagon
side 18

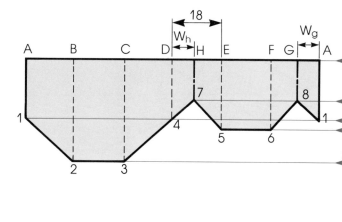

DEVELOPMENT of part A

H7 and G8 are located in the plan by W_h and W_g from D4 and A1 respectively.
The position of H7 and G8 was chosen to coincide with the ridge, to analyse the ridge and hexagonal prism relationship.

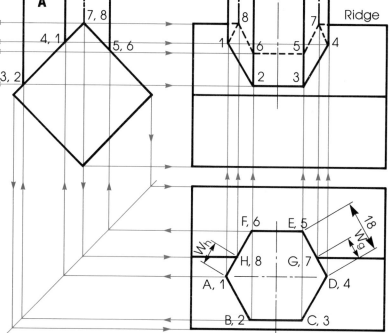

Drawing No.	TITLE: **Lines of intersection (hexagonal with squares).**	NOTE: **First Angle projection used.**	SCALE:
G39			

0 10 20 30 40 50 60 70 80
mm

Draw and complete the 2 given principal views and produce a plan of the angled entry hexagonal tube mounted astride the square tube. Produce a development of the hexagonal tube to suit.

Auxiliary elevation on arrow X to Third Angle projection for convenience

DEVELOPMENT

Widths from auxiliary elevation

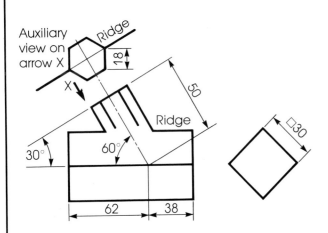

Auxiliary view on arrow X

Ridge

18

X

30°

60°

Ridge

50

□30

62   38

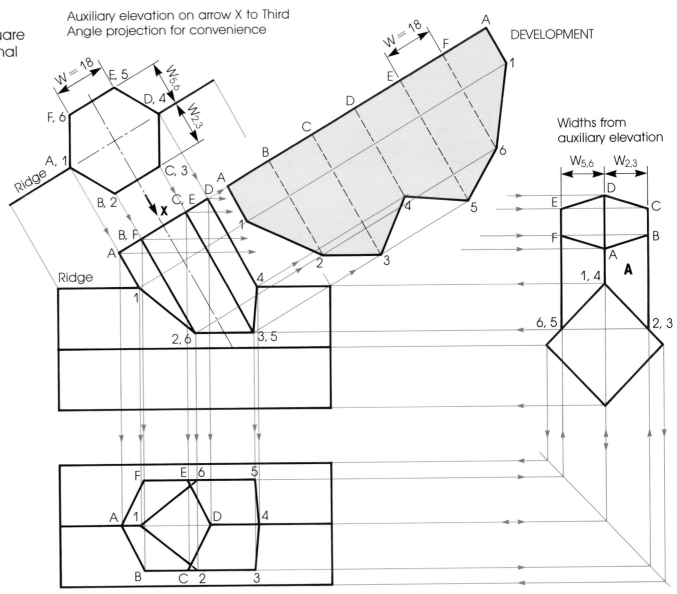

W = 18

| Drawing No.
G39 | TITLE: **Lines of intersection (hexagonal with square prisms).** | NOTE: **First Angle projection used.** | SCALE:
0 10 20 30 40 50 60 70 80
mm |

Complete the given elevations of an angled entry offset hexagonal tube fitted to the square tube. Show the intersection between the tubes and draw a plan. Develop the hexagonal tube to suit.

Auxiliary elevation on arrow X to Third Angle projection for convenience

Widths W, W₈, W₂,₃ etc. from auxiliary elevation

DEVELOPMENT

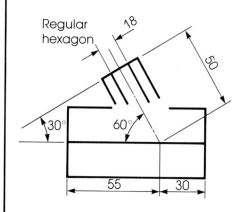

Regular hexagon

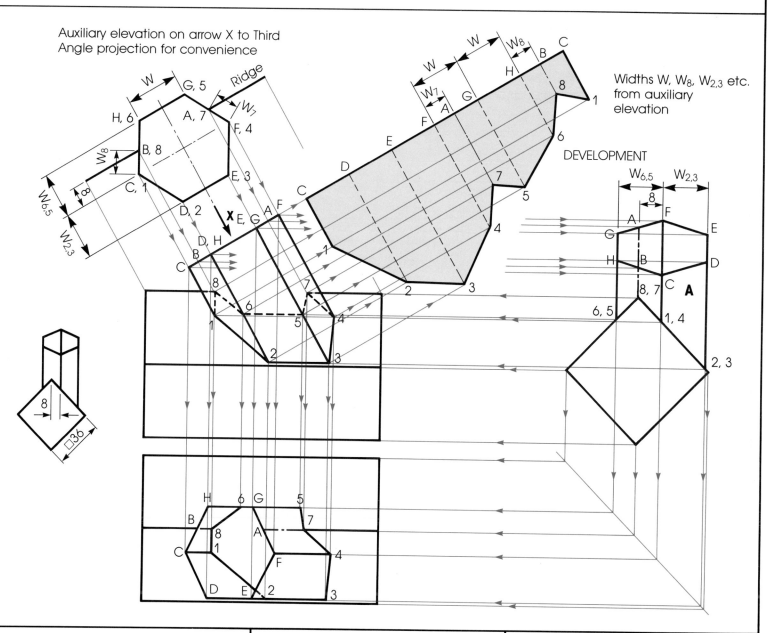

Drawing No.	TITLE: **Lines of intersection (hexagonal with square prisms).**	NOTE: **First Angle projection used.**	SCALE:
G39			

0 10 20 30 40 50 60 70 80
mm

The drawing below shows an incomplete
front elevation of a cylinder sat
astride 2 plane sloping surfaces and inclined
at 45° in the end elevation. Draw the
plan and complete the front elevation
determining the intersection.

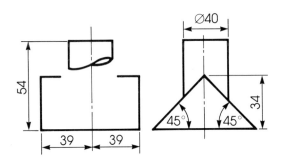

Curve of
intersection is
semicircular for
45° planes

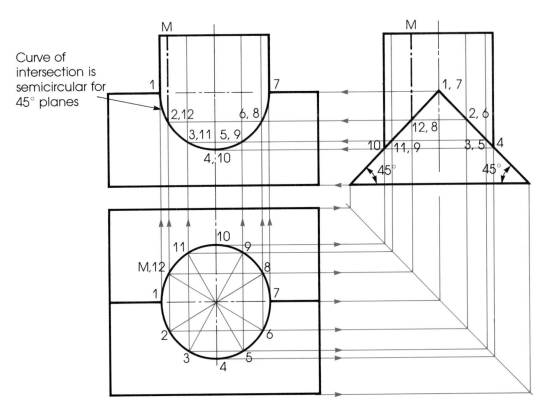

The position of the line M12 along the cylinder is vertical
in the plan, i.e. M is directly above 12. In the end elevation
the length of M12 is determined by the 45° angle and this
length is projected to the front elevation. Repeat for 2, 3 etc.

Drawing No.	TITLE: **Curves of intersection (the cylinder**	NOTE: **First Angle projection**	SCALE:
G40	**and plane surface).**	**used.**	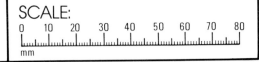

A partial front elevation and a complete
end elevation of a cylinder sat astride
2 plane sloping surfaces is shown
with the centre of the cylinder coincident
with the intersection of the planes.
Draw the complete front elevation.

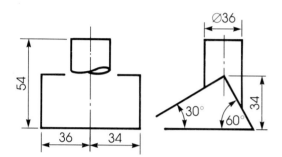

Section A–A

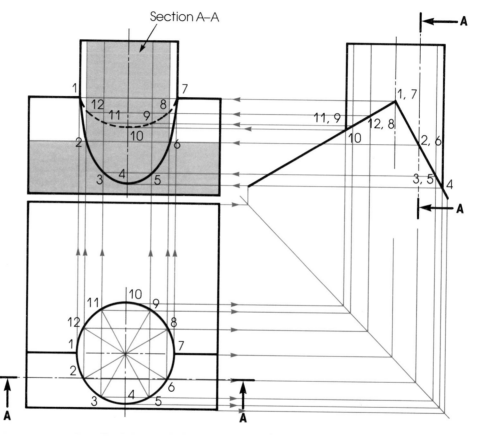

An alternative method of analysing the problem is to take a convenient section
through the combined solids (section A–A is illustrated). Points 2 and 6 give the
intersection between the cylinder section A and the triangular prism section A–A.

| Drawing No. | TITLE: **Curves of intersection (the cylinder** | NOTE: **First Angle projection** | SCALE: |
| **G40** | **and plane surface).** | **used.** | 0 10 20 30 40 50 60 70 80 |

mm

203

Draw and complete the given
elevations of the cylinder sat astride
the 2 planes as shown by determining
the curve of intersection between
the cylinder and the plane surfaces.

A plan is useful!

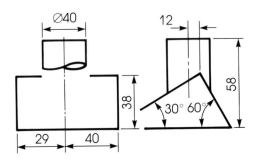

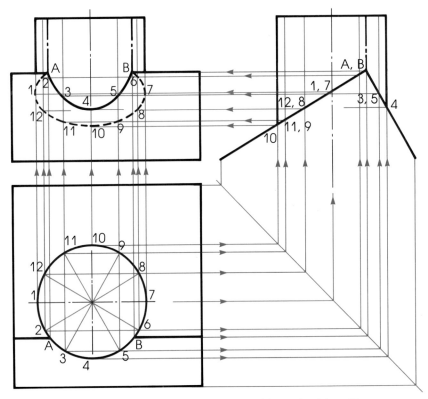

2 extra lines down the cylinder are utilised to coincide with
the ridge, to determine the exact position where the curve of
intersection rises over the ridge in the front elevation, i.e. the
lines have ends A and B.

Drawing No.	TITLE: **Curves of intersection (the cylinder**	NOTE: **First Angle projection**	SCALE:
G40	**and plane surface).**	**used.**	

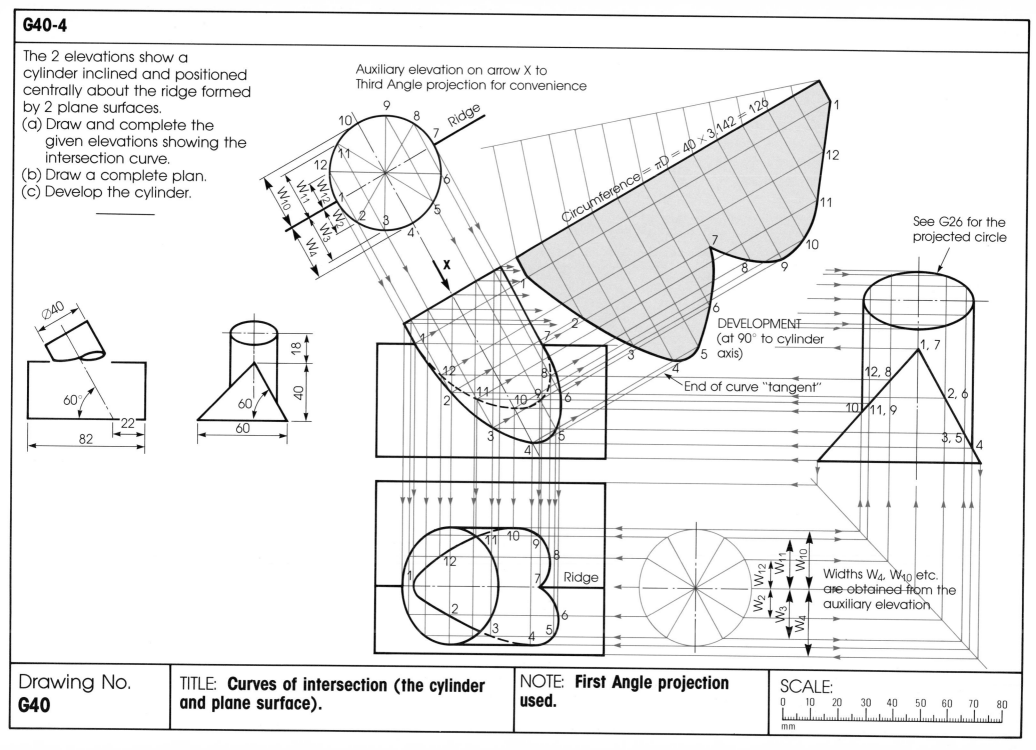

G40-4

The 2 elevations show a cylinder inclined and positioned centrally about the ridge formed by 2 plane surfaces.
(a) Draw and complete the given elevations showing the intersection curve.
(b) Draw a complete plan.
(c) Develop the cylinder.

Auxiliary elevation on arrow X to Third Angle projection for convenience

Circumference $= \pi D = 40 \times 3.142 = 126$

DEVELOPMENT (at 90° to cylinder axis)

End of curve "tangent"

See G26 for the projected circle

Ridge

Ø40

60°

82   22

18

40

60

60

Ridge

Widths W_4, W_{10} etc. are obtained from the auxiliary elevation

| Drawing No. **G40** | TITLE: **Curves of intersection (the cylinder and plane surface).** | NOTE: **First Angle projection used.** | SCALE: |

G40-5

The given elevations show a cylinder inclined at 60° to the ridge formed by the intersection of 2 plane surfaces with its axis offset behind the ridge by 13 mm.
(a) Complete the given views.
(b) Draw a plan.
(c) Develop the cylinder to suit.

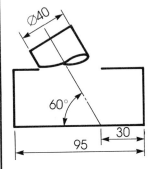

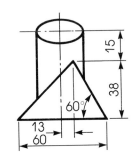

Auxiliary elevation on arrow X to Third Angle projection for convenience

Distance 11 to A from auxiliary elevation

Distance 3 to B from auxiliary elevation

Circumference = 126

DEVELOPMENT

See G26-3

See G40-4

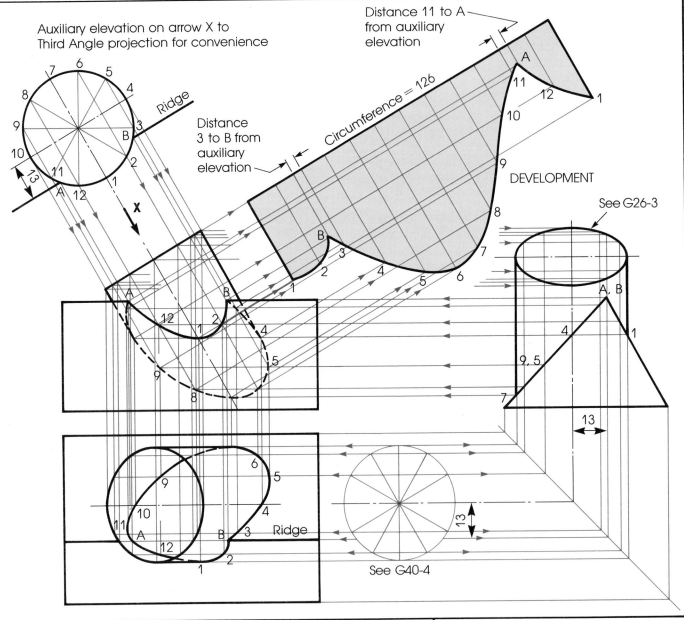

| Drawing No. **G40** | TITLE: **Curves of intersection (the cylinder and plane surface).** | NOTE: **First Angle projection used.** | SCALE: |

206

G41-1

The diagram shows an end view and an incomplete front elevation of a right-angled tee junction between two 50 mm diameter pipes. Complete the front elevation by determining the curve of intersection.

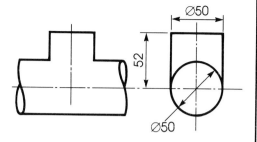

See G35-2 for development

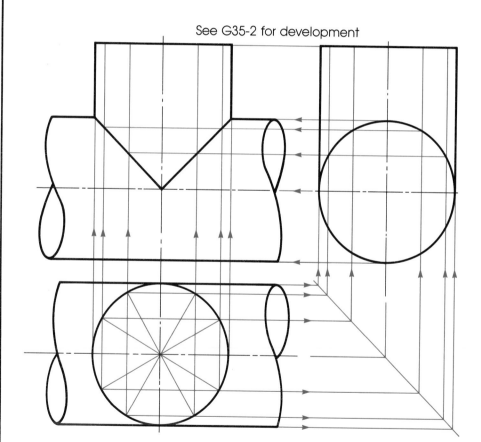

G41-2

A 40 mm diameter pipe forms a right-angled tee junction with a pipe of diameter 48 mm as shown. Draw and complete the given elevations by determining the curve of intersection.

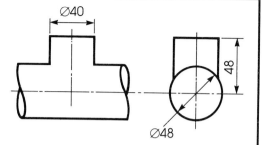

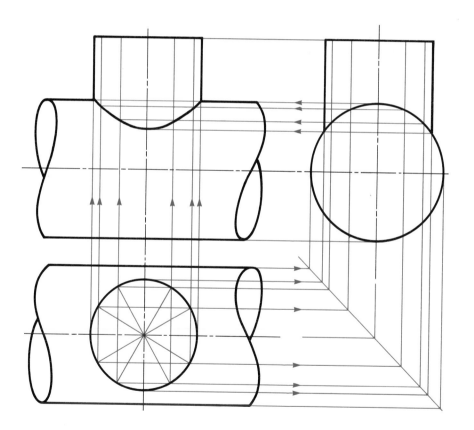

| Drawing No. **G41** | TITLE: **Curves of intersection (cylinders and curved surfaces).** | NOTE: **First Angle projection used.** | SCALE: |

The given elevations show 2
intersecting cylinders with the axis
of cylinder A offset by 4 mm behind
the axis of cylinder B and at 90° to
it. Draw both elevations completed.

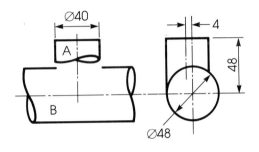

Ø40

A

B

4

48

Ø48

Detail enlarged

See G35-5 for development

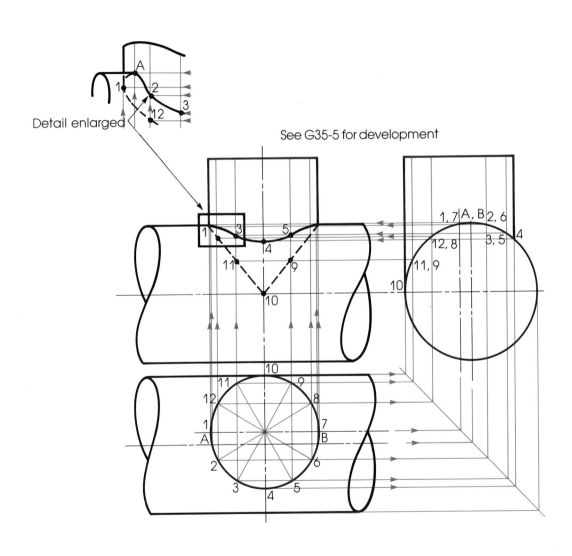

Drawing No.	TITLE: **Curves of intersection (cylinders and**	NOTE: **First Angle projection**	SCALE:
G41	**curved surfaces).**	**used.**	

The given end elevation shows a pipe A joining a pipe of diameter 46 mm. The incomplete front elevation shows the angle of entry of pipe A (diameter 38 mm) with the pipe of diameter 46 mm.

(a) Construct the front elevation.
(b) Draw a plan.
(c) Develop pipe A to suit.

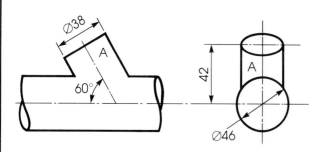

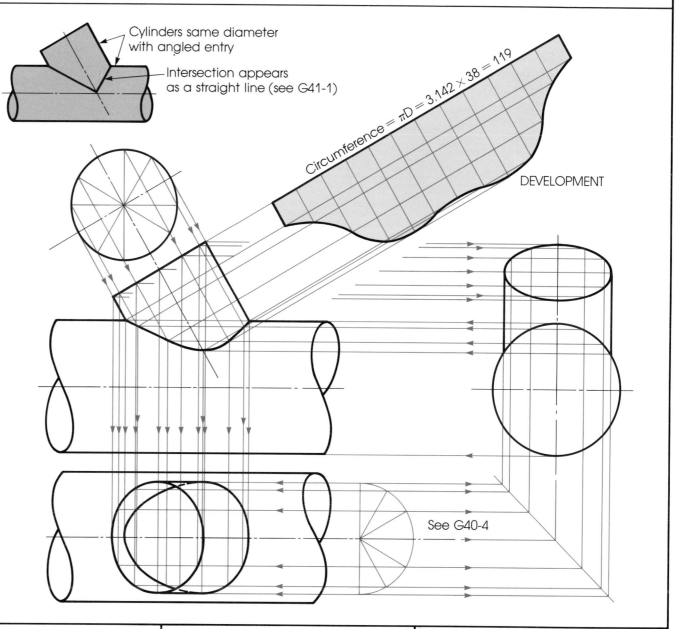

Cylinders same diameter with angled entry

Intersection appears as a straight line (see G41-1)

Circumference = πD = 3.142 × 38 = 119

DEVELOPMENT

Ø38

A

60°

42

A

Ø46

See G40-4

Drawing No. **G41**	TITLE: **Curves of intersection (cylinders and curved surfaces).**	NOTE: **First Angle projection used.**	SCALE:

0 10 20 30 40 50 60 70 80
mm

209

The given elevations show 2 intersecting cylinders with the axis of cylinder A offset by 4 mm in front of the axis of cylinder B. The angle of entry of cylinder A with cylinder B is shown as 60° in the incomplete elevation.

(a) Complete the given elevations.
(b) Draw the plan.
(c) Develop pipe A to suit.

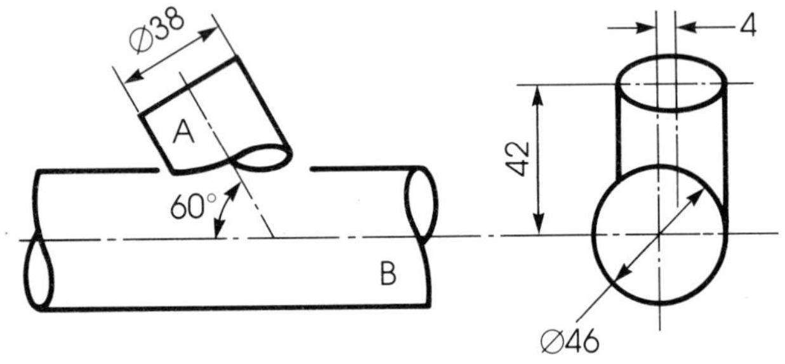

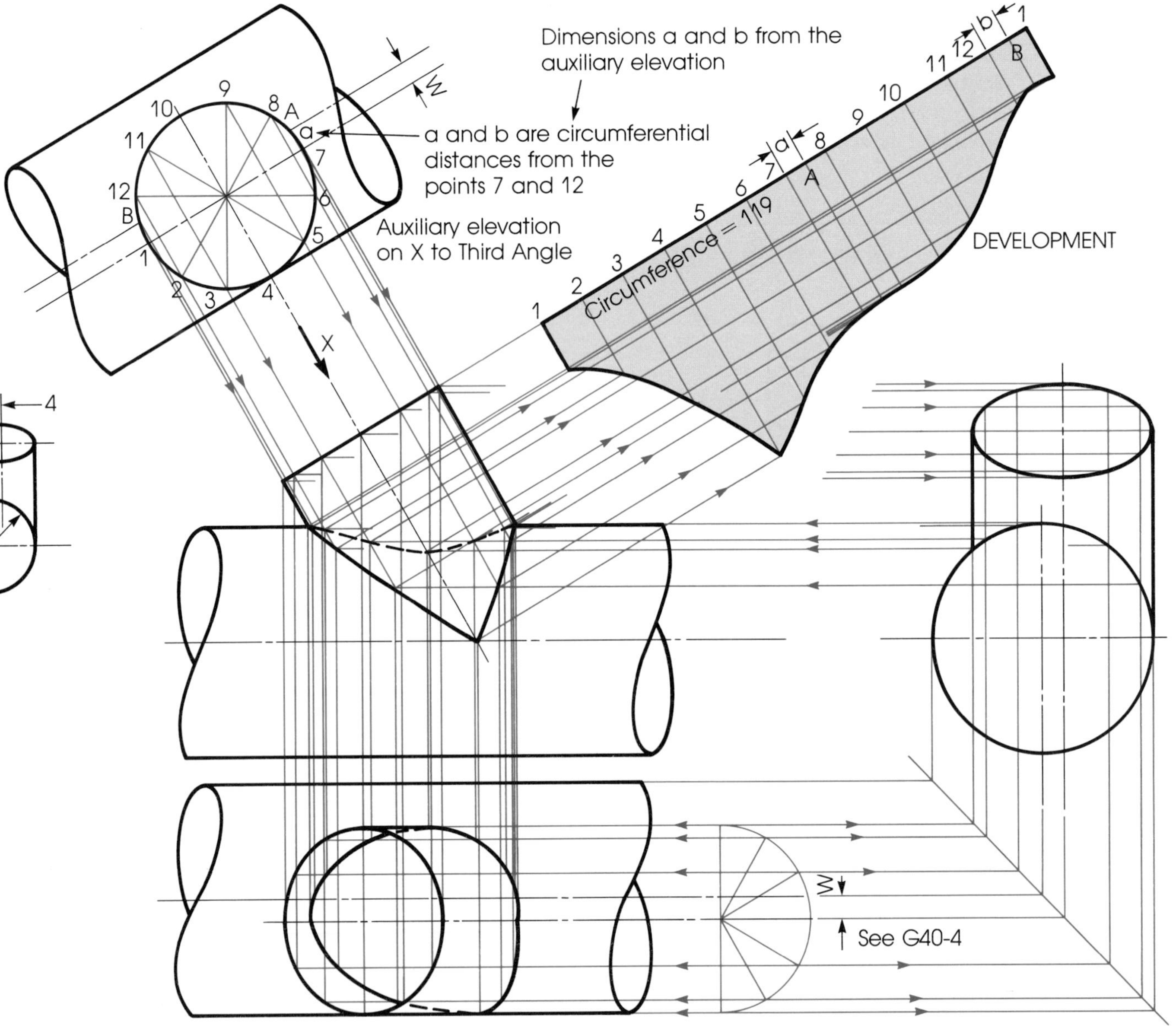

Dimensions a and b from the auxiliary elevation

a and b are circumferential distances from the points 7 and 12

Auxiliary elevation on X to Third Angle

DEVELOPMENT

Circumference = 119

Ø38

4

42

Ø46

60°

A

B

See G40-4

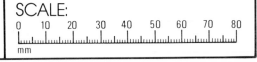

Drawing No. G41	TITLE: **Curves of intersection (cylinders and curved surfaces).**	NOTE: **First Angle projection used.**	SCALE:

0 10 20 30 40 50 60 70 80
mm

Draw and complete the 2 given elevations
by constructing the intersection
between the prism and the pyramid.
Project a plan from the incomplete
elevation.

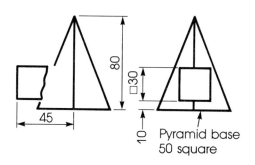

80

□30

45

10

Pyramid base
50 square

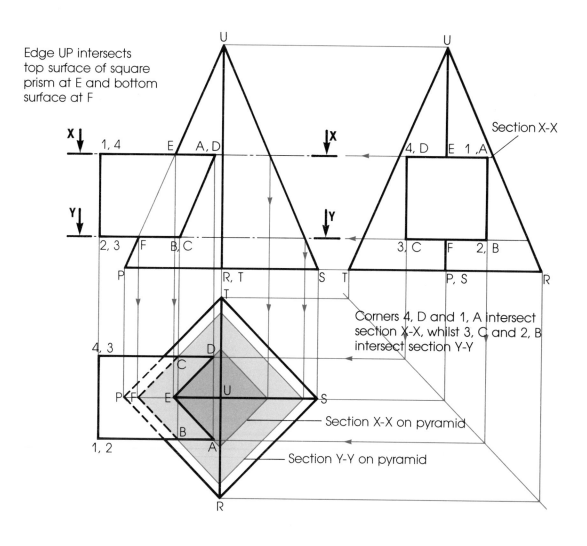

Edge UP intersects
top surface of square
prism at E and bottom
surface at F

U

U

Section X-X

X   1, 4   E   A,D

X   4, D   E 1 ,A

Y   2, 3   F   B, C

Y   3, C   F   2, B

P   R, T   S T   P, S   R

T

Corners 4, D and 1, A intersect
section X-X, whilst 3, C and 2, B
intersect section Y-Y

4, 3

D

C

P F   E   U   S

B

1, 2   A

R

Section X-X on pyramid

Section Y-Y on pyramid

Drawing No.	TITLE: **Intersection of solids (square pyramid**	NOTE: **First Angle projection**	SCALE:
G42	**with prisms and cylinders).**	**used.**	0 10 20 30 40 50 60 70 80
			mm

211

G42-2

Draw and complete the 2 given elevations by constructing the intersection between the prism and the pyramid. Project a plan from the incomplete elevation.

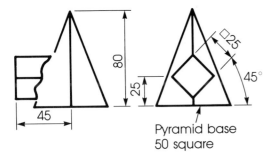

□25
45°

80

25

45

Pyramid base
50 square

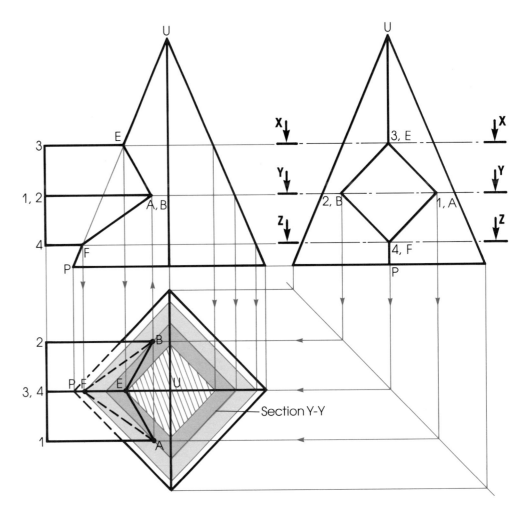

Section Y-Y

Corners 3, E and 4, F meet pyramid edge
UP at E and F (see both elevations). Sections
X-X and Z-Z provide an alternative to using UP

Drawing No. **G42**	TITLE: **Intersection of solids (square pyramid with prisms and cylinders).**	NOTE: **First Angle projection used.**	SCALE:

mm

Draw and complete the 2 given elevations
by constructing the intersection
between the prism and the pyramid.
Project a plan from the incomplete
elevation.

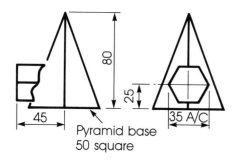

80

25

45

35 A/C

Pyramid base
50 square

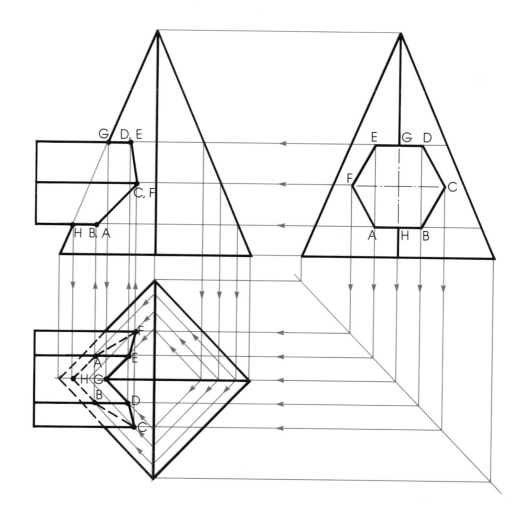

Drawing No. **G42**	TITLE: **Intersection of solids (square pyramids with prisms and cylinders).**	NOTE: **First Angle projection used.**	SCALE:

0 10 20 30 40 50 60 70 80

mm

Draw and complete the 2 given elevations by constructing the intersection between the prism and the pyramid. Project a plan from the incomplete elevation.

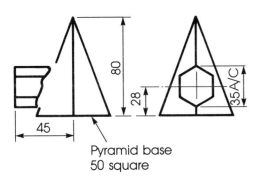

45

80

28

35 A/C

Pyramid base
50 square

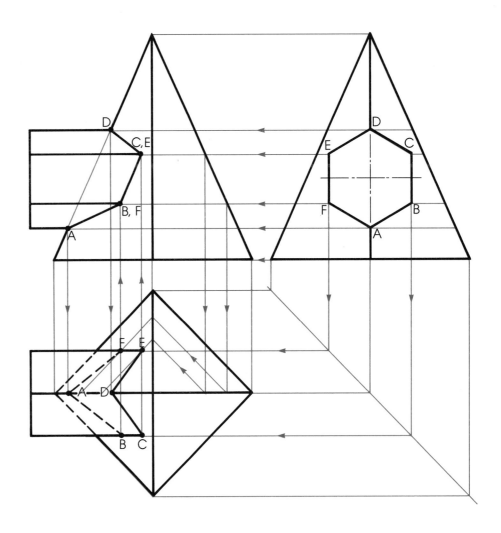

| Drawing No.
G42 | TITLE: **Intersection of solids (square pyramid with prisms and cylinders).** | NOTE: **First Angle projection used.** | SCALE:
 |

Draw and complete the 2 given elevations by constructing the intersection between the cylinder and the pyramid. Project a plan from the incomplete elevation.

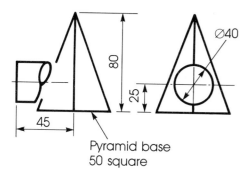

Ø40

Pyramid base
50 square

80

25

45

Sections A-A, B-B etc. can be used as an alternative to the sections X-X, Y-Y etc.

Sections A-A and B-B

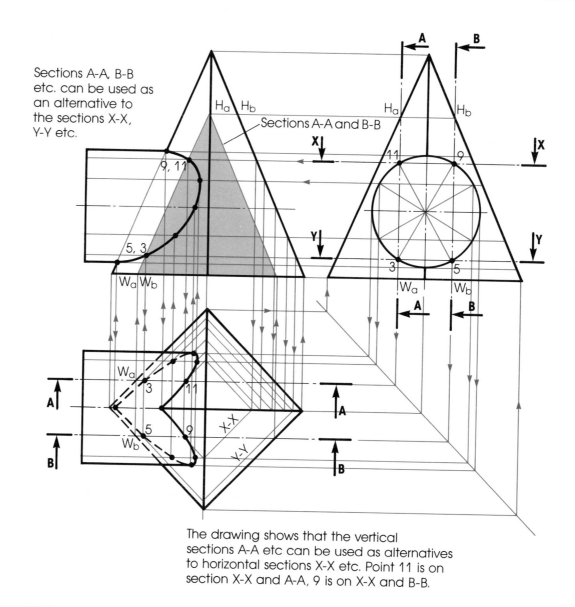

H$_a$ H$_b$

H$_a$ H$_b$

X

X

9, 11

11 9

Y

Y

5, 3

3 5

W$_a$ W$_b$

W$_a$ W$_b$

A

A

B

B

X-X

X-X

Y-Y

W$_a$

3 11

5 9

W$_b$

The drawing shows that the vertical sections A-A etc can be used as alternatives to horizontal sections X-X etc. Point 11 is on section X-X and A-A, 9 is on X-X and B-B.

Drawing No.	TITLE: **Intersection of solids (square pyramid with prisms and cylinders).**	NOTE: **First Angle projection used.**	SCALE:
G42			

SCALE:
0 10 20 30 40 50 60 70 80
mm

215

Draw and complete the 2 given elevations
by constructing the curve of intersection
between the cylinder and the pyramid.
Project a plan from the incomplete
elevation.

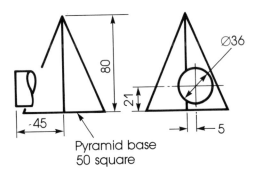

Ø36

80

21

-45

5

Pyramid base
50 square

Points A and B
are on the edge UP

Extra points A and B
are required to determine
where cylinder wraps
around edge UP
(see G40-5)

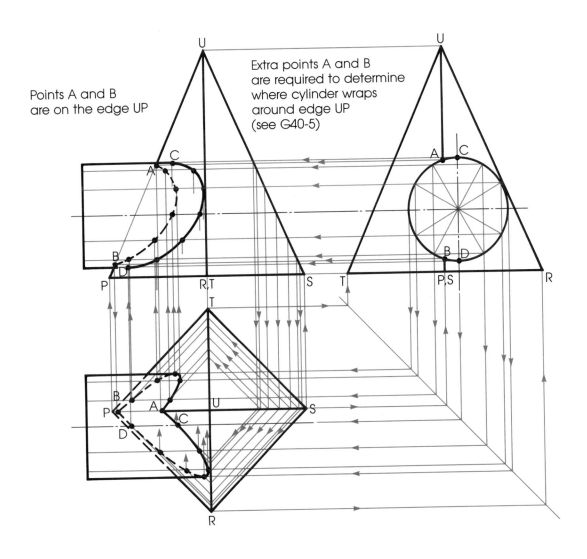

| Drawing No. G42 | TITLE: **Intersection of solids (square pyramid with prisms and cylinders).** | NOTE: **First Angle projection used.** | SCALE: 0 10 20 30 40 50 60 70 80 mm |

Worksheets for G43 to G46

G43 **INTERSECTION OF SOLIDS: HEXAGONAL PYRAMID WITH PRISMS AND CYLINDERS (FIRST ANGLE PROJECTION).**

G43-1 Draw and complete the 2 given elevations by constructing the intersection between the prism and the pyramid. Project a plan from the complete elevation.

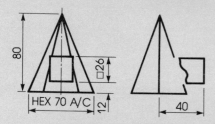

G43-2 Draw and complete the 2 given elevations by constructing the intersection between the prism and the pyramid. Project a plan from the incomplete elevation.

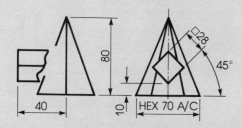

G43-3 Draw and complete the 2 given elevations by constructing the intersection between the prism and the pyramid. Project a plan from the incomplete elevation.

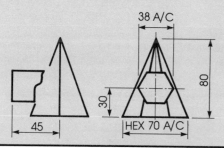

G43-4 Draw and complete the 2 given elevations by constructing the intersection between the prism and the pyramid. Project a plan from the incomplete elevation.

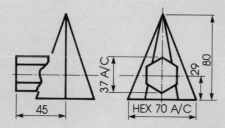

G43-5 Draw and complete the 2 given elevations by constructing the intersection between the cylinder and the pyramid. Project a plan from the incomplete elevation.

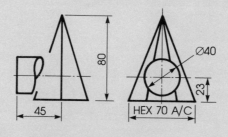

G43-6 Draw and complete the 2 given elevations by constructing the curve of intersection of the cylinder resting in the lower part of a hexagonal pyramid.

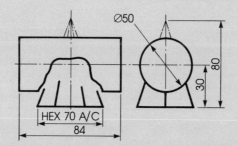

G44 **INTERSECTION OF SOLIDS: CONE WITH PRISMS AND CYLINDERS (FIRST ANGLE PROJECTION).**

G44-1 Draw and complete the 2 given elevations by constructing the curve of intersection between the cone and the prism. Project a plan from the incomplete elevation.

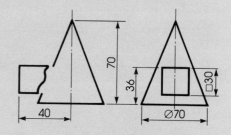

G44-2 Draw and complete the 2 given elevations by constructing the curves of intersection between the cone and the prism. Project a plan from the incomplete elevation.

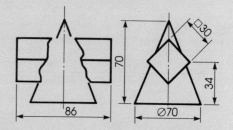

G44-3 Draw and complete the 2 given elevations by constructing the curve of intersection between the cone and the prism. Project a plan from the incomplete elevation.

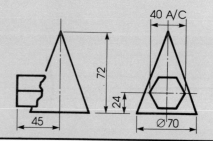

G44-4 Draw and complete the 2 given elevations by constructing the curve of intersection between the cone and the prism. Project a plan from the incomplete elevation.

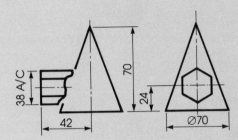

G44-5 Draw and complete the 2 given elevations by constructing the curves of intersection between the cone and the cylinder. Project a plan from the incomplete elevation.

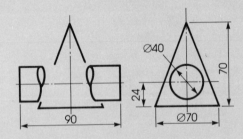

G44-6 Draw and complete the 2 given elevations by constructing the curves of intersection between the cone and the cylinder. Project a plan from the incomplete elevation.

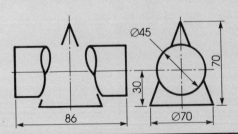

G45 INTERSECTION OF SOLIDS: ANGLED ENTRY TO PYRAMIDS AND CONES (FIRST ANGLE PROJECTION).

G45-1 Draw and complete the 2 given elevations by constructing the lines of intersection between the pyramid and the tube. Project a plan from the incomplete elevation.

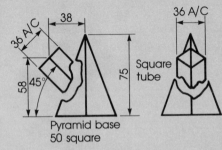

G45-2 Draw and complete the 2 given elevations by constructing the lines of intersection between the pyramid and the tube. Project a plan from the incomplete elevation.

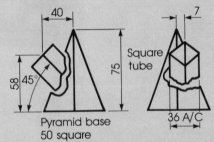

G45-3 Draw and complete the 2 given elevations by constructing the lines of intersection between the hexagonal pyramid and hexagonal tube. Project a plan from the incomplete elevation.

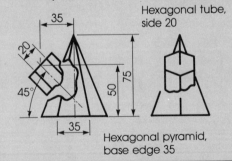

G45-4 Draw and complete the 2 given elevations by constructing the lines of intersection between the hexagonal pyramid and hexagonal tube. Project a plan from the incomplete elevation.

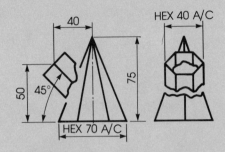

G45-5 Draw and complete the 2 given elevations by constructing the curve of intersection between the cylinder and hexagonal pyramid. Project a plan from the incomplete elevation.

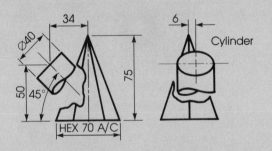

G45-6 Draw and complete the 2 given elevations by constructing the curve of intersection between the cylinder and cone. Project a plan from the incomplete elevation.

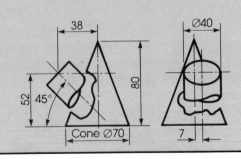

G46 INTERPENETRATION OF SOLIDS: CONE, CYLINDER AND SPHERE (FIRST ANGLE PROJECTION).

G46-1 Draw the given plan and complete the elevation shown by constructing the curve of intersection as the solids meet.

G46-2 Draw the given plan of the pipe inlet to the hemispherical end of a cylindrical pressure vessel and complete the given elevation by constructing the intersection formed by the joint between the pipe and the hemisphere.

G46-3 Complete the 2 given views of the cone and sphere by constructing the curve of intersection between the 2 solids as they meet.

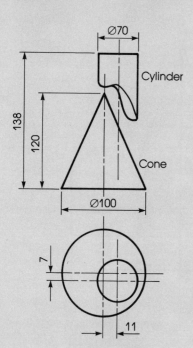

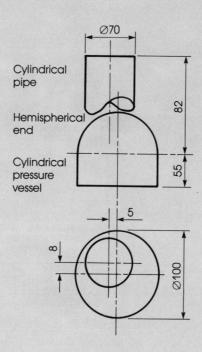

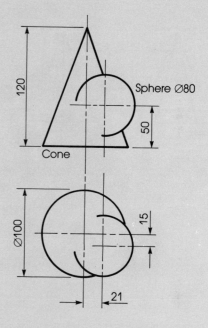

Draw and complete the 2 given elevations
by constructing the intersection between
the prism and the pyramid. Project a plan
from the complete elevation.

All corners except 1 and 2 can be located
without taking sections. Points 1 and 2 are
located on section Y-Y. Alternative method is
to use G1 produced to give P

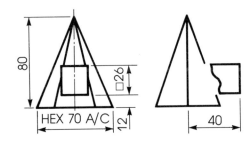

HEX 70 A/C

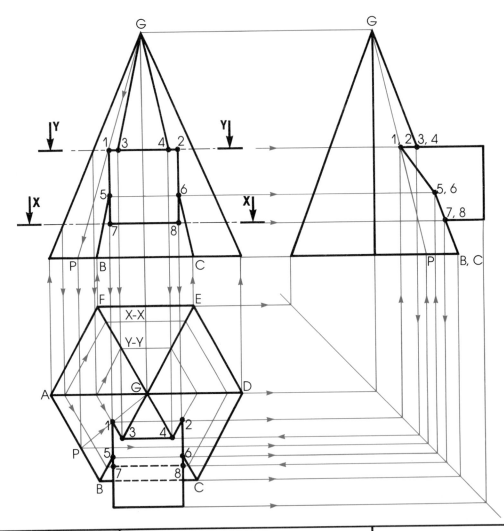

Drawing No.	TITLE: **Intersection of solids (hexagonal**	NOTE: **First Angle projection**	SCALE:
G43	**pyramid with prisms and cylinders).**	**used.**	0 10 20 30 40 50 60 70 80 mm

Draw and complete the 2 given elevations
by constructing the intersection between
the prism and the pyramid. Project a plan
from the incomplete elevation.

Points 1 and 2 are determined in the plan using
section X-X or G2 produced to P, i.e. invent a line
GP which is in a useful position

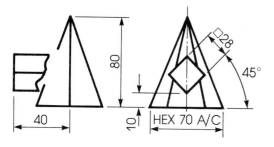

80

40

10

28

45°

HEX 70 A/C

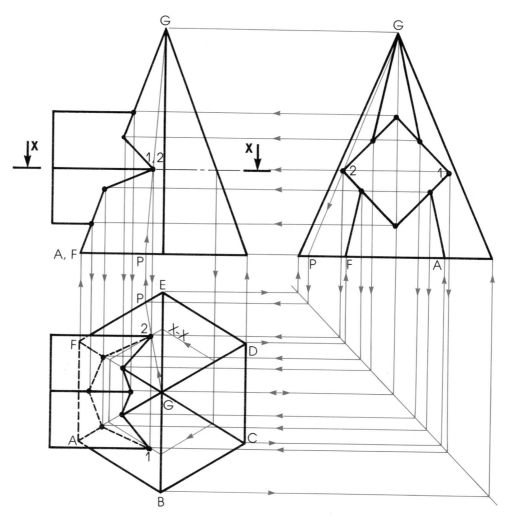

Drawing No.	TITLE: **Intersection of solids (hexagonal**	NOTE: **First Angle projection**	SCALE:
G43	**pyramid with prisms and cylinders).**	**used.**	0 10 20 30 40 50 60 70 80

mm

Draw and complete the 2 given elevations
by constructing the intersection between
the prism and the pyramid. Project a plan
from the incomplete elevation.

See notes on G43-1 and G43-2

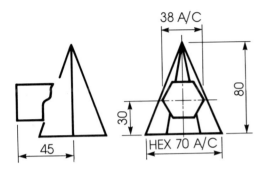

38 A/C

80

30

45

HEX 70 A/C

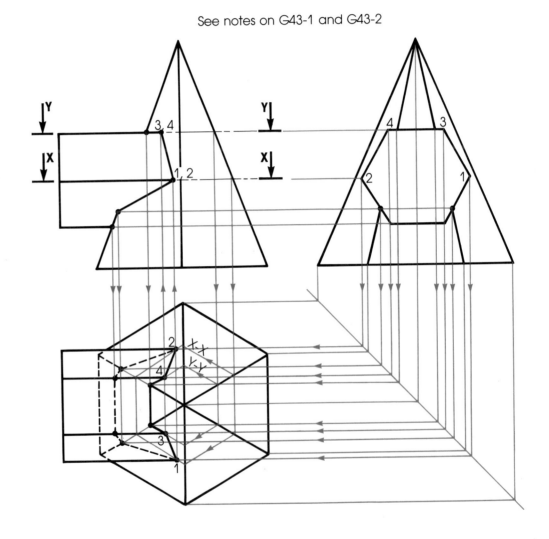

| Drawing No. **G43** | TITLE: **Intersection of solids (hexagonal pyramid with prisms and cylinders).** | NOTE: **First Angle projection used.** | SCALE: 0 10 20 30 40 50 60 70 80 mm |

Draw and complete the 2 given elevations
by constructing the intersection between
the prism and the pyramid. Project a plan
from the incomplete elevation.

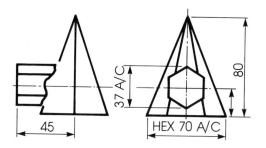

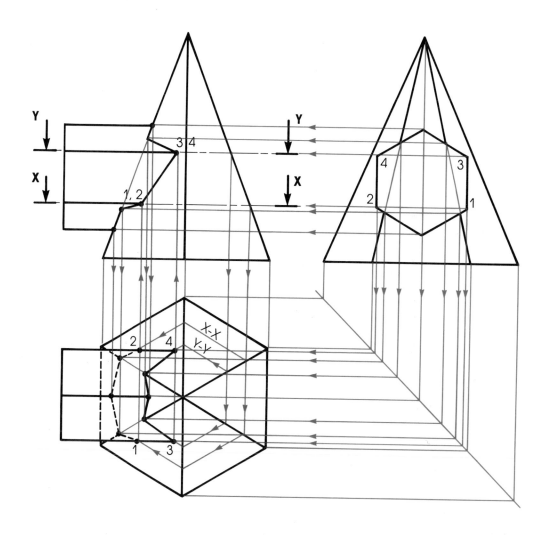

Drawing No.	TITLE: **Intersection of solids (hexagonal**	NOTE: **First Angle projection**	SCALE:
G43	**pyramid with prisms and cylinders).**	**used.**	0 10 20 30 40 50 60 70 80 mm

G43-5

Draw and complete the 2 given elevations by constructing the intersection between the cylinder and the pyramid. Project a plan from the incomplete elevation.

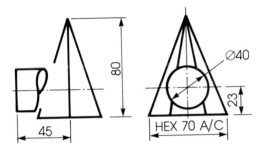

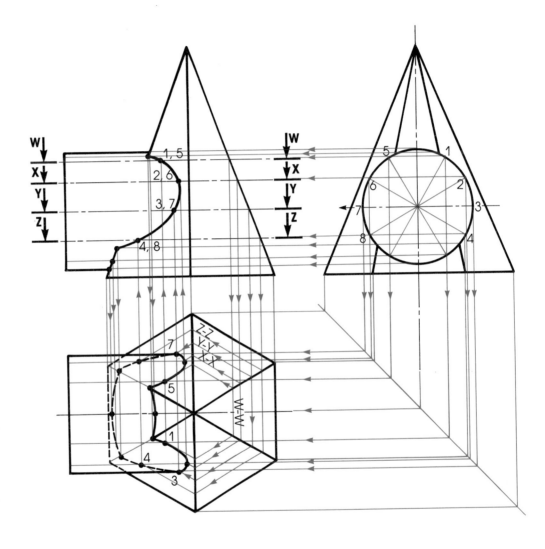

Drawing No. G43	TITLE: **Intersection of solids (hexagonal pyramid with prisms and cylinders).**	NOTE: **First Angle projection used.**	SCALE:

Draw and complete the 2 given elevations by constructing the curve of intersection of the cylinder resting in the lower part of a hexagonal pyramid.

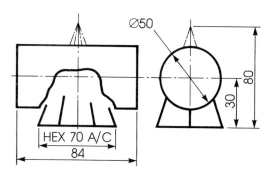

Ø50

HEX 70 A/C

84

80

30

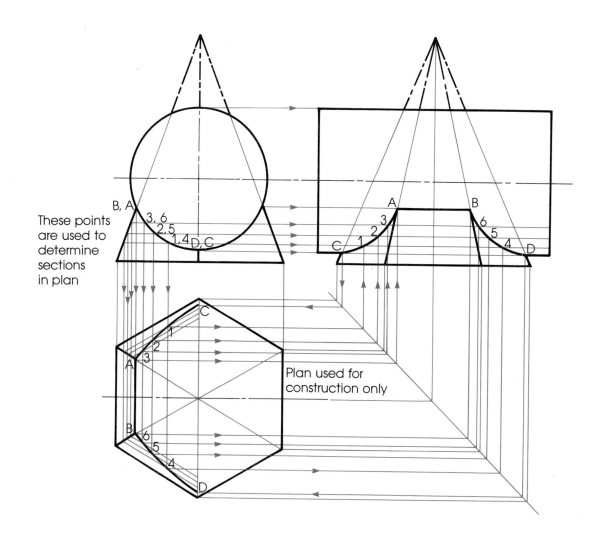

These points are used to determine sections in plan

B, A

3, 6
2, 5
1, 4 D, C

A
2 3
C 1
6 5
4 D

B

Plan used for construction only

C
1
2
3
A

B
6
5
4
D

Drawing No. **G43**	TITLE: **Intersection of solids (hexagonal pyramid with prisms and cylinders).**	NOTE: **First Angle projection used.**	SCALE:

SCALE:
0 10 20 30 40 50 60 70 80
mm

Draw and complete the 2 given elevations
by constructing the curve of intersection
between the cone and the prism. Project a
plan from the incomplete elevation.

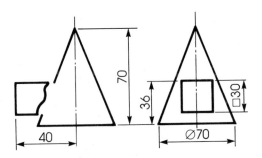

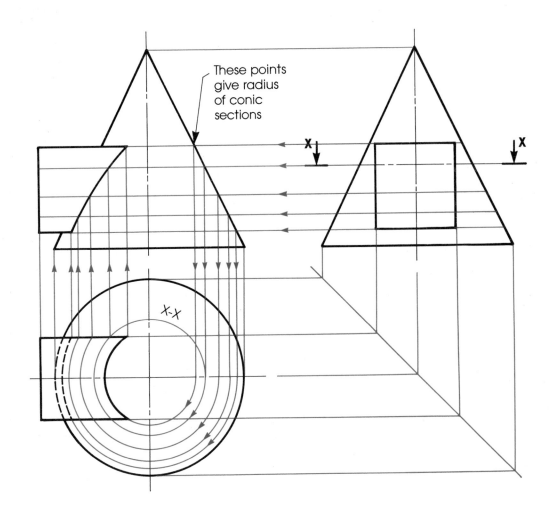

These points
give radius
of conic
sections

| Drawing No.
G44 | TITLE: **Intersection of solids (cone with prisms and cylinders).** | NOTE: **First Angle projection used.** | SCALE:
0 10 20 30 40 50 60 70 80
mm |

Draw and complete the 2 given elevations
by constructing the curves of intersection
between the cone and the prism. Project
a plan from the incomplete elevation.

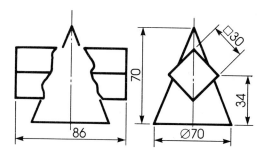

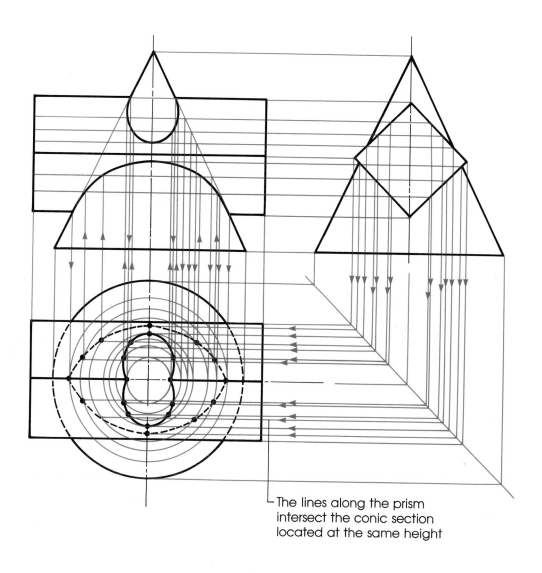

The lines along the prism
intersect the conic section
located at the same height

Drawing No.	TITLE: **Intersection of solids (cone with**	NOTE: **First Angle projection**	SCALE:
G44	**prisms and cylinders).**	**used.**	0 10 20 30 40 50 60 70 80 mm

Draw and complete the 2 given elevations
by constructing the curve of intersection
between the cone and the prism. Project
a plan from the incomplete elevation.

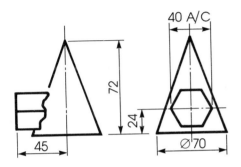

40 A/C

72

24

45

⌀70

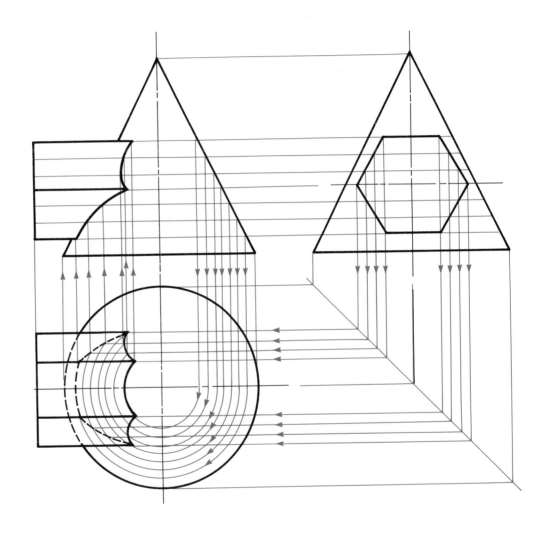

| Drawing No. G44 | TITLE: **Intersection of solids (cone with prisms and cylinders).** | NOTE: **First Angle projection used.** | SCALE: 0 10 20 30 40 50 60 70 80 mm |

Draw and complete the 2 given elevations
by constructing the curve of intersection
between the cone and the prism. Project
a plan from the incomplete elevation.

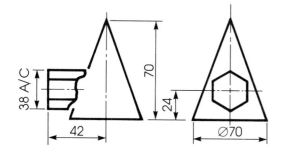

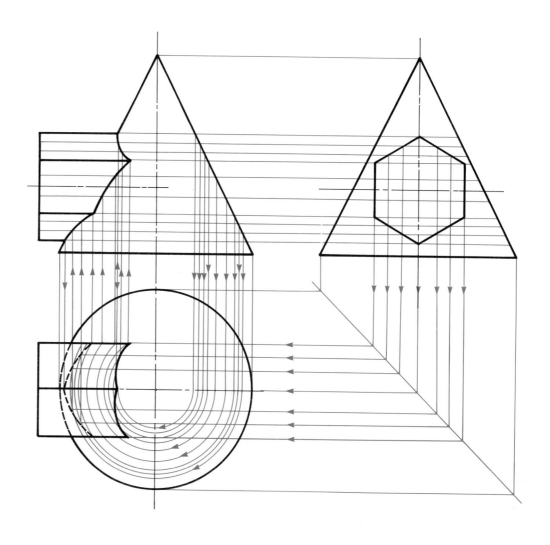

Drawing No.
G44

TITLE: **Intersection of solids (cone with prisms and cylinders).**

NOTE: **First Angle projection used.**

SCALE:
0   10   20   30   40   50   60   70   80
mm

Draw and complete the 2 given elevations by constructing the curves of intersection between the cone and the cylinder. Project a plan from the incomplete elevation.

D = diameter of section X-X through cone

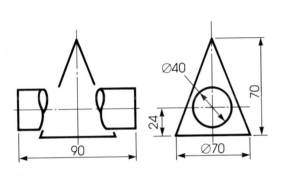

Ø40

70

24

90

Ø70

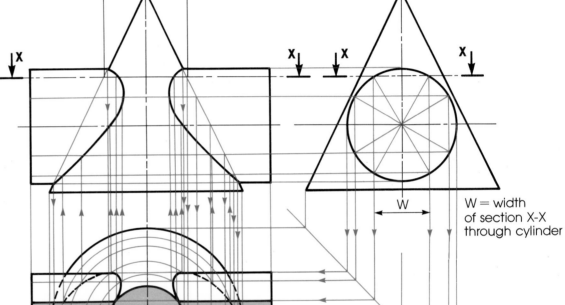

X

X X X

W

W = width of section X-X through cylinder

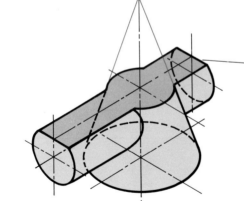

Section X-X

| Drawing No. **G44** | TITLE: **Intersection of solids (cone with prisms and cylinders).** | NOTE: **First Angle projection used.** | SCALE: |

0 10 20 30 40 50 60 70 80

mm

Draw and complete the 2 given elevations by constructing the curves of intersection between the cone and the cylinder. Project a plan from the incomplete elevation.

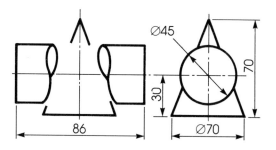

Ø45

70

30

86

Ø70

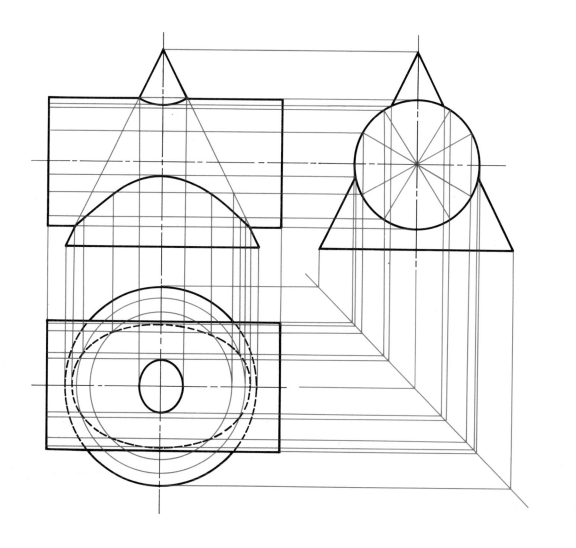

Drawing No. **G44**	TITLE: **Intersection of solids (cone with prisms and cylinders).**	NOTE: **First Angle projection used.**	SCALE: 0 10 20 30 40 50 60 70 80 mm

231

G45-1

Draw and complete the 2 given elevations by constructing the lines of intersection between the pyramid and the tube. Project a plan from the incomplete elevation.

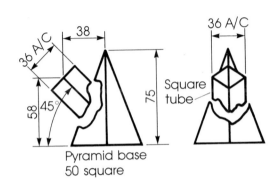

36 A/C
38
36 A/C
75
58
45°
Square tube
Pyramid base
50 square

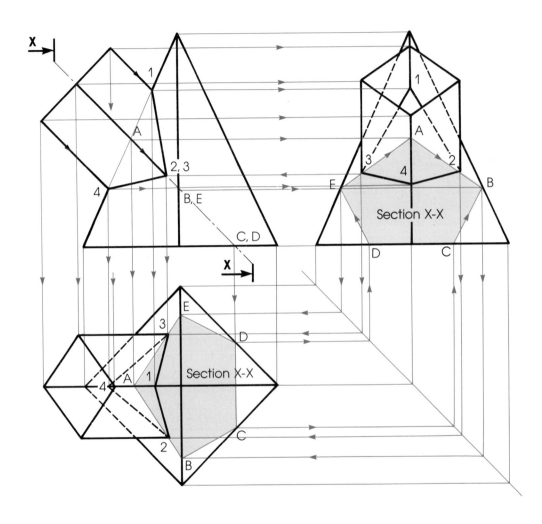

Section X-X

Section X-X

Drawing No. **G45**	TITLE: **Intersection of solids (angled entry to pyramids and cones).**	NOTE: **First Angle projection used.**	SCALE:

Draw and complete the 2 given elevations
by constructing the lines of intersection
between the pyramid and the tube. Project
a plan from the incomplete elevation.

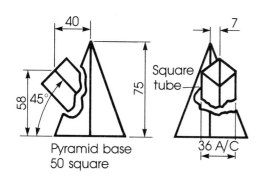

40

58 45°

75

Pyramid base
50 square

7

Square
tube

36 A/C

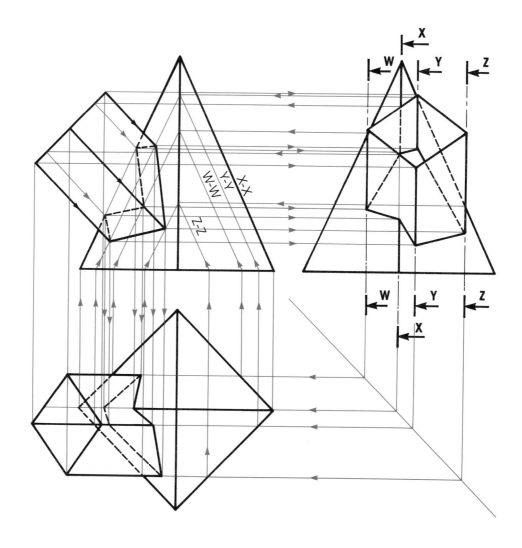

X

W Y Z

X-X
Y-Y
W-W

Z-Z

W Y Z

X

Drawing No.
G45

TITLE: **Intersection of solids (angled entry to
pyramids and cones).**

NOTE: **First Angle projection
used.**

SCALE:

0 10 20 30 40 50 60 70 80

mm

233

Draw and complete the 2 given elevations by constructing the lines of intersection between the hexagonal pyramid and hexagonal tube. Project a plan from the incomplete elevation.

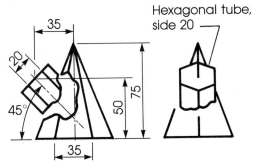

Hexagonal tube, side 20

Hexagonal pyramid, base edge 35

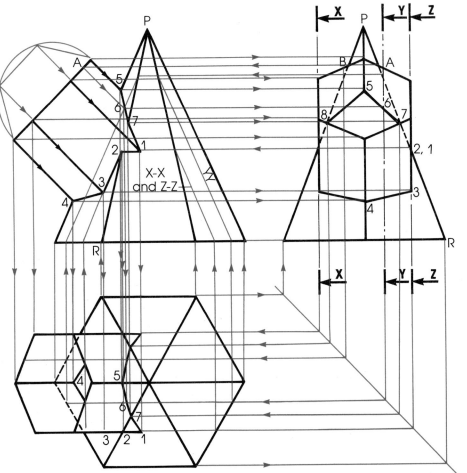

X-X and Z-Z

Point 7 is determined by taking a section to the right of point 5 (i.e. section Y-Y to obtain point 6). Since the intersection between plane surfaces produces a straight line, the point 7 is on the line 5 to 6 produced to meet the pyramid corner PR. Point 8 is obtained by the same method.

Note: A to 6 is the section edge of Y-Y with the hexagonal prism.

Drawing No. G45	TITLE: **Intersection of solids (angled entry to pyramids and cones).**	NOTE: **First Angle projection used.**	SCALE: 0 10 20 30 40 50 60 70 80 mm

Draw and complete the 2 given elevations
by constructing the lines of intersection
between the hexagonal pyramid and
hexagonal tube. Project a plan from the
incomplete elevation.

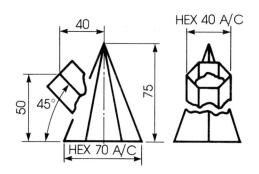

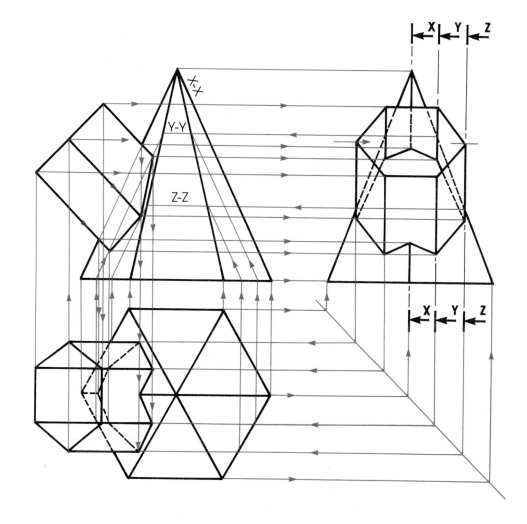

| Drawing No.
G45 | TITLE: **Intersection of solids (angled entry to pyramids and cones).** | NOTE: **First Angle projection used.** | SCALE:
0 10 20 30 40 50 60 70 80
mm |

Draw and complete the 2 given elevations
by constructing the curve of intersection
between the cylinder and hexagonal
pyramid. Project a plan from the
incomplete elevation.

See G28 for sections through hexagonal pyramid
and G26-2 for cylinder

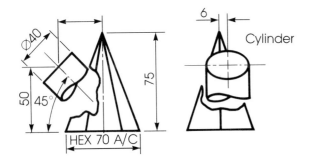

Cylinder

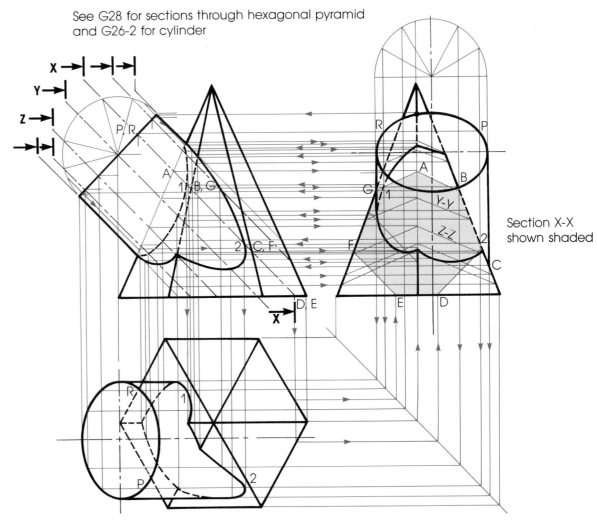

Section X-X
shown shaded

Point 2 is on the line from P down the cylinder
and on section X-X, i.e. intersection between
line and section gives point 2

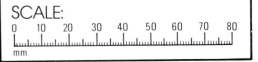

Drawing No.	TITLE: **Intersection of solids (angled entry to pyramids and cones).**	NOTE: **First Angle projection used.**	SCALE:
G45			0 10 20 30 40 50 60 70 80 mm

Draw and complete the 2 given elevations
by constructing the curve of intersection
between the cylinder and cone. Project
a plan from the incomplete elevation.

Cylinder and cone
See G29 for
construction of
conical sections

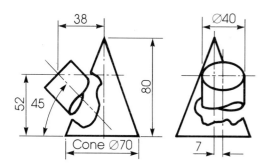

38

⌀40

80

52   45

Cone ⌀70

7

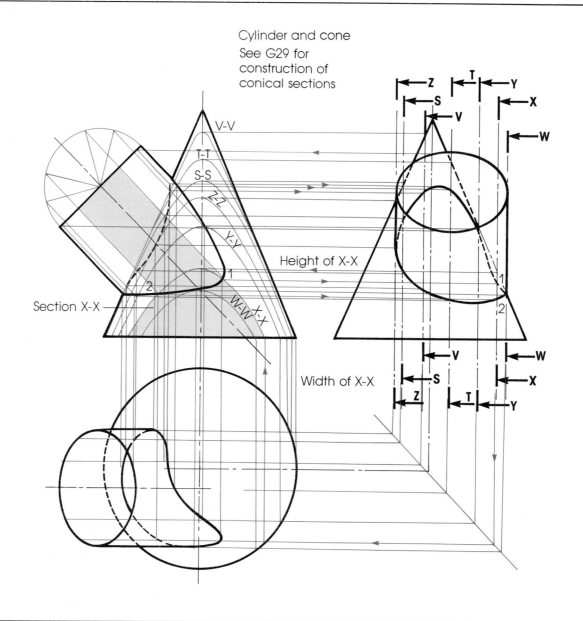

V-V

T-T

S-S

Z-Z

V-V

1

2

W-W   X-X

Section X-X

Height of X-X

Width of X-X

Z   T   Y

S   X

V

W

V   W

S   X

Z   T   Y

1

2

| Drawing No.
G45 | TITLE: **Intersection of solids (angled entry to**
pyramids and cones). | NOTE: **First Angle projection**
used. | SCALE:
0 10 20 30 40 50 60 70 80
mm |

237

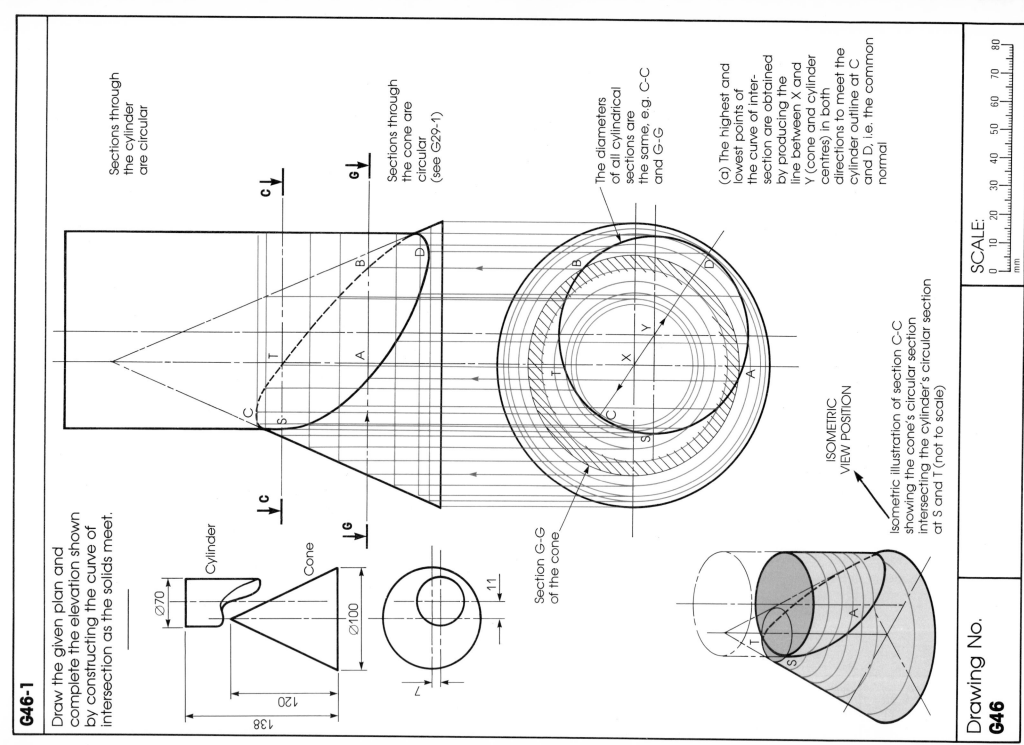

G46-1

Draw the given plan and complete the elevation shown by constructing the curve of intersection as the solids meet.

Sections through the cylinder are circular

Sections through the cone are circular (see G29-1)

The diameters of all cylindrical sections are the same, e.g. C-C and G-G

(a) The highest and lowest points of the curve of inter-section are obtained by producing the line between X and Y (cone and cylinder centres) in both directions to meet the cylinder outline at C and D, i.e. the common normal

Section G-G of the cone

ISOMETRIC VIEW POSITION

Isometric illustration of section C-C showing the cone's circular section intersecting the cylinder's circular section at S and T (not to scale)

Cylinder

Cone

Ø70

Ø100

120

138

11

7

SCALE:

mm

Drawing No.
G46

238

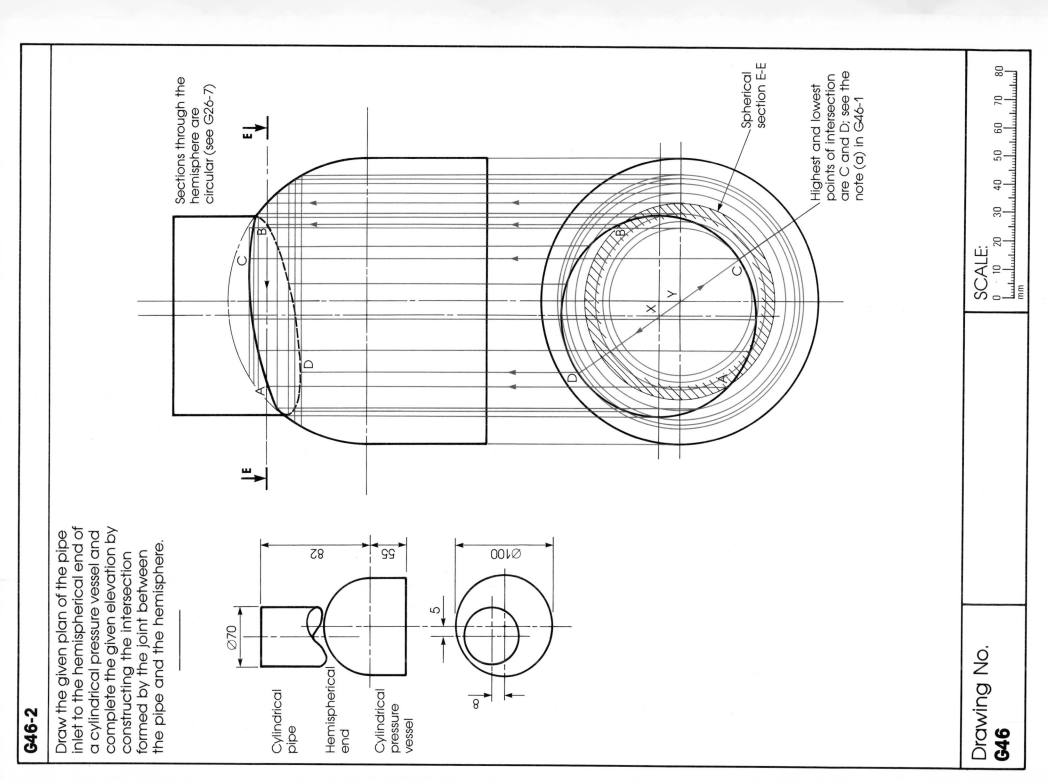

G46-2

Draw the given plan of the pipe inlet to the hemispherical end of a cylindrical pressure vessel and complete the given elevation by constructing the intersection formed by the joint between the pipe and the hemisphere.

Sections through the hemisphere are circular (see G26-7)

Spherical section E-E

Highest and lowest points of intersection are C and D; see the note (a) in G46-1

Cylindrical pipe

Hemispherical end

Cylindrical pressure vessel

Ø70

82

55

Ø100

5

8

SCALE:

0 10 20 30 40 50 60 70 80
mm

Drawing No.
G46

239

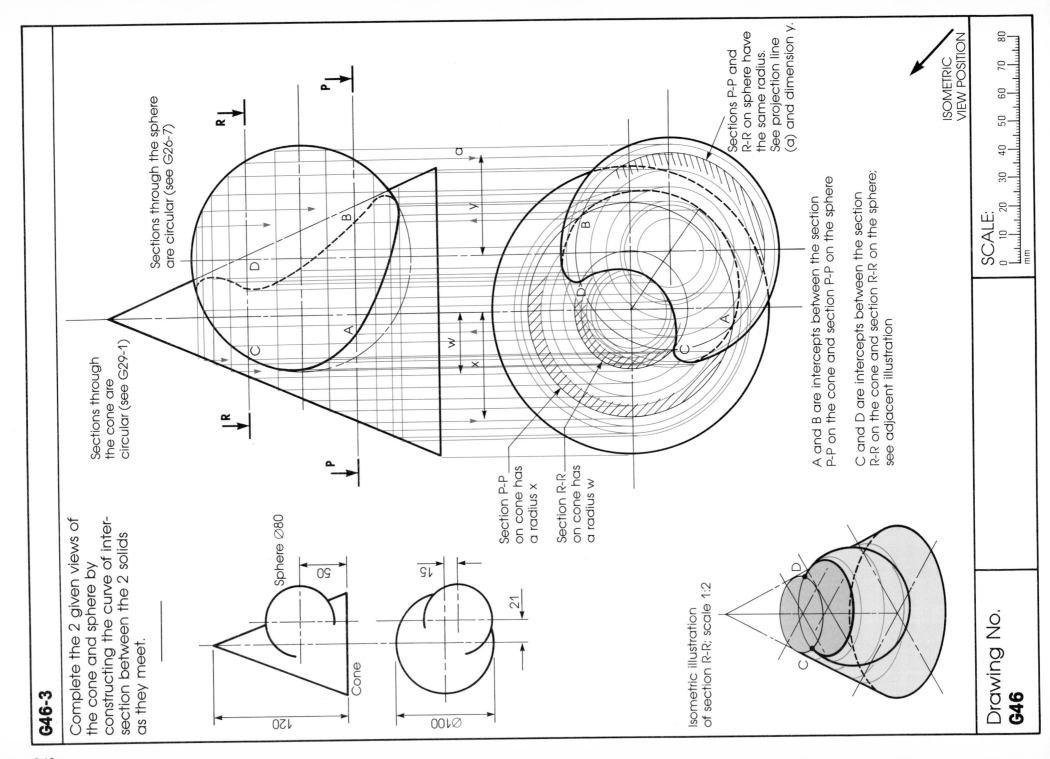

G46-3

Complete the 2 given views of the cone and sphere by constructing the curve of inter-section between the 2 solids as they meet.

Sections through the sphere are circular (see G26-7)

Sections through the cone are circular (see G29-1)

Section P-P on cone has a radius x

Section R-R on cone has a radius w

Sections P-P and R-R on sphere have the same radius. See projection line (a) and dimension y.

A and B are intercepts between the section P-P on the cone and section P-P on the sphere

C and D are intercepts between the section R-R on the cone and section R-R on the sphere; see adjacent illustration

Sphere ⌀80

50

15

21

120

⌀100

Cone

Isometric illustration of section R-R; scale 1:2

ISOMETRIC VIEW POSITION

SCALE:

mm
0 10 20 30 40 50 60 70 80

Drawing No.
G46

Worksheets for G47 to G50

G47 INTRODUCTION TO ISOMETRIC DRAWING (PROJECTION AS STATED).

G47-1 Produce an isometric drawing of the block shown looking in the direction of arrow Y.

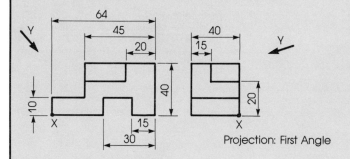

Projection: First Angle

G47-2 Produce an isometric drawing of the triangular prism shown, with corner AP in view.
Note: The given drawing is to Third Angle projection and involves a subtle twist!

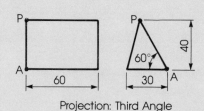

Projection: Third Angle

G47-3 Produce an isometric drawing of the hexagonal prism shown, with the view taken from above in the direction of arrow Z.

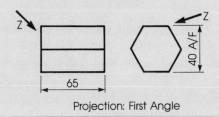

Projection: First Angle

G47-4 Produce an isometric drawing of the cylinder shown, with its axis represented isometrically horizontal.

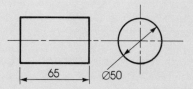

G47-5 Produce an isometric drawing of the cut cylinder shown, looking down onto the angled cut face.

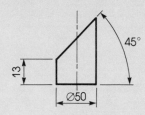

G47-6 Produce an isometric drawing of the Woodruff key shown, with the semicircular face represented as vertical.

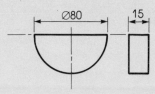

G47-7 Produce an isometric drawing of the Feather key shown.

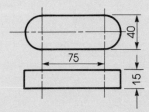

G48 INTRODUCTION TO OBLIQUE DRAWING (PROJECTION AS STATED).

G48-1a Produce a cavalier oblique drawing of the block shown in Fig 1. The view should be drawn to correspond with the direction of observation which is indicated by arrow A and the edge XY should be represented horizontally.
1b Produce a 45° cabinet oblique drawing of Fig 1 looking in the direction of arrow A with the edge XY represented horizontally.
1c Produce a 60° cabinet oblique drawing of Fig 1 looking in the direction of arrow A with the edge XY represented horizontally.

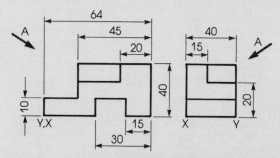

Fig 1   Projection: First Angle

G48-2a Using 45° cabinet oblique produce a drawing of the prism in Fig 2, which uses the true shape of the hexagonal face A.
2b Using 45° cabinet oblique produce a drawing of the prism in Fig 2 which incorporates the true shape of the rectangular face B.

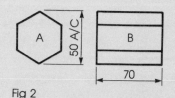

Fig 2

G48-3a Using 45° cabinet oblique draw a cylinder ⌀50 mm × 78 mm long with its axis horizontal and the true shape of the circular faces utilised.

3b Produce a 45° cabinet oblique drawing of a cylinder ⌀50 mm × 78 mm with its axis vertical.

3c Produce a 45° cabinet oblique drawing of a cylinder ⌀50 mm × 78 mm long with its axis represented horizontally and not using a true shape.

G48-4 Produce a 45° cabinet oblique drawing of the cut cylinder in Fig 3 looking onto the angled face.

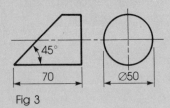

Fig 3

G48-5 Using the 45° cabinet oblique method produce a drawing of the coupling shown in Fig 4. Use the easiest viewing position for construction purposes.

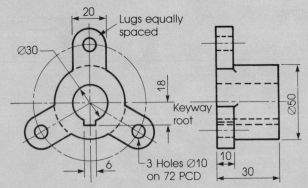

Fig 4   Projection: Third Angle

G49   ORTHOGRAPHIC TO ISOMETRIC AND OBLIQUE (PROJECTION AS STATED).

G49-1 Produce an isometric drawing of the object shown in Fig 1 viewed in the direction of arrow Y with corner A nearest the viewing position. Omit hidden detail.

G49-2 Produce an isometric drawing of the object shown in Fig 2 viewed in the direction of arrow Y.

G49-3 Produce an isometric drawing of the object shown in Fig 3 viewed from arrow Y with corners AB and AC visible. Hidden detail not required.

G49-4 Produce an isometric drawing of the frustum of a pyramid shown in Fig 4 viewed in the direction of arrow Y.

G49-5 Produce an oblique drawing, viewed from the direction of arrow W, of the object shown in Fig 1. Use the 45° cabinet method with edge AB horizontal.

G49-6 Produce a 45° cabinet oblique drawing of the object shown in Fig 2. The view should be in the direction of arrow Y with AB horizontal.

G49-7 Produce an oblique drawing of the object shown in Fig 3 and viewed in the direction of arrow W, with BD horizontal and visible.

G49-8 Represent the frustum of a pyramid shown in Fig 4, by an oblique drawing with the view taken in the direction of arrow Y.

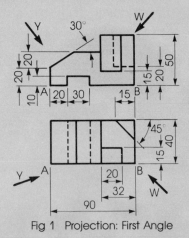

Fig 1   Projection: First Angle

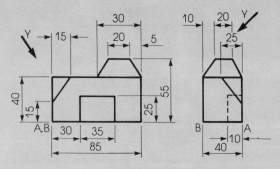

Fig 2   Projection: First Angle

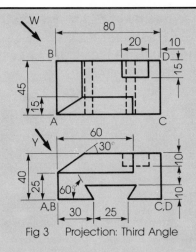

Fig 3   Projection: Third Angle

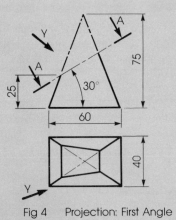

Fig 4   Projection: First Angle

242

G50 ISOMETRIC AND OBLIQUE EXAMPLES INVOLVING CURVES (PROJECTION AS STATED).

G50-1 Produce an isometric drawing of the component shown in Fig 1 with the corner A nearest to the viewing position.

G50-2 Produce an oblique drawing of the object in Fig 1 with edge AB horizontal and A, B and C in view.

G50-3 Produce an isometric drawing of the M/C slide shown in Fig 2 with corner A nearest the viewing position.

G50-4 Draw an oblique interpretation of the M/C slide shown in Fig 2 with the edge AB horizontal.

G50-5 Produce an isometric drawing of the clevis joint shown in Fig 3 viewed from the direction of arrow X and with the centre line (℄) represented horizontal.

G50-6 Produce an oblique drawing of the clevis joint in Fig 3 viewed from the direction of arrow Y with the centre line receding at 45°.

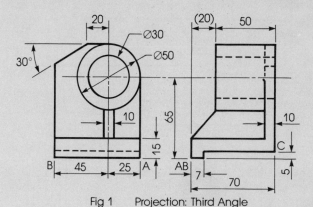

Fig 1   Projection: Third Angle

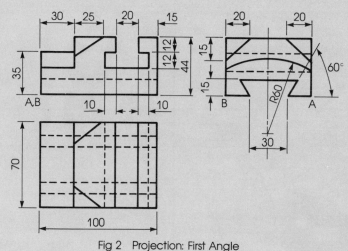

Fig 2   Projection: First Angle

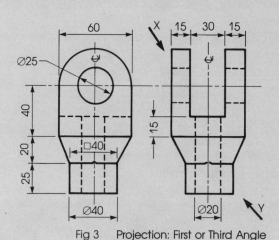

Fig 3   Projection: First or Third Angle

243

Introduction

Isometric projection is a special form of a type of orthographic projection which is referred to as axonometric projection. Axonometric projection is derived by projecting from 2 orthographic views located in any position, but the special isometric case uses the angles given in Fig 1 to reduce all 3 dimensions by the same proportion.

The resulting pictorial view has its edges reduced in length from the original views due to the lengths being projected and formed by the intersection of the projection lines from the corners.

This form of isometric is <u>true</u> <u>isometric</u> or <u>isometric projection</u>. It can also be produced by using the scale shown in Fig 2 and the isometric axis, with the scale reducing the mutually perpendicular edges by the correct proportion.

Conventional isometric drawing is thus derived from the true isometric, using the same axis but with all lengths to a full size scale when they are parallel to the axis. Drawings tend to appear oversize when directly compared to orthographic projection.

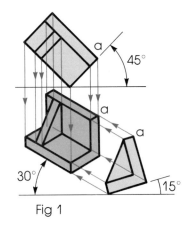

Fig 1

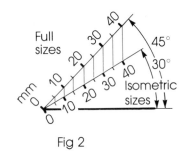

Fig 2

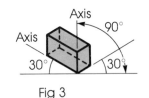

Fig 3

G47-1

Produce an isometric drawing of the block shown (right) looking in the direction of arrow Y.

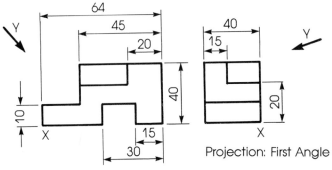

Projection: First Angle

All the plane surfaces of the block illustrated are mutually perpendicular as are all intersecting corners. Angle A represents 90° but is drawn at 60° with angle C also representing 90° but drawn at 120°. Angle B = A

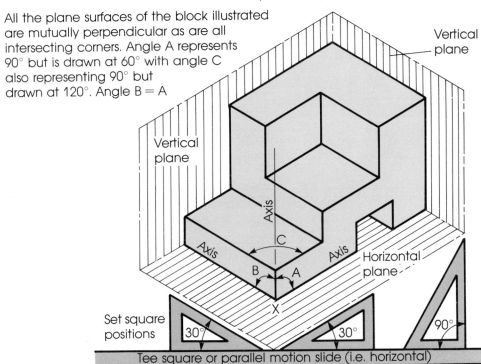

Conventional isometric drawing

All dimensions are drawn full size along isometric lines.
Isometric lines are at 30° and 90° to the horizontal.
Isometric angles are not true. Angles A,B and C represent 90°

| Drawing No. G47 | TITLE: **Introduction to isometric projection and isometric drawing.** | | SCALE: |

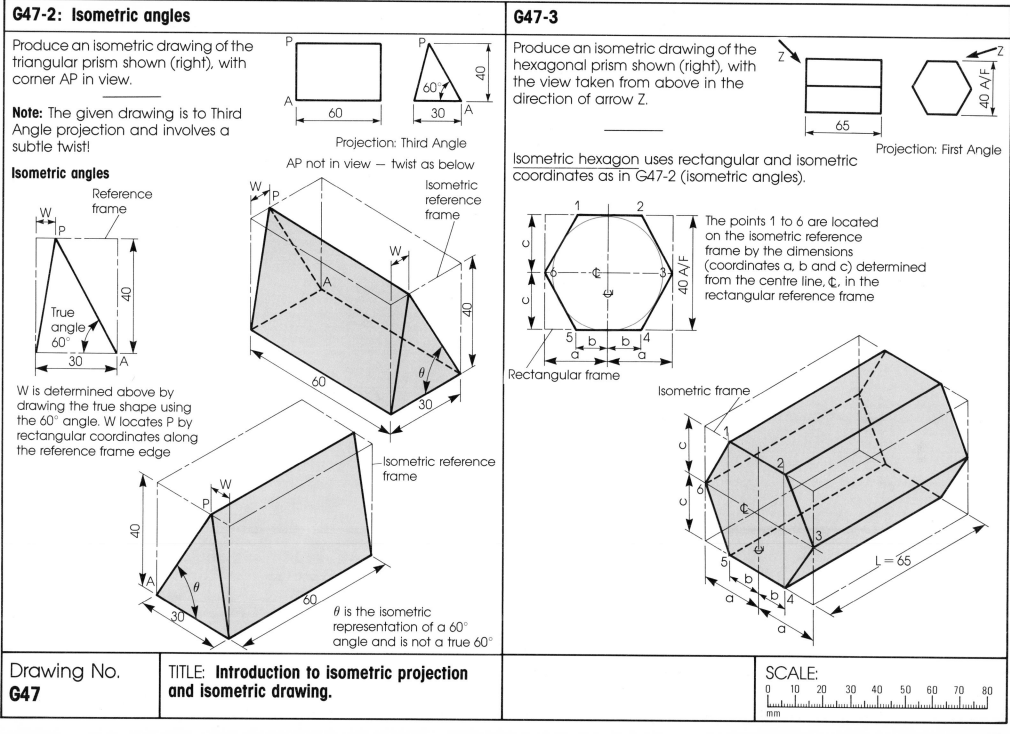

G47-2: Isometric angles

Produce an isometric drawing of the triangular prism shown (right), with corner AP in view.

Note: The given drawing is to Third Angle projection and involves a subtle twist!

Isometric angles

Reference frame

W

P

True angle 60°

40

30

A

W is determined above by drawing the true shape using the 60° angle. W locates P by rectangular coordinates along the reference frame edge

P

A

60

Projection: Third Angle

AP not in view — twist as below

W P

Isometric reference frame

W

A

60

40

30

θ

Isometric reference frame

W

P

40

A

θ

30

60

θ is the isometric representation of a 60° angle and is not a true 60°

G47-3

Produce an isometric drawing of the hexagonal prism shown (right), with the view taken from above in the direction of arrow Z.

Z

40 A/F

65

Projection: First Angle

Isometric hexagon uses rectangular and isometric coordinates as in G47-2 (isometric angles).

1   2

c

6   ℄   3

c

40 A/F

5   b   b   4

a   a

Rectangular frame

The points 1 to 6 are located on the isometric reference frame by the dimensions (coordinates a, b and c) determined from the centre line, ℄, in the rectangular reference frame

Isometric frame

1

c

6

c

℄

2

3

5

b

a   b   4

a

L = 65

Drawing No.
G47

TITLE: **Introduction to isometric projection and isometric drawing.**

SCALE:

0 10 20 30 40 50 60 70 80
mm

245

G47-4: Isometric circles

Produce an isometric drawing of the cylinder shown (right), with its axis represented isometrically horizontal.

Isometric circle:

Treat as a changing angle.

Rectangular coordinates, e.g. (d,f), give point 5 on circle

Transfer to isometric coordinates

Reference frame

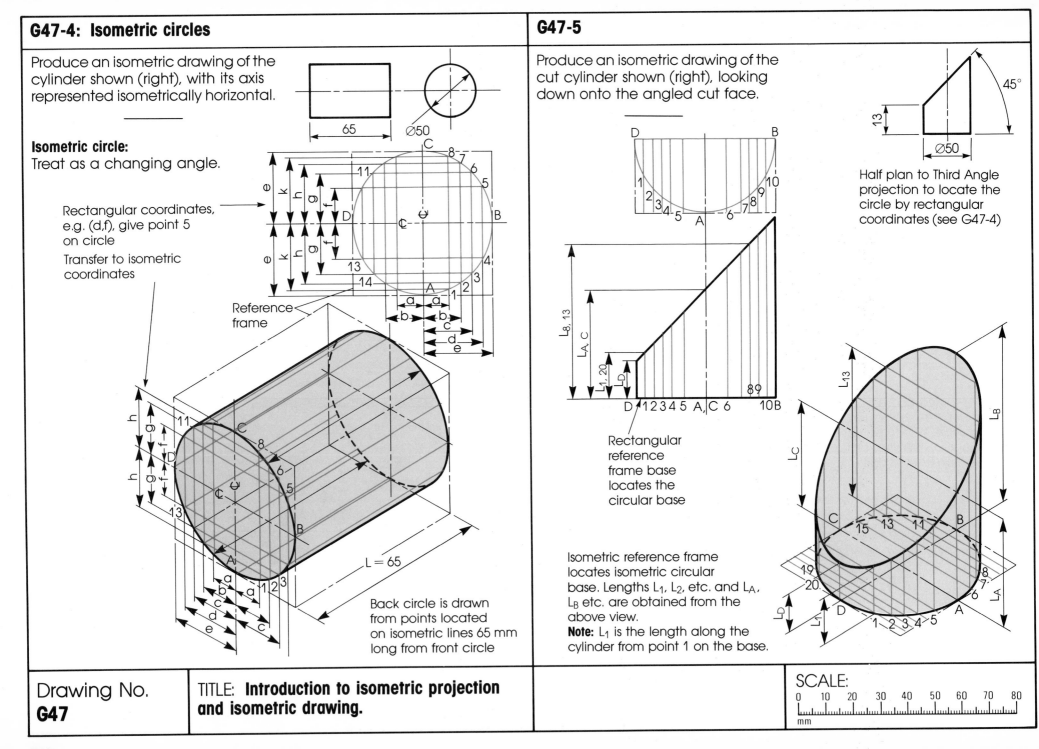

Back circle is drawn from points located on isometric lines 65 mm long from front circle

65   Ø50

L = 65

G47-5

Produce an isometric drawing of the cut cylinder shown (right), looking down onto the angled cut face.

45°

13   Ø50

Half plan to Third Angle projection to locate the circle by rectangular coordinates (see G47-4)

Rectangular reference frame base locates the circular base

Isometric reference frame locates isometric circular base. Lengths L_1, L_2, etc. and L_A, L_B etc. are obtained from the above view.

Note: L_1 is the length along the cylinder from point 1 on the base.

Drawing No.	TITLE: **Introduction to isometric projection and isometric drawing.**	
G47		

SCALE:
0 10 20 30 40 50 60 70 80
mm

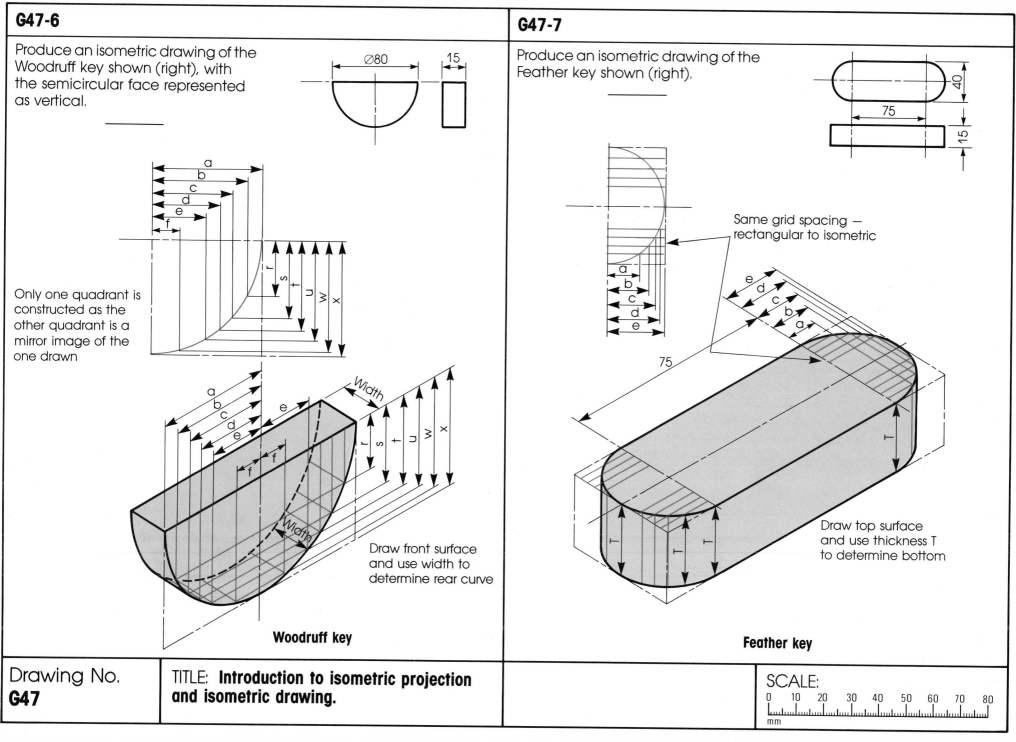

G47-6

Produce an isometric drawing of the Woodruff key shown (right), with the semicircular face represented as vertical.

⌀80   15

Only one quadrant is constructed as the other quadrant is a mirror image of the one drawn

Width

Draw front surface and use width to determine rear curve

Woodruff key

G47-7

Produce an isometric drawing of the Feather key shown (right).

40   75   15

Same grid spacing — rectangular to isometric

75

Draw top surface and use thickness T to determine bottom

Feather key

| Drawing No. **G47** | TITLE: **Introduction to isometric projection and isometric drawing.** | | SCALE: |

SCALE:
0 10 20 30 40 50 60 70 80
mm

G48-1

1(a) Produce a cavalier oblique drawing of the block shown opposite. The view should be drawn to correspond with the direction of observation which is indicated by arrow A. The edge XY should be represented horizontally.

1(b) Produce a 45° cabinet oblique drawing of the figure opposite looking in the direction of arrow A with the edge XY represented horizontally.

1(c) Produce a 60° cabinet oblique drawing of the figure opposite looking in the direction of arrow A with the edge of XY represented horizontally.

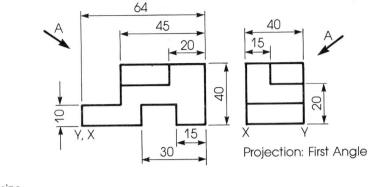

Projection: First Angle

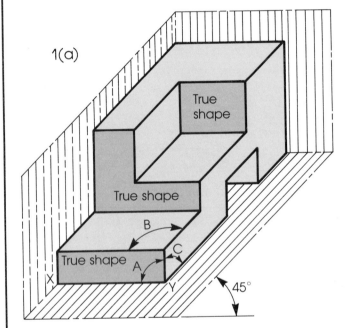

1(a)

Cavalier oblique drawing

Oblique axes are horizontal, vertical and at 45°. All lines drawn parallel to the axes are to full scale sizes.
Angle A is 90° and represents a true angle of 90°. The shaded faces are true shapes.
Angle B is 135° but represents 90°; angle C is 45° and also represents 90°.

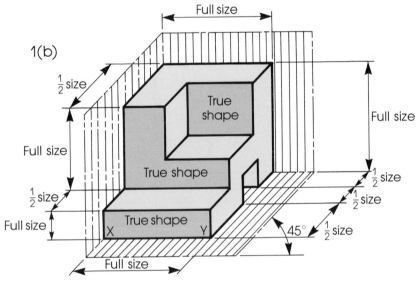

1(b)

45° cabinet oblique

Oblique axes are horizontal, vertical and at 45°. Lines drawn parallel to the horizontal and vertical axes are to full scale sizes but when drawn parallel to 45° axis are $\frac{1}{2}$ scale size.

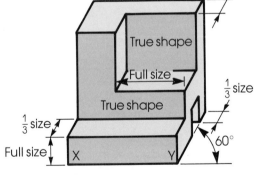

1(c)

60° cabinet oblique

$\frac{1}{3}$ size for lines parallel to 60° axis.

Drawing No.	TITLE: **Introduction to oblique drawing.**	NOTE: **45° cabinet with lines $\frac{1}{2}$ size when parallel to 45° axis is required for C.S.E. and G.C.E. exams.**	SCALE:
G48			0 10 20 30 40 50 60 70 80 mm

G48-2: Oblique angles

2(a) Using 45° cabinet oblique produce a drawing of the prism shown below which uses the true shape of the hexagonal face A.

2(b) Using the 45° cabinet oblique method produce a drawing of the prism shown below which incorporates the true shape of the rectangular face B.

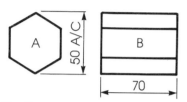

Fig 2

2(b)

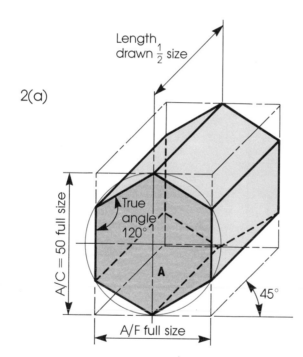

2(a)

Length drawn ½ size

45° cabinet oblique drawing

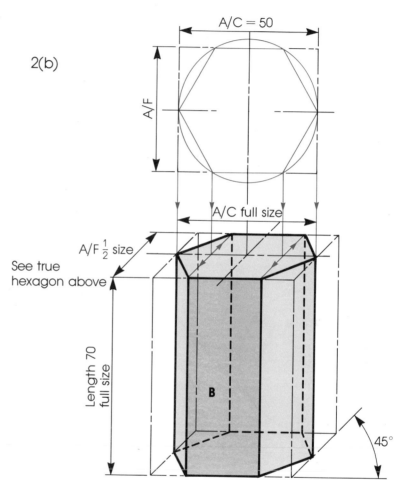

45° cabinet oblique drawing

Drawing No. G48	TITLE: **Introduction to oblique drawing.**	NOTE: **45° cabinet with lines ½ size when parallel to 45° axis is required for C.S.E. and G.C.E. exams.**	SCALE:

G48-3: Oblique circles

3(a) Using the 45° cabinet oblique method draw a cylinder of diameter 50 mm × 78 mm long with its axis horizontal and the true shape of the circular faces utilised.

3(b) Produce a 45° cabinet oblique drawing of a cylinder of diameter 50 mm × 78 mm with its axis vertical.

3(c) Produce a 45° cabinet oblique drawing of a cylinder of diameter 50 mm × 78 mm long with its axis represented horizontally and not using a true shape.

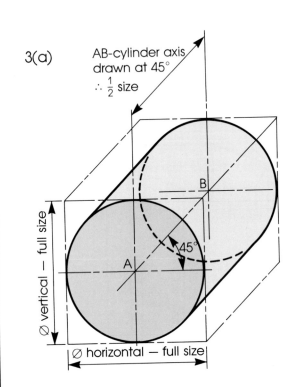

3(a)

AB-cylinder axis drawn at 45°
∴ ½ size

∅ vertical – full size

∅ horizontal – full size

45°

A

B

Use compass to draw circle as it appears true. Coordinates remain rectangular

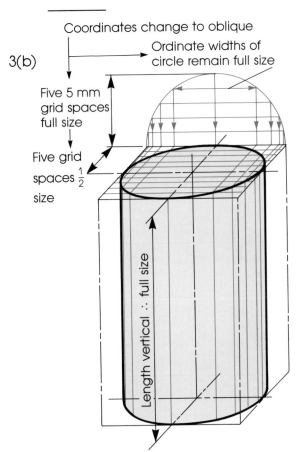

Coordinates change to oblique

Ordinate widths of circle remain full size

3(b)

Five 5 mm grid spaces full size

Five grid spaces ½ size

Length vertical ∴ full size

Note: Production of circular face is easier if presented as in Fig G48–3(a)

3(c)

∅ D C

Grid spaces

∅

A B

Full size

L = length of axis full size

L

Axis

L

L

A

B

∅

Grid spaces are at 45°
∴ ½ size

½ size at 45°

Coordinates change to oblique

45° cabinet oblique drawing

| Drawing No.
G48 | TITLE: **Introduction to oblique drawing.** | NOTE: **45° cabinet with lines ½ size when parallel to 45° axis is required for C.S.E. and G.C.E. exams.** | SCALE:
0 10 20 30 40 50 60 70 80
mm |

G48-4

Produce a 45° cabinet oblique drawing of the cut cylinder opposite looking on to the angled face.

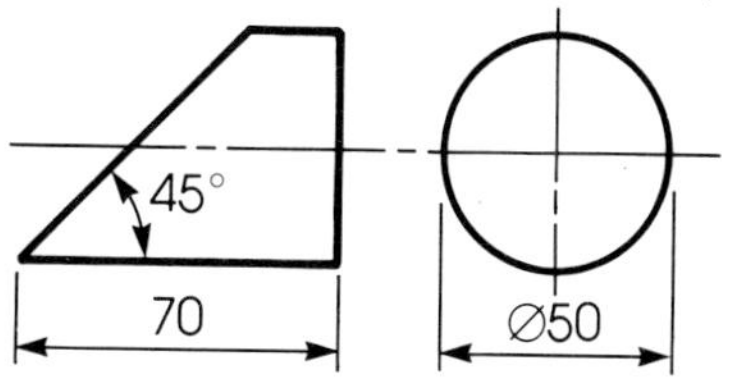

45°

70   Ø50

45° cabinet oblique drawing

A
B
C
D
E
F
G

Draw circular back face first

True lengths halved for use at 45° in the oblique drawing below

A
B
C
D   D
E
F   G

45°

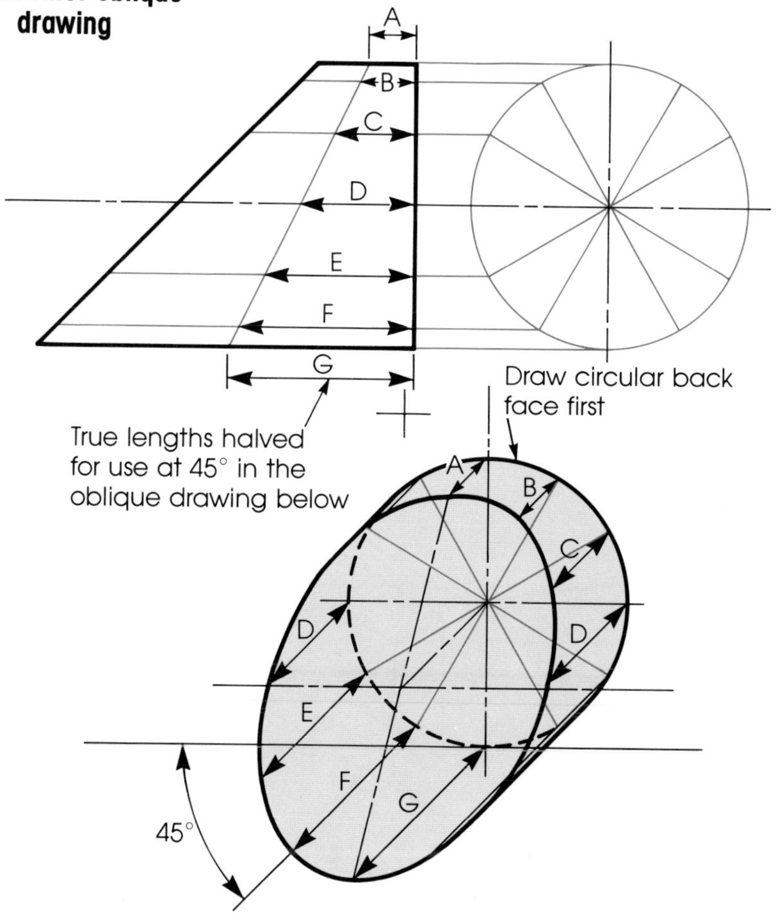

G48-5

Using the 45° cabinet oblique method produce a drawing of the coupling shown opposite. Use the easiest viewing position for construction purposes.

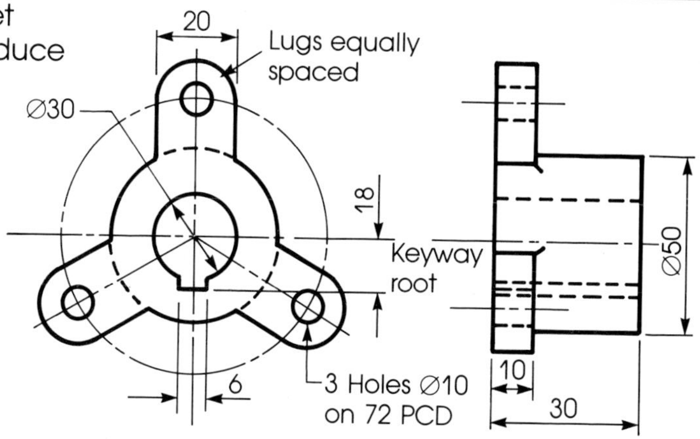

20   Lugs equally spaced

Ø30

18

Keyway root

6   3 Holes Ø10 on 72 PCD

Ø50

10   30

Projection: Third Angle

Length of boss is at 45° ∴ ½ size

Lug thickness is at 45° ∴ ½ size

45° cabinet oblique drawing

Produce shape of shaded face first as per the given orthographic elevation

45°

45°

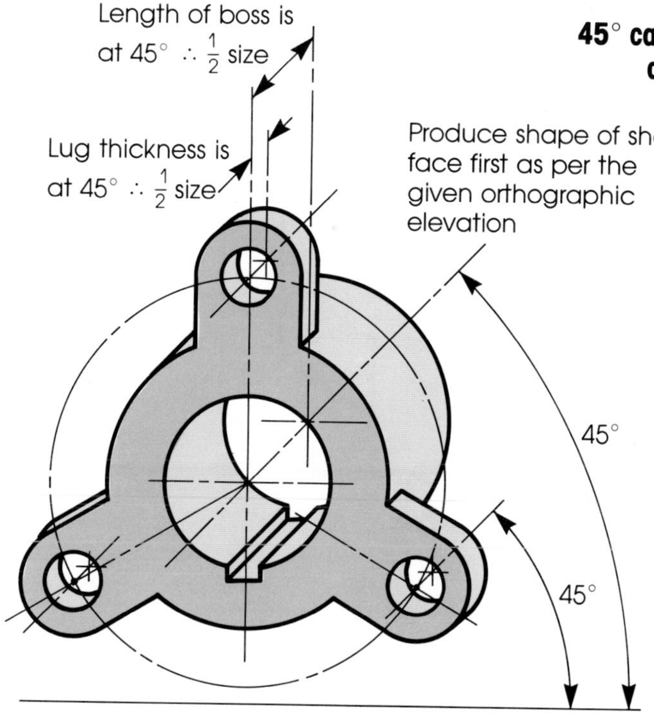

| Drawing No. **G48** | TITLE: **Introduction to oblique drawing.** | NOTE: **45° cabinet with lines ½ size when parallel to 45° axis is required for C.S.E. and G.C.E. exams.** | SCALE: 0 10 20 30 40 50 60 70 80 mm |

251

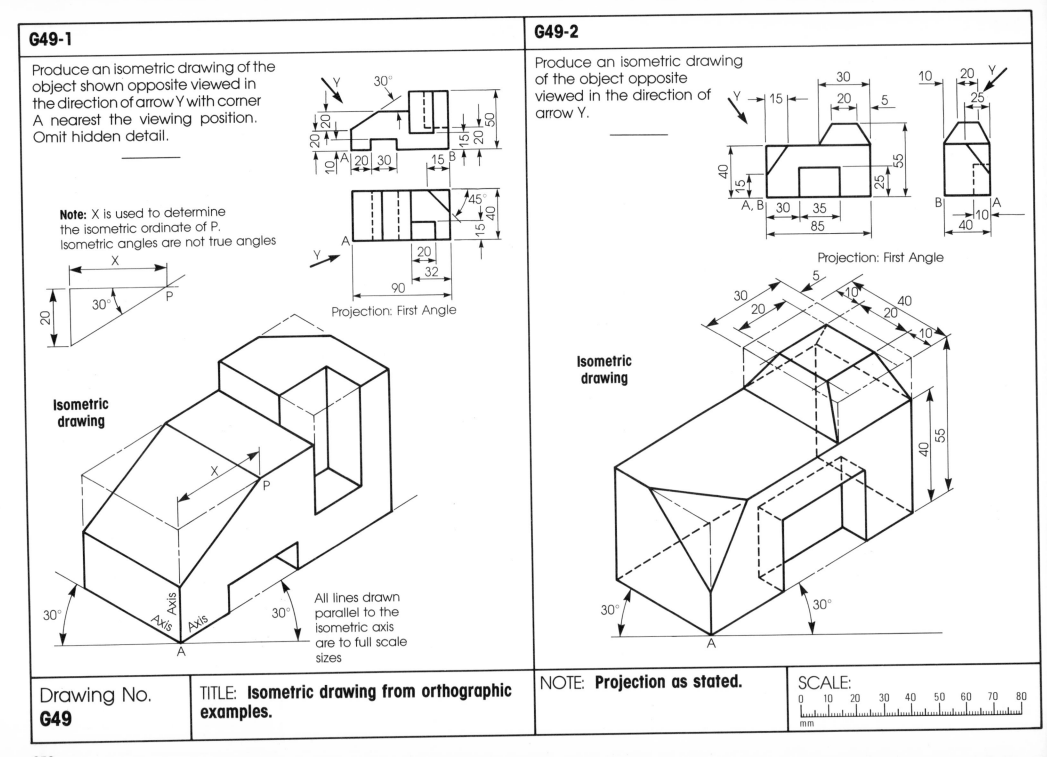

G49-1

Produce an isometric drawing of the object shown opposite viewed in the direction of arrow Y with corner A nearest the viewing position. Omit hidden detail.

Note: X is used to determine the isometric ordinate of P. Isometric angles are not true angles

Projection: First Angle

Isometric drawing

All lines drawn parallel to the isometric axis are to full scale sizes

G49-2

Produce an isometric drawing of the object opposite viewed in the direction of arrow Y.

Projection: First Angle

Isometric drawing

Drawing No.
G49

TITLE: **Isometric drawing from orthographic examples.**

NOTE: **Projection as stated.**

SCALE:
0 10 20 30 40 50 60 70 80
mm

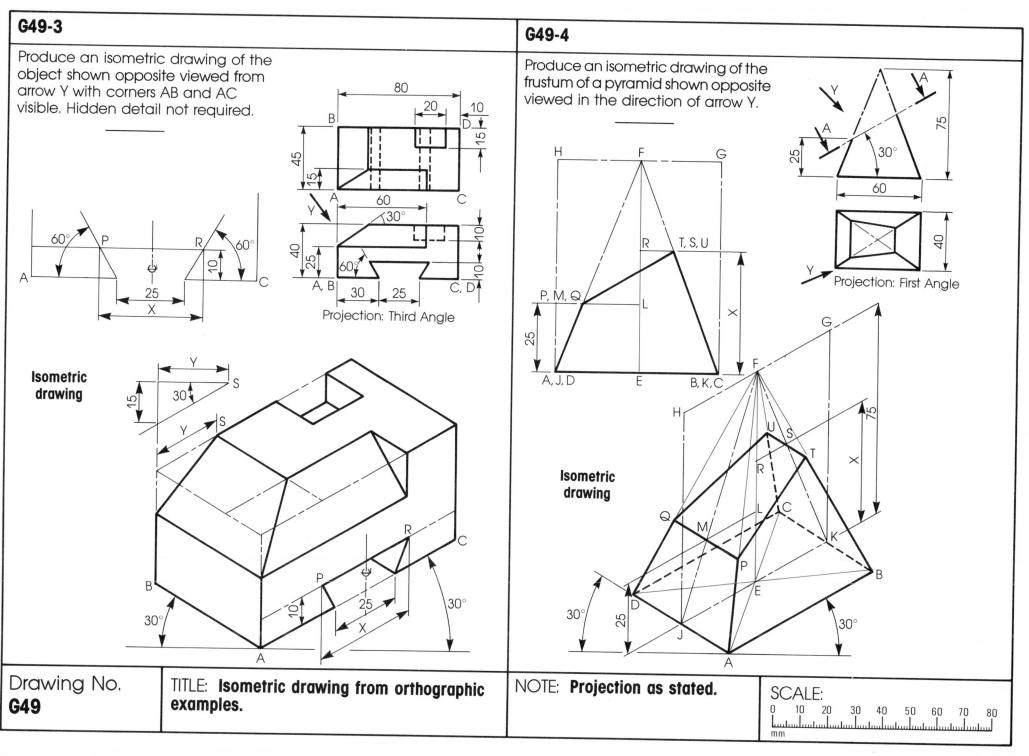

G49-3

Produce an isometric drawing of the object shown opposite viewed from arrow Y with corners AB and AC visible. Hidden detail not required.

80

20

10

B

D

15

45

15

A

60

C

Y

30°

40

25

60°

A, B

30

25

C, D

10

10

Projection: Third Angle

60°

P

R

60°

A

C

10

25

X

Isometric drawing

Y

S

15

30°

Y

S

R

C

B

P

10

25

30°

30°

X

A

G49-4

Produce an isometric drawing of the frustum of a pyramid shown opposite viewed in the direction of arrow Y.

Y

A

A

75

25

30°

60

Projection: First Angle

40

Y

H

F

G

R

T, S, U

P, M, Q

L

X

25

A, J, D

E

B, K, C

G

F

H

75

U

S

X

R

T

Isometric drawing

Q

M

L

C

K

P

B

30°

E

30°

25

D

J

A

Drawing No. **G49**

TITLE: **Isometric drawing from orthographic examples.**

NOTE: **Projection as stated.**

SCALE:

0 10 20 30 40 50 60 70 80

mm

253

G49-5

Produce an oblique drawing, viewed from the direction of arrow W, of the object shown opposite. Use the 45° cabinet method with edge AB horizontal.

Projection: First Angle

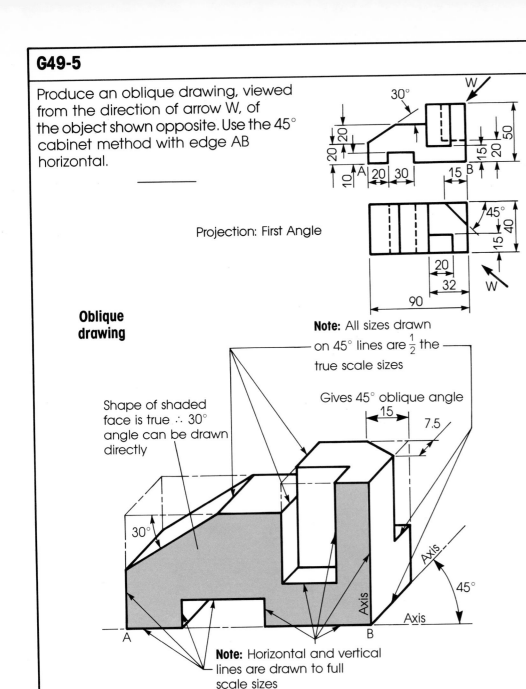

Oblique drawing

Note: All sizes drawn on 45° lines are ½ the true scale sizes

Gives 45° oblique angle

Shape of shaded face is true ∴ 30° angle can be drawn directly

Note: Horizontal and vertical lines are drawn to full scale sizes

G49-6

Produce a 45° cabinet oblique drawing of the object shown opposite. The view should be in the direction of arrow Y with AB horizontal.

Projection: First Angle

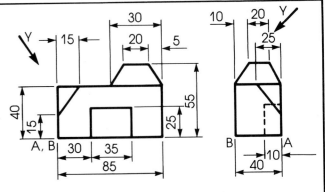

Oblique drawing

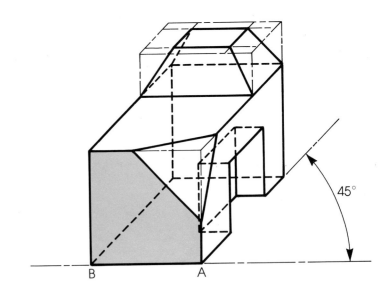

Drawing No.
G49

TITLE: **Oblique drawing from orthographic examples.**

NOTE: **Projection as stated.**

SCALE:
0 10 20 30 40 50 60 70 80
mm

G49-7

Produce an oblique drawing of the object shown opposite and viewed in the direction of arrow W, with BD horizontal and visible.

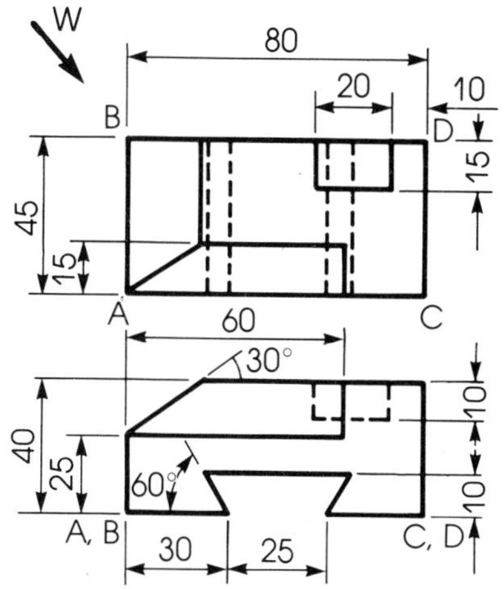

W

80

20

10

B

D

45

15

15

A

60

C

30°

40

25

60°

10

10

A, B

30

25

C, D

Projection: Third Angle

Oblique drawing

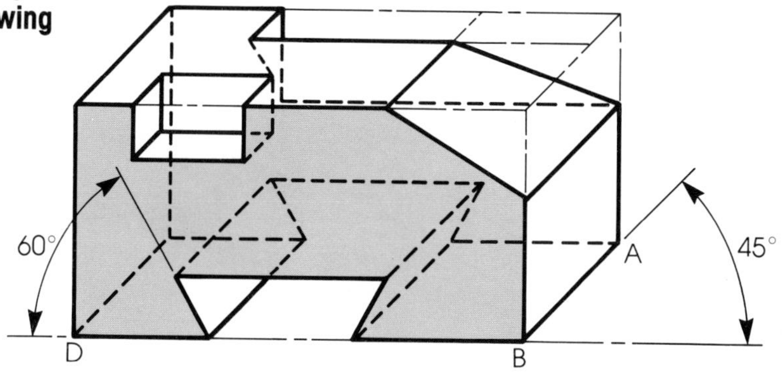

60°

D

A

B

45°

G49-8

Represent the frustrum of a pyramid shown opposite, by an oblique drawing with the view taken in the direction of arrow Y.

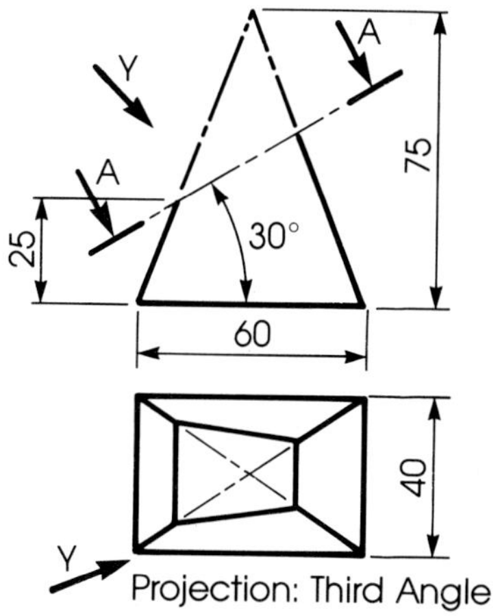

Y

A

A

25

30°

75

60

40

Y

Projection: Third Angle

Note: Point L is determined by the 30° angle from J which intersects KF to give height H

Oblique drawing

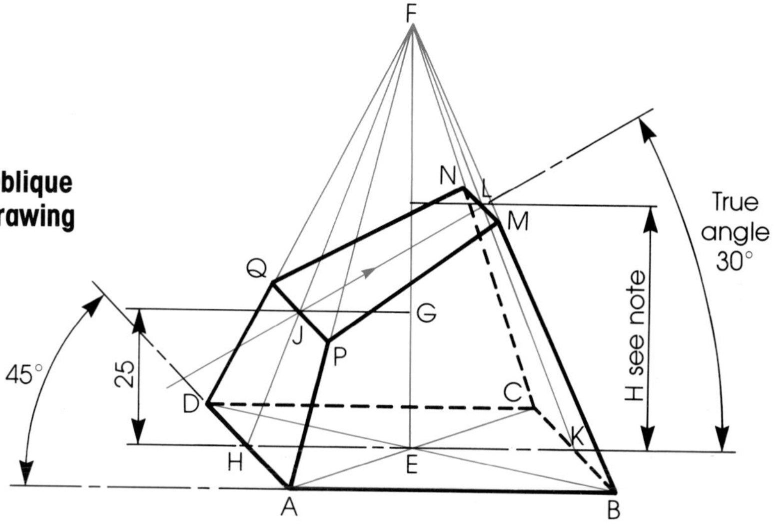

F

N

L

M

True angle 30°

Q

G

J

P

H see note

45°

25

D

C

H

E

K

A

B

None of the faces appears as a true shape

Drawing No. G49	TITLE: **Oblique drawing from orthographic examples.**	NOTE: **Projection as stated.**	SCALE:

SCALE:
0 10 20 30 40 50 60 70 80
mm

G50-1

Produce an isometric drawing of the component shown below with the corner A nearest to the viewing position.

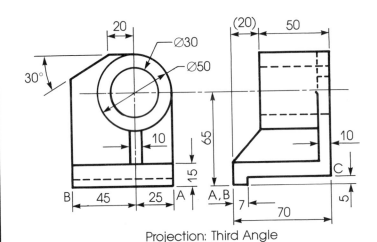

Projection: Third Angle

Isometric drawing

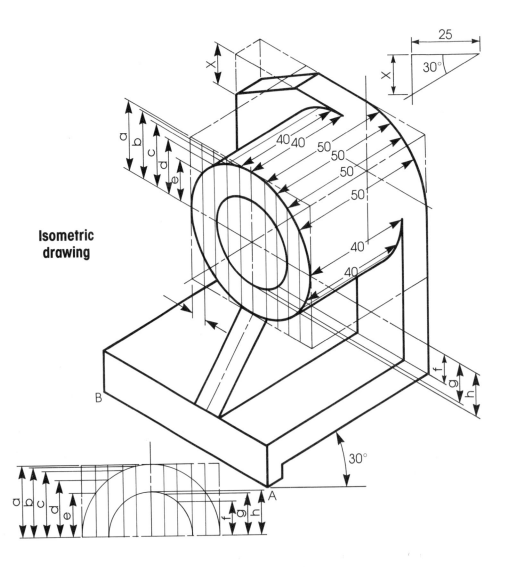

| Drawing No. **G50** | TITLE: **Isometric and oblique examples involving curves.** | NOTE: **Projection as stated.** | SCALE:
0 10 20 30 40 50 60 70 80
mm |

Produce an oblique drawing of the object below
with edge AB horizontal and A, B and C in view.

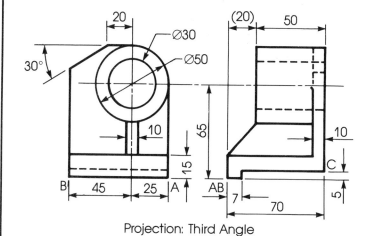

20

⌀30

⌀50

30°

65

10

15

B | 45 | 25 | A

Projection: Third Angle

(20) | 50

10

C

AB

7

70

5

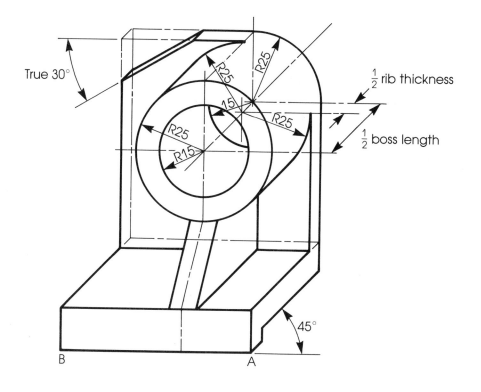

True 30°

R25

R25

R25

45

R25

R15

$\frac{1}{2}$ rib thickness

$\frac{1}{2}$ boss length

45°

B

A

45° cabinet oblique drawing

| Drawing No.
G50 | TITLE: **Isometric and oblique examples involving curves.** | NOTE: **Projection as stated.** | SCALE:
0 10 20 30 40 50 60 70 80
mm |

G50-3

Produce an isometric drawing of the M/C slide shown
below with corner A nearest the viewing position.

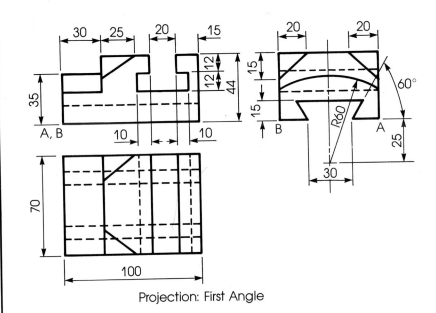

Projection: First Angle

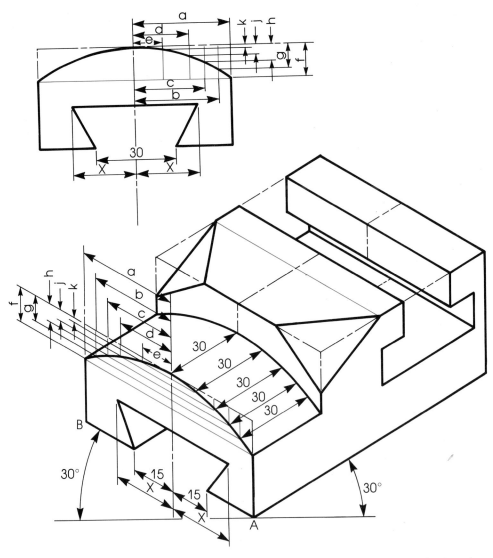

Isometric drawing

Drawing No. **G50**	TITLE: **Isometric and oblique examples involving curves.**	NOTE: **Projection as stated.**	SCALE:

Draw an oblique interpretation of the M/C slide shown
below with the edge AB horizontal.

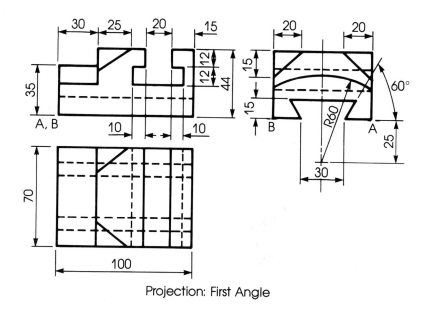

Projection: First Angle

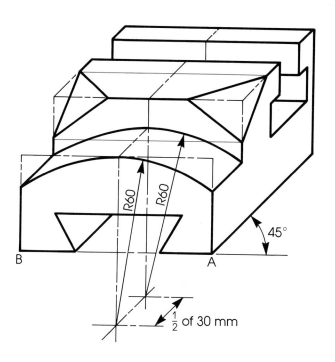

45° cabinet oblique drawing

Drawing No.	TITLE: **Isometric and oblique examples involving curves.**	NOTE: **Projection as stated.**	SCALE:
G50			0 10 20 30 40 50 60 70 80 mm

G50-5

Produce an isometric drawing of the clevis joint shown below viewed from the direction of arrow X and with the centre line represented horizontally.

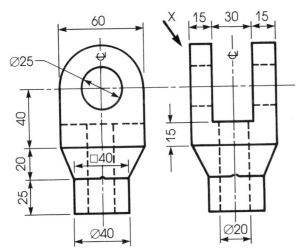

Projection: First or Third Angle

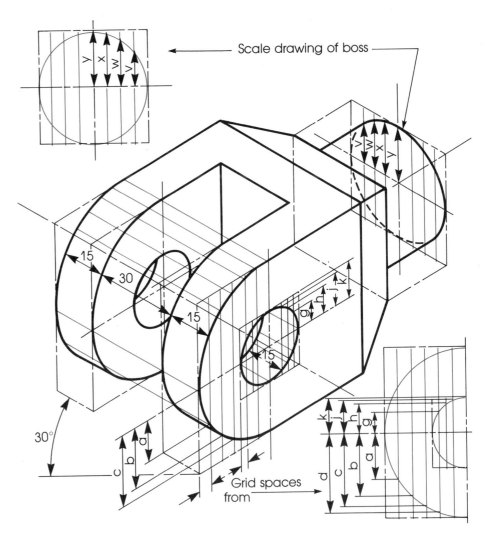

Scale drawing of boss

Grid spaces from

Isometric drawing

Drawing No. **G50**	TITLE: **Isometric and oblique examples involving curves.**	NOTE: **Projection as stated.**	SCALE: 0 10 20 30 40 50 60 70 80 mm

Produce an oblique drawing of the clevis joint below viewed from the direction of arrow Y with the centre line receding at 45°.

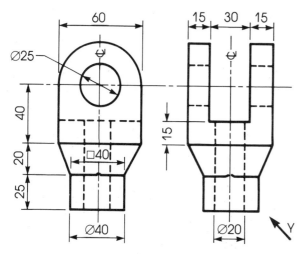

Projection: First or Third Angle

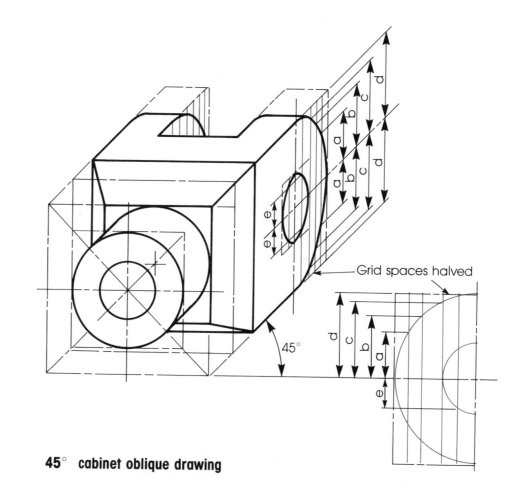

Grid spaces halved

45°

45° cabinet oblique drawing

Drawing No.	TITLE: **Isometric and oblique examples involving curves.**	NOTE: **Projection as stated.**	SCALE:
G50			0 10 20 30 40 50 60 70 80 mm

EXAMINATION-STYLE QUESTIONS

PLANE GEOMETRY

(a) Construct a polygon ABCDE which has the following dimensions: AB = 65 mm, BC = 41 mm, CD = 100 mm, DE = 75 mm, EC = 54 mm, angle ABC = 126° and angle BCD = 114°. A protractor may be used to determine angles.

(b) Divide the polygon drawn in (a) into 3 sections of equal area with 2 straight lines from E. Designate the lines EF and EG.

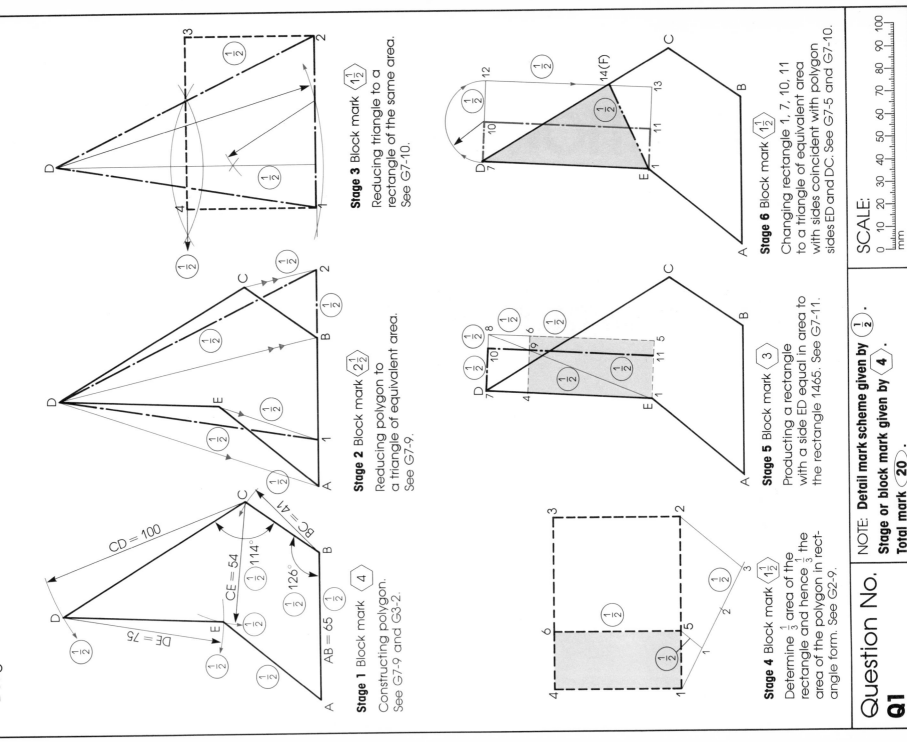

Stage 1 Block mark ⟨4⟩

Constructing polygon.
See G7-9 and G3-2.

Stage 2 Block mark ⟨2½⟩

Reducing polygon to a triangle of equivalent area.
See G7-9.

Stage 3 Block mark ⟨1½⟩

Reducing triangle to a rectangle of the same area.
See G7-10.

Stage 4 Block mark ⟨1½⟩

Determine ⅓ area of the rectangle and hence ⅓ the area of the polygon in rect-angle form. See G2-9.

Stage 5 Block mark ⟨3⟩

Producting a rectangle with a side ED equal in area to the rectangle 1465. See G7-11.

Stage 6 Block mark ⟨1½⟩

Changing rectangle 1, 7, 10, 11 to a triangle of equivalent area with sides coincident with polygon sides ED and DC. See G7-5 and G7-10.

SCALE:

0 10 20 30 40 50 60 70 80 90 100
mm

Question No.
Q1

NOTE: **Detail mark scheme given by** ⟨½⟩ .
Stage or block mark given by ⟨4⟩ .
Total mark ⟨20⟩ .

264

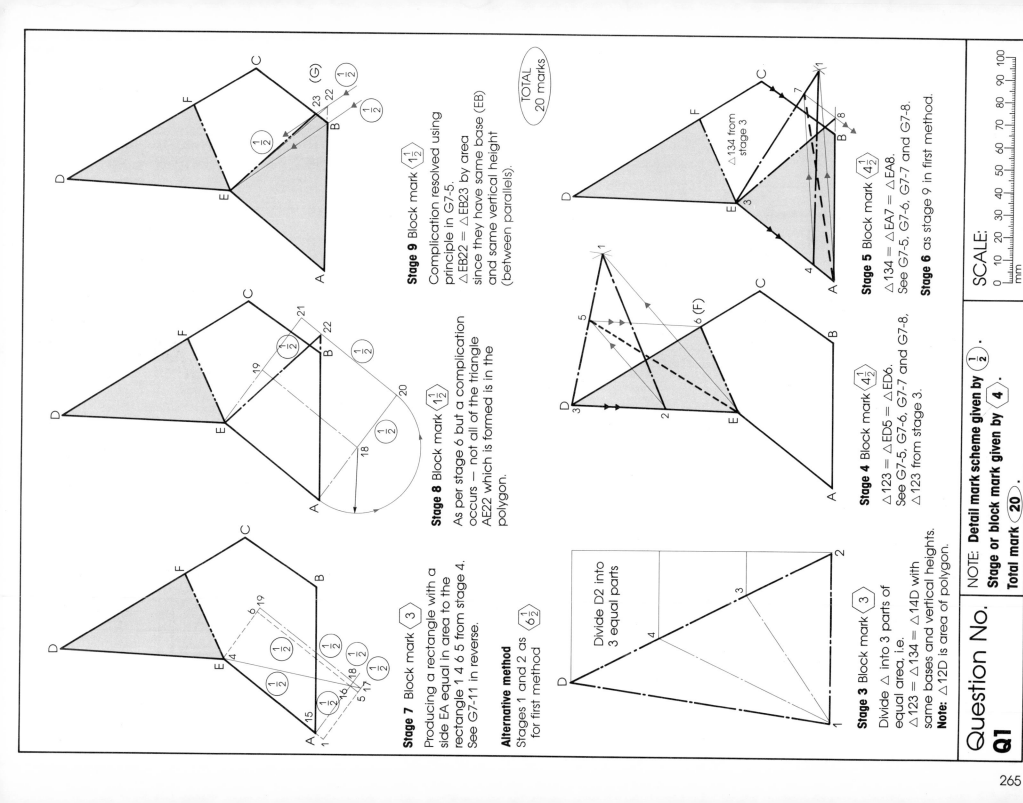

Stage 9 Block mark $\langle 1\frac{1}{2}\rangle$

Complication resolved using principle in G7-5.
△EB22 = △EB23 by area since they have same base (EB) and same vertical height (between parallels).

TOTAL 20 marks

Stage 8 Block mark $\langle 1\frac{1}{2}\rangle$

As per stage 6 but a complication occurs – not all of the triangle AE22 which is formed is in the polygon.

Stage 7 Block mark $\langle 3\rangle$

Producing a rectangle with a side EA equal in area to the rectangle 1 4 6 5 from stage 4.
See G7-11 in reverse.

Alternative method

Stages 1 and 2 as for first method $\langle 6\frac{1}{2}\rangle$

Stage 5 Block mark $\langle 4\frac{1}{2}\rangle$

△134 = △EA7 = △EA8.
See G7-5, G7-6, G7-7 and G7-8.

Stage 6 as stage 9 in first method.

Stage 4 Block mark $\langle 4\frac{1}{2}\rangle$

△123 = △ED5 = △ED6.
See G7-5, G7-6, G7-7 and G7-8.
△123 from stage 3.

Stage 3 Block mark $\langle 3\rangle$

Divide △ into 3 parts of equal area, i.e.
△123 = △134 = △14D with same bases and vertical heights.
Note: △12D is area of polygon.

Divide D2 into 3 equal parts

Question No.
Q1

NOTE: **Detail mark scheme given by** $\langle\frac{1}{2}\rangle$.
Stage or block mark given by $\langle 4\rangle$.
Total mark $\langle 20\rangle$.

SCALE:

mm
0 10 20 30 40 50 60 70 80 90 100

265

(a) Construct a rectangle which has a side of 87 mm and an area equal to that of a square which has a side of 50 mm.

(b) Construct a right-angled triangle which has a base of 100 mm and an area equal to that of an equilateral triangle which has a side of 70 mm.

(c) Construct an obtuse-angled triangle which has the same base and area as the right-angled triangle in (b) but with one of its other sides 47 mm long.

(d) Draw a square ABCD which has a side of 55 mm and a centre E. Construct a square equal in area to the irregular pentagon ABCDE; that is the square with triangle AED removed.

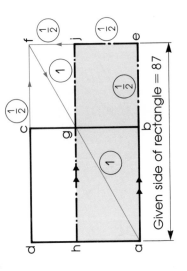

Part (a) Block mark ⟨4⟩

See G8-8 but reverse the method.
See G3-6 to find centre, f, of the semicircle.

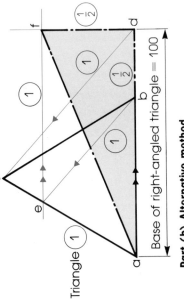

Part (b) Block mark ⟨5⟩

See G7-11 for proof of method when considering rectangles.
See G7-10 to understand why it also applies to triangles.

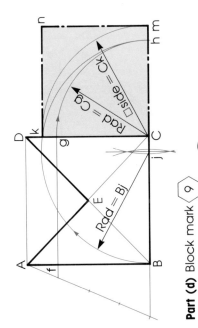

Part (c) Block mark ⟨2⟩

See G7-5.

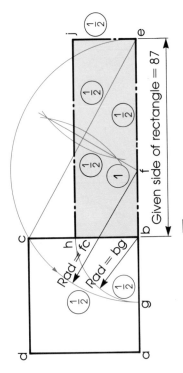

Part (a) Alternative method
See G7-11.

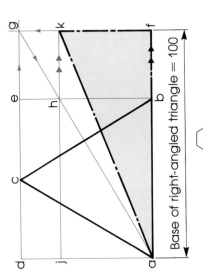

Triangle ①

Part (b) Alternative method
See G7-6, G7-7 and G7-8.

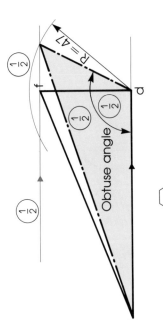

Part (d) Block mark ⟨9⟩

② marks for ABCDE plus ③ marks for reducing polygon ABCDE to rectangle BCgf (see G2-9) and ④ marks for reducing rectangle BCgf to square Cknm (see G8-8).

(TOTAL 20 marks)

Question No. | NOTE: **Lower case letter sequence gives order of construction.**

Q2

SCALE:

0 10 20 30 40 50 60 70 80 90 100
mm

266

(a) Produce the largest rectangle having sides in the ratio of 1:2.5 which is circumscribed by a circle of diameter 86 mm.

(b) Construct the plan of a rectangular plot of land which has sides of 32.5 m and 23.5 m to a scale of 1:500.

(c) If it costs £236 to fence the perimeter of the plot of land described in (b) determine, completely by construction, the cost of fencing a similar rectangular plot which has an area 2¼ times greater.

Part (a) Block mark ⟨4⟩

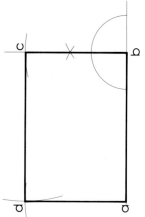

Start with any rectangle which has sides in the ratio of 2.5:1, e.g. ab = 100, bc = 40.
See G9 for similar figures, also G4-5.

Part (b) Block mark ⟨4⟩

⟨2⟩ marks for construction plus ⟨2⟩ marks for calculating scale sizes. See G11-1 and G6-4.

Scale length of ab = $\dfrac{32\,500\ mm}{500}$ = 65 mm.

bc = $\dfrac{23\,500\ mm}{500}$ = 47 mm.

Side of new rectangle with 2¼ times the area

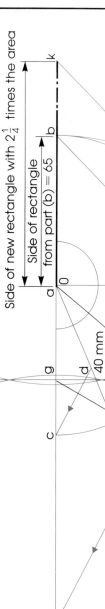

Part (c) Stage 1 Block mark ⟨6⟩

Determining proportional increase in length of side for a given proportional increase in area. See G9-5. **Note:** increase in perimeter is in same proportion as increase in side. The length of side of any polygon will increase in proportion by the root of the proportional increase in area, i.e. linear increase = √$2\frac{1}{4}$ = 1.5.
See ratio of ab:ak constructed above, i.e. 65:97.5 = 1:1.5. The cost derived arithmetically for the increased length of perimeter = 1.5 × £236 = £354.

Ratio of areas = $2\frac{1}{4}$:1 or 9:4, i.e. a linear ratio of 90 mm to 40 mm is used to obtain points e and d

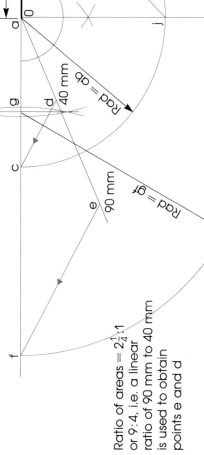

Part (c) Stage 2 Block mark ⟨6⟩

See G2-9 to G2-13 and G11-8.

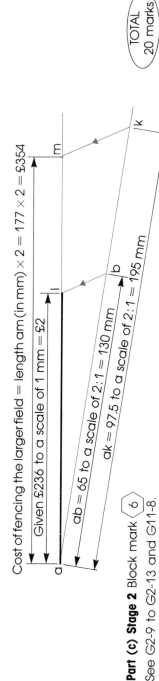

Cost of fencing the larger field = length am (in mm) × 2 = 177 × 2 = £354
Given £236 to a scale of 1 mm = £2
ab = 65 to a scale of 2:1 = 130 mm
ak = 97.5 to a scale of 2:1 = 195 mm

Question No. Q3

NOTE: **Lower case letter sequence gives order of construction.**

SCALE:

0 10 20 30 40 50 60 70 80 90 100
mm

TOTAL 20 marks

267

(a) Construct a regular pentagon given that it has diagonals of 95 mm.
(b) Construct a regular pentagon given that it has a perimeter of 207 mm.
(c) Construct a regular pentagon which is inscribed by a circle of diameter 90 mm.

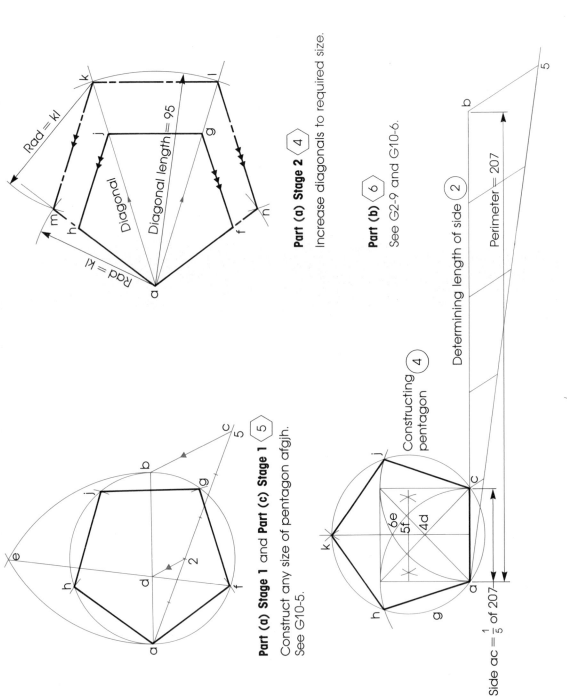

Rad = kl

Diagonal length = 95

Diagonal

Diagonal

Rad = kl

Part (a) Stage 2 ④

Increase diagonals to required size.

Part (b) ⑥

See G2-9 and G10-6.

Determining length of side ②

Perimeter = 207

Constructing pentagon ④

Side ac = 1/5 of 207

6e
5f
4d

Part (a) Stage 1 and **Part (c) Stage 1** ⑤

Construct any size of pentagon afgjh.
See G10-5.

Part (c) Stage 2 ⑤

Reproducing pentagon afgjh from stage 1.
See G3-8 and G10.

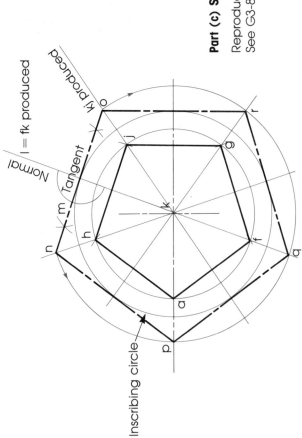

Normal

kl produced

l = fk produced

m Tangent

Inscribing circle

Question No.
Q4

NOTE: **Lower case letter sequence gives order of construction.**

SCALE:
0 10 20 30 40 50 60 70 80 90 100
mm

TOTAL
20 marks

268

(a) Construct a regular heptagon (septagon) which is circumscribed by a circle of diameter 110 mm.

(b) Produce a regular heptagon which has an area of $\frac{9}{25}$ of the heptagon described in part (a).

(c) Determine by construction the length of side of a regular polygon which has an area double that of a regular polygon of side 40 mm.

(d) Construct a triangle having sides of 53 mm, 110 mm and 80 mm and produce a second triangle which has the same shortest side and area as the given triangle but is also circumscribed by a circle 85 mm in diameter.

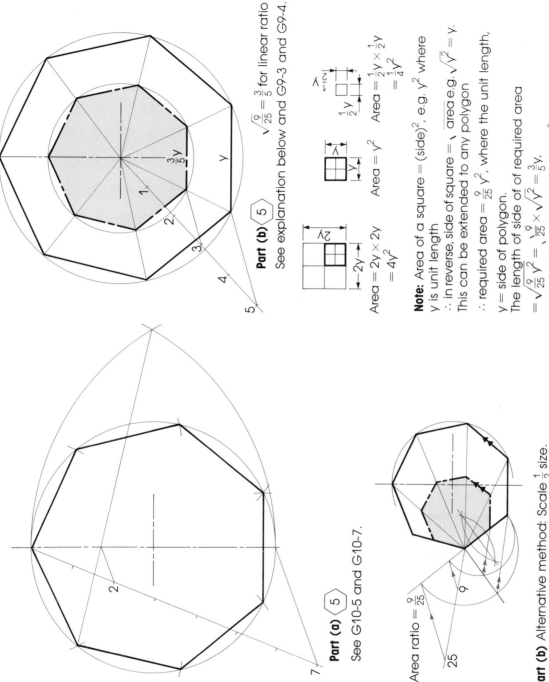

Part (a) ⬡ 5

See G10-5 and G10-7.

Part (b) ⬡ 5

See explanation below and G9-3 and G9-4.

$\sqrt{\frac{9}{25}} = \frac{3}{5}$ for linear ratio

Area = $2y \times 2y$
= $4y^2$

Area = y^2

Area = $\frac{1}{2}y \times \frac{1}{2}y$
= $\frac{1}{4}y^2$

Note: Area of a square = (side)^2, e.g. y^2 where y is unit length

∴ in reverse, side of square = $\sqrt{\text{area}}$ e.g. $\sqrt{y^2} = y$. This can be extended to any polygon

∴ required area = $\frac{9}{25}y^2$, where the unit length, y = side of polygon.

The length of side of of required area
= $\sqrt{\frac{9}{25}y^2} = \sqrt{\frac{9}{25}} \times \sqrt{y^2} = \frac{3}{5}y$,
i.e. the side of new polygon is $\frac{3}{5}$ of original, y.

Part (c) ⬡ 5

See G9-5 and G9-6.

Area ratio = $\frac{9}{25}$

Part (b) Alternative method: Scale $\frac{1}{2}$ size.
See G9-7.

Side = 56.5
ab = 40

Part (d) ⬡ 5

See G7-5.

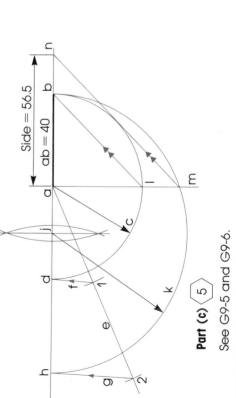

R = 42.5

110

80

Smallest side = 53

TOTAL
20 marks

Question No.
Q5

NOTE: **Lower case letter sequence gives order of construction.**

SCALE:

0 10 20 30 40 50 60 70 80 90 100
mm

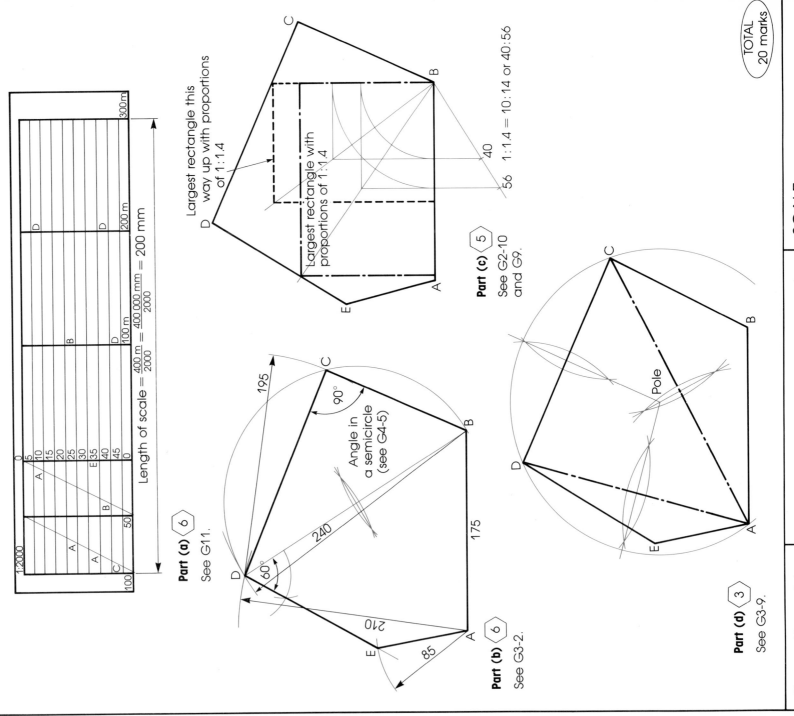

(a) Produce a diagonal scale of 1:2000 to read to a maximum of 400 m in 100 m, 50 m and 5 m increments.

(b) Use the scale produced in (a) to construct the plan of a piece of land which takes the form of an irregular polygon ABCDE with AB = 175 m, AD = 210 m, BD = 240 m, CD = 195 m, AE = 85 m, ∠BCD = 90° and ∠BDE = 60° with angle BAE being obtuse.

(c) Produce the largest rectangular sports area which fits on the land ABCDE, has sides in the ratio of 1:1.4 and has one side coincident with side AB of the polygon.

(d) Determine the position of a survey pole which is equal in distance to the corners ACD of the land.

Length of scale = $\dfrac{400\ m}{2000} = \dfrac{400\,000\ mm}{2000} = 200\ mm$

Part (a) 6

See G11.

Part (b) 6

See G3-2.

Angle in a semicircle (see G4-5)

Part (c) 5

See G2-10 and G9.

Largest rectangle this way up with proportions of 1:1.4

Largest rectangle with proportions of 1:1.4

1:1.4 = 10:14 or 40:56

Part (d) 3

See G3-9.

Pole

Question No.
Q6

(TOTAL 20 marks)

SCALE:

270

(a) Construct an ellipse given that 3 points A, B and C are on the ellipse with AB, the major axis, being 150 mm long, AC = 120 mm and BC = 60 mm.

(b) Construct a tangent to the ellipse at the point C.

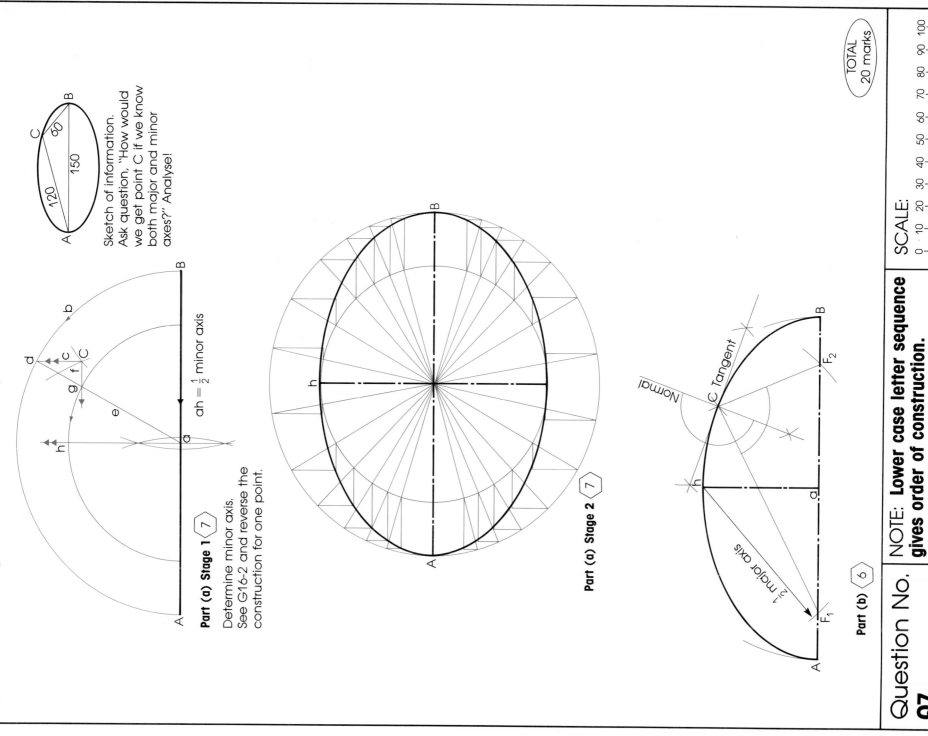

Sketch of information. Ask question, "How would we get point C if we know both major and minor axes?" Analyse!

Part (a) Stage 1 ⟨7⟩

Determine minor axis. See G16-2 and reverse the construction for one point.

ah = ½ minor axis

Part (a) Stage 2 ⟨7⟩

Part (b) ⟨6⟩

Question No.	NOTE: **Lower case letter sequence gives order of construction.**	SCALE:
Q7		

(TOTAL 20 marks)

271

(a) Produce a rectangle ABCD with AB = 120 mm and BC = 85 mm. Using AB as the directrix construct a parabola which passes through corners C and D.

(b) Produce a rectangle WXYZ with WX = 140 mm and XY = 70 mm. Using WX as the directrix and a focal point 20 mm from WX, construct a hyperbola which terminates at Y and Z.

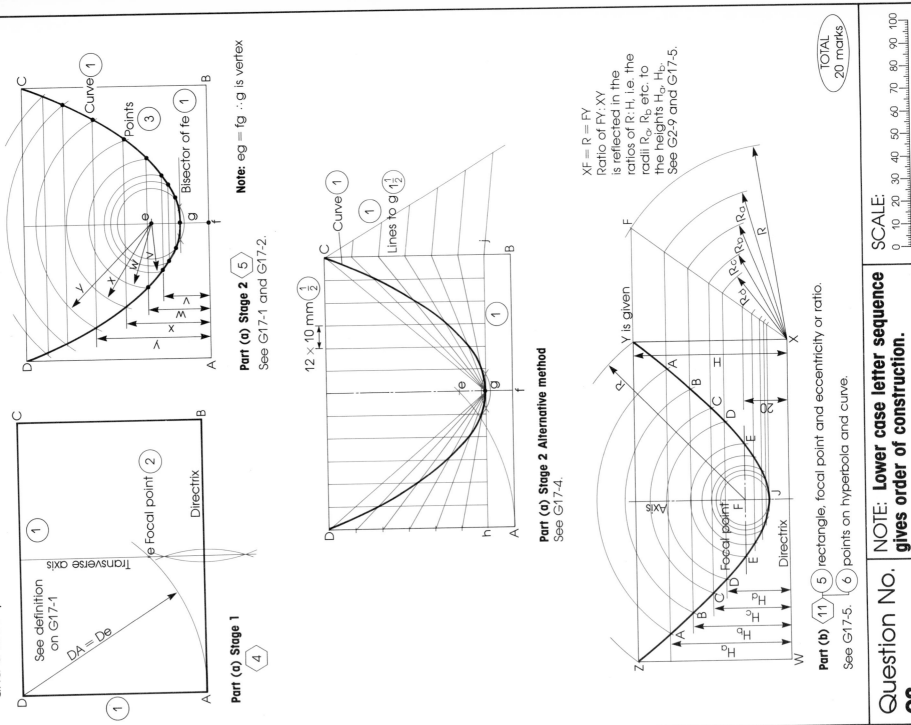

Part (a) Stage 1 ⬡4

See definition on G17-1

DA = De

Focal point e ②

Transverse axis

Directrix

Part (a) Stage 2 ⬡5

See G17-1 and G17-2.

Curve ① Points ③ Bisector of fe ①

Note: eg = fg ∴ g is vertex

Part (a) Stage 2 Alternative method

See G17-4.

12 × 10 mm ½

Curve ① Lines to g (1½) ① ½ ①

Part (b) ⟨11⟩ ⬡5

See G17-5.

⬡5 rectangle, focal point and eccentricity or ratio.

⬡6 points on hyperbola and curve.

XF = R = FY
Ratio of FY:XY is reflected in the ratios of R:H, i.e. the radii Rₐ, R_b etc. to the heights Hₐ, H_b.
See G2-9 and G17-5.

Y is given

Axis Focal point F Directrix

Question No. | **NOTE: Lower case letter sequence gives order of construction.**

Q8

SCALE:
0 10 20 30 40 50 60 70 80 90 100 mm

TOTAL 20 marks

272

Fig 1 shows a disc, diameter 70 mm, which is to roll without slipping around a triangle ABC which has sides in the ratio of 3:4:5 and a perimeter equal to the circumference of the disc.
Plot the locus of point P on the disc for one complete revolution with P starting and finishing in the position shown in Fig 1.

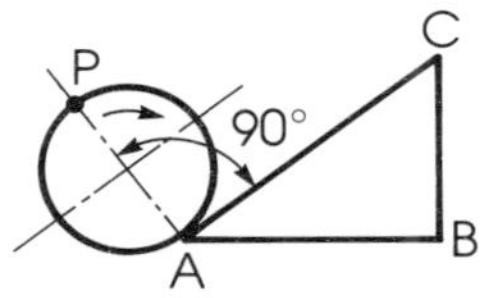

BC:AB:CA = 3:4:5

Fig 1

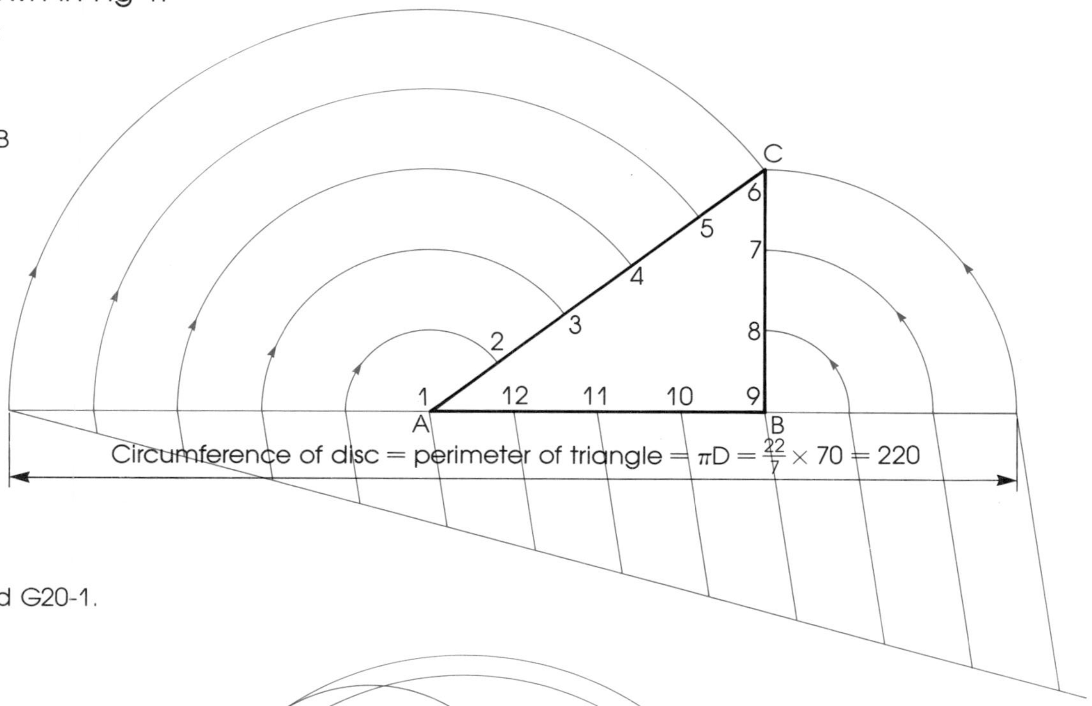

Circumference of disc = perimeter of triangle = $\pi D = \frac{22}{7} \times 70 = 220$

Stage 1 ⟨6⟩

See G2-13 and G20-1.

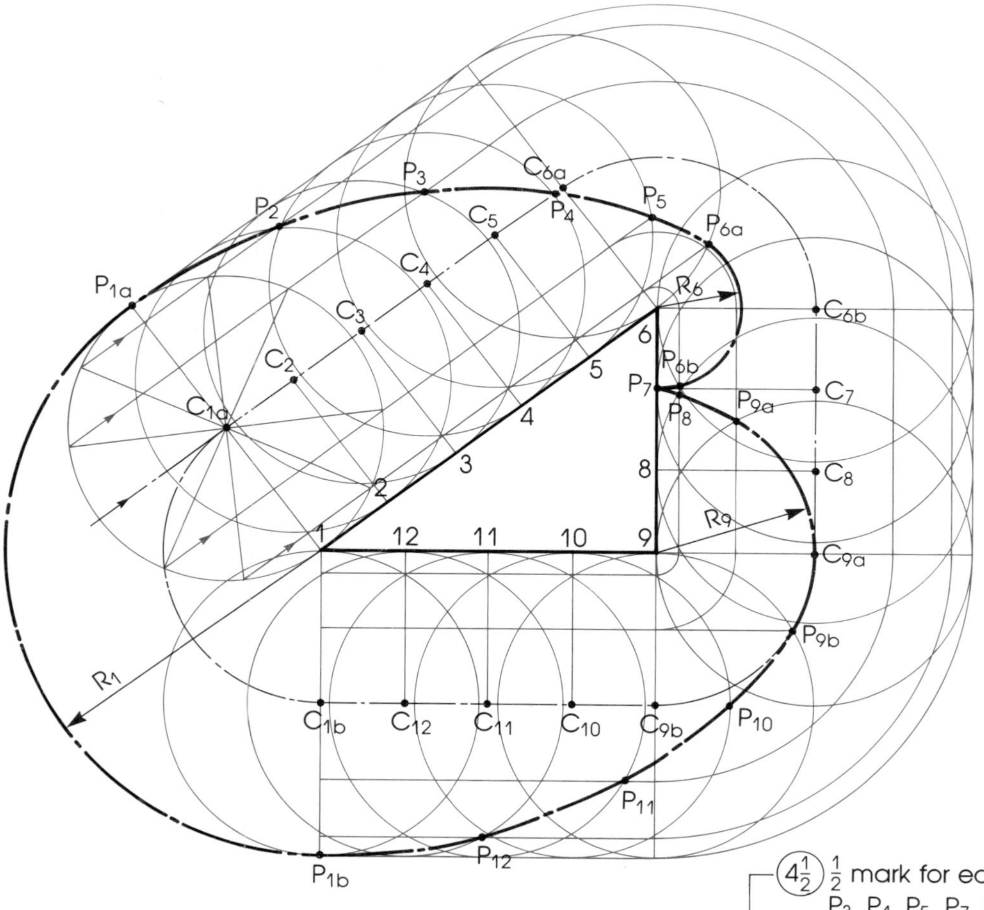

Stage 2 ⟨14⟩

⟨3⟩ $\frac{1}{2}$ mark each for P_{1a}, P_{1b}, P_{6a}, P_{6b}, P_{9a}, P_{9b}.

⟨2⟩ all disc centres C_{1a}, C_2, C_3 etc. —·—·—·—

⟨$4\frac{1}{2}$⟩ $\frac{1}{2}$ mark for each point P_2 P_3, P_4, P_5, P_7, P_8, P_{10}, P_{11}, P_{12}.

⟨$1\frac{1}{2}$⟩ cycloidal curve.

⟨3⟩ 1 mark each for arcs P_{6a} to P_{6b}, P_{9a} to P_{9b} and P_{1b} to P_{1a}.

⟨TOTAL 20 marks⟩

Question No.
Q9

SCALE:

mm

273

Construct a triangle ABC with AB = 90 mm, BC = 80 mm and CA = 70 mm. Draw a circle of diameter 50 mm with A as its centre, a circle of diameter 30 mm with B as its centre and a circle of diameter 60 mm with C as its centre.
Determine, using loci, the centre and diameter of a circle which will circumscribe the 3 given circles as shown in Fig 1.

Fig 1

Theory: See Figs (a) and (b) and G12-17.
Point P_1 is the centre of a circle having a radius R_1 which will touch the circles A and B at S and T. Since ST is the common normal, S to P_1 equals T to P_1, i.e. P_1 bisects ST. If R_1 is increased to R_2 then its centre P_2 is $R_2 - R_a$ from A and $R_2 - R_b$ from B. See G12-17, where R_2 can be any convenient size. If R_2 is now increased to R_3 then its centre P_3 is $R_3 - R_a$ from A and $R_3 - R_b$ from B, i.e. we can determine P for any circle R_X which touches A and B. See R_3 in Fig (b), and Table A for stage 1 locus. The circle with the smallest radius R_1 to touch both circles A and B has a radius

$$R_1 = \frac{R_a + R_b + (A \text{ to } B)}{2}$$

$$R_1 = \frac{25 + 15 + 90}{2}$$

$$R_1 = 65$$

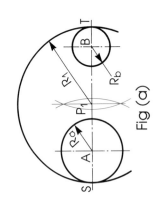

Fig (a)

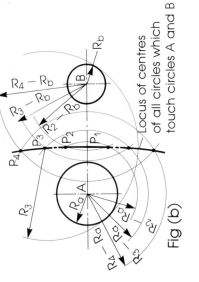

Locus of centres of all circles which touch circles A and B

Fig (b)

Table A (used in stage 1)

R_X	R_a	R_b	A to P = $R_X - R_a$	B to P = $R_X - R_b$
65	25	15	65 − 25 = 40	65 − 15 = 50
70	25	15	70 − 25 = 45	70 − 15 = 55
75	25	15	75 − 25 = 50	75 − 15 = 60
80	25	15	80 − 25 = 55	80 − 15 = 65
90	25	15	90 − 25 = 65	90 − 15 = 75

Question No. **Q10**

NOTE: **Letter sequence gives order of construction.**

SCALE:

0 10 20 30 40 50 60 70 80 90 100
mm

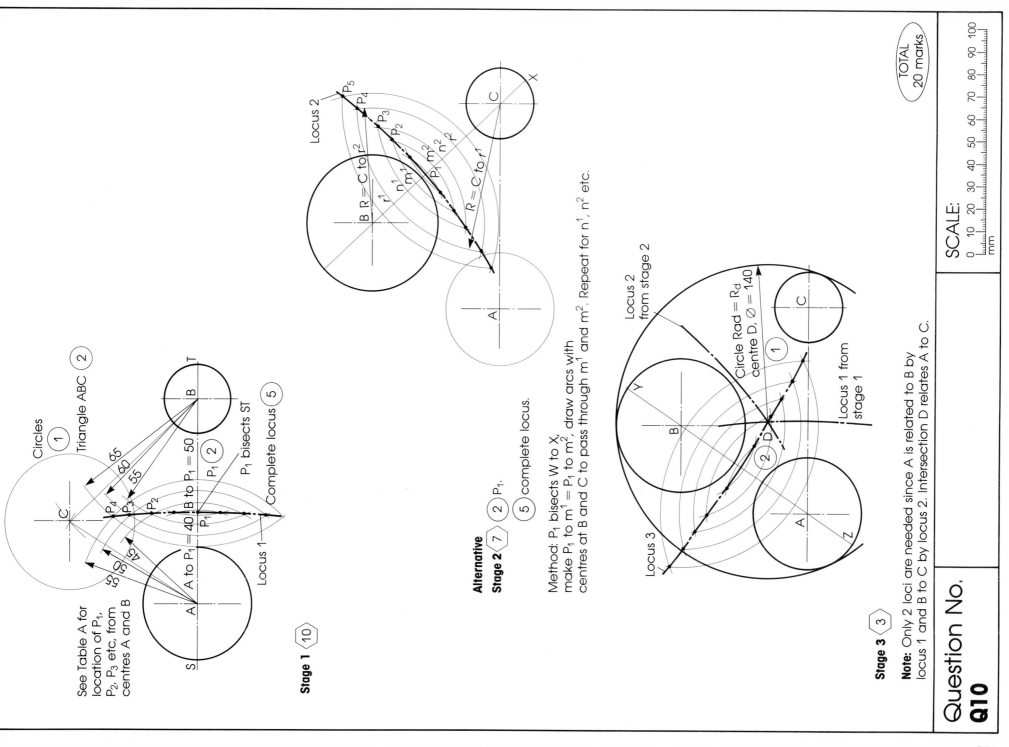

Circles ①

Triangle ABC ②

See Table A for location of P₁, P₂, P₃ etc, from centres A and B

65
60
55
50
45

A to P₁ = 40. B to P₁ = 50 ②

P₁ bisects ST

Locus 1

Complete locus ⑤

Stage 1 ⑩

Locus 2

B R = C to r²

r^1 r^2
n^1 m^2
m^1 P_1 n^2
P_1 m^2
P_2
P_3
P_4
P_5

R = C to r¹

Alternative
Stage 2 ⑦ ② P₁.

⑤ complete locus.

Method: P₁ bisects W to X,
make P₁ to m¹ = P₁ to m², draw arcs with
centres at B and C to pass through m¹ and m². Repeat for n¹, n² etc.

Locus 2
from stage 2

Circle Rad = R_d
centre D, ⌀ = 140

①

② D

Locus 1 from
stage 1

Locus 3

Stage 3 ③

Note: Only 2 loci are needed since A is related to B by
locus 1 and B to C by locus 2. Intersection D relates A to C.

Question No.
Q10

SCALE:

0 10 20 30 40 50 60 70 80 90 100
mm

TOTAL
20 marks

275

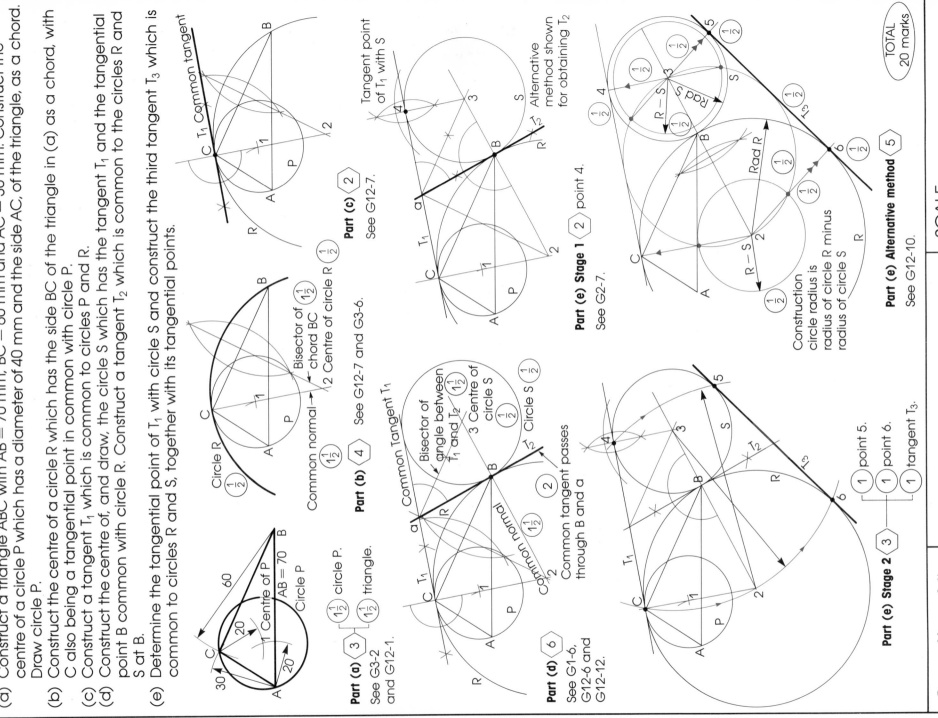

(a) Construct a triangle ABC with AB = 70 mm, BC = 60 mm and AC = 30 mm. Construct the centre of a circle P which has a diameter of 40 mm and the side AC, of the triangle, as a chord. Draw circle P.

(b) Construct the centre of a circle R which has the side BC of the triangle in (a) as a chord, with C also being a tangential point in common with circle P.

(c) Construct a tangent T_1 which is common to circles P and R.

(d) Construct the centre of, and draw, the circle S which has the tangent T_1 and the tangential point B common with circle R. Construct a tangent T_2 which is common to the circles R and S at B.

(e) Determine the tangential point of T_1 with circle S and construct the third tangent T_3 which is common to circles R and S, together with its tangential points.

Part (a) ⬡3
See G3-2
and G12-1.

(1½) circle P.
(1½) triangle.

Circle P

Centre of P
AB = 70
30
20
20
20
C
A
B
60

Part (b) ⬡4   See G12-7 and G3-6.

Circle R
C
A
P
B

Bisector of chord BC (1½)
Centre of circle R (1½)

Common normal (1½)

Part (c) ⬡2
See G12-7.

C T_1 Common tangent
R
P
A
B
1
2

Part (d) ⬡6
See G1-6,
G12-6 and
G12-12.

a Common Tangent T_1
C T_1
R
P
A
B
1
2
Common normal T_2

Bisector of angle between T_1 and T_2 (1½)
Centre of circle S (1½)
Circle S (1½)
T_2
Common tangent passes through B and a (2)

T_1
C
P
A
B
R
1
2
3
S
T_2
T_3
4
5
6

point 5. (1)
point 6. (1)
tangent T_3. (1)

Part (c) ⬡2
See G12-7.

C T_1
P
A
B
R
1
2
3
S
Tangent point of T_1 with S
4
Alternative method for obtaining T_2

Part (e) Stage 1 ⬡2 point 4.
See G2-7.

C
A
P
B
R – S
R – S
2
Rad R
Rad S
R – S
3
S
R
4
5
6
T_3
(½) (½) (½) (½) (½) (½) (½) (½)

Construction circle radius is radius of circle R minus radius of circle S

Part (e) Alternative method ⬡5
See G12-10.

Part (e) Stage 2 ⬡3

(TOTAL 20 marks)

SCALE:
mm
0 10 20 30 40 50 60 70 80 90 100

Question No.
Q11

276

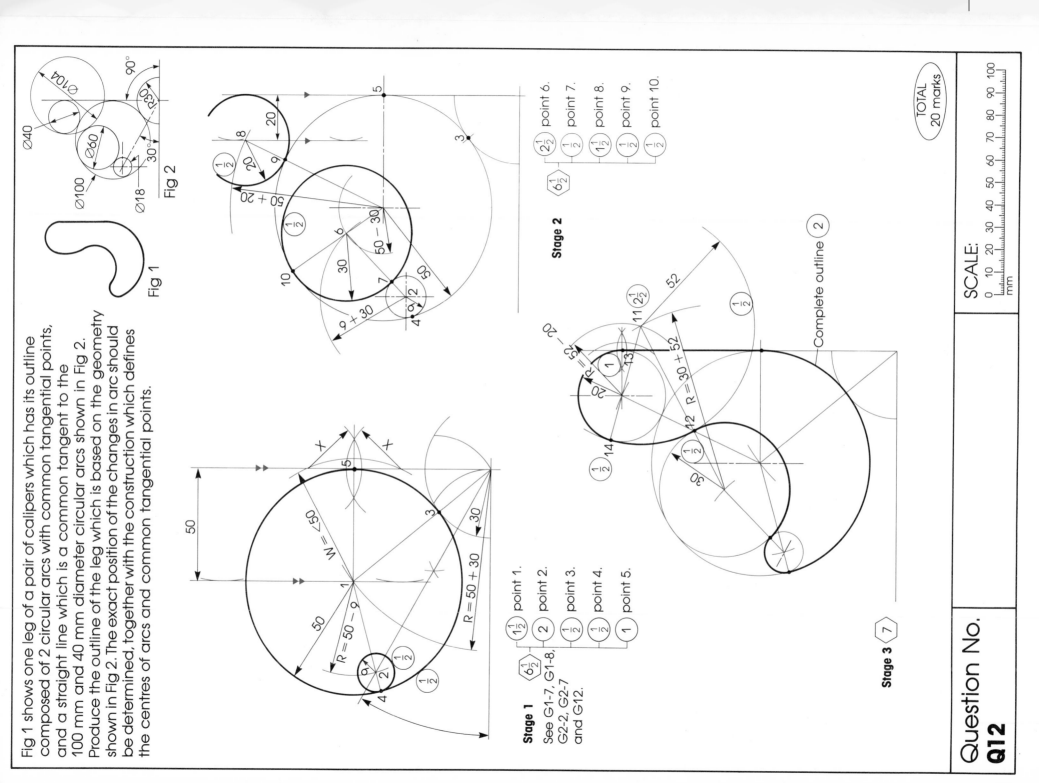

Fig 1 shows one leg of a pair of calipers which has its outline composed of 2 circular arcs with common tangential points, and a straight line which is a common tangent to the 100 mm and 40 mm diameter circular arcs shown in Fig 2.

Produce the outline of the leg which is based on the geometry shown in Fig 2. The exact position of the changes in arc should be determined, together with the construction which defines the centres of arcs and common tangential points.

Fig 1

Fig 2

∅40 ∅104 90° R30 30° ∅60 ∅100 ∅18

Stage 1

See G1-7, G1-8, G2-2, G2-7 and G12.

⬡6½

1½ point 1.
2 point 2.
½ point 3.
½ point 4.
1 point 5.

Stage 2

⬡6½

2½ point 6.
½ point 7.
1½ point 8.
½ point 9.
½ point 10.

Stage 3 ⟨7⟩

Complete outline ②

Question No.
Q12

SCALE:

0 10 20 30 40 50 60 70 80 90 100
mm

TOTAL
20 marks

277

(a) Two circles, which have centres Y and Z and diameters of 80 mm and 40 mm respectively, are located on the same side of a straight line WX with WX-to-Y = 65 mm and WX-to-Z = 40 mm. The distance between centres Y and Z is 103 mm. Draw the line and the circles at Y and Z.

(b) Determine the centre of, and draw a third circle, which lies between the 2 given circles and the line WX, has WX as a tangent and has tangential points in common with the circles at Y and Z. Determine the common tangential points of the third circle with the circles at Y and Z and the point of contact between the circle and the line WX.

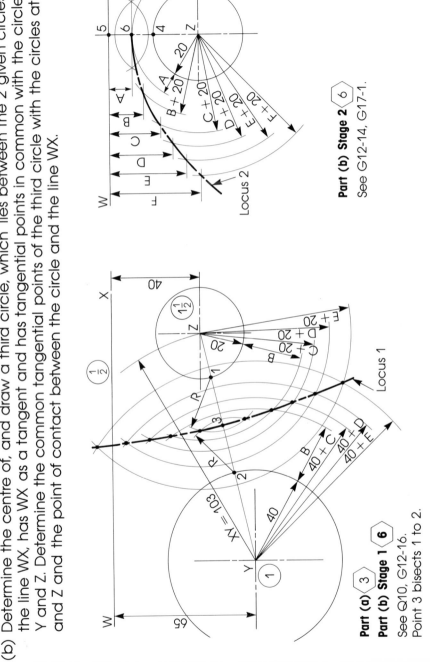

Part (a) ③

Part (b) Stage 1 ⑥

See Q10, G12-16.
Point 3 bisects 1 to 2.

Part (b) Stage 2 ⑥

See G12-14, G17-1.

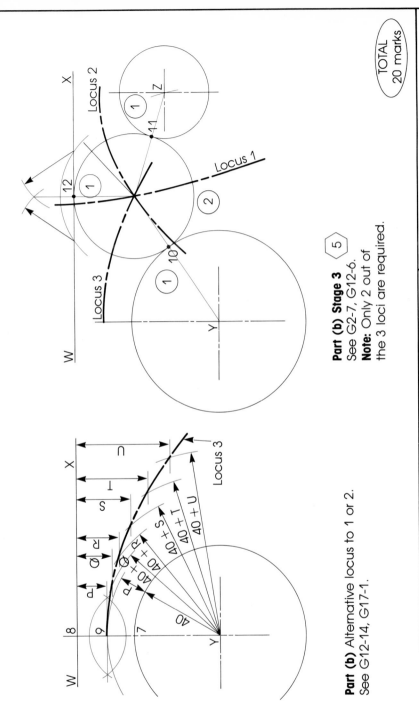

Part (b) Stage 3 ⑤

See G2-7, G12-6.
Note: Only 2 out of the 3 loci are required.

Part (b) Alternative locus to 1 or 2.
See G12-14, G17-1.

Question No.
Q13

SCALE:

0 10 20 30 40 50 60 70 80 90 100
mm

(TOTAL
20 marks)

278

Two centres A and B are 70 mm apart with A positioned horizontally to the left of B. A rod AD which rotates about A is positioned vertically above A and a rod BC which rotates about B is positioned with C to the right of B and BC horizontal. AD is 99 mm long and BC is 70 mm long. D starts to rotate with a clockwise uniform angular velocity about A at the same instant that C starts to rotate about B with an anticlockwise uniform angular velocity, which is double the angular velocity of DA (CB completes 2 revolutions whilst AD completes one revolution). Plot the complete locus of the points of intersection of the rods during one complete revolution of AD.

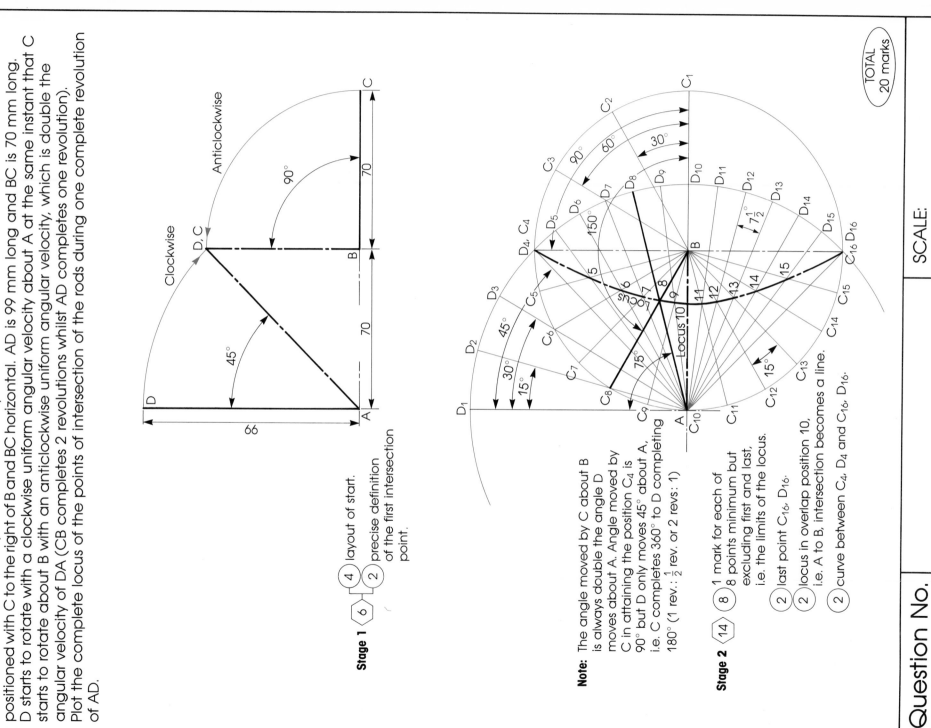

Stage 1 ⬡6 ⟨4⟩ layout of start.

⟨2⟩ precise definition of the first intersection point.

Note: The angle moved by C about B is always double the angle D moves about A. Angle moved by C in attaining the position C_4 is 90° but D only moves 45° about A, i.e. C completes 360° to D completing 180° (1 rev.: $\frac{1}{2}$ rev. or 2 revs: 1)

Stage 2 ⬡14 ⟨8⟩ 1 mark for each of 8 points minimum but excluding first and last, i.e. the limits of the locus.

⟨2⟩ last point C_{16}, D_{16}.

⟨2⟩ locus in overlap position 10, i.e. A to B, intersection becomes a line.

⟨2⟩ curve between C_4, D_4 and C_{16}, D_{16}.

Question No.
Q14

TOTAL
20 marks

SCALE:

0 10 20 30 40 50 60 70 80 90 100
mm

The line diagram illustrates a crank OA with a rod AP pin jointed to OA at A. A rotates about O and the rod AP is constrained to rest on the 50 mm diameter cylinder by the tension spring B.

Construct the locus of point P as A completes one revolution about O. OA = 40 mm, AP = 140 mm.

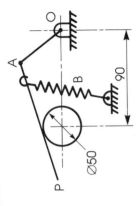

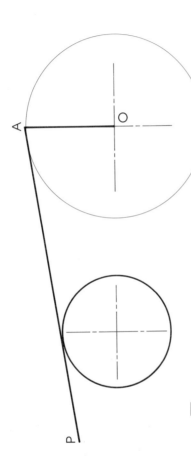

Stage 1 ① Correct layout which gives one position of P.

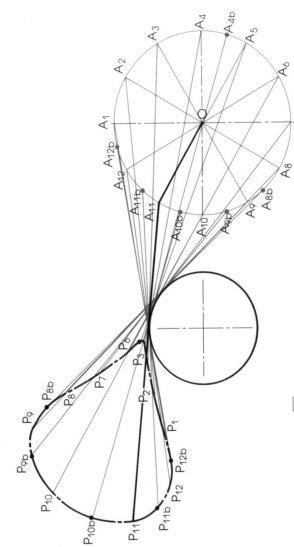

Stage 2 ⑪ Initial points from A₂, A₃, A₄, A₅, A₆, A₇, A₈, A₉, A₁₀, A₁₁, A₁₂.

Stage 3 ⑥ At least 6 extra points in the critical areas where the locus is not clearly defined e.g. from A₄ᵦ, A₈ᵦ, A₉ᵦ etc.

Stage 4 ② Curve of locus.

Question No.
Q15

SCALE:

TOTAL
20 marks

0 10 20 30 40 50 60 70 80 90 100
mm

280

(a) Construct a right-hand helix which has a pitch of 60 mm and a pitch diameter of 60 mm for one complete turn with the start at position 1, as illustrated in the line diagram.

(b) Determine the true length of the helix for one complete turn.

(c) Ten spheres having a diameter of 16 mm are located with their centres equally spaced along the helix with one centre at 1 and one at the end of the helix after one complete turn.
Locate the centres of, and draw, the spheres.

Note: Whilst the helix is strictly part of solid geometry it is illustrated here within plane geometry, under the general topic heading 'loci'.

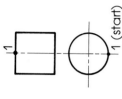

1

1 (start)

Projection: First Angle

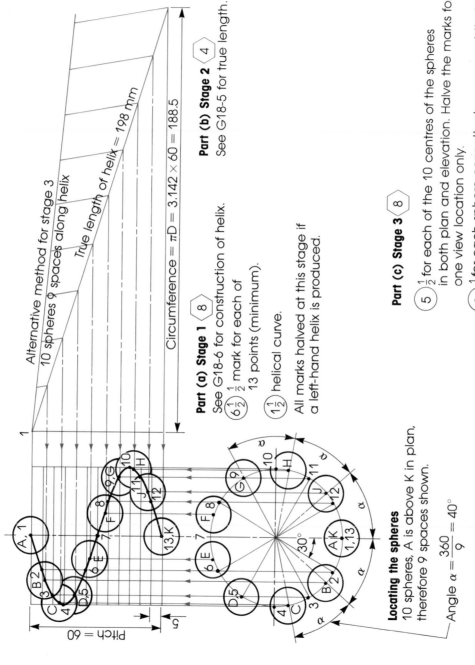

Alternative method for stage 3
10 spheres 9 spaces along helix

True length of helix = 198 mm

Circumference = πD = 3.142 × 60 = 188.5

Part (a) Stage 1 ⟨8⟩

See G18-6 for construction of helix.

(6½) ½ mark for each of 13 points (minimum).

(1½) helical curve.

All marks halved at this stage if a left-hand helix is produced.

Part (b) Stage 2 ⟨4⟩

See G18-5 for true length.

Part (c) Stage 3 ⟨8⟩

(5) ½ for each of the 10 centres of the spheres in both plan and elevation. Halve the marks for one view location only.

(3) ⅓ for each sphere correctly drawn except that in position number one.

Locating the spheres

10 spheres, A is above K in plan, therefore 9 spaces shown.

Angle $\alpha = \dfrac{360}{9} = 40°$

Centre positions of spheres are projected to the constructed helix in the elevation.
See alternative method which uses heights determined in the development of the helix projected across to the helix curve and on to the plan – less accurate.
Best method uses both other methods combined.

Question No. | **NOTE: First Angle projection used.** | SCALE:
Q16 | |

Projection | TOTAL 20 marks

0 10 20 30 40 50 60 70 80 90 100
mm

281

(a) Construct the plan and elevation of a left-hand helix which has a pitch of 72 mm and a pitch diameter of 60 mm with the start at A as shown in the line diagram.

(b) Determine the helix angle.

(c) Construct the plan and elevation of a tangent to point P on the helix using the helix angle found in (b). The position of point P is located in the line diagram.

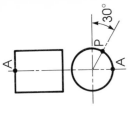

Projection: First Angle

Helix angle $\theta = 21°$ from drawing

By calculation $\tan \theta = \dfrac{72}{188.5}$

$\theta = 20°54'$

Circumference $= \pi D = 3.142 \times 60 = 188.5$

Pitch = 72

Part (a) Stage 1 ⬡ 8

See G18-5 for construction of helix.

Part (b) Stage 2 ⬡ 3

See G18-5 for true helix angle.

Part (c) Stage 3 ⬡ 9

See G31 and G32 for lines in space and G3-8 for tangent.

① P in elevation.

①½ any tangent to P in plan – any length.

③ any $X^1 Y^1$ to pass through P with angle θ (2 for elevation, 1 for plan).

②½ projected angle, α, of tangent and tangent XY in elevation.

① determination of X_1 and Y_1 in plan.

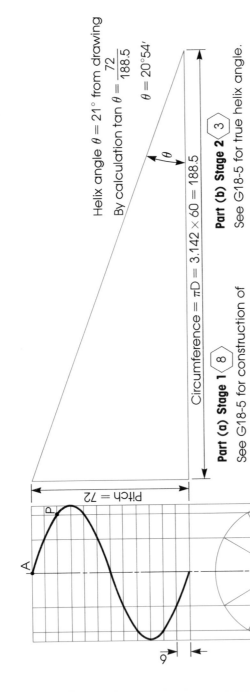

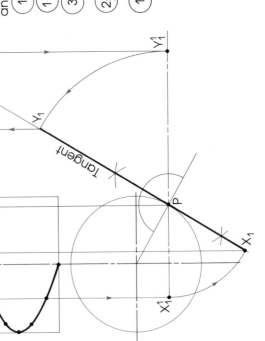

EXAMINATION-STYLE QUESTIONS

SOLID GEOMETRY

A, B and C are 3 points which lie on a horizontal plane and form the corners of an equilateral triangle where AB = BC = CA = 70 mm. AC is at 90° to the FVP (front vertical plane) and all 3 points lie on the surface of a sphere. The surface of the sphere also contains another point, D, which is located vertically 24 mm above the centre of the triangle ABC. Determine the centre of, and draw, the sphere which has the points A,B,C and D on its surface. State sphere diameter.

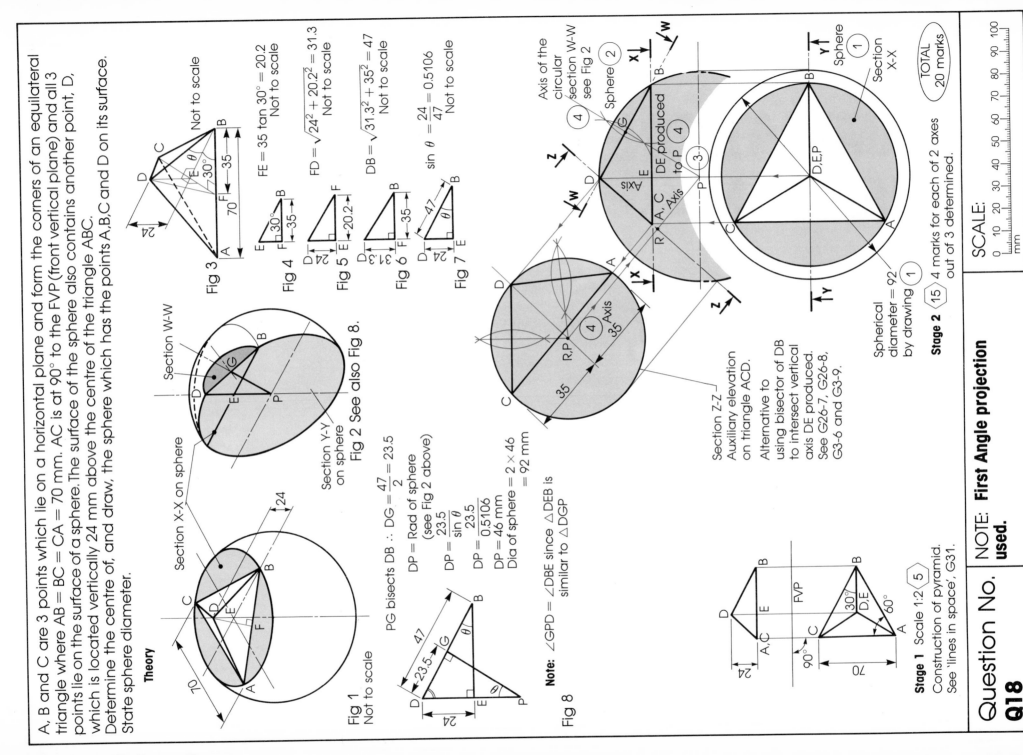

Theory

Fig 1
Not to scale

Section X-X on sphere

Section Y-Y
on sphere
Fig 2 See also Fig 8.

Section W-W

Fig 3
Not to scale

FE = 35 tan 30° = 20.2
Not to scale

Fig 4

Fig 5

Fig 6

Fig 7

$FD = \sqrt{24^2 + 20.2^2} = 31.3$
Not to scale

$DB = \sqrt{31.3^2 + 35^2} = 47$
Not to scale

$\sin\theta = \dfrac{24}{47} = 0.5106$
Not to scale

PG bisects DB ∴ DG = $\dfrac{47}{2}$ = 23.5

DP = Rad of sphere
(see Fig 2 above)

$DP = \dfrac{23.5}{\sin\theta}$

$DP = \dfrac{23.5}{0.5106}$

DP = 46 mm

Dia of sphere = 2 × 46
= 92 mm

Fig 8

Note: ∠GPD = ∠DBE since △DEB is
similar to △DGP

Section Z-Z
Auxiliary elevation
on triangle ACD.

Alternative to
using bisector of DB
to intersect vertical
axis DE produced.
See G26-7, G26-8,
G3-6 and G3-9.

Axis of the
circular
section W-W
see Fig 2

Sphere 2

DE produced
to P 4

Section
X-X

Sphere 1

Spherical
diameter = 92
by drawing 1

Stage 2 15 ⟨ 4 marks for each of 2 axes
out of 3 determined.

Stage 1 Scale 1:2 5
Construction of pyramid.
See 'lines in space', G31.

Question No. | NOTE: **First Angle projection**
Q18 | **used.**

SCALE:

0 10 20 30 40 50 60 70 80 90 100
mm

TOTAL
20 marks

284

A, B and C are 3 points located on a plane that is inclined at 60° to the HP (horizontal plane). Fig 1 shows the location of the points in the plan view together with the HT (horizontal trace) of the plane which contains the points. The 3 points A, B and C also lie on the periphery of the major segment of a circle with BC being the chord of the segment and A a point on the arc BC.

Draw a plan and front elevation of the segment ABC and state its radius.

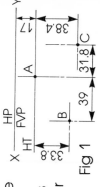

Fig 1

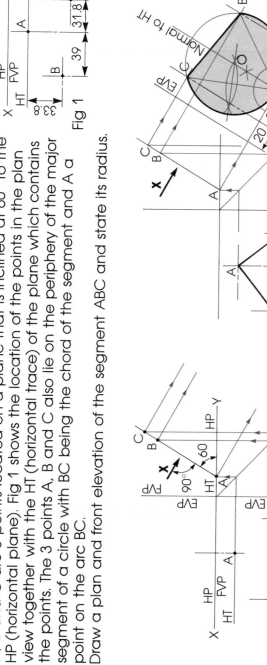

Stage 1 ③½ Scale: 1:2

② to determine the plane in the end elevation.

①½ to locate A, B and C on the plane.
See G32 for traces.

Stage 2 ⑦½ Scale: 1:2

④½ to determine true shape of triangle ABC.

② 1 mark each for any 2 out of 3 bisectors of the chords AB, BC and AC or any chord bisector and the normal to A as shown above. See G3-6 and G5-8.

① centre O and circle.

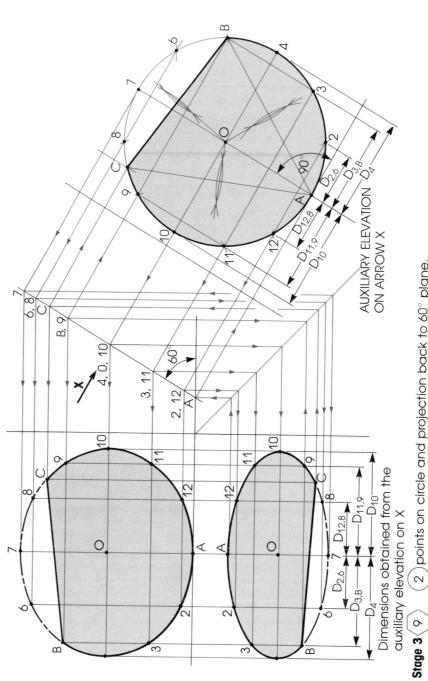

AUXILIARY ELEVATION ON ARROW X

Dimensions obtained from the auxiliary elevation on X

Stage 3 ⑨

See G26.

② points on circle and projection back to 60° plane.

③½ points 2,3,4,9,10,11 and 12 in plan and front elevation, i.e. ¼ each.

①½ curve in plan and front elevation.

①½ A, B and C in front elevation.

①½ radius = 45 mm.

Question No. **NOTE:** **First Angle projection used.**
Q19

SCALE:
0 10 20 30 40 50 60 70 80 90 100
mm

TOTAL
20 marks

285

The plan of a hemisphere is shown in Fig 1 with 3 points A, B, and C located on its spherical surface. The plane surface of the hemisphere rests on the HP with point O as its centre and the true length from O to A is 55 mm.

(a) Draw the given plan together with a front elevation of the hemisphere with the position of points A, B and C located on its surface.

(b) Determine the shortest distance between the centre O and the inclined plane defined by the traces HT and VT in Fig 1. Also state which of the 3 points A, B or C is nearest the inclined plane.

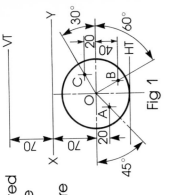

Fig 1

True length of OA = 55
OA = OB = OC = spherical radius,
since O is the sphere's centre and A, B and C are on the sphere's surface

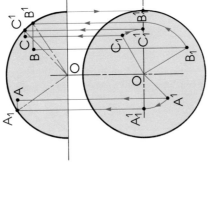

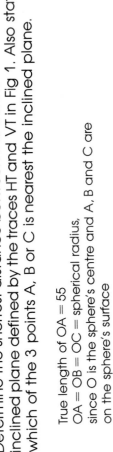

Alternative to the method below
— See G31-5. Scale: 1:2

OA = 55

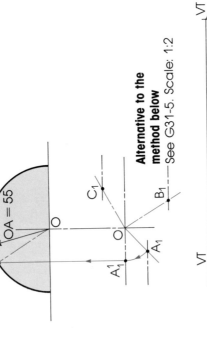

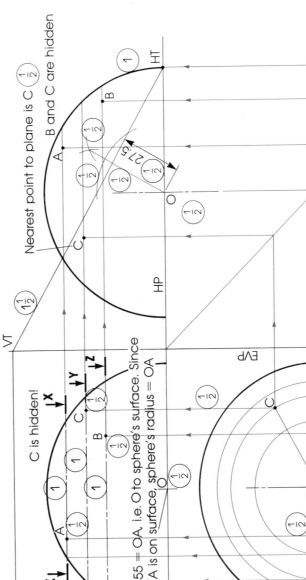

Nearest point to plane is C ($\frac{1}{2}$)

B and C are hidden

C is hidden!

55 = OA, i.e. O to sphere's surface. Since A is on surface, sphere's radius = OA

Section X-X
Section Y-Y
Section Z-Z

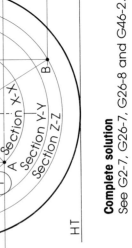

Complete solution
See G2-7, G26-7, G26-8 and G46-2.

Question No. **Q20**

NOTE: **First Angle projection used.**

SCALE:

0 10 20 30 40 50 60 70 80 90 100
mm

TOTAL
20 marks

286

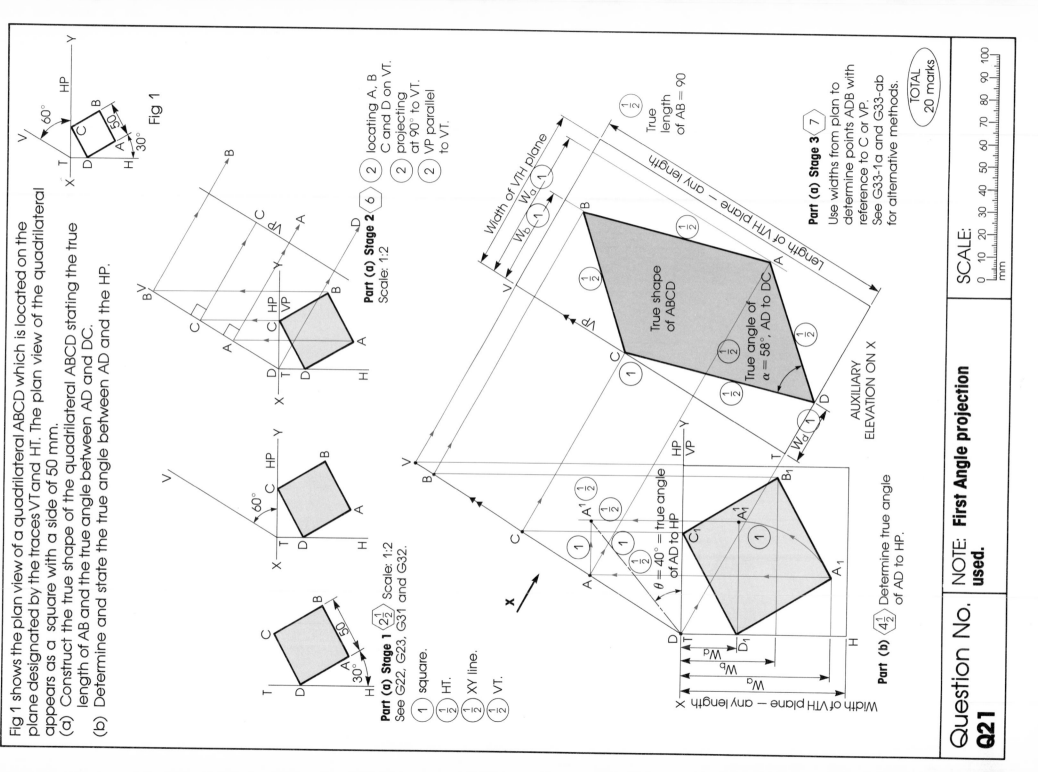

Fig 1 shows the plan view of a quadrilateral ABCD which is located on the plane designated by the traces VT and HT. The plan view of the quadrilateral appears as a square with a side of 50 mm.

(a) Construct the true shape of the quadrilateral ABCD stating the true length of AB and the true angle between AD and DC.

(b) Determine and state the true angle between AD and the HP.

Fig 1

Part (a) Stage 1 ②½ Scale: 1:2
See G22, G23, G31 and G32.

① square.
①½ HT.
①½ XY line.
①½ VT.

Part (a) Stage 2 ⑥

② locating A, B C and D on VT.
② projecting at 90° to VT.
② VP parallel to VT.

Part (a) Stage 2 ⑥ Scale: 1:2

Part (a) Stage 3 ⑦

Use widths from plan to determine points ADB with reference to C or VP. See G33-1a and G33-ab for alternative methods.

True length of AB = 90

True shape of ABCD

True angle of α = 58°, AD to DC

AUXILIARY ELEVATION ON X

Width of VTH plane

Length of VTH plane – any length

$\theta = 40° =$ true angle of AD to HP

Part (b) ④¼ Determine true angle of AD to HP.

Width of VTH plane – any length

(TOTAL 20 marks)

Question No. NOTE: **First Angle projection used.**
Q21

SCALE:

0 10 20 30 40 50 60 70 80 90 100
mm

287

The line diagram shows the basic geometric pattern involved in the design of a stained glass window when it is viewed from the vantage point illustrated. The design appears to be a symmetrical stylised cross in a circular window with the points A, B, C, D, E, F, G and H forming an octagon which is enclosed by the circumscribed square wxyz.

Determine the true shape of the window to a scale of 1:10 for it to appear as shown when viewed in the direction illustrated.

Complete solution See G26 for principles but note the reversal in the role of the auxiliary elevation – its shape is known, as in the sphere.

② $\frac{1}{2}$ for auxiliary circle, $\frac{1}{2}$ for square, 1 for cross arcs.

① 1 for window plane (face).

⑤ $\frac{1}{4}$ for each point to form true shape of circle and 1 for quality of curve.

④ 2 for points on curve BOG, 2 for points on curve COF.

④ 2 for points on curve AOD, 2 for points on curve HOE.

② $\frac{1}{2}$ each for quality of curves BOG, COF, AOD and HOE.

② $\frac{1}{4}$ each for lines wA, wH, xG, xF, yE, yD, zD and zC.

Apparent shape of the window when viewed from position illustrated

R400

Ø800

30°

Window

Viewing position

Eye

Wall

Widths W_1, W_2 etc. from auxiliary elevation

True shape of window

Window face

AUXILIARY ELEVATION GIVEN

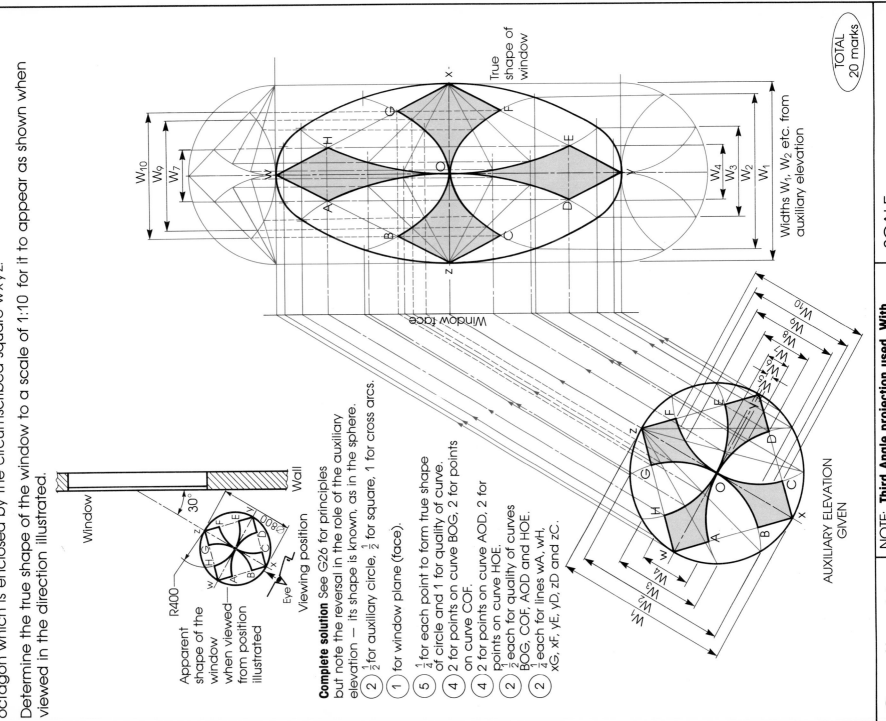

Question No. Q22

NOTE: **Third Angle projection used. With exception of lettering sequence, First Angle projection would also be possible.**

SCALE:

0 10 20 30 40 50 60 70 80 90 100
mm

288

The plan of a piece of sheet metal 100 mm square is shown in the line diagram with a vertical crease 40 mm from one edge. The incomplete front elevation shows the sheet with one edge resting on the horizontal plane.
A pipe, 50 mm diameter, runs parallel to the horizontal plane and front vertical plane and has its axis located by the centre of the metal sheet.
A hole which appears as a circle in the view on arrow P is cut in the sheet to receive the pipe.

Draw the plan, complete the front elevation, and produce a development of the metal sheet.

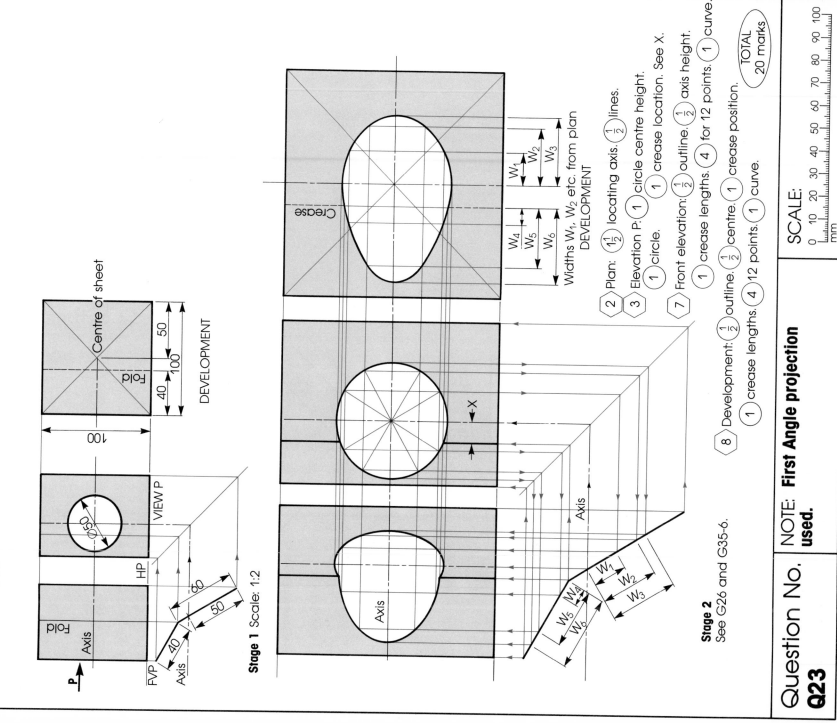

Stage 1 Scale: 1:2

Stage 2
See G26 and G35-6.

Widths W_1, W_2 etc. from plan
DEVELOPMENT

(2) Plan: (1½) locating axis. (½) lines.
(3) Elevation P: (1) circle centre height.
   (1) circle. (1) crease location. See X.
(7) Front elevation: (½) outline. (½) axis height.
   (1) crease lengths. (4) for 12 points. (1) curve.
(8) Development: (½) outline. (½) centre. (1) crease position.
   (1) crease lengths. (4) 12 points. (1) curve.

(TOTAL 20 marks)

Question No.	NOTE: **First Angle projection used.**	SCALE:
Q23		mm 0 10 20 30 40 50 60 70 80 90 100

Draw the 2 orthographic views given in the line diagram to a scale of 1:1 and, using a consistent method of projection, produce an auxiliary elevation to show the true shape of the shaded face A. Hidden detail is not required in the auxiliary elevation.

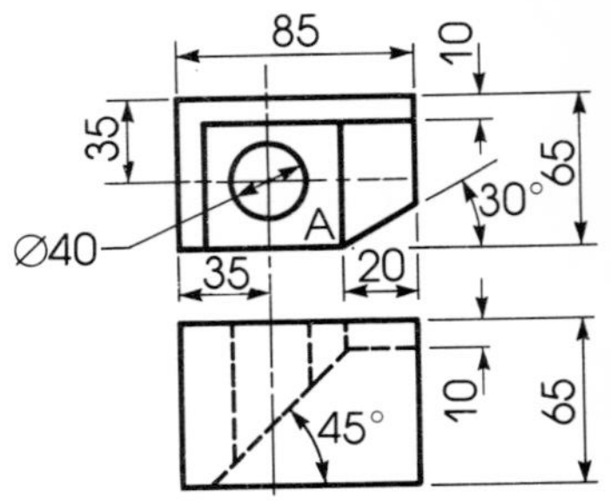

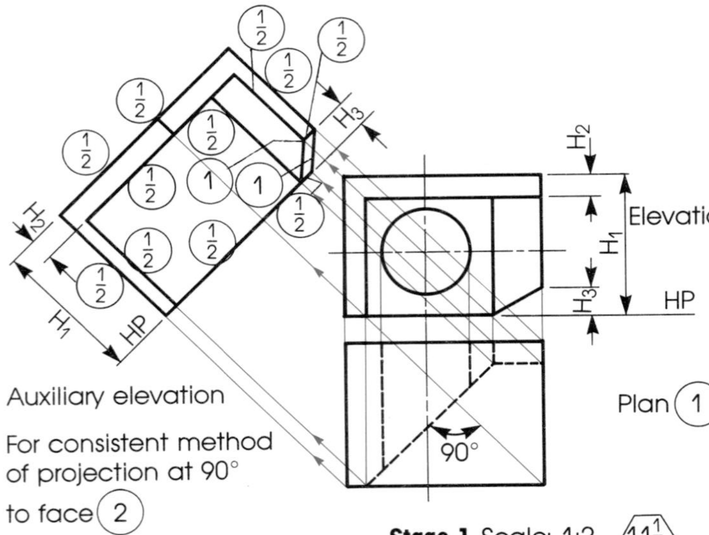

10
9·5
30°
65
85
20
A
Ø40
35
35
10
45°

Elevation (1)
H₁
H₂
H₃
HP

Plan (1)

Auxiliary elevation

For consistent method of projection at 90°
to face (2)

90°

H₃
H₁
HP
H₂

(½) (½) (½)
(½) (1)
(½) (1) (½)
(1) (½)
(½) (½) (½)

Stage 1 Scale: 1:2
See G23 to G25.

(11½)

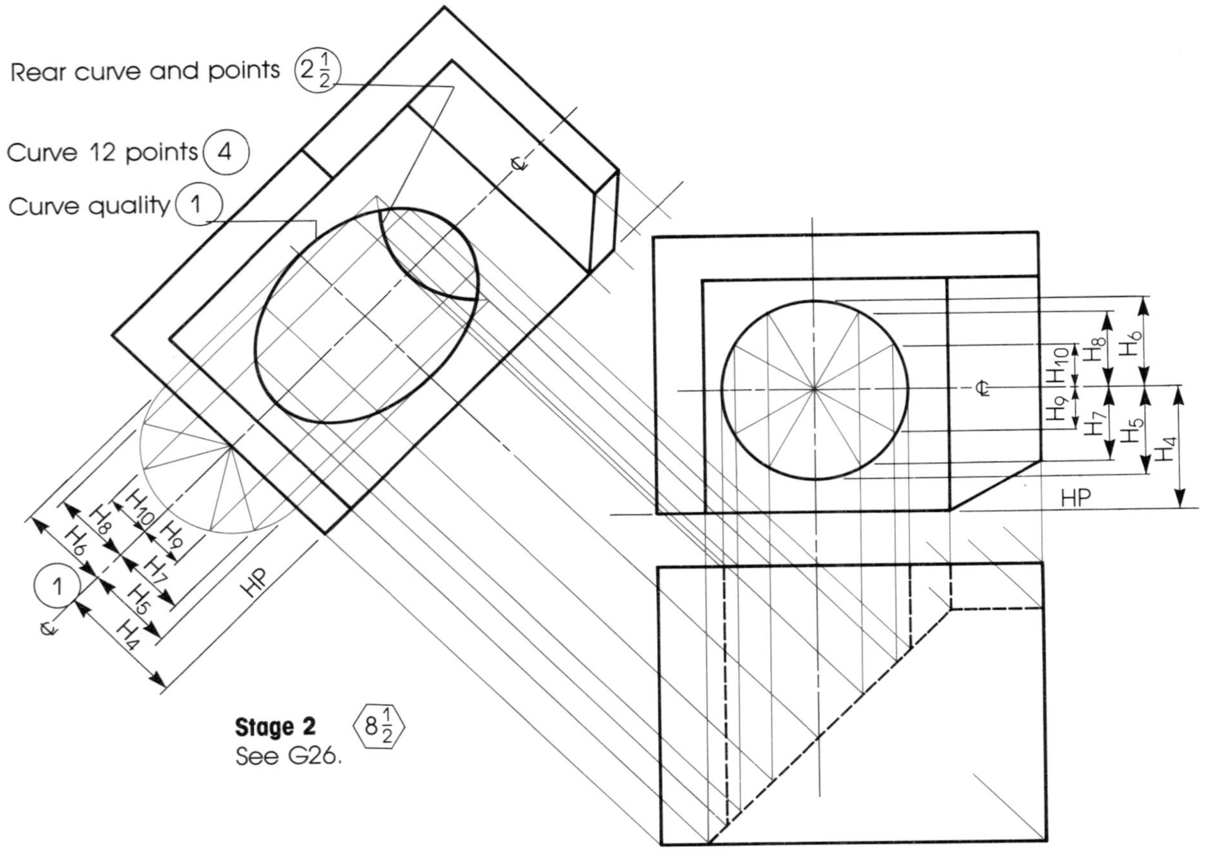

Rear curve and points (2½)

Curve 12 points (4)

Curve quality (1)

H₁₀ H₉
H₈ H₇
H₆ H₅
H₄
HP

Stage 2 (8½)
See G26.

H₆
H₈ H₅
H₇
H₄
H₁₀ H₉
HP

Question No. | NOTE: **First Angle projection**
Q24 | **used.**

SCALE:

0 10 20 30 40 50 60 70 80 90 100
mm

TOTAL
20 marks

An hexagonal prism rests with a rectangular face in contact with the horizontal plane and its axis at 30° to the front vertical plane as shown in the line diagram. The distance across flats on the hexagon is 46 mm with 75 mm between hexagonal faces. The prism is cut by a plane which is designated by the traces HTV.

Draw the plan and elevation of the part of the prism which lies below the HTV plane and project an auxiliary elevation from the plan on to the X₁ Y₁ line.

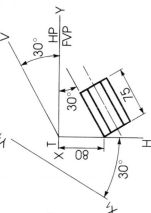

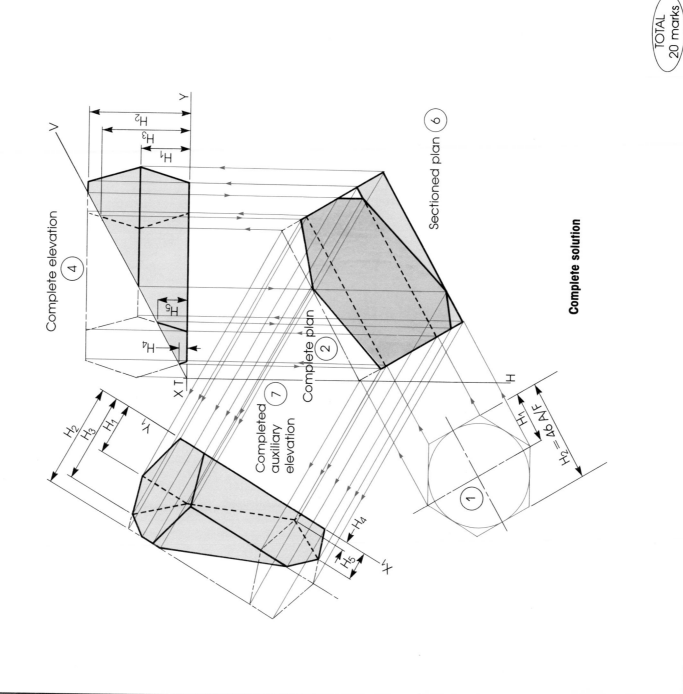

Complete elevation ④

Completed auxiliary elevation ⑦

Complete plan ②

Sectioned plan ⑥

Complete solution

Question No.	NOTE: **First Angle projection used.**	SCALE:
Q25		

TOTAL 20 marks

0 10 20 30 40 50 60 70 80 90 100 mm

291

The line diagram shows an auxiliary elevation of a regular hexagonal prism fixed to a cylinder and with a common axis. The combined solid is cut by a plane A-A.

Draw the plan and elevation of the solid to the right of the plane A-A and with the views relative to the X-Y line. Hidden detail is required.

Hexagonal prism 50 A/F

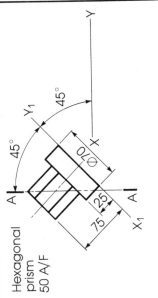

Stage 1 Scale: 1:2
See G25, G26 and G30.

Auxiliary elevation ②

Elevation ②½

Plan ③

Setsquare orientation for plan of hexagon

Parallel slide

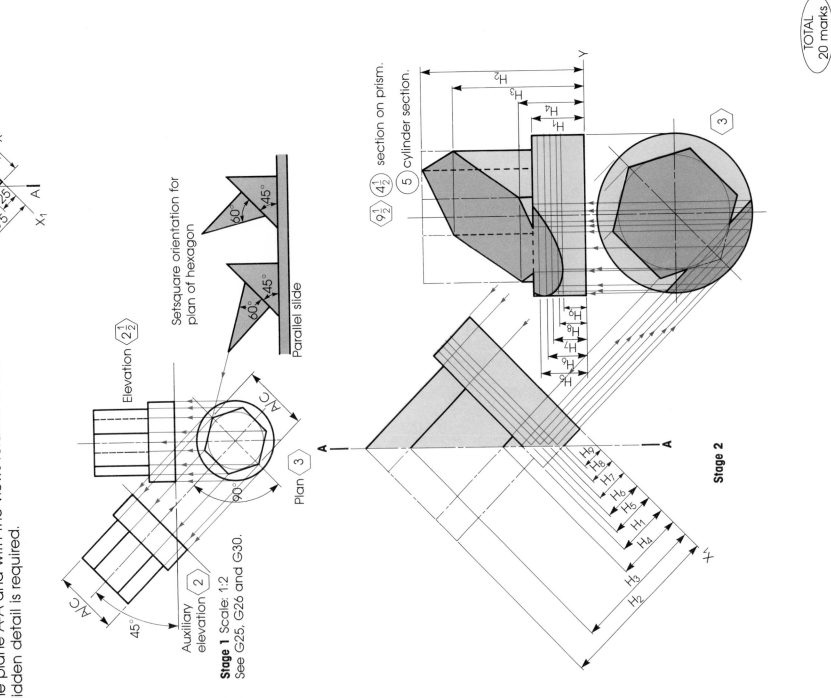

Stage 2

⑨½   ④½ section on prism.
⑤ cylinder section.

Question No. | NOTE: **First Angle projection used.**

Q26

SCALE:

0 10 20 30 40 50 60 70 80 90 100
mm

TOTAL 20 marks

The line diagram shows 2 views of a stone lintel for the top of an arched church window.

Draw the 2 given views to a scale of 1:10 and project an auxiliary elevation on to the $X_1 Y_1$ line. Hidden detail not required.

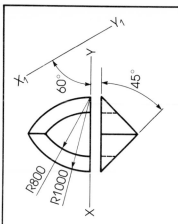

R800
R1000
60°
45°

3 marks for points defining curve and 1 for curve quality

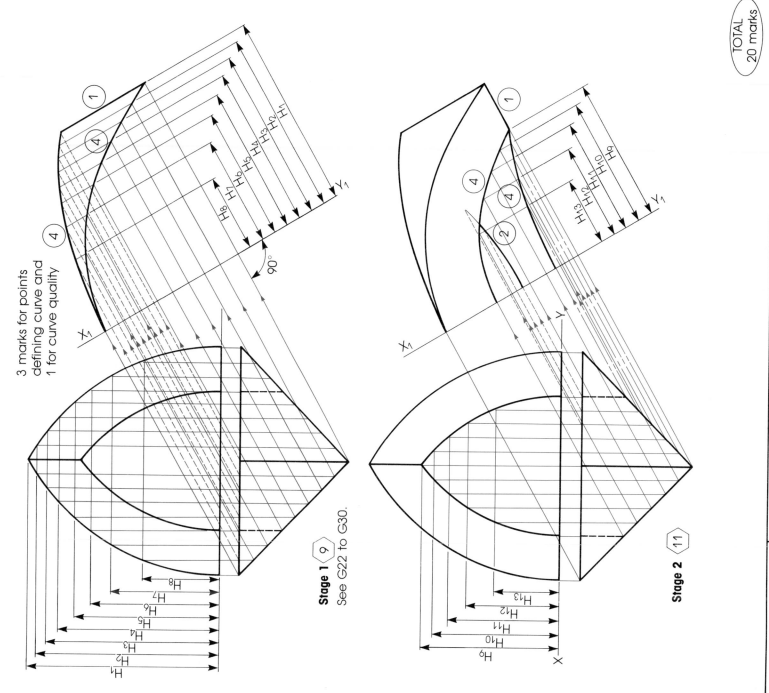

90°

H_8
H_7
H_6
H_5
H_4
H_3
H_2
H_1

Stage 1 ⬡9
See G22 to G30.

H_{13}
H_{12}
H_{11}
H_{10}
H_9

Stage 2 ⬡11

TOTAL
20 marks

SCALE:
0 10 20 30 40 50 60 70 80 90 100
mm

Question No. | NOTE: **First Angle projection used.**
Q27

293

The orthographic view given in the line diagram shows the frustrum of a cone standing on a hexagonal prism and located by a common axis.

Draw the given elevation and project the plan of the parts which lie below the cutting plane designated by the HTV traces. Also draw an auxiliary elevation to show the true shape of section of the combined solid which exists below the cutting plane. Hidden detail not required.

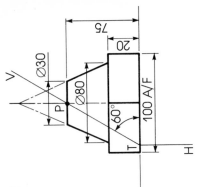

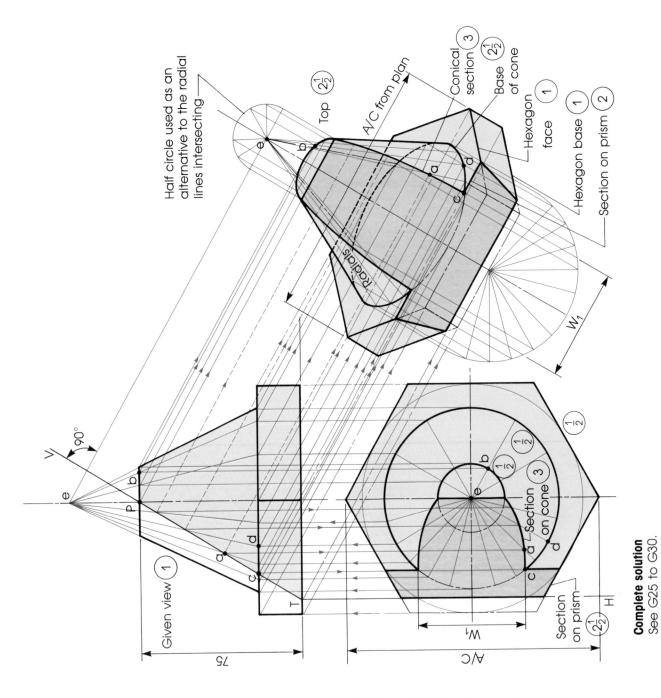

Half circle used as an alternative to the radial lines intersecting

Radials

A/C from plan

Top ②½

Conical section ③

Base of cone

Hexagon face ①

Hexagon base ①

Section on prism ②

W₁

90°

Given view ①

75

T

Section on prism ②½

A/C

W₁

HI

Section on cone ③

½

½

3

Complete solution
See G25 to G30.

Question No. | NOTE: **First Angle projection used.**
Q28

SCALE:

0 10 20 30 40 50 60 70 80 90 100
mm

TOTAL 20 marks

294

An auxiliary elevation of the outlet nozzle from a ventilation duct is shown in the line diagram together with a partly completed plan view.

Draw full size:
(a) the given auxiliary elevation,
(b) the completed plan,
(c) the elevation located on the X-Y line.

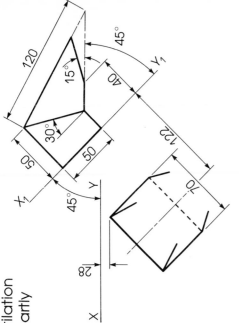

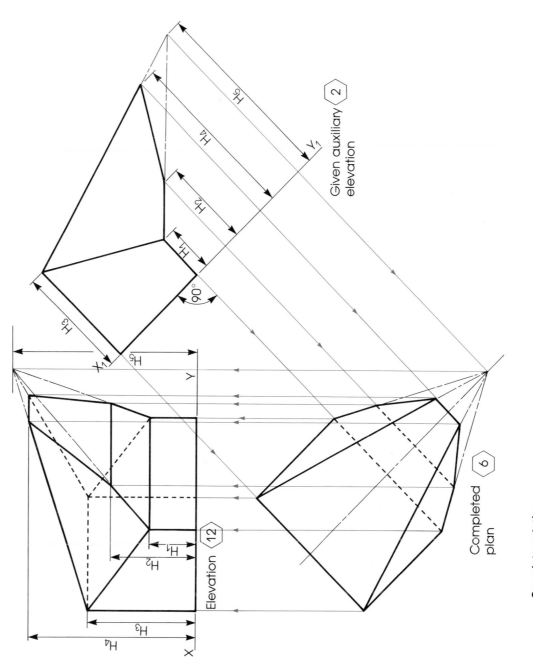

Given auxiliary elevation ②

Completed plan ⑥

Elevation ⑫

Complete solution
See G23 and G27.

Question No. | NOTE: **First Angle projection**
Q29 | **used.**

SCALE:

0 10 20 30 40 50 60 70 80 90 100
mm

TOTAL
20 marks

295

The triangular face of a right square pyramid rests on the horizontal plane in the position shown in the line diagram. The pyramid is cut by a plane designated by the traces HTV.

(a) Draw the plan and elevation of the part of the pyramid which exists below the cutting plane.

(b) Produce a development of the surface of the part of the pyramid which is below the cutting plane but excluding the cut face.

The vertical trace (VT) and horizontal trace (HT) are often combined as the VTH or HTV in order to define a plane.

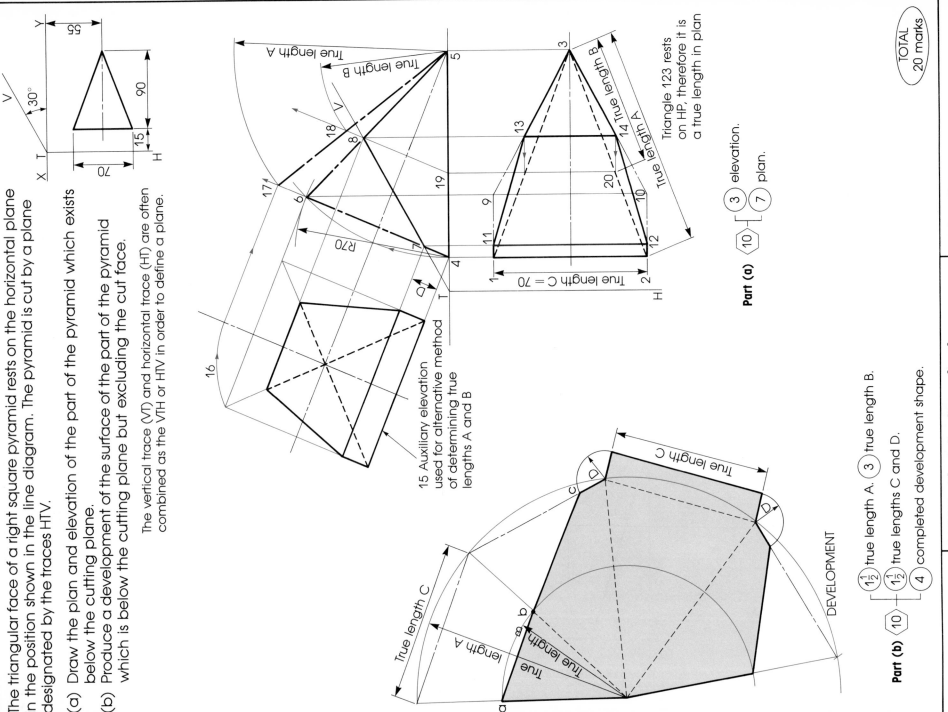

15 Auxiliary elevation used for alternative method of determining true lengths A and B

Triangle 123 rests on HP, therefore it is a true length in plan

Part (a) ⟨10⟩ ─┬─ ③ elevation.
                └─ ⑦ plan.

Part (b) ⟨10⟩ ─┬─ (1½) true length A. ③ true length B.
                ├─ (1½) true lengths C and D.
                └─ ④ completed development shape.

DEVELOPMENT

Question No.
Q30

NOTE: **First Angle projection used.**

SCALE:
0 10 20 30 40 50 60 70 80 90 100
mm

TOTAL
20 marks

296

The plan of a right square pyramid is shown in the line diagram together with the traces of a cutting plane shown by the line HTV. The pyramid rests with one of its triangular faces on the horizontal plane and has a base 60 mm square and a vertical height of 75 mm.

(a) Draw the plan and elevation of the part of the pyramid which lies below the HTV plane.

(b) Produce the development of the part of the pyramid which lies below the cutting plane excluding the face produced by the HTV plane and any part of the square base.

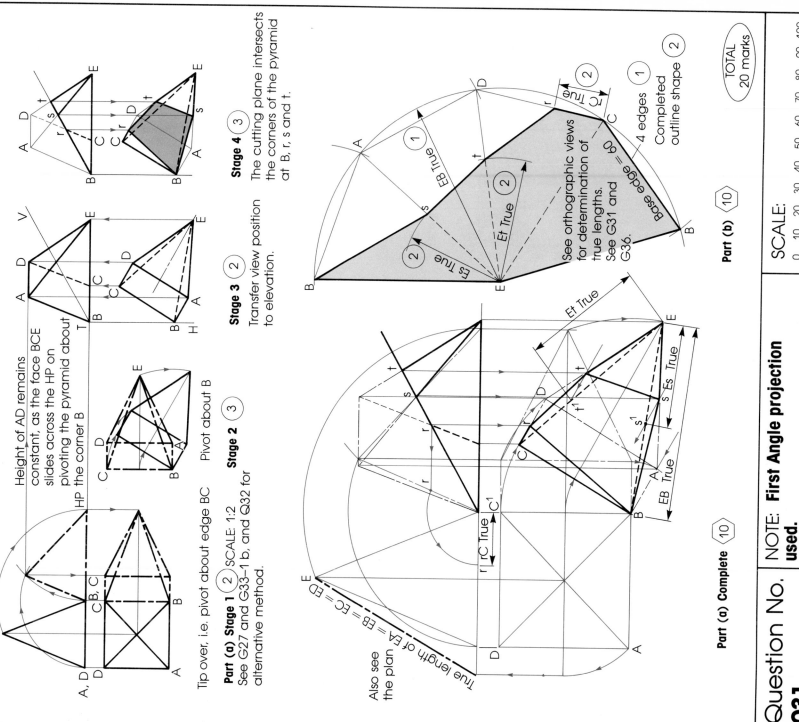

Height of AD remains constant, as the face BCE slides across the HP on pivoting the pyramid about the corner B

Tip over, i.e. pivot about edge BC   Pivot about B

Part (a) Stage 1 ② SCALE: 1:2   **Stage 2** ③
See G27 and G33–1 b, and Q32 for alternative method.

Stage 3 ②
Transfer view position to elevation.

Stage 4 ③
The cutting plane intersects the corners of the pyramid at B, r, s and t.

See orthographic views for determination of true lengths. See G31 and G36.

① EB True   ② Et True   ② ES True   ② Ct True
① 4 edges
② Completed outline shape

Part (a) Complete ⑩

Part (b) ⑩

Also see the plan

True length of EA = EB = EC = EB

(TOTAL 20 marks)

Question No. **Q31** | NOTE: **First Angle projection used.** | SCALE:

0 10 20 30 40 50 60 70 80 90 100
mm

297

The plan of a right hexagonal pyramid is shown in the line diagram with a corner A located 80 mm from the X-Y line. The pyramid has a vertical height of 75 mm from the base to the apex and rests with one of its triangular faces (AFG) on the horizontal plane.

Draw the front elevation and plan of the part of the pyramid which lies below the cutting plane designated by the traces HTV, showing clearly the projected shape of the section.

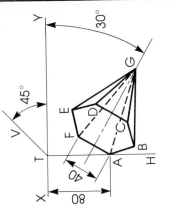

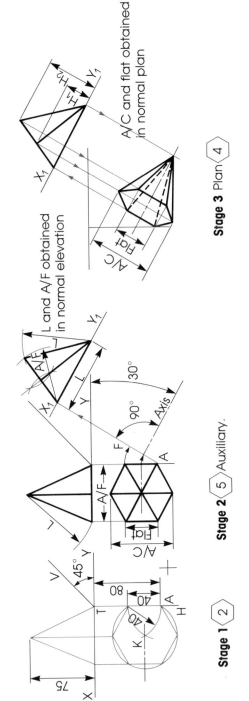

Stage 1 ②

Stage 2 ⑤ Auxiliary.

Stage 3 Plan ④

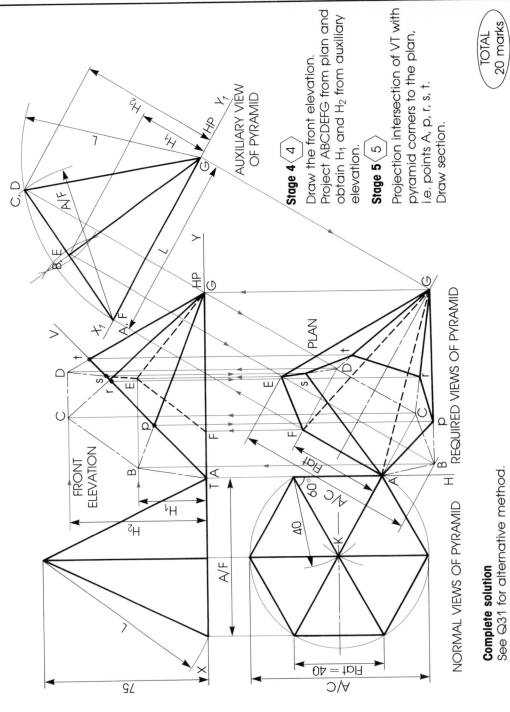

Stage 4 ④
Draw the front elevation. Project ABCDEFG from plan and obtain H_1 and H_2 from auxiliary elevation.

Stage 5 ⑤
Projection intersection of VT with pyramid corners to the plan, i.e. points A, p, r, s, t. Draw section.

Complete solution
See Q31 for alternative method.

Question No. | NOTE: **First Angle projection**
Q32 | **used.**

SCALE:

(TOTAL 20 marks)

0 10 20 30 40 50 60 70 80 90 100
mm

A rectangular label 45 mm wide by 134 mm long is stuck on to a hexagonal bottle and smoothed round the corners without it creasing. Unfortunately the label had a crooked start and slopes downwards, with the corner A located on the front face of the bottle as shown in the line diagram.

Complete the elevation of the part of the bottle below the plane B-B to a scale of 1:1 showing the label stuck to the bottle. All hidden detail is required.

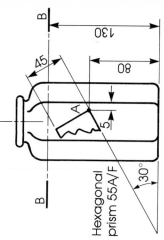

Hexagonal prism 55A/F

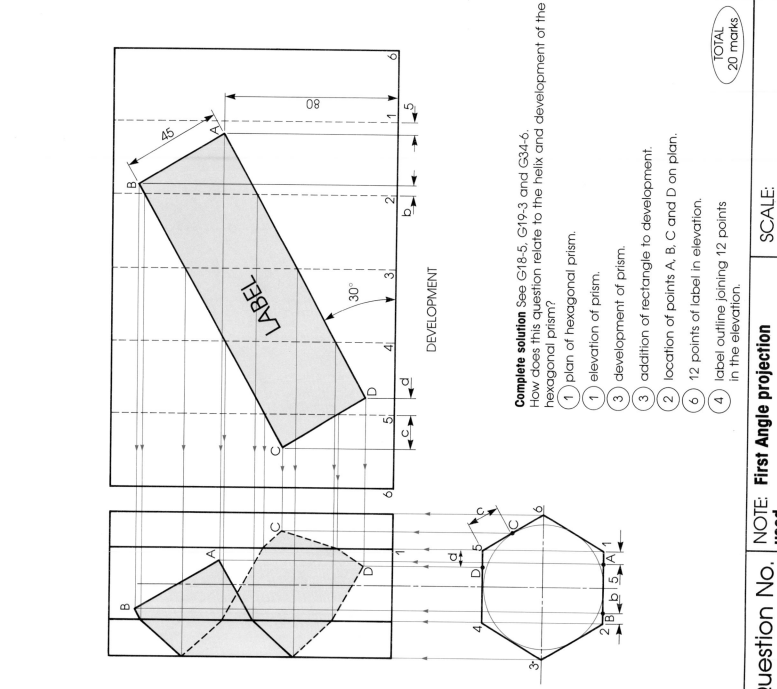

DEVELOPMENT

LABEL

30°

Complete solution See G18-5, G19-3 and G34-6.

How does this question relate to the helix and development of the hexagonal prism?

(1) plan of hexagonal prism.

(1) elevation of prism.

(3) development of prism.

(3) addition of rectangle to development.

(2) location of points A, B, C and D on plan.

(6) 12 points of label in elevation.

(4) label outline joining 12 points in the elevation.

Question No. **Q33**

NOTE: **First Angle projection used.**

SCALE:

TOTAL 20 marks

mm
0 10 20 30 40 50 60 70 80 90 100

299

The line diagram shows a fabricated support stay constructed from thin sheet steel and welded along one corner.

Construct the development which uses the most economical length of weld.

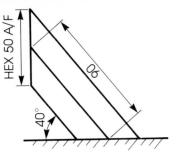

HEX 50 A/F

90

40°

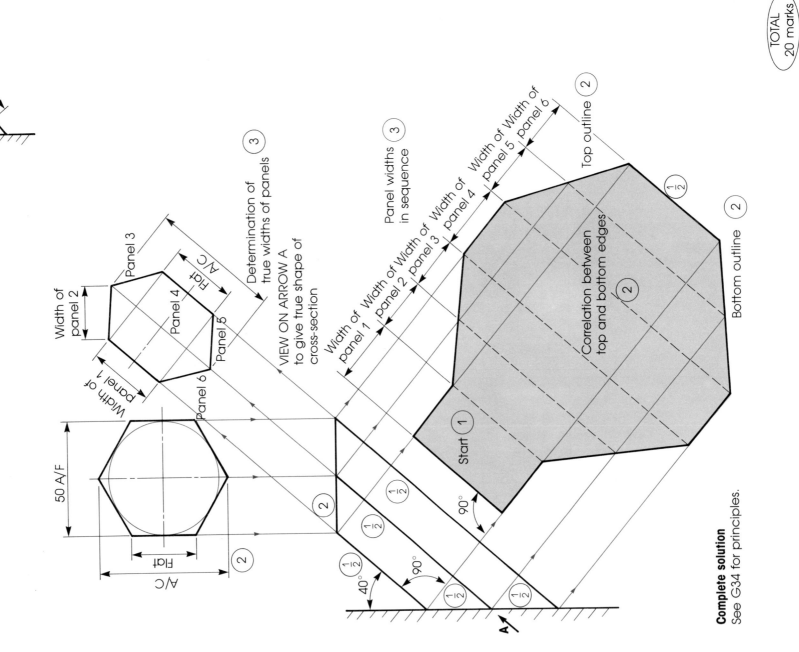

Width of panel 2

Panel 3

Panel 4

A/C Flat

Panel 5

Panel 6

Determination of true widths of panels ③

VIEW ON ARROW A to give true shape of cross-section

Width of panel 1

50 A/F

Flat

A/C

②

Width of Width of Width of Width of Width of Width of panel 1 panel 2 panel 3 panel 4 panel 5 panel 6

Panel widths in sequence ③

Top outline ②

½

Bottom outline ②

Correlation between top and bottom edges

②

Start ①

90°

½

½

②

90°

½

½

40°

A

Complete solution
See G34 for principles.

Question No.
Q34

NOTE: **First Angle projection used.**

SCALE:

0 10 20 30 40 50 60 70 80 90 100
mm

TOTAL 20 marks

The front and end elevations of the junction between a rectangular prism and a cylinder are shown in the line diagram.

Draw the given elevations and project a plan from the front elevation. Also produce a development of the rectangular prism. Hidden detail is required.

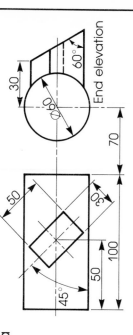

End elevation

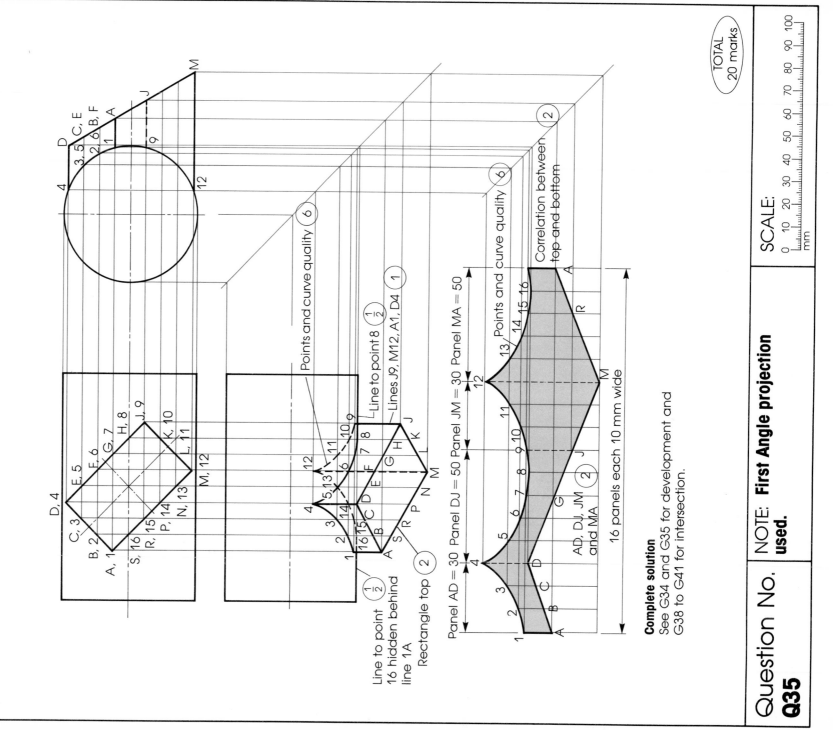

Complete solution
See G34 and G35 for development and G38 to G41 for intersection.

Question No.
Q35

NOTE: **First Angle projection used.**

SCALE:

mm
0 10 20 30 40 50 60 70 80 90 100

TOTAL
20 marks

301

The line diagram shows the elevation of a regular octagonal prism penetrated by an equilateral triangular prism, with the horizontal axis P of the triangular prism intersecting the vertical axis of the octagonal prism. The axis of the triangular prism is located as shown with the disposition of the corner R given in relation to P. The triangular prism is 120 mm long and its triangular end faces are equally displaced about the vertical axis of the octagonal prism when viewed in the direction of arrow X.

Draw:
(a) the given elevation,
(b) an elevation looking in the direction of arrow Y,
(c) an elevation looking in the direction of arrow X.

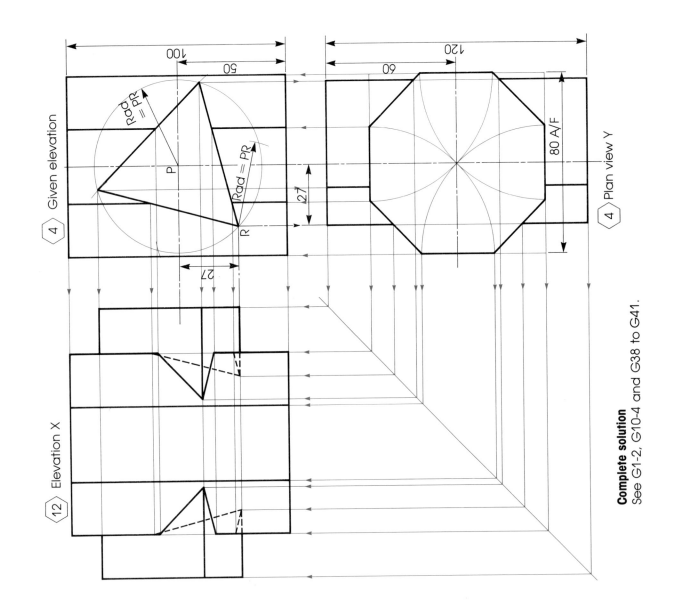

④ Given elevation

⑫ Elevation X

④ Plan view Y

Complete solution
See G1-2, G10-4 and G38 to G41.

Question No. | NOTE: **First Angle projection used.**

Q36

SCALE:
0 10 20 30 40 50 60 70 80 90 100
mm

TOTAL
20 marks

An incomplete elevation of the junction between a triangular prism and a cylinder is shown in the line diagram. The auxiliary view on arrow X shows the true shape of the prism and its disposition about the axis of the cylinder.

(a) Draw and complete the given elevation.
(b) Produce an end elevation in the direction of arrow Y.
(c) Project a plan from the given view.

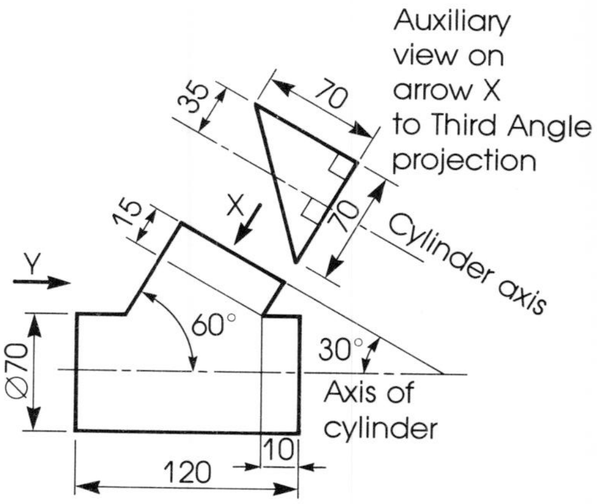

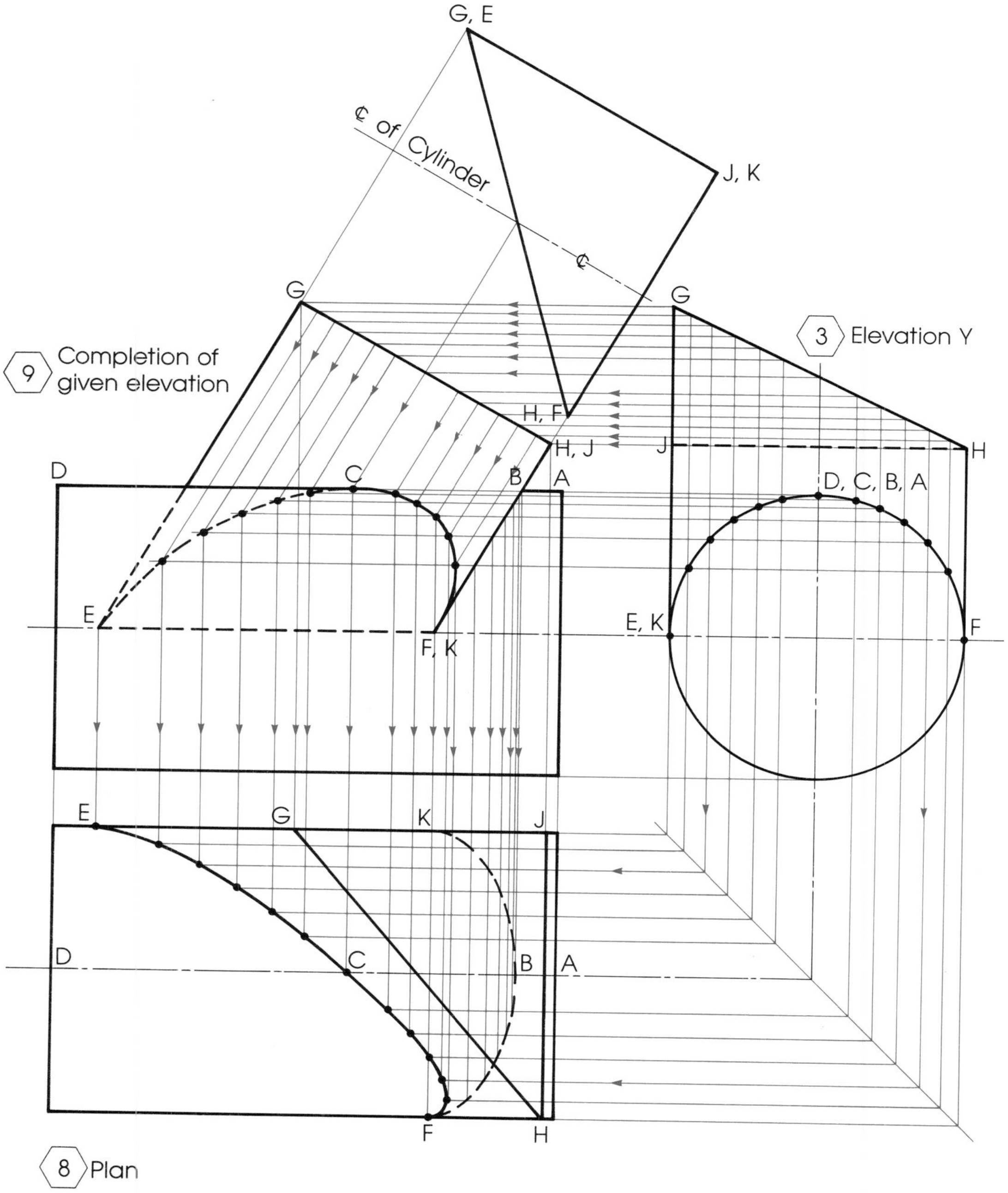

Auxiliary view on arrow X to Third Angle projection

Cylinder axis

70

R

X

35

75

60°

30°

Axis of cylinder

120

10

Ø70

Y

3 Elevation Y

H

F

D, C, B, A

G

J

E, K

9 Completion of given elevation

J, K

G, E

₡ of Cylinder

H, F

H, J

A

B

C

F, K

D

E

G

K

B

C

J

A

H

F

E

D

G

8 Plan

Complete solution
See G38 to G41.

Question No.
Q37

NOTE: **First Angle projection used.**

SCALE:

0 10 20 30 40 50 60 70 80 90 100
mm

303

The line diagram shows the elevation of an equilateral triangular prism which is 80 mm long and shaped to receive a 50 mm diameter cylinder which intersects the prism as illustrated. The axis of the cylinder passes through the top edge of the prism at 90° to the edge and half way along its length.

(a) Draw the given elevation.
(b) Project a plan from the given elevation.
(c) Produce a development of the 2 adjacent surfaces of the prism which have been cut to receive the cylinder.

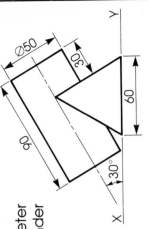

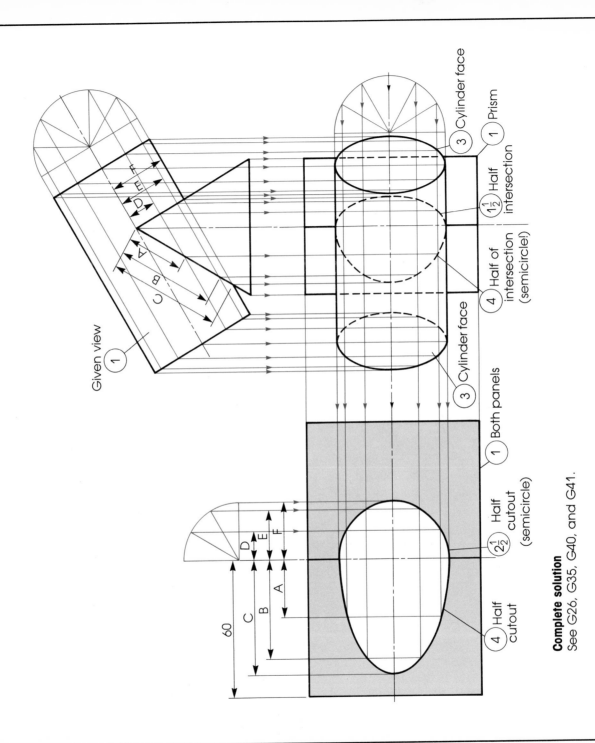

Given view ①

③ Cylinder face ① Prism

①½ Half intersection

④ Half of intersection (semicircle)

③ Cylinder face

① Both panels

②½ Half cutout (semicircle)

④ Half cutout

Complete solution
See G26, G35, G40, and G41.

Question No. | NOTE: **First Angle projection**
Q38 | **used.**

SCALE:

0 10 20 30 40 50 60 70 80 90 100
mm

(TOTAL 20 marks)

304

Part of a child's construction kit has a pentagonal prism with a coaxial circular hole and number of cylindrical pegs.

Construct an oblique (cabinet 45°) view of the prism with a mating peg 160 mm long located in the hole with 100 mm protruding towards the viewing position from the pentagonal face. One rectangular face of the prism is located on the horizontal plane and the axis of the peg is represented as horizontal by a 45° oblique line. Prism: pentagon side 60 mm, length 60 mm, hole ∅50 mm.

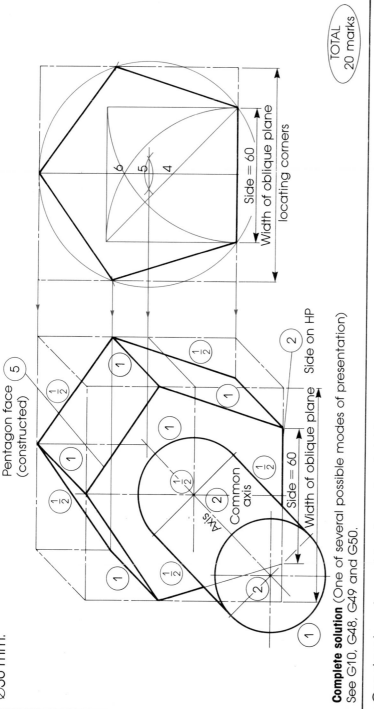

Complete solution (One of several possible modes of presentation)
See G10, G48, G49 and G50.

(TOTAL 20 marks)

Construct an isometric view of a right hexagonal pyramid standing on the octagonal face of a regular octagonal prism. 2 sides of the pyramid base are parallel to 2 sides of the prism, and the pyramid and prism have a common axis which is vertical.

Pyramid: vertical height = 70 mm, base is hexagonal and 50 mm across flats.
Prism: octagonal with octagon 80 mm across corners and prism 20 mm long.
Hidden detail not required.

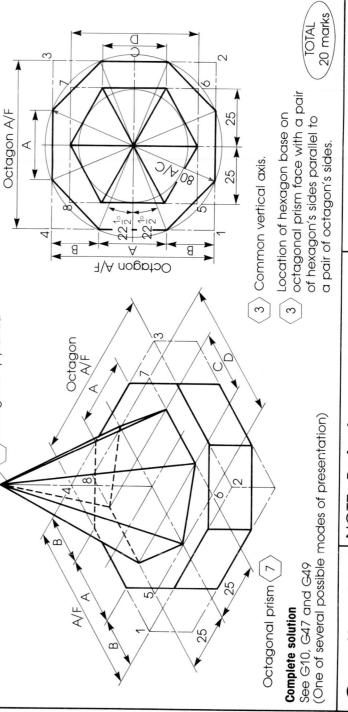

⬡7 Hexagonal pyramid

⬡7 Octagonal prism

Complete solution
See G10, G47 and G49
(One of several possible modes of presentation)

⬡3 Common vertical axis.

⬡3 Location of hexagon base on octagonal prism face with a pair of hexagon's sides parallel to a pair of octagon's sides.

(TOTAL 20 marks)

The line diagram shows a solid together with the ghosted outline of a mating piece which combines to make a solid rectangular prism 100 mm long, 60 mm wide and 80 mm tall.

Produce to a scale of 1:1 the 3 orthographic views of the mating solid indicated by the arrows A, B and C.

The views must be in a consistent method of projection and all hidden detail is required.

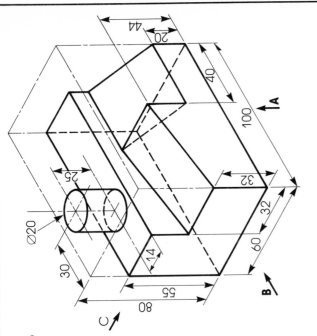

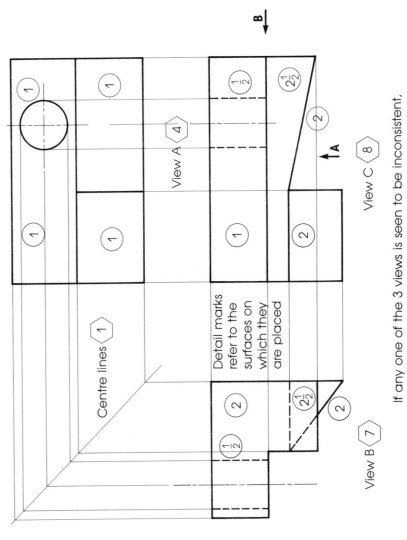

Centre lines ⟨1⟩

Detail marks refer to the surfaces on which they are placed

View A ⟨4⟩

View B ⟨7⟩

View C ⟨8⟩

If any one of the 3 views is seen to be inconsistent, total the marks of the 2 views projected correctly.

TOTAL
20 marks

SCALE:

0 10 20 30 40 50 60 70 80 90 100
mm

Question No. | **NOTE: First Angle projection used.**
Q41

306

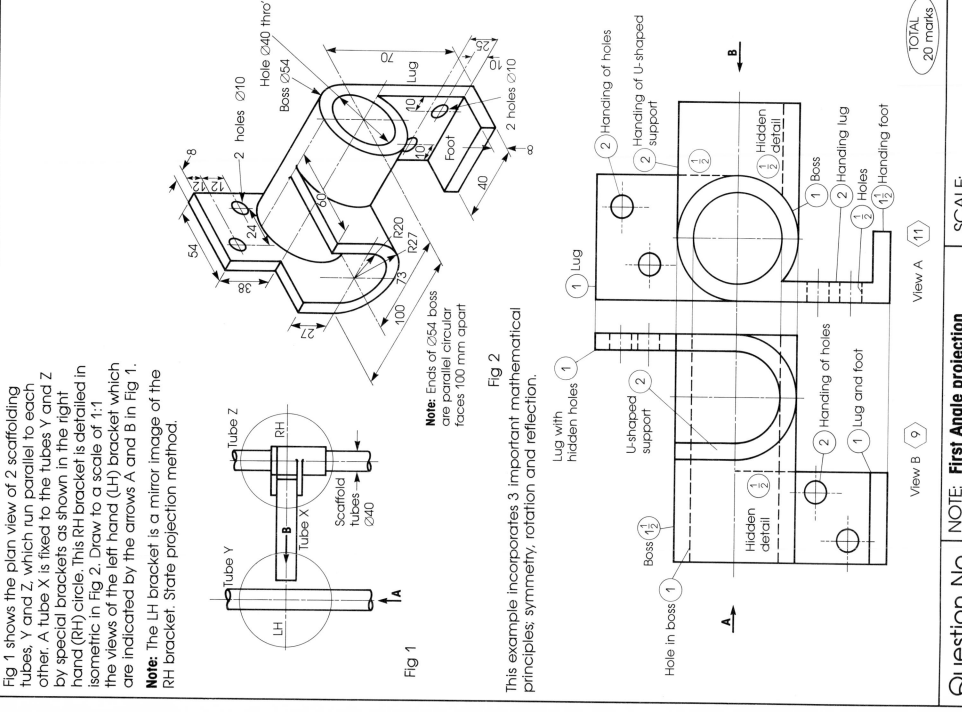

Fig 1 shows the plan view of 2 scaffolding tubes, Y and Z, which run parallel to each other. A tube X is fixed to the tubes Y and Z by special brackets as shown in the right hand (RH) circle. This RH bracket is detailed in isometric in Fig 2. Draw to a scale of 1:1 the views of the left hand (LH) bracket which are indicated by the arrows A and B in Fig 1.

Note: The LH bracket is a mirror image of the RH bracket. State projection method.

Tube Z

Tube Y

RH

LH

Tube X

B

Scaffold tubes Ø40

A

Fig 1

Hole Ø40 thro'

Boss Ø54

Lug

70

25

10

2 holes Ø10

10

Foot

10

2 holes Ø10

8

40

8

12 12

54

24

38

R20

R27

60

73

100

27

Note: Ends of Ø54 boss are parallel circular faces 100 mm apart

Fig 2

This example incorporates 3 important mathematical principles; symmetry, rotation and reflection.

Lug with hidden holes ①

U-shaped support ②

Boss 1½ ①

Hidden detail ½

Handing of holes ②

Lug and foot ①

View B ⟨9⟩

Lug ①

②② Handing of holes

②② Handing of U-shaped support

Hidden detail ½

½

½

Boss ①

②② Handing lug

½ Holes ②

1½ Handing foot

Hole in boss ①

A

B

View A ⟨11⟩

TECHNICAL GRAPHICS

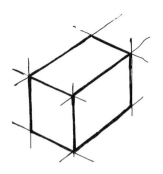

Fig 1 Vertical corners should appear vertical.

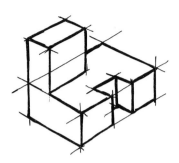

Fig 2 Build in blocks and cut away parts not required.

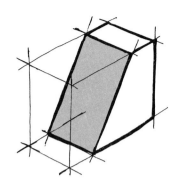

Fig 3 Perceive the block and cut to shape.

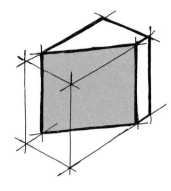

Fig 4 Do not draw from point to point as you will lose your overall line of progression.

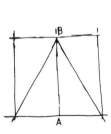

Fig 5a

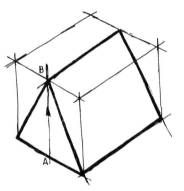

Fig 5b Locate the corners in a box and 'cut' to shape.

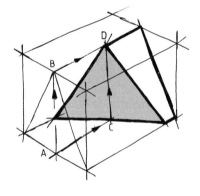

Fig 6 Perceived as a rectangular block, cut to a triangular prism and then cut by oblique plane.

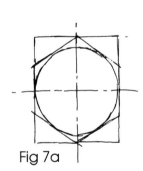

Fig 7a

Fig 7b

| Section No. **T1** | TITLE: **Freehand sketching.** | **Basic forms.** | |

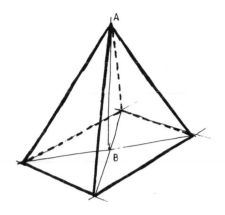

Fig 8a Point A is perceived
as vertically above
point B.

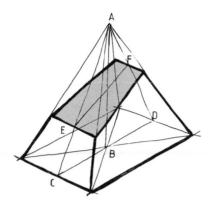

Fig 8b Points C, D, E and F are
perceived in the same
plane. B is central on the
base and A vertically above B.

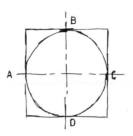

Fig 9a Circle is a
tangent to A,
B, C, and D.

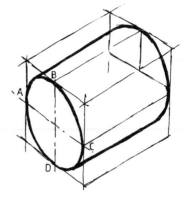

Fig 9b Picture of circle
is tangential to the
'square' frame.

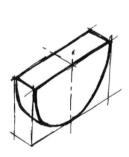

Fig 10 Woodruff key.

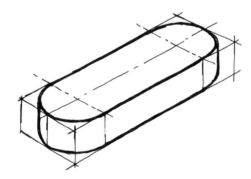

Fig 11 Feather key.

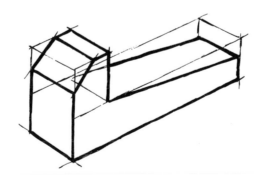

Fig 12 Gib head taper key. First perceived
as 2 blocks and then head is
chamfered and key is tapered.

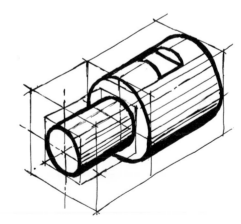

Fig 13 Pin is first perceived as 2
square coaxial blocks and then
as cylinders.

Section No.	TITLE: **Freehand sketching.**	**Basic forms.**	
T1			

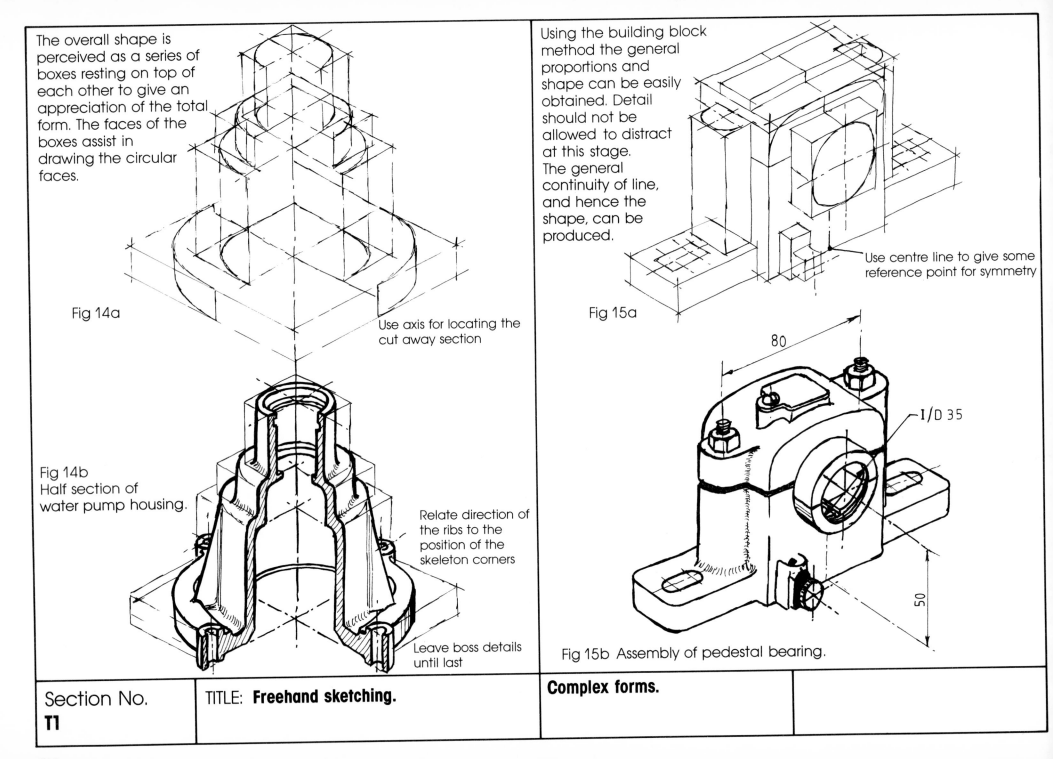

The overall shape is perceived as a series of boxes resting on top of each other to give an appreciation of the total form. The faces of the boxes assist in drawing the circular faces.

Fig 14a

Use axis for locating the cut away section

Fig 14b
Half section of water pump housing.

Relate direction of the ribs to the position of the skeleton corners

Leave boss details until last

Using the building block method the general proportions and shape can be easily obtained. Detail should not be allowed to distract at this stage. The general continuity of line, and hence the shape, can be produced.

Use centre line to give some reference point for symmetry

Fig 15a

80

I/D 35

50

Fig 15b Assembly of pedestal bearing.

| Section No. | TITLE: **Freehand sketching.** | **Complex forms.** |
| T1 | | |

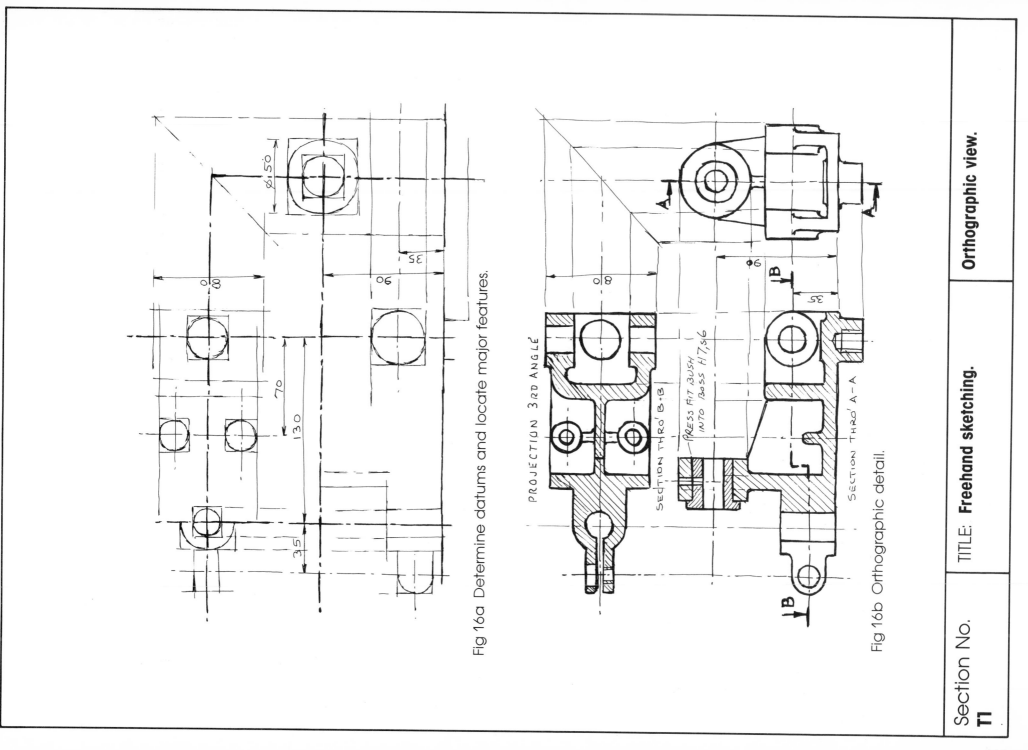

Fig 16a Determine datums and locate major features.

PROJECTION 3RD ANGLE

SECTION THRO' B-B

PRESS FIT BUSH INTO BOSS H7,S6

SECTION THRO' A-A

Fig 16b Orthographic detail.

Section No.
T1

TITLE: **Freehand sketching.** **Orthographic view.**

313

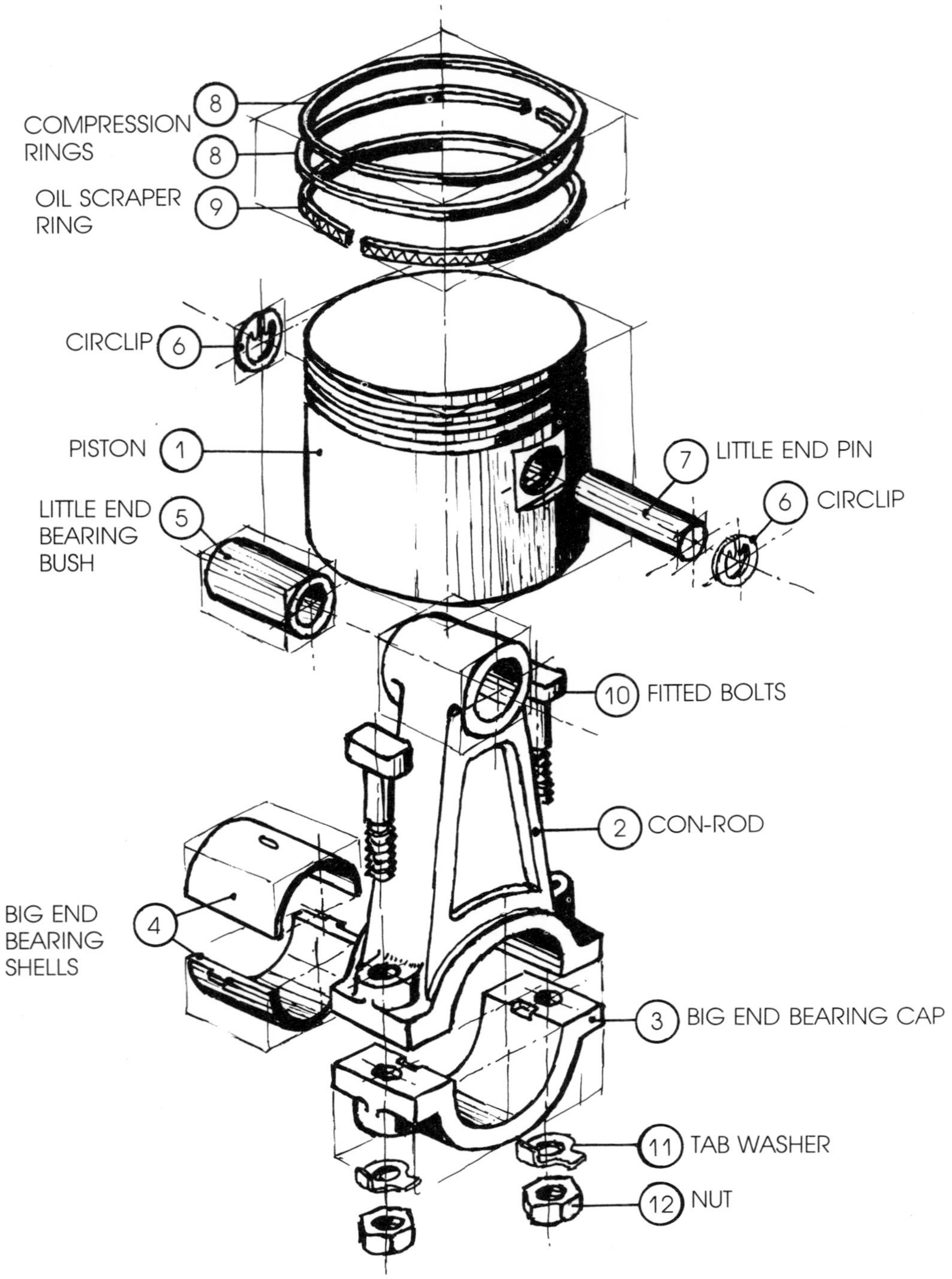

Fig 17 Exploded assembly.

COMPRESSION RINGS — 8
OIL SCRAPER RING — 9
CIRCLIP — 6
PISTON — 1
LITTLE END BEARING BUSH — 5
BIG END BEARING SHELLS — 4

LITTLE END PIN — 7
CIRCLIP — 6
FITTED BOLTS — 10
CON-ROD — 2
BIG END BEARING CAP — 3
TAB WASHER — 11
NUT — 12

Section No.

T1

TITLE: **Freehand sketching.**   **Exploded assembly.**

Planometric drawing is a pictorial method which utilises the true shape of the plan. Draw the plan view in one of the planometric positions as shown in Fig 2a or Fig 3a. Erect perpendicular corners from the plan but referring to the given elevations for positions and lengths of the vertical corners above the plan position. When the 45° mode of presentation is used, i.e. Fig 3b, it is normal to foreshorten the vertical corners to improve the proportions. $\frac{3}{4}$, $\frac{1}{2}$, and $\frac{2}{3}$ size are common reduction ratios for the verticals.

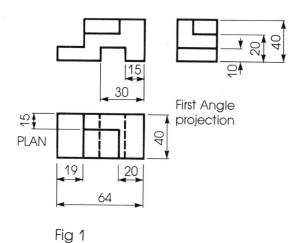

First Angle projection

Fig 1

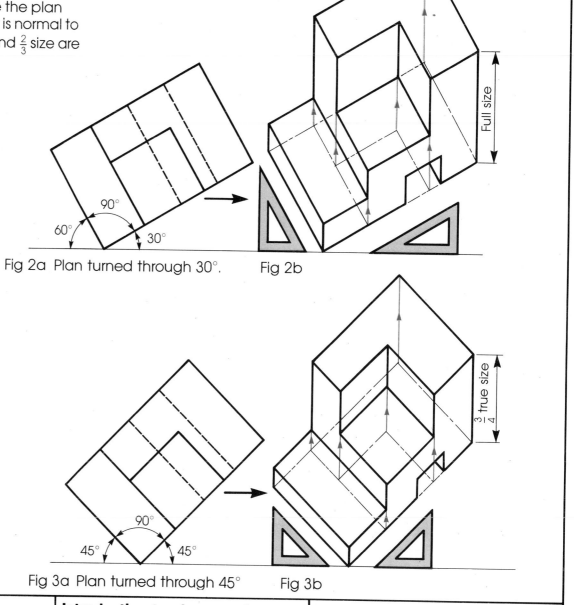

Fig 2a Plan turned through 30°.   Fig 2b

Fig 3a Plan turned through 45°   Fig 3b

Section No.	TITLE: **Planometric views.**	**Introduction to planometric drawing.**	
T2			

Many of the principles used are similar to those involved in isometric and oblique drawing. See G47 to G50.

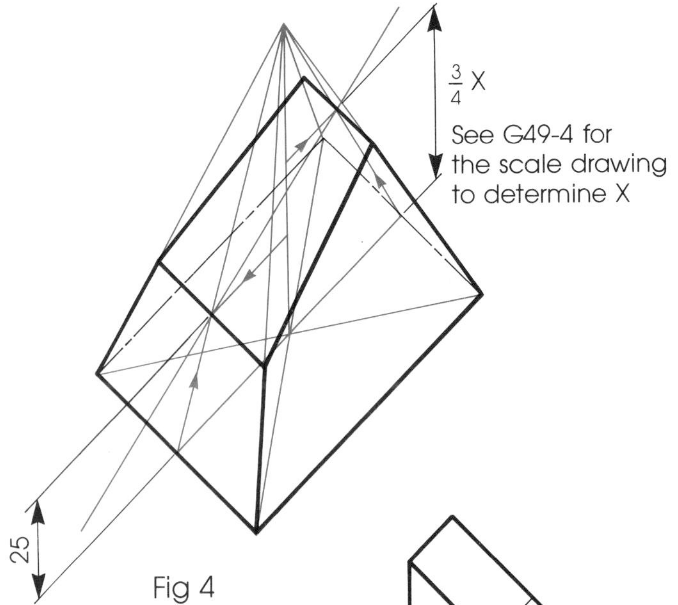

$\frac{3}{4}$ X

See G49-4 for the scale drawing to determine X

25

Fig 4

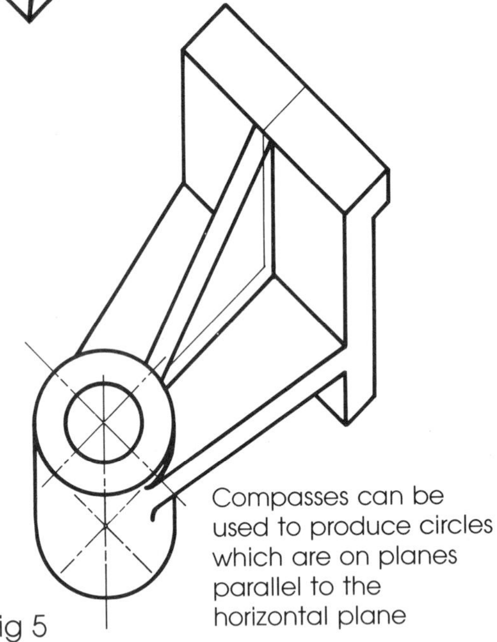

Fig 5

Compasses can be used to produce circles which are on planes parallel to the horizontal plane

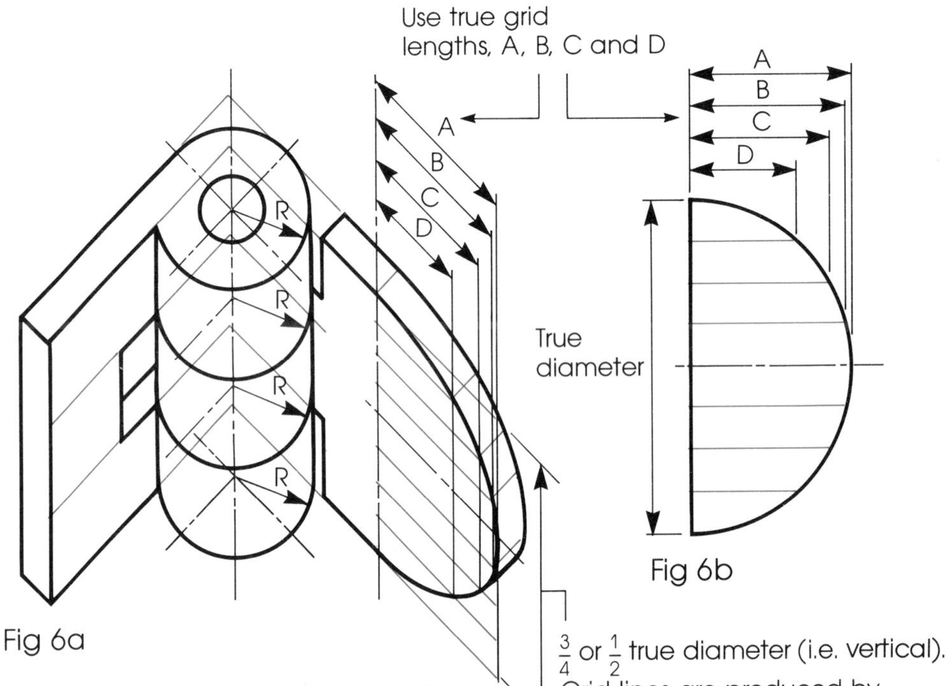

Use true grid lengths, A, B, C and D

A
B
C
D

True diameter

Fig 6a

A
B
C
D

Fig 6b

Circles on vertical planes are distorted and need to be constructed. Method used is similar to that used for oblique drawing. See G48-3b.

$\frac{3}{4}$ or $\frac{1}{2}$ true diameter (i.e. vertical). Grid lines are produced by dividing scaled down diameter into the same number of parts as the true arc in Fig 6b.

| Section No. T2 | TITLE: **Planometric views.** | **Introduction to planometric drawing.** | |

Perspective drawing is a method used to produce an image which represents the picture perceived by the eye when an object is viewed from a given position. Fig 1 and Fig 2 show how the length of a line is perceived to be shorter than its true length for the purpose of producing a perspective drawing. The view on arrow A analyses heights and the view on arrow B analyses the widths.

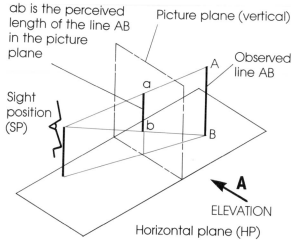

Fig 1 Perspective of a vertical line.

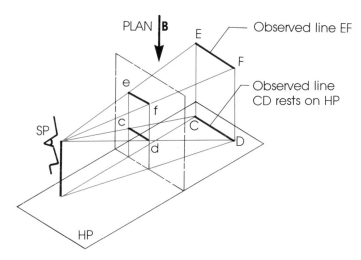

Fig 2 Perspective widths of horizontal lines.

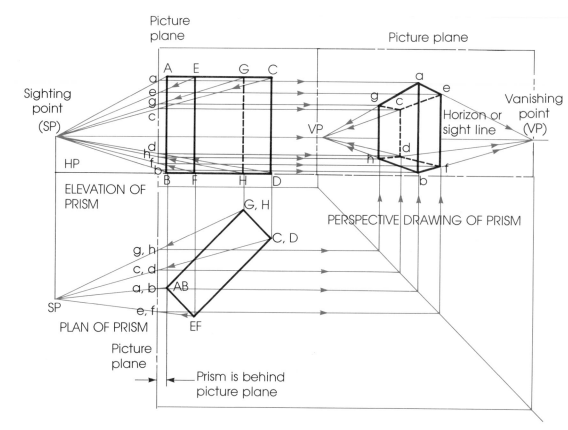

The elevation analyses the heights at which the corners appear in the picture plane. The plan analyses the widths as they appear across the picture plane. The perspective drawing synthesises (puts together) the picture plane heights and widths on the picture plane.

Fig 3 Perspective of a solid derived from orthographic views.

Section No.	TITLE: **Perspective drawing.**	**Introduction.**	
T3			

317

The points in the perspective drawing in Fig 3 are located by the intersection of the projectors from the elevation and the plan of the points on those picture planes. Corner G is located as point g on the picture plane in both the elevation and the plan using the sighting or station point (SP). Point g is then projected from the elevation and the plan of the picture plane to the perspective picture plane.

When full use is made of the vanishing points (VP) much of the projection work from the orthographic elevation can be eliminated, providing a useful alternative method of locating points. See Fig 4.

The perspective drawing in Fig 4 has used a higher viewing, or station, position in relation to the object in the elevation. The front corner AB has been placed conveniently in the picture plane, thus its perspective height will also be a true height. Point x has been used to relate the perspective height of the object above the corner AB. Lines are then drawn from the points a, b and x to the vanishing points. Corners c, d, e, f, g and h are then located by the intersection of the projectors from the points on the picture plane in the plan and the lines from the vanishing points. Further lines are drawn from the points obtained to the vanishing points to give points k, l and m.

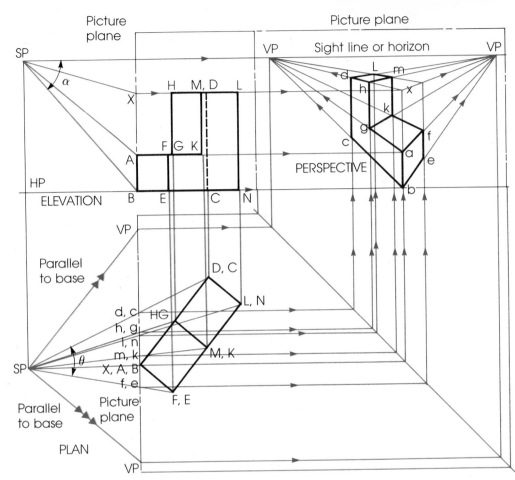

The vanishing points (VP) in the plan are determined in the plan of the picture plane by drawing lines parallel to the rectangular base from the station point (SP). The vanishing points are then projected from the plan to intersect the sight line.

Note: If the station position (SP) is too close to the object the image appears distorted. The best proportions are obtained when the angles θ and α are kept between 20° and 30°.

Fig 4 Perspective drawing using vanishing points.

Section No.	TITLE: **Perspective drawing.**	**Making use of vanishing points.**	
T3			

The measured point method is directly derived from the method which has been described on p 318 but there is no need to produce the orthographic views in this case. The vanishing points VP1 and VP2 are obtained in a similar way to those in Fig 4 on p 318 but note that the plan has been turned through 90° and amalgamated with the perspective in this method. Stage one shows how to set up the measuring points MP1 and MP2. These points are used to rotate the true lengths, measured along the ground line, into the perspective.

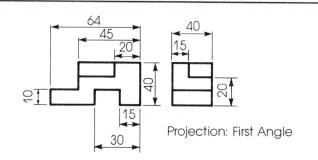

Projection: First Angle

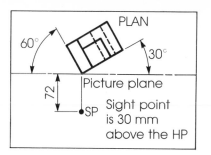

PLAN

Picture plane

SP Sight point is 30 mm above the HP

Example

Produce a perspective drawing of the 3-D object shown above in orthographic projection with the object located and viewed from the station (or sight point) shown in the adjoining plan.

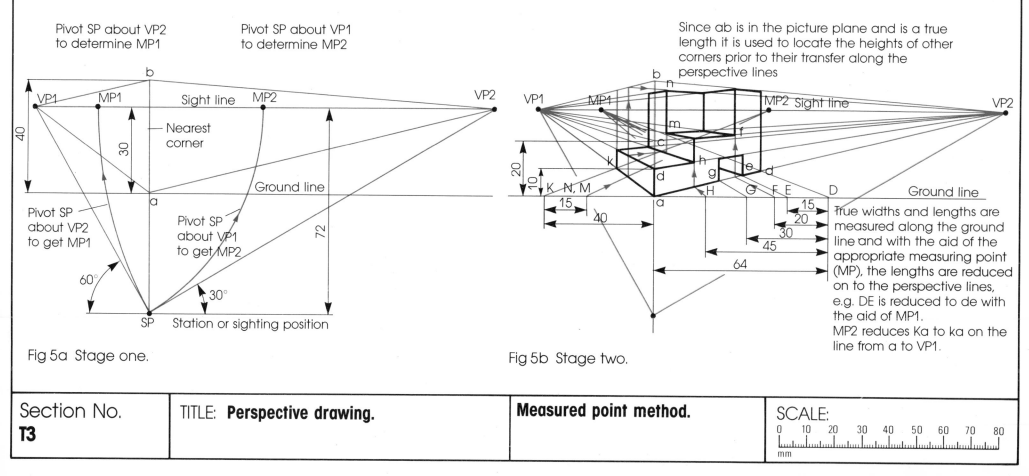

Pivot SP about VP2 to determine MP1

Pivot SP about VP1 to determine MP2

Since ab is in the picture plane and is a true length it is used to locate the heights of other corners prior to their transfer along the perspective lines

Fig 5a Stage one.

Fig 5b Stage two.

True widths and lengths are measured along the ground line and with the aid of the appropriate measuring point (MP), the lengths are reduced on to the perspective lines, e.g. DE is reduced to de with the aid of MP1.
MP2 reduces Ka to ka on the line from a to VP1.

Section No.	TITLE: **Perspective drawing.**	**Measured point method.**	SCALE:
T3			0 10 20 30 40 50 60 70 80 mm

This method is referred to as parallel since the object is located with a face or faces parallel to the picture plane. It is useful for illustrating objects which have circular faces, since the faces can be drawn with compasses if they are maintained parallel to the picture plane.

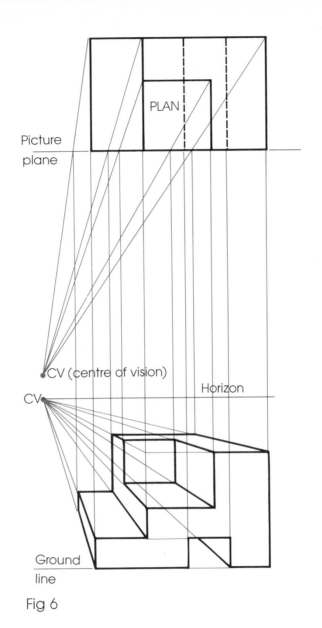

PLAN

Picture plane

CV (centre of vision)

CV

Horizon

Ground line

Fig 6

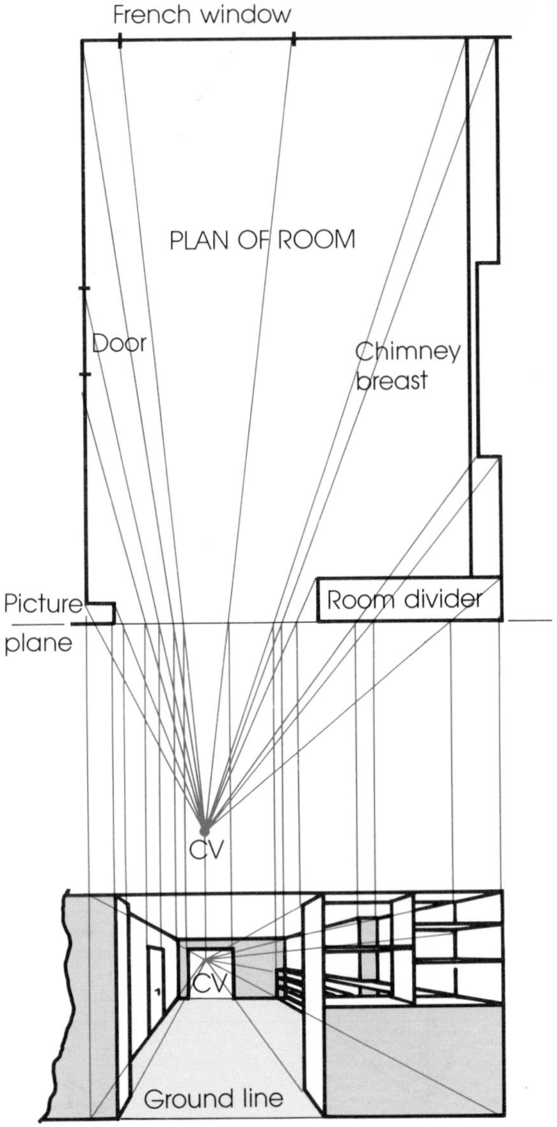

French window

PLAN OF ROOM

Door

Chimney breast

Picture plane

Room divider

CV

CV

Ground line

Fig 7 Interior of a room.

Section No. **T3**	TITLE: **Perspective drawing.**	**Parallel or single point perspective.**	

Numerical information in tabular form is often difficult to absorb but when it is displayed in 'pictures' it can provide a useful impression which may highlight various aspects of the information provided.

Perhaps the simplest form of graphical display is the <u>pictogram</u>, examples of which are shown in Fig 1 and Fig 2.

EXAMPLE 1

Information about the employees of a medium-sized engineering company is shown in the table below. Produce a pictogram to illustrate the information given in the table with the difference between office and production workers also shown.

Table 1

	Machine operatives	180
PRODUCTION WORKERS	Assembly and Fitting	80
	Foundry Pattern making	48
	Fabrication and Tinsmiths	40
	Maintenance and Labourers	37
OFFICE STAFF	Drawing and Design	65
	Estimating Buying, O. & M. Supervisors	32
	General office Finance and Personnel etc.	30

JOB DESCRIPTION	No. EMPLOYED: ⚒=10 Production; ⚒= 10 Office
Machine operators, turners, millers etc.	⚒⚒⚒⚒⚒⚒⚒⚒⚒⚒⚒⚒⚒⚒⚒⚒⚒⚒
Assembly, fitting, M/C erection.	⚒⚒⚒⚒⚒⚒⚒⚒
Foundry workers, moulders, pattern makers	⚒⚒⚒⚒⚒
Fabrication, platers, welders, tinsmiths.	⚒⚒⚒⚒
Maintenance, electricians, general lab.	⚒⚒⚒⚒
Draughtsmen, designers, tracers.	⚒⚒⚒⚒⚒⚒⚒
Estimating, buying, O. & M., Supervisors.	⚒⚒⚒°
General office, finance, personnel, etc.	⚒⚒⚒

Fig 1

EXERCISE 1

A company produces a poster to remind its workforce of its production commitments and to show the amount of work completed to date, against the annual target. The chart is brought up to date each month and after 8 months it appears as shown in Fig 2.

Which aircraft are (a) ahead of production schedule, (b) behind schedule, (c) on schedule?

Completed aircraft are in silhouette form.

Fig 2

Tornado 40	
Hawk 60	
Harrier 75	
Jaguar 35	
Nimrod 2	

| Section No. T4 | TITLE: **Representing data.** | **Pictograms.** | |

A bar chart is similar to a pictogram but is easier to construct since the group size is represented by the area of a rectangle (i.e. bar). It is normal to make the bar widths of each group the same, thus making the group size proportional to the lengths of the bars; see Fig 3 and Fig 4. These 2 examples relate the lengths of the bars to a linear scale since the bar widths are the same, but the scale relating their areas is also generally accepted. Fig 3 shows a horizontal bar chart which illustrates the number of people employed at 5-year intervals by a company. Fig 4 is a vertical bar chart which illustrates the company's profits in each of the previous 7 years.

Note: When all bars have the same width they can be directly related to their linear scales as in Fig 3 and Fig 4, but in Fig 5 the widths vary therefore a linear scale cannot be used and an area scale has been provided. The bar chart in Fig 5 represents the same information as that in Fig 2. It is difficult to interpret and relate the values of the bars in Fig 5 to the given scale but if the scale areas can also be illustrated by a grid, as in Fig 6, this makes analysis of the information much easier.

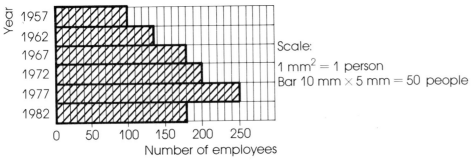

Scale:
1 mm^2 = 1 person
Bar 10 mm × 5 mm = 50 people

Fig 3 Horizontal Bar Chart.

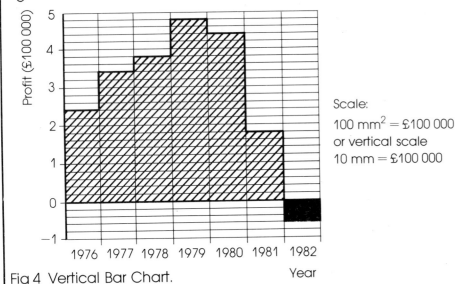

Scale:
100 mm^2 = £100 000
or vertical scale
10 mm = £100 000

Fig 4 Vertical Bar Chart.

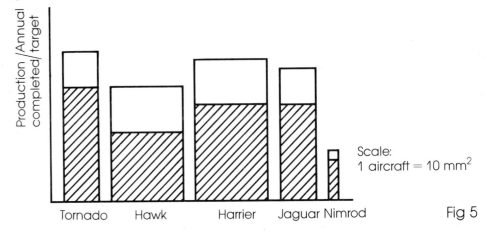

Scale:
1 aircraft = 10 mm^2

Fig 5

EXERCISE 2
A company owns 5 production plants and in its statement to shareholders it represents the value of its production output at the 5 plants on the bar chart in Fig 6. Determine from the information given the value of the production from each of the 5 plants.

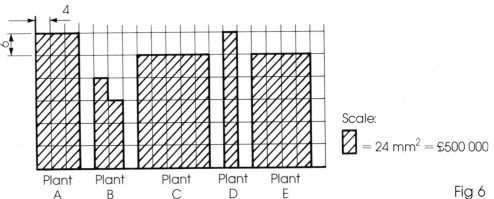

Scale:
⬚ = 24 mm^2 = £500 000

Fig 6

Section No.	TITLE: **Representing data.**	**Bar charts.**	
T4			

322

The numerical value of each element is expressed as an area which is a percentage of the total of the represented elements.

Sectional bar or **block chart:** The chart shown in Fig 7 illustrates the total area as a rectangle which is divided into rectangular elements or bars.

EXAMPLE 2

A company which produces paper-making machinery exports much of its production. The quantity and destination of its products over a 5-year period are as follows: North America 14%, Eastern bloc (Russia, Poland, East Germany etc.) 9%, Northern Europe (Finland, Norway, Sweden) 18%, EEC 5%, Asia (India, Pakistan, China) 13%, Africa 7%, Australasia 12%, and the remainder to the home market. Represent this information on a block chart 60 mm tall by 25 mm wide for inclusion in an information booklet on the company. See Fig 7 for answer.

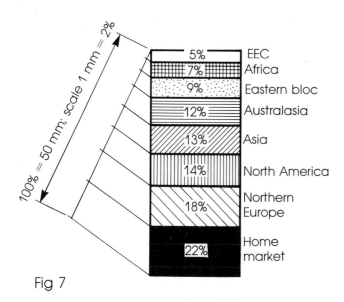

Fig 7

EXAMPLE 3

The cost of producing a car is broken down as follows: castings £300, forgings £200, machining £700, bought-out components £1550, assembly £500, steel pressings £900, painting and finishing £100. Represent these costs by a sectional bar chart which is 70 mm long by 30 mm wide. The special size is required to fit the illustration into a page layout for an automobile magazine. See Fig 8 for answer.

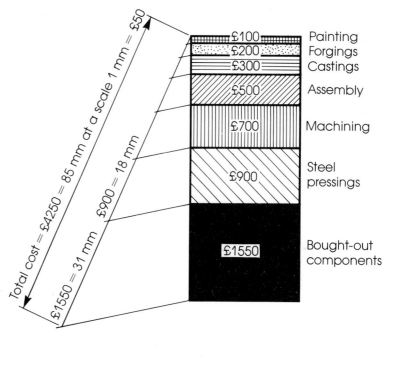

Fig 8

Section No.	TITLE: **Representing data.**	**100% charts.**	
T4			

Pie charts: These are similar to the block charts in principle but the area is in circular form with the elements represented by sectors of the circle. The value of each element is the area of the sector which is directly proportional to the angle of the sector at the centre of the circle.

EXAMPLE 4

Produce a pie chart to illustrate the distribution of a company's capital costs which are given as: wages £300 000, materials and overheads £520 000, investment in new equipment £240 000, profit paid to share-holders £130 000. Total £1 190 000.

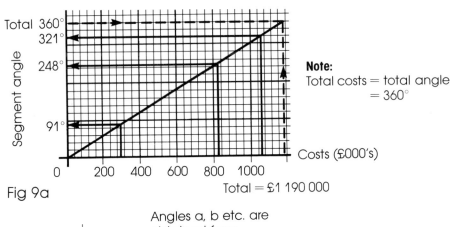

Fig 9a

Note:
Total costs = total angle
= 360°

Total = £1 190 000

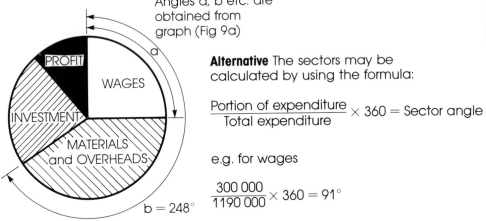

Angles a, b etc. are obtained from graph (Fig 9a)

Alternative The sectors may be calculated by using the formula:

$$\frac{\text{Portion of expenditure}}{\text{Total expenditure}} \times 360 = \text{Sector angle}$$

e.g. for wages

$$\frac{300\,000}{1\,190\,000} \times 360 = 91°$$

b = 248°

Fig 9b Pie chart.

A <u>histogram</u> illustrates the number of times (frequency) a defined variable occurs. The variable is divided into classes.

Class intervals: In Table 2, the first class is 1.53–1.56. The numbers 1.53 and 1.56 are called the <u>class limits</u>.

Class boundaries: In Table 2, the heights have been recorded to the nearest centimetre. The class interval 1.53–1.56 theoretically includes all the heights between 1.525 m and 1.565 m. These numbers are called the lower and upper class boundaries respectively.

The bars in the histogram <u>must</u> be the same width (the class interval) as the areas in each bar represent the frequencies of each of the classes. The frequency can then be related by a linear scale. The Histogram should not be confused with the bar chart which appears to be similar.

EXAMPLE 5

It was decided to design the cockpit of a military aircraft to accommodate men whose height varied between 1.73 m and 1.84 m after a survey produced the statistics given in Table 2 below.

Table 2

Variable height of males age 20 to 35	Frequency No. of times variable occurs
1.53 to 1.56 m	0
1.57 to 1.60 m	2
1.61 to 1.64 m	10
1.65 to 1.68 m	40
1.69 to 1.72 m	110
1.73 to 1.76 m	200
1.77 to 1.80 m	250
1.81 to 1.84 m	215
1.85 to 1.88 m	120
1.89 to 1.92 m	45
1.93 to 1.96 m	15
1.97 to 2.00 m	5

Section No. T4	TITLE: **Representing data.**	**100% charts.** **Histograms.**	

Produce a histogram which illustrates the given information and indicate on the illustration the proportion of the population who would be available for recruitment as a pilot for the aircraft.

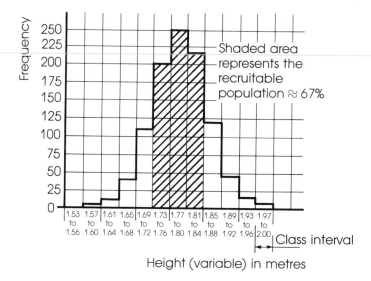

Shaded area represents the recruitable population ≈ 67%

Height (variable) in metres

Fig 10

EXAMPLE 6

Twenty samples of 10 components each are checked during a quality control process with the same outside diameter being measured on each component. The frequency of the measured sizes was recorded in Table 3. Produce a histogram based on the tabulated information and indicate the acceptable size boundary if the limits of size on the measured diameter are 79.965 and 80.065. Indicate, by shading the appropriate part of the diagram, the rejects which are scrap.

Table 3

O/D Size in mm	Frequency
79.93 to 79.94	1
79.95 to 79.96	5
79.97 to 79.98	18
79.99 to 80.00	40
80.01 to 80.02	60
80.03 to 80.04	44
80.05 to 80.06	23
80.07 to 80.08	6
80.09 to 80.10	2
80.11 to 80.12	1

Note: If the components are oversize they are not scrap as they can be recovered by machining down to the correct size. Metal cannot, however, be added if under size.

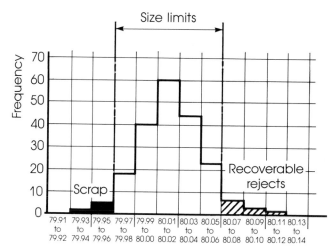

Fig 11

| Section No. T4 | TITLE: **Representing data.** | **Histograms.** | |

A <u>topic web</u> is a diagram used to illustrate a progression of ideas, concepts etc. which are related to a topic. The diagram has no inherent logic and is usually stimulus-response orientated. See below.

Example 1
Produce a topic web as a first step to organising ideas on metal manufacturing processes.

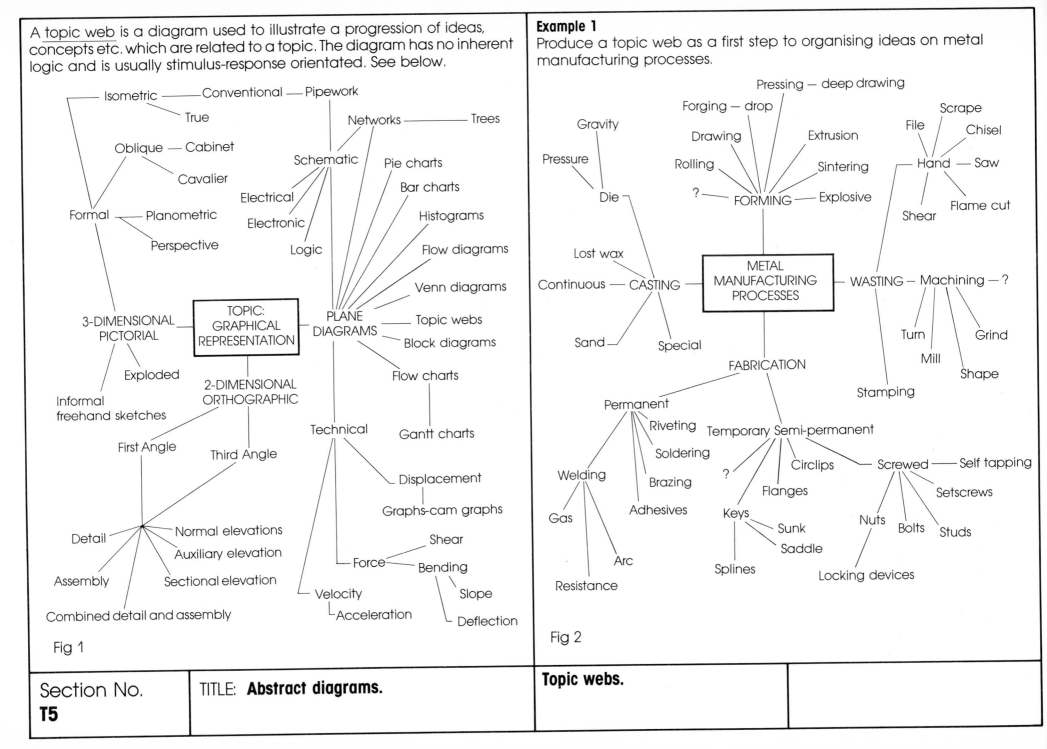

Fig 1

Fig 2

Section No.	TITLE: **Abstract diagrams.**	**Topic webs.**	
T5			

Classification: A process which groups related elements into recognisable sets.

Element: A single entity, symbol, object, number, value, individual etc.

Set: A collection of related elements.

Partition: The division of a set into subsets where:
(a) every element belongs to one subset of the partition,
(b) no 2 subsets intersect, i.e. an element cannot belong to 2 or more subsets.

Subset: A set which has special qualities or relationships between its elements.

Note: The subset shown shaded in Fig 3 is the set of all regular plane shapes. It is a subset of the set of all plane shapes defined by straight edges. The circle has been included as it can be considered to have an infinite number of infinitely small straight sides.

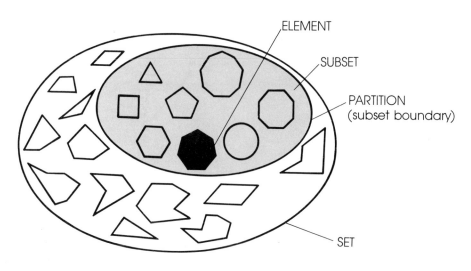

Fig 3

Venn diagrams: Abstract diagrams used to represent sets and the relationships between sets. See Fig 4 and Fig 5.

Intersection: The intersection of set A with set B produces set C whose elements belong to <u>both</u> A and B. Symbol for intersection is $\cap$, e.g. $A \cap B = C$ (shaded).

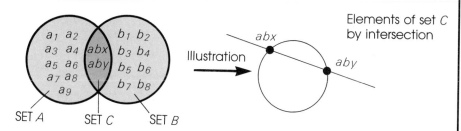

Set A, a line defined by an infinite number of points a_1, a_2, a_3, a_4, etc.

Set B, a circle defined by points b_1, b_2, b_3, etc.

Fig 4

Union: The union of 2 sets A and B produces a third set C whose elements belong to <u>either</u> A or B <u>or</u> A and B. Symbol for union is $\cup$, e.g. $A \cup B = C$ (shaded).

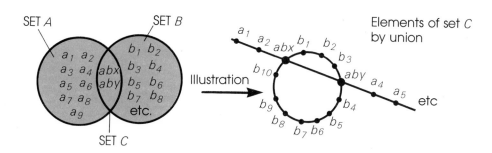

Fig 5

Section No.	TITLE: **Abstract diagrams.**	**Venn diagrams.**	
T5			

327

A network is represented by a number of lines or <u>arcs</u> which join together a number of reference positions termed <u>nodes.</u> See Fig 1.

Arc: A route which joins a pair of nodes. See Fig 1.

Node: A point of arrival or departure, or both. The order of the node refers to the number of arcs which meet at the node. See Fig 1 where order of node A is 2, B is 3, C is 4, D is 4, and E is 3, i.e. A is an even node, B is an odd node.

Planar network: A network which can be drawn on a plane surface without the arcs intersecting. See Fig 1, Fig 2 and Fig 4 for examples.

Non-planar network: A network which requires a third dimension, i.e. a 3-D space. Fig 3 represents a 3-D network where the arc A to C weaves behind the arc E to B and in front of the arc B to D. The arc A to C is in fact complete with the break being used to give the impression of it curving behind the arc E to B.

Complete network: A network where every node is linked <u>directly</u> to every other node. See Fig 2 and Fig 3 for examples.

Path: A path is a sequence of connected arcs which can be followed with an arc being used only once. See Fig 4 for an illustration of a path from A to D which follows the route A-B-F-E-D.

Circuit: A circuit is a path which starts and finishes at the same node, that is, the path is closed. Applications include electric circuits. See Fig 6, where the path completes a circuit A-B-E-D-C-A.

Open path: A path which starts and finishes at different nodes. Fig 4 illustrates an open path A-B-F-E-D.

Traverse: A path is said to traverse the network if <u>every</u> arc is used only once. Fig 5 can be traversed using the path A-B-C-D-E-D-E-A, which is also closed. Fig 7 can be traversed by a path A-B-C-D-E-D-F-E-F-B-G which is an open path. A path cannot traverse a network if the network has more than 2 odd nodes. If an open path traverses a network the start and finish must have odd nodes. If all nodes are even, a closed path exists which can traverse the network. In Fig 8 the odd node C can be the start of an open path which traverses the network, e.g. C-A-B-D-E-D-C-E.

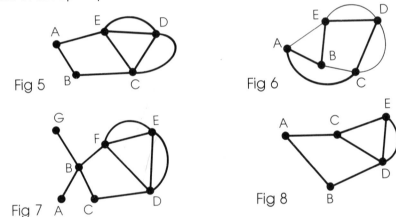

Fig 5   Fig 6

Fig 7   Fig 8

EXERCISE 1

(a) Can the network shown in Fig 9 be traversed?
(b) Draw Fig 9 and illustrate 2 different circuits which use a common arc.
(c) Draw the network shown in Fig 6 and produce a path which traverses it. List the nodes in order to describe the path.

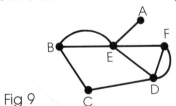

Fig 9

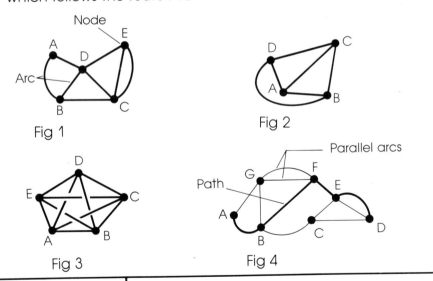

Fig 1

Fig 2

Fig 3

Fig 4

| Section No. **T6** | TITLE: **Logical diagrams.** | **Networks.** | |

A tree diagram is a network with the number of arcs being one less than the number of nodes, i.e. No. of arcs = no. of nodes − 1.
Fig 10 illustrates a tree which has 10 nodes and 9 arcs.
A tree is the mathematical counterpart to the topic web and is logical in its progression. It is often used to classify elements or order processes. Tree diagrams are generally used to describe static situations although they may be used in a dynamic (moving) situation. Alternative courses of action may be clarified by using a tree, see Fig 11, e.g. If I do A then I can do C or D, but if I do B then I can do E or F or G.

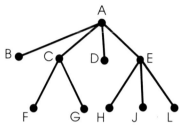

Fig 10

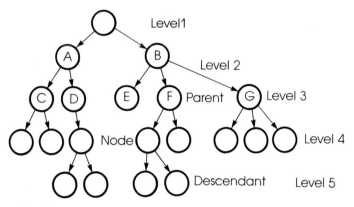

Fig 11 Arrows are omitted when the tree form makes the subordinate obvious.

Node: an element in the hierarchy.
Parent: the node above the observed level.
Descendant: the node below the observed level.
(Level 4 is the observed level illustrated in Fig 11.)

EXAMPLE 1
Produce a tree which classifies the permanent methods of joining materials.

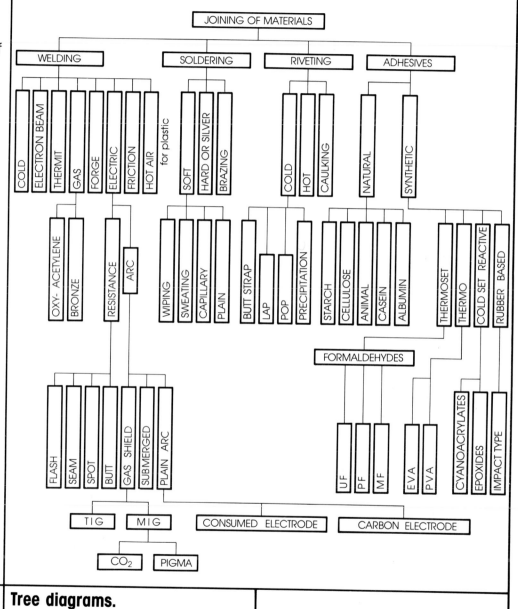

Section No.	TITLE: **Logical diagrams.**	**Tree diagrams.**	
T6			

329

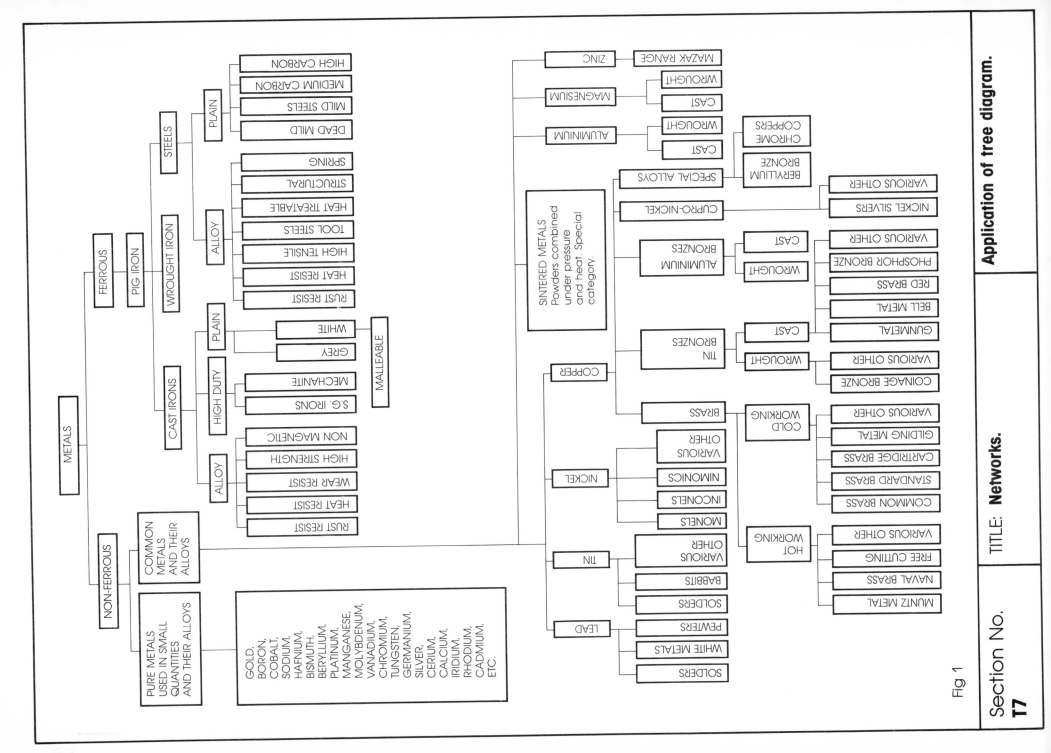

Fig 1

Section No.
T7

TITLE: **Networks.**

Application of tree diagram.

Consider the way in which a simple on/off switch works in an electric circuit.

When the switch is open the path in Fig 2 starts at D and finishes at C, therefore the path is open. Since the path is open, electrons are prevented from flowing due to the break in the conductor and since the lamp relies on a flow of electrons for its illumination, it remains off.

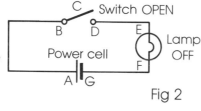

Fig 2

When the switch is closed the path forms a circuit since C and D become the same node (see p 328 Fig 4 and Fig 6). The electrons can now flow round the circuit and through the lamp to illuminate it, i.e. the lamp is switched on. See Fig 3.

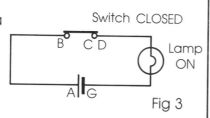

Fig 3

On/off switches can be arranged in (a) series and (b) parallel as shown in Figs 4a, b, c and d, and Figs 6a, b, c and d.

SERIES

When switches are in series it can be seen from the sequence below that current flow is permitted only on condition that both x and y are in the closed (ON) position. A circuit or closed path is shown in Fig 4d.

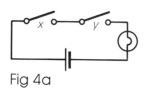

Fig 4a

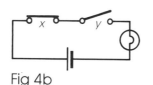

Fig 4b

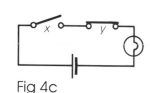

Fig 4c

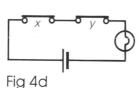

Fig 4d

0 and 1 are binary numbers and in logic they are the conventions used to signify switch conditions, i.e. 0 is OFF, 1 is ON, 0 is no current flow, 1 is current flow, 0 is false, 1 is true.

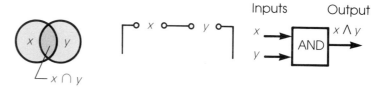

Fig 5a Venn = Fig 5b Switch = Fig 5c Logic gate

The shaded area of the Venn diagram (Fig 5a) represents elements belonging to both set x and set y. The corresponding switch arrangement shown in Fig 5b is referred to as an AND gate in logic and can be replaced by a block as shown in Fig 5c. See Figs 4a, b, c and d.

Note: In set theory, intersection is written $x \cap y$ for use with Venn diagrams but the symbol changes to $x \wedge y$ for the corresponding switch and logic networks. Similarly, union, which is written $x \cup y$ changes to $x \vee y$ for switching and logic networks.

Truth table for Figs 5a, b and c

SWITCH x	SWITCH y	SERIES $x \wedge y$
0 off	0 off	0 off
1 on	0 off	0 off
0 off	1 on	0 off
1 on	1 on	1 on

Section No.	TITLE: **Networks.**	**Introduction to logic networks.**	
T7			

PARALLEL

When switches are arranged in parallel as in the sequence below, current flow is permitted when <u>either</u> switch x or switch y is closed or both switches x <u>and</u> y are closed. A circuit or closed path is shown in Figs 6b, c and d.

The Venn diagram (Fig 7a) represents union with the corresponding switch arrangement in Fig 7b being replaced by an OR gate, its logic equivalent, as in Fig 7c.
See Figs 6a, b, c and d.

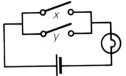

Fig 6a

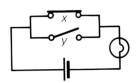

Fig 6b

Truth table for Figs 7a, b and c

SWITCH x	SWITCH y	SERIES $x \lor y$
0 off	0 off	0 off
1 on	0 off	1 on
0 off	1 on	1 on
1 on	1 on	1 on

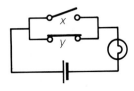

Fig 6c

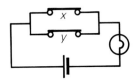

Fig 6d

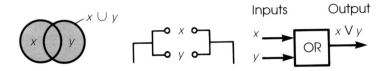

Fig 7a Venn = Fig 7b Switch = Fig 7c Logic gate

Section No.	TITLE: **Networks.**	**Introduction to logic networks.**
T7		

An expansion of series switching, AND gates, and parallel switching, OR gates, follows with the introduction of 3 switches or input conditions.

Venn diagram: Members of the intersection set must all belong to each of the sets x, y and z for there to be an intersection between x AND y AND z, i.e. the shaded set $s = x \cap y \cap z$ (See Fig 8a).

Switching diagram: Similarly, a closed path would only exist between A and B if x AND y AND z are closed; that is, in condition 1. See truth table for output of series switching.

Logic gate: There must be an input condition 1 to x AND y AND z in order to obtain a positive output signal 1. See truth table for output $s = x \wedge y \wedge z$ from the AND gate.

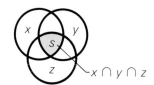

Fig 8a

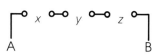

A   B

Fig 8b

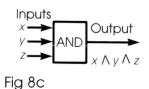

Fig 8c

Truth table for Figs 8a, b and c

Switch condition INPUT			SYSTEM OUTPUT
x	y	z	$x \wedge y \wedge z$
0	0	0	0
0	0	1	0
0	1	0	0
0	1	1	0
1	0	0	0
1	0	1	0
1	1	0	0
1	1	1	1

Venn diagram: The union of the sets x, y and z produces a set which has elements belonging to x OR y OR z, or x AND y, or x AND z, or y AND z, or x AND y AND z, i.e. the tinted set $s = x \cup y \cup z$.

Switching diagram: Similarly, a closed path would exist between A and B if either x OR y OR z is in the closed (i.e. 1 condition) or if x AND y, or x AND z, or y AND z, or x AND y AND z are closed. A closed path exists if one or more switches are closed.

Logic gate: There must be an input to any one of the input terminals of the gate to obtain a <u>positive</u> output.

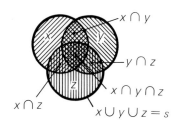

Fig 9a

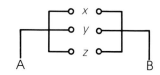

A   B

Fig 9b

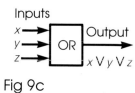

Fig 9c

Truth table for Figs 9a, b and c

Switch condition INPUT			SYSTEM OUTPUT
x	y	z	$x \vee y \vee z$
0	0	0	0
0	0	1	1
0	1	0	1
0	1	1	1
1	0	0	1
1	0	1	1
1	1	0	1
1	1	1	1

Section No. T7	TITLE: **Networks.**	**AND and OR gates.**	

Combinations of gates: Gates may be combined to form a network which will give a desired output.

EXAMPLE 1

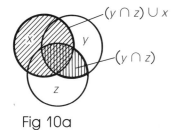

$(y \cap z) \cup x$

$(y \cap z)$

Fig 10a

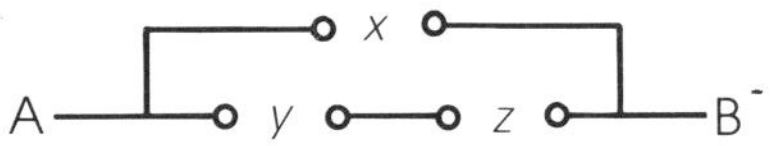

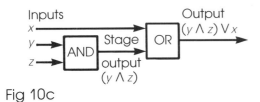

Fig 10b

Fig 10c

Inputs
Output $(y \wedge z) \vee x$

Stage output $(y \wedge z)$

Truth table for Figs 10a, b and c

INPUT	INPUT	STAGE	INPUT	OUTPUT
y	z	$y \wedge z$	x	$(y \wedge z) \vee x$
0	0	0	0	0
0	0	0	1	1
0	1	0	0	0
0	1	0	1	1
1	0	0	0	0
1	0	0	1	1
1	1	1	0	1
1	1	1	1	1

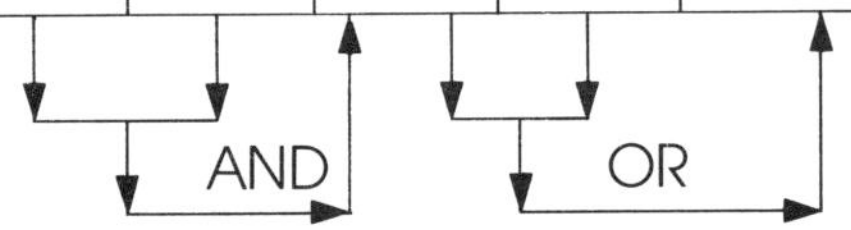

AND   OR

EXAMPLE 2

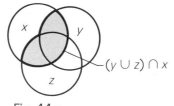

$(y \cup z) \cap x$

Fig 11a

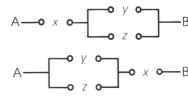

Fig 11b

Inputs
Output $(y \vee z) \wedge x$

Stage output $(y \vee z)$

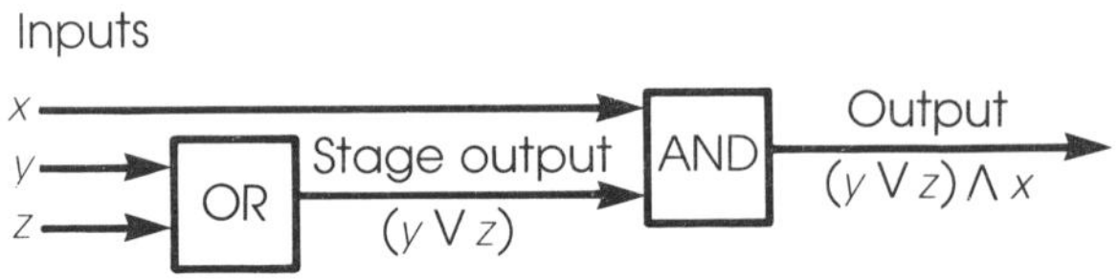

Fig 11c

Truth table for Figs 11a, b and c

INPUT	INPUT	STAGE	INPUT	OUTPUT
y	z	$y \vee z$	x	$(y \vee z) \wedge x$
0	0	0	0	0
0	0	0	1	0
0	1	1	0	0
0	1	1	1	1
1	0	1	0	0
1	0	1	1	1
1	1	1	0	0
1	1	1	1	1

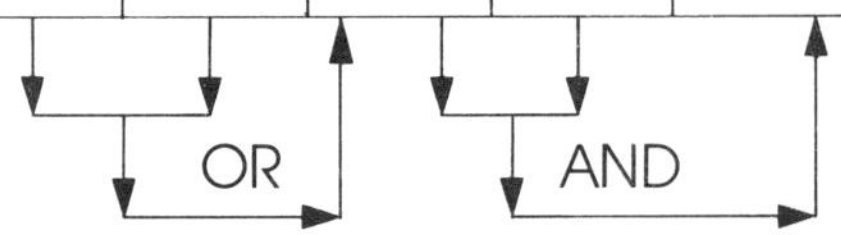

OR   AND

| Section No. **T7** | TITLE: **Networks.** | **Logic and switching networks.** | |

EXAMPLE 3

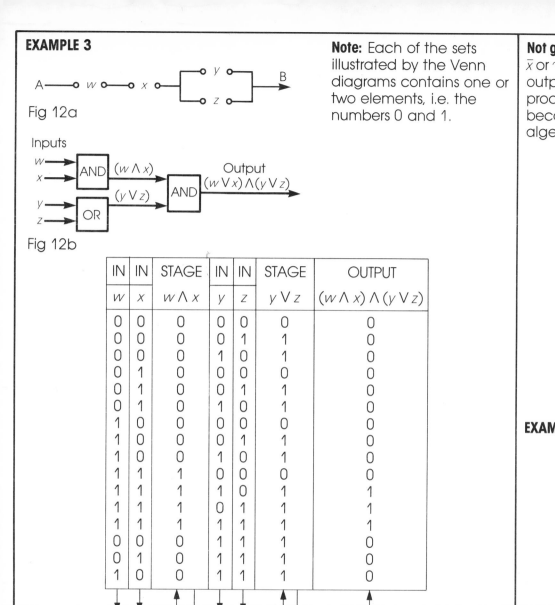

Fig 12a

Inputs

Fig 12b

IN	IN	STAGE	IN	IN	STAGE	OUTPUT
w	x	$w \wedge x$	y	z	$y \vee z$	$(w \wedge x) \wedge (y \vee z)$
0	0	0	0	0	0	0
0	0	0	0	1	1	0
0	0	0	1	0	1	0
0	1	0	0	0	0	0
0	1	0	0	1	1	0
0	1	0	1	0	1	0
1	0	0	0	0	0	0
1	0	0	0	1	1	0
1	0	0	1	0	1	0
1	1	1	0	0	0	0
1	1	1	1	0	1	1
1	1	1	0	1	1	1
1	1	1	1	1	1	1
0	0	0	1	1	1	0
0	1	0	1	1	1	0
1	0	0	1	1	1	0

AND   OR

AND

Note: Each of the sets illustrated by the Venn diagrams contains one or two elements, i.e. the numbers 0 and 1.

Not gates: The NOT gate reverses the value of the signal x to NOT x, written $\bar{x}$ or $\sim x$. When the input (x) is 0 the NOT gate would produce a positive output, i.e. a 1 signal. If the input to the NOT gate is 1 the gate would produce a 0 output signal. If NOT x passes into a NOT gate the output becomes NOT, NOT x, i.e. $\sim(\bar{x})$ which compares with $-(-x) = x$ in algebra. Therefore $\sim(\bar{x}) = x$.

Fig 13a

A ———o $\bar{x}$ o——— B

Fig 13b

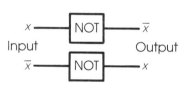

Fig 13c

INPUT	OUTPUT
x	$\sim x$
0	1
1	0

EXAMPLE 4 NOT gate effect

$\sim(x \cap y)$

Fig 14a

A ———o x o——o y o——o $\bar{z}$ o——— B

$z = x \wedge y$

Fig 14b

Inputs

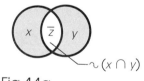

$z = x \wedge y$ $\sim(x \wedge y)$

Fig 14c

IN	IN	STAGE	OUTPUT
x	y	$x \wedge y$	$\sim(x \wedge y)$
0	0	0	1
1	0	0	1
0	1	0	1
1	1	1	0

Section No.	TITLE: **Networks.**	**Switching networks and NOT gates.**	
T7			

The examples of switching and logic networks which have been considered so far have dealt with ON or OFF conditions only. Two-way (one-gang) switches open one path of a network but close another path simultaneously. See Fig 15 where the condition of path A to B relies on the condition of the path A to C in the switch wiring diagram.

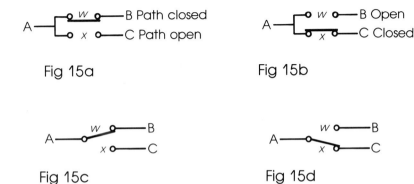

Fig 15a

Fig 15b

Fig 15c

Fig 15d

The conditions of the switch are w AND NOT x or x AND NOT w which is written $(w \wedge \bar{x}) \vee (x \wedge \bar{w})$.

Note: The switch is not an OR logic switch as it does not contain the w AND x combination. See T7 Figs 6a, b, c and d and Fig 9b. In logic OR means w or x or (w and x). The corresponding switching network to Figs 15a and 15b is illustrated in Fig 16a together with the logic network in Fig 16b and the truth table which follows.

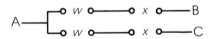

Fig 16a Switching network

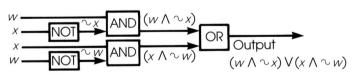

Fig 16b Logic network.

IN		IN		STAGE	STAGE	OUTPUT
w	$\sim w$	x	$\sim x$	$w \wedge \sim x$	$x \wedge \sim w$	$(w \wedge \sim x) \vee (x \wedge \sim w)$
0	1	0	1	0	0	0
1	0	1	0	0	0	0
0	1	1	0	0	1	1
1	0	0	1	1	0	1

Application of a system using two-way switching

Perhaps the most common application of two-way switches is to be found in the normal two-storey house where a switch at the bottom of a stairway can switch the stair light on or off and the switch at the top of the stairway can perform the same function. It must be possible to switch the light on from each end of the stairway and off from each end of the stairway. See Figs 17a, b, c and d.

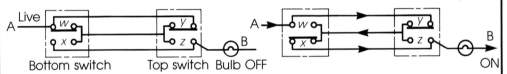

Fig 17a Wiring diagram — switch condition 1.

Fig 17b Switch condition 2.

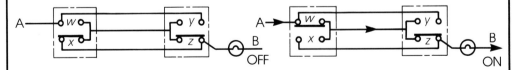

Fig 17c Switch condition 3. See truth table opposite.

Fig 17d Switch condition 4.

Section No.	TITLE: **Networks.**		**Two-way switching logic.**	
T7				

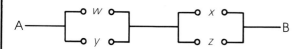

A————[w] / [y]————[x] / [z]————B

Fig 18a Switching network.

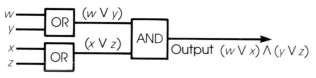

Fig 18b Logic network.

IN	IN	IN	IN	STAGE	STAGE	OUTPUT
w	y	x	z	$w \vee y$	$x \vee z$	$(w \vee y) \wedge (x \vee z)$
1	1	0	0	1	0	0
0	1	1	0	1	1	1
0	0	1	1	0	1	0
1	0	0	1	1	1	1

NAND gate: This is a logic gate which combines the function of the AND and NOT gates shown in Fig 19a. This combination can be simplified to the single gate shown in Fig 19b. Note the use of the symbol &, to represent AND and the negation symbol ○, at the exit from the gate to illustrate that the gate is a NOT AND, i.e. NAND gate. The output from a NAND gate is the reverse of the outputs from an AND gate. See truth table.

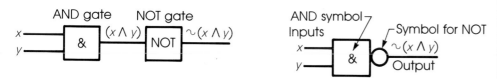

Fig 19a AND and NOT equals Fig 19b NAND gate.

IN	IN	STAGE	NAND OUTPUT
x	y	$x \wedge y$	$\sim(x \wedge y)$
0	0	0	1
1	0	0	1
0	1	0	1
1	1	1	0

NOR gate: This is a logic gate which combines the functions of the OR and NOT gates shown in Fig 20a. This combination can be simplified to the single gate shown in Fig 20b. Note the use of the symbol ≦ 1 to represent OR. See the truth table output on T7, Fig 9c, where a 1 output will be obtained if one or more inputs are in a 1 condition. The output from a NOR gate is the reverse of the outputs from an OR gate. Compare the outputs from the truth table below with those in the truth table for Fig 9c.

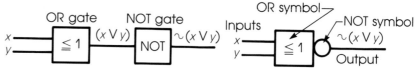

Fig 20a OR and NOT equals Fig 20b NOR gate.

IN	IN	STAGE	NOR OUTPUT
x	y	$x \vee y$	$\sim(x \vee y)$
0	0	0	1
1	0	1	0
0	1	1	0
1	1	1	0

Section No.	TITLE: **Networks.**	**NAND and NOR gates.**	
T7			

Use of logic gates

Logic gates find general use in electronic equipment and computers where they often take the form of integrated circuits (ICs). These are produced from semiconductor material which is in wafer form and consists of individual transistors linked in a switching network by conducting paths together with other electrical features. The transistors or semiconductor material act as the switches but the circuits may involve other electrical features such as resistors and capacitors.

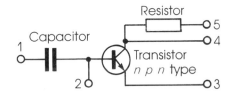

Fig 21a   Electronic schematic.

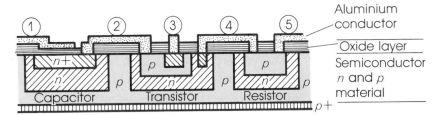

Fig 21b   Semiconductor integrated circuit equivalent to Fig 21a.

TYPE OF LOGIC GATE					
	AND	OR	NOT	NAND	NOR
BRITISH STANDARD SYMBOLS (BS 3939)	⊐&⊐	⊐≦1⊐	⊐1⊳	⊐&⊳	⊐≦1⊳
AMERICAN ANSI STANDARD SYMBOLS	⊐⊐	⊐⊐	⊳◦	⊐⊐◦	⊐⊐◦

Conventions

Paths connected   Path not connected

Logic problems

(a) Produce a switching network corresponding to the logic network shown and determine an expression for its output.

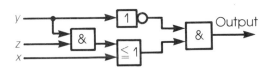

(b) Produce a logic network which corresponds to the switching network and determine an expression for its output.

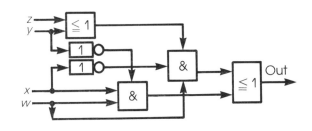

(c) Produce an equivalent switching network to the logic network shown.

Section No.	TITLE: **Networks.**	**Use of logic gates and logic problems.**	
T7			

338

Schematic circuit diagram: This type of diagram shows the connection to every component with the components represented by standard symbols. The components are usually specified on the diagram or listed separately.

Fig 1a shows a schematic circuit diagram for an electric bell, bell push, and transformer-rectifier.

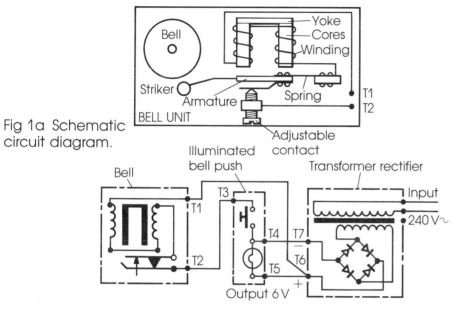

Fig 1a Schematic circuit diagram.

Block diagram: A form of diagram which represents the functional or working relationship that exists between separate complete units or assemblies. The units are represented by rectangles or blocks which indicate an interdependence, transfer of energy or transmission of signals between the functional units.

The block diagram provides a means of analysing a system's overall workings without the distraction of the detailed working of the individual units. This simplification is better illustrated by the block diagram on p 344 which describes an electronic digital voltmeter.

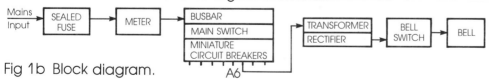

Fig 1b Block diagram.

Installation diagram: A diagram which locates the components within their frame of reference. The components are shown in symbolic form within the building which acts as the frame of reference for their location. Conductors are not shown.

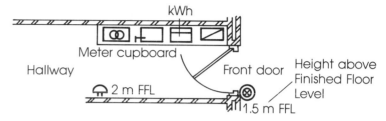

Fig 1c Installation diagram.

Wiring diagram: The wiring diagram illustrates the network of conducting paths between the terminals of the individual components. Where several conductors travel in parallel between components a cable may be used which carries several insulated conductors. A wiring harness can also be formed to carry several individual conductors which travel in parallel for a part of the distance but may split into groups to travel to separate destinations. The insulation around the conductors is colour coded to differentiate between the individual conductors of the cable, to simplify their tracing and connection.

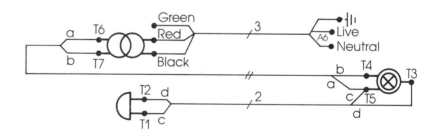

a and c — red or brown, +DC.
b and d — black or blue, −DC.

Fig 1d Wiring diagram.

Section No.	TITLE: **Electrical networks.**	**Schematic, block, installation and wiring diagrams.**	
T8			

Schematic circuit, wiring and layout diagram symbols

Cell		Rheostat		Circuit breaker		Ohmmeter		Electric bell
Battery		Potentiometer		Make contactor		Generator		Buzzer
Battery (alternative)		Impedance		Break contactor		Motor		Chassis-ground
Polarity POSITIVE		Capacitor		Winding with one tapping		DC Generator		Earth
Polarity NEGATIVE		p n Diode		Transformer		DC Motor		Pyrometer Thermometer
Direct current DC		p n Diode on a "chip"		Single element relay		Alternator AC Generator		Thermocouple
Alternating current AC		Light sensitive p n Diode		Heater		AC Motor		Single stroke bell
Suitable for AC and DC		Thyristor		Heater alternative		Oscilloscope		
Conductor		p n p Transistor		Mechanical coupling		Discharge lamp		
Conductors not connected		n p n Transistor		Relay coil		Clock-timer		**Installation symbols**
Conductors connected		Microphone		Socket (female)		Make contact		Main control or supply
Separable contact		Earphone		Plug (male)		Break contact		Main switch
Fixed or bolted contact		Loudspeaker		Multiple pole plug and socket		Push button make contact		Meter
Fuse		Headphones		4-pole plug and socket		Push button break contact		Spotlight
Fuse		Conductors twisted		Coaxial socket		Mechanically coupled make contactors		Wall light with built in switch
Fuse-supply side indicated		Cable with 3 conductors		Coaxial plug		Change over contact		Lighting point built in switch
Winding		1 line to mean 3 conductors		Jack sleeve and spring		Change over contact		Wall mounted light point
Transformer		2 conductors in one line		3-pole concentric jack and plug		Change over diagonally		Single tube fluorescent
Resistor		Link (separable)		Ammeter		Change over contact unit		Multiple lamp fluorescent
Resistor (alternative)		Link (fixed)		Voltmeter		Make/break contact unit		Fluorescent lamp-multiple
Variability		Filament lamp		Wattmeter		Mech. operated break pulse		Multiple light point
Variable resistor		Signal lamp						

Lamp or lighting point	
Switch with a pilot light	
Cord operated one-way switch	
Single pole one-way switch	
Push button contact	
Illuminated push button	
Transformer	
2-pole one-way switch	
Two-way switch	
Electrical appliance	
Intermediate switch	
Rheostat or dimmer switch	
Socket outlet	
Switched socket	
Multiple socket outlet	
Socket with pilot light	
Switched socket with pilot light	
Consumer's earth point	
Fan	
Thermostat	
Time switch	
Aerial	

Section No.	TITLE: **Electrical networks.**	**Electrical symbols.**
T8		

340

Ring main socket outlets: Each socket on the ring main may obtain its supply by 2 routes from the supply unit, that is clockwise or anticlockwise around the ring, see Fig 1. The mains supply is distributed to the ring via the main switch and distribution fuse box containing the miniature circuit breakers, see T8 Fig 1b. The miniature circuit breaker for the ring main is fused, rated at 30 amperes (30 A). In a multi-storey building each floor will normally have a separate ring although a house having a floor area less than 100 square metres may have an unlimited number of socket outlets. A typical ring is illustrated in Fig 1 which also shows sockets located on spurs. The number of sockets on an unfused spur is limited to 2 and the total number of sockets on spurs must not exceed half the number of sockets on the ring.

The paths between the sockets are PVC-sheathed cables with each cable carrying 3 insulated conductors each having a cross-sectional area of 2.5 mm^2. The insulation around the conductors is colour coded, red for live, black for neutral and green for earth.

Flexible cables distribute power to the appliances from the sockets via a plug with the conductors carried in the cable having their insulation colour coded as follows: brown for live, blue for neutral, and green and yellow for earth.

Appliances which require an earth must not be connected to a lighting circuit.

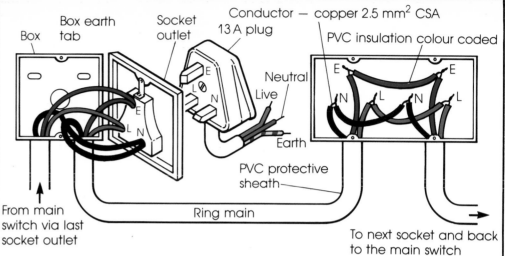

Fig 2   Wiring for a single socket on a ring main.

Fig 3   Wiring for a double socket on a ring main.

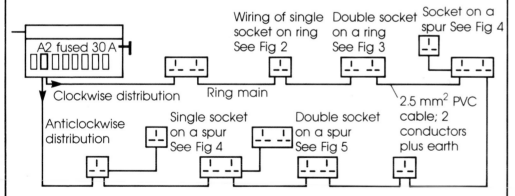

Fig 1   Typical ring main block diagram. Suffices as a wiring diagram since the electrician is aware of the individual connections of the conductors in each box. These connections are illustrated in Figs 2, 3, 4 and 5.

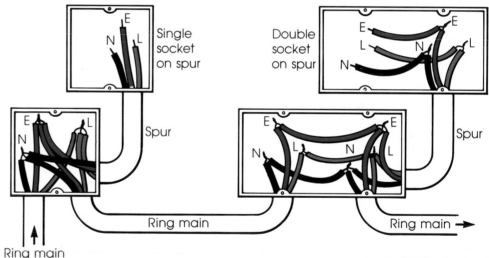

Fig 4   Wiring for a spur off a single socket outlet on the ring main.

Fig 5   Wiring for a spur with a double socket outlet from a double socket on the ring main.

Section No.	TITLE: **House wiring networks.**	**Power supply and ring main.**	
T9			

Installation diagram: The architect or engineer specifies the electrical services required for a building on an installation diagram as shown in Fig 6. The electrician would produce the wiring diagrams from each of the miniature circuit breakers.

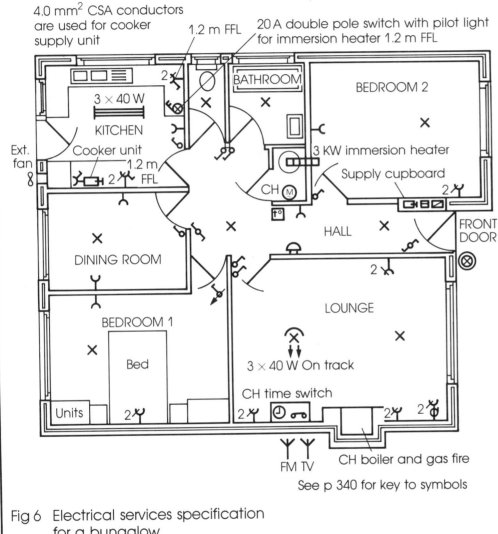

4.0 mm² CSA conductors are used for cooker supply unit

1.2 m FFL

20 A double pole switch with pilot light for immersion heater 1.2 m FFL

3 × 40 W

KITCHEN

Cooker unit

1.2 m FFL

Ext. fan

2

BATHROOM

BEDROOM 2

3 KW immersion heater

Supply cupboard

2

DINING ROOM

CH

HALL

FRONT DOOR

BEDROOM 1

Bed

Units

2

LOUNGE

3 × 40 W On track

CH time switch

2

FM TV

CH boiler and gas fire

See p 340 for key to symbols

Fig 6 Electrical services specification for a bungalow.

There are several methods of distributing the power from the main switch unit to the light switches and lighting points. The block diagram in Fig 7 illustrates the different methods of distribution and connection generally in use, with the actual wiring at the switches, joint boxes and ceiling roses detailed in Figs 8 to 14. The block diagram illustrates the maximum number of lighting points on a network which uses the standard 1.0 mm² CSA conductors, but more generally the number is kept down to 8 or 9 points. Since the miniature circuit breaker for the lighting network is fused, rated at 5 A, and the circuit voltage is 240 V, then the maximum power, in watts, which can be transmitted through the network is 240 V × 5 A = 1200 W (since watts = volts × amps). (Note result gives 12 × 100 W bulbs.) Two-core-and-earth PVC-sheathed cable with the conductors insulated by PVC colour coded red for live and black for neutral is generally used with the conductors of 1.0 mm² CSA and the earth contained in the sheath.

Note: In Fig 8 a black insulated conductor is supplied with a red tab to show its use as a live conductor. Figs 13 and 14 show a 3-core-and-earth cable, colour coded red, blue, yellow and green with the red, blue and yellow all potentially live conductors as in their 3-phase general use. The use of 3 types of switches is illustrated with Fig 8 showing a one-way switch, Fig 13 a 2-gang switch (2 one-way switches in one box) and Fig 14 a 2-way switch.

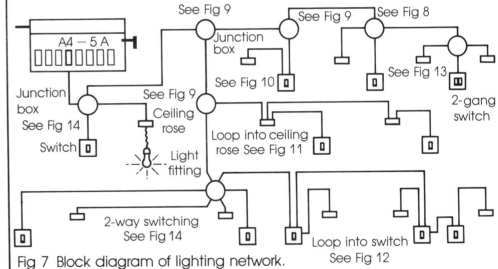

Fig 7 Block diagram of lighting network.

| Section No. | TITLE: **House wiring networks.** | **Installation and lighting.** |

T9

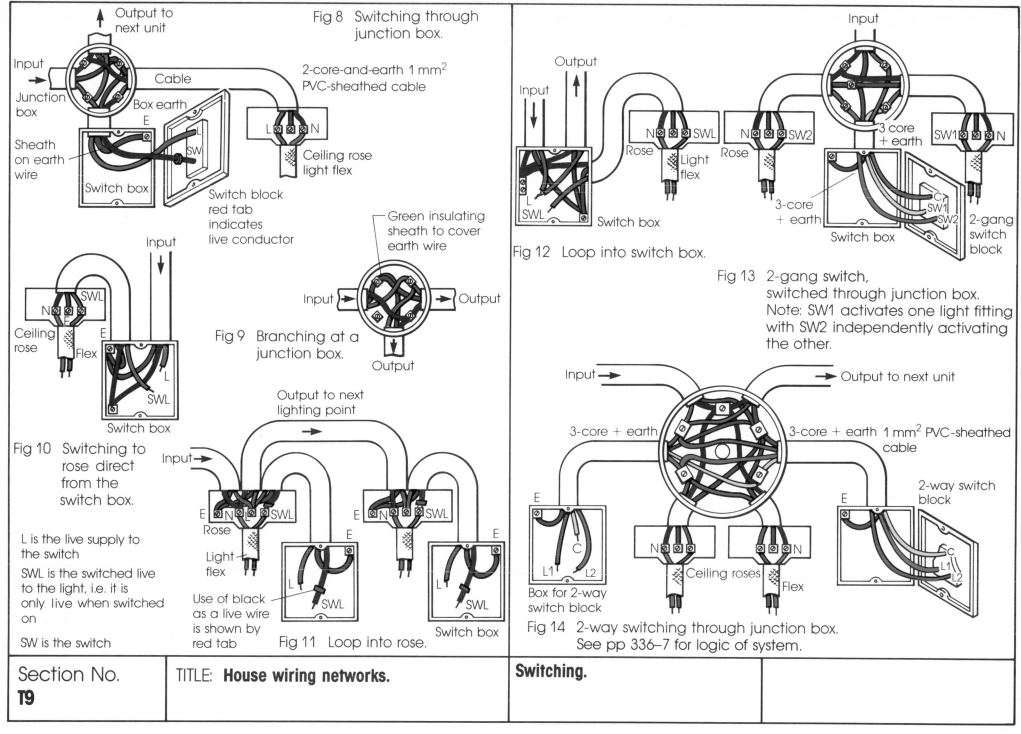

Fig 8 Switching through junction box.

Output to next unit

Input

Junction box

Box earth

Sheath on earth wire

Switch box

Cable

E

L

SW

2-core-and-earth 1 mm² PVC-sheathed cable

L N

Ceiling rose light flex

Switch block red tab indicates live conductor

Green insulating sheath to cover earth wire

Input

Output

Output

Fig 9 Branching at a junction box.

SWL

N

E

Ceiling rose

Flex

E

L

SWL

Switch box

Input

Fig 10 Switching to rose direct from the switch box.

L is the live supply to the switch

SWL is the switched live to the light, i.e. it is only live when switched on

SW is the switch

Input

Output to next lighting point

E N SWL

Rose

Light flex

Use of black as a live wire is shown by red tab

E N SWL

E

L

SWL

E

L

SWL

Switch box

Fig 11 Loop into rose.

Input

Output

N SWL

Rose

Light flex

Switch box

L

SWL

Input

N SW2

Rose

3 core + earth

3-core + earth

SW1 N

C

SW1

SW2

Switch box

2-gang switch block

Fig 12 Loop into switch box.

Fig 13 2-gang switch, switched through junction box.
Note: SW1 activates one light fitting with SW2 independently activating the other.

Input

Output to next unit

3-core + earth

3-core + earth 1 mm² PVC-sheathed cable

E

C

L1 L2

Box for 2-way switch block

N

Ceiling roses

N

Flex

E

2-way switch block

C

L1

L2

Fig 14 2-way switching through junction box.
See pp 336–7 for logic of system.

| Section No. T9 | TITLE: **House wiring networks.** | **Switching.** |

The following diagrams describe a digital electronic voltmeter in different ways and are provided as examples of the various stages of illustrating an electronics network.

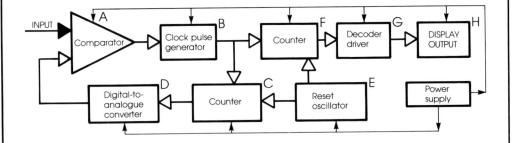

Fig 1 Block diagram. Similar to Fig 1b p 339. The block diagram elements A, B, C, D and E are represented in the left-hand side of the circuit diagram and this in turn in Figs 3a and 4a; F, G, and H by the right-hand side and in Figs 3b and 4b.

Note the symbols shown on the integrated circuits (ICs), locate the pin number 1 with the other pins numbered consecutively around the IC:

This consecutive numbering is not strictly necessary on the schematic circuit diagram shown in Fig 2.

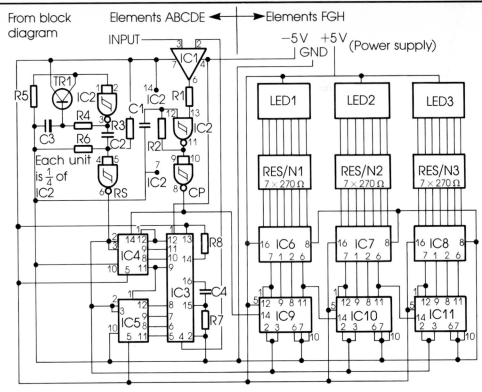

Fig 2 Circuit diagram: Similar to Fig 1a p 339. Schematic layout only.

TR1	BC109	Transistor
IC1	741	Op. Amp
IC2	74132	Quad Schmitt trigger
IC3	MC1408	8-bit DAC
IC4 and 5	7493	4-bit binary counters
IC6, 7 and 8	7447	Decoder driver
IC9, 10 and 11	7490	Decade counter
LED1, 2 and 3		Light emitting diode

RES/N1, 2 and 3 $7 \times 270\ \Omega$	
R1	2.2 kΩ
R2	330 Ω
R3	1 kΩ
R4	3.3 kΩ
R5	330 Ω
R6	2.2 kΩ
R7	2.7 kΩ
R8	2.7 kΩ

C1	10 nF
C2	10 nF
C3	10 μF polarised
C4	50 pF

Note: GND = ground or earth.
CP = clock pulse.
RS = reset.
DAC = digital to analogue converter

Section No. **T10**	TITLE: **Electronics networks.**	**Block diagram and circuit diagram.**	

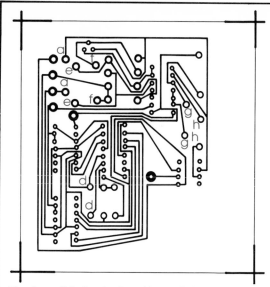

Fig 3a Printed circuit part 1.
The through board foil print as
it is known, is the counterpart
of the wiring diagram on T8 Fig 1d.

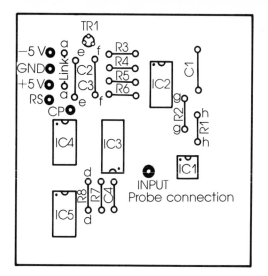

Fig 4a Component location diagram.
This diagram provides a similar function to
the installation diagram on T8 Fig 1c locating
the components within a frame of reference.

Wired connections are required between the 2
boards, CP to CP, RS to RS, GND to GND and +5 V to
+5 V with an external supply provided to the +5 V and
−5 V. Unlike the schematic in Fig 2 the conductors
on the boards cannot cross but where this is
necessary insulated wired links are provided, i.e.
a to a, b to b, and c to c. The links have only been
included to illustrate their use and could have
been avoided.

EXERCISE 1

Determine the paths of conducting tracks on the
boards which would have made the links a-a, b-b
and c-c redundant. Extra space between existing
conductors would have to be provided in some
areas.

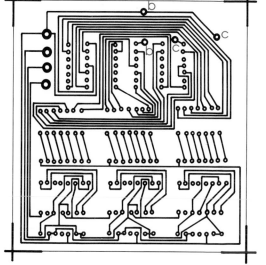

Fig 3b Printed circuit part 2.

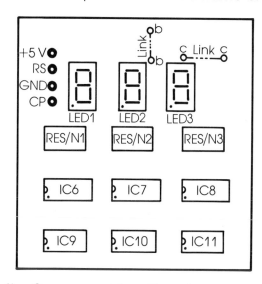

Fig 4b Component location diagram.

Section No.	TITLE: **Electronics networks.**	**Printed circuits and**	
T10		**component location diagrams.**	

Pipe networks are usually produced as plain schematics in the design stage where the routes between the network elements can be more easily analysed (see Fig 1 below). The network or system consists of a number of components which are connected to form routes between the functional elements of the system. In the plain schematic we generally define only the functional elements (i.e. valves, pumps, vessels, heat-exchangers etc.) with the pipe routes between them shown by lines. The content of the pipes and its condition may be designated as illustrated in Fig 4 with the network elements described by the symbols shown opposite.

The isometric schematic (see Fig 2) is usually drawn to scale and relates the elements spatially. The components which form the route or pipe and the method of their connection is also shown symbolically. Fig 2 contains all the information necessary to manufacture the system shown by the plain schematic, Fig 1. Alternatively, the spatial representation may be achieved through orthographic projection using the normal physical representation of the components although the symbols are often used once again to simplify the drawing process. See Fig 3.

It is important that the engineer is conversant with the symbols and their use together with the components and elements they represent. The table on the following page illustrates many of the standard symbols together with a range of composites (e.g. see 62 which involves 1, 12, 37, 46, 48, 51 and 60).

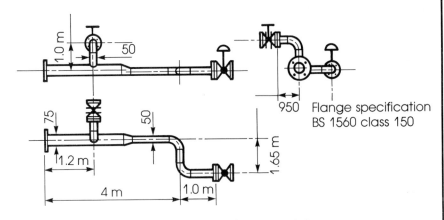

Fig 3   Orthographic projection (First Angle).

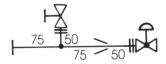

Fig 1   Plain schematic.

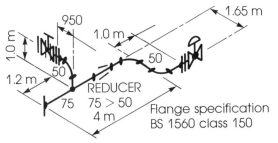

Fig 2   Isometric schematic.

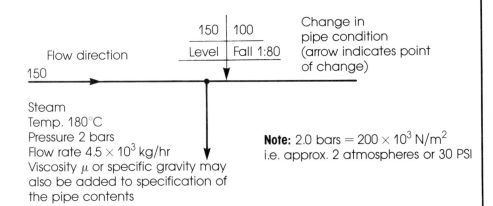

Flow direction

Steam
Temp. 180°C
Pressure 2 bars
Flow rate 4.5×10^3 kg/hr
Viscosity μ or specific gravity may also be added to specification of the pipe contents

Note: 2.0 bars = 200×10^3 N/m^2 i.e. approx. 2 atmospheres or 30 PSI

Fig 4   Designation of pipe contents.

| Drawing No. **T11** | TITLE: **Pipe networks.** | **Schematic presentation.** | |

Pipe; major flow line	1	Soldered tee	22	Globe valve	40
Pipe; minor flow line	2	Screwed tee	23	Butterfly valve	41
Pipes connect, i.e. junction	3	Flanged tee	24	Diaphragm valve	42
4-way junction	4	Soldered bend or elbow	25	Needle valve	43
Pipes cross but not connected	5	Screwed bend	26	Valve closed	44
Butt welded joint	6	Flanged bend	27	Valve; hand operated	45
Soldered or joint made by adhesive	7	Open vent	28	Valve; power operated	46
Screwed joint	8	Instrument; temperature gauge	29	Motor operated valve	47
Sleeve joint	9	Instrument; pressure gauge	30	Pressure control valve	48
Compression joint	10	Discharge to atmosphere	31	Power operated pressure control valve	49
Socket welded	11	Trap; release or retention	32	Flanged, hand operated valve	50
Flanged and bolted	12	Trapped vent	33	Valve to open on failure	51
Flanges welded on	13	Sight flow indicator	34	Flanged, power operated pressure control valve to close on failure	52
Flanges screwed on	14	Strainer or filter	35	Valve to maintain its position on failure	53
Pipe bore change	15	Orifice plate	36	Float operated valve e.g. cistern ball cock	54
End capped	16	Valve (in line); general symbol	37	Non return valve flow direction	55
End cap screwed	17	Parallel slide valve	38		
End, blank flanged and bolted	18	Wedge gate valve	39		
Pipe guide	19				
Pipe support	20				
Pipe hanger	21				

Plug or cock annotated T or L according to style of porting	56
3-way plug or cock with style of porting annotated T or L	57
Safety valve spring loaded	58
Safety valve; flanged and weight loaded	59
Angled valve	60
Angled valve; flanged and hand operated	61
Flanged, power operated, angled pressure control valve to open on failure	62
Radiator	63
Convector	64
Towel rail	65
Pump	66
Boiler	Blr	67
Hot water cylinder	HWC	68
Hot water tank	HWT	69
Freed and expansion tank	F&ET	70
Condensate tank	CT	71
Air vessel	72

Section No.	TITLE: **Pipe networks.**	**Pipe symbols.**	
T11			

347

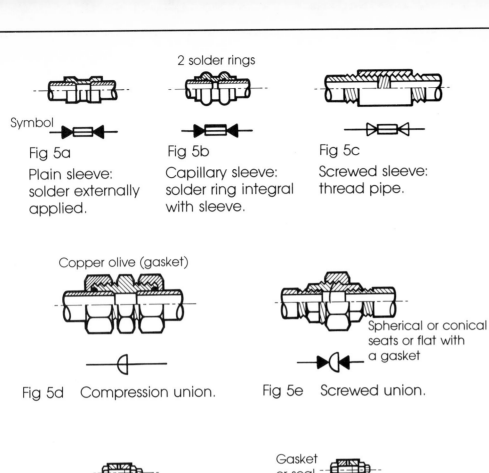

Symbol ◄■► Fig 5a

Fig 5a
Plain sleeve:
solder externally
applied.

Fig 5b
Capillary sleeve:
solder ring integral
with sleeve.

Fig 5c
Screwed sleeve:
thread pipe.

2 solder rings

Copper olive (gasket)

Spherical or conical
seats or flat with
a gasket

Fig 5d   Compression union.

Fig 5e   Screwed union.

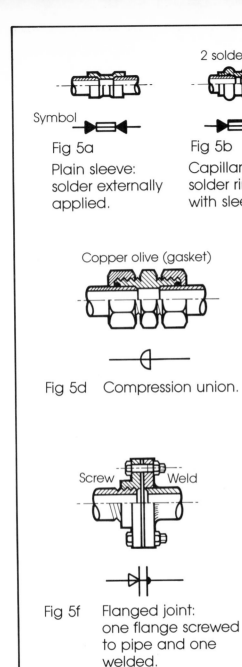

Screw   Weld

Fig 5f   Flanged joint:
one flange screwed
to pipe and one
welded.

Gasket
or seal

Fig 5g   Flanged joint:
flanges cast as integral
part of pipe.

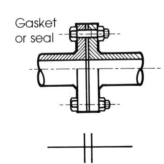

The bungalow shown in Fig 6 on p 342 would be adequately serviced
by this system with the hot water cylinder (HWC), motorised pump
and the manifold located in the airing cupboard next to the
bathroom.
Note: HWC and pump motor are shown in that location on p 342. This
system can be used for a house but requires 2 manifolds, one for the
first and one for the ground floor. Special entry/exit valves are fitted to
the radiators and connected to the manifold via 8 mm soft copper
tube and compression fittings as shown on the typical radiator 7
below.

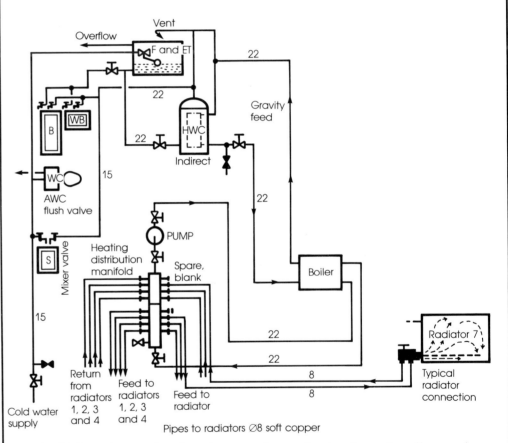

Fig 6   Plain schematic of water supply and microbore heating system.

Section No.	TITLE: **Pipe networks.**	**Joining the network elements.**
T11		

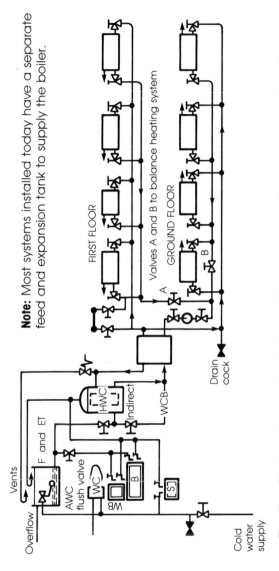

Note: Most systems installed today have a separate feed and expansion tank to supply the boiler.

Fig 7   Plain schematic of domestic water supply and central heating system (2-pipe) for typical 3 bedroom house.

The contents of pipes are often illustrated by different types of line on plumbing diagrams:

– – – – – hot water
———— fresh water
–·–·–·– salt water

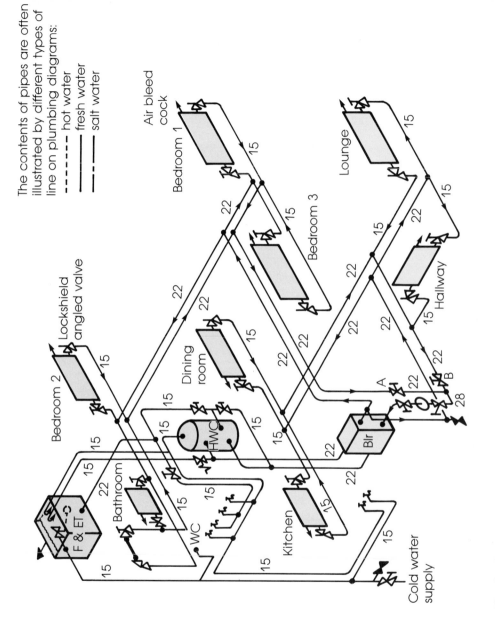

Fig 8   Isometric schematic of system shown in Fig 7.

Flow charts: Networks which graphically represent the ordered relationships which exist between the operations forming a process, or the components comprising a system.

The different types of elements (the operations, processes and various other components) of the system are distinguished by a variety of symbols which are connected by routes. These routes, or flow lines, joining the symbols indicate the sequence of operations or flow of data which should normally flow from left to right or top to bottom of the diagram, as shown in Figs 1 and 2.

Table A, below, shows examples of symbols in general use, but for a more detailed source of information see BS 4058.

Table A FLOW CHART SYMBOLS			
←	Flow lines — arrows used to increase clarity of flow direction.	⊥	Flow lines which intersect should be staggered. Arrows need only be shown to increase clarity, e.g. if flow is other than right to left or top to bottom.
+	Flow lines which do not join but cross should be avoided if possible.		
⬭	Start, stop, halt, delay.	▱	Input or output to the flow chart or diagram.
▭	Process or data. Defines an operation or group of operations.	NO ◇ YES	Decision — exit from symbol identified by a route specification.
3▭2	Process reference for identification, top left e.g. 3, cross-reference top right e.g. 2.	⬡	Modification of an instruction, index register or starting a routine.
⫾▭⫾	Process which has been predefined by a lower order program.	To sheet 2 ⬠	Exit or entry from another flow chart on another sheet.
▭--[	Annotation — addition of descriptive comments or explanatory notes.	To 4 ◯	Connector — entry to or exit from another part of the same flow chart.

Let us examine a simple process and analyse its sequence of operations.

EXAMPLE 1

Produce a flow diagram to illustrate the series or sequence of operations used in constructing a line at 60° to a line defined by its ends A and X. The line AX is 65 mm long and is intersected by the second line at A which forms a 60° angle. Refer to G1-4.

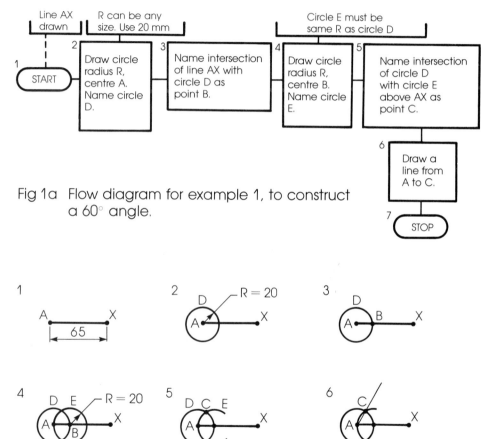

Fig 1a   Flow diagram for example 1, to construct a 60° angle.

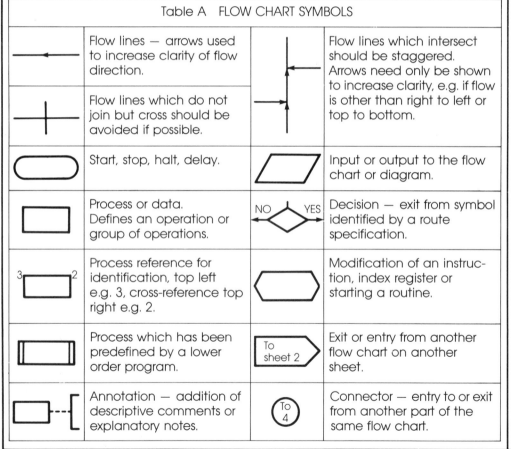

Fig 1b   Processes described by the routine given in Fig 1a.

Section No.	TITLE: **Flow networks.**	**Flow chart symbols and processes.**	
T12			

EXAMPLE 2

Produce a flow diagram to illustrate the sequence of operations used in each of the following processes:

(a) bisecting an angle — given an angle produced by any 2 lines which meet at a point A,

(b) bisecting a line — given any line defined by its ends A and B.

EXERCISES

(1) Perform the processes described in the flow diagrams shown in Figs 2a and 2b following exactly the given routines. (The routine given in Fig 1a is performed step by step as an example in Fig 1b.) Refer to G1-6 and G2-6 to check the constructions but note a change in annotated letters.

(2) Produce a flow diagram to illustrate the sequence of operations used in constructing a triangle defined by its corners A, B and C, where A to B is 70 mm, angle at corner A is 60° and angle at corner B is 30°.
Solution is shown in Fig 3 on the following page.

(3) Produce a flow diagram to illustrate the sequence of operations used when circumscribing a triangle which is already drawn and defined by the corners A, B and C. Predefined programmes, i.e. Fig 1a can be used.
Solution is shown in Fig 4 on the following page.

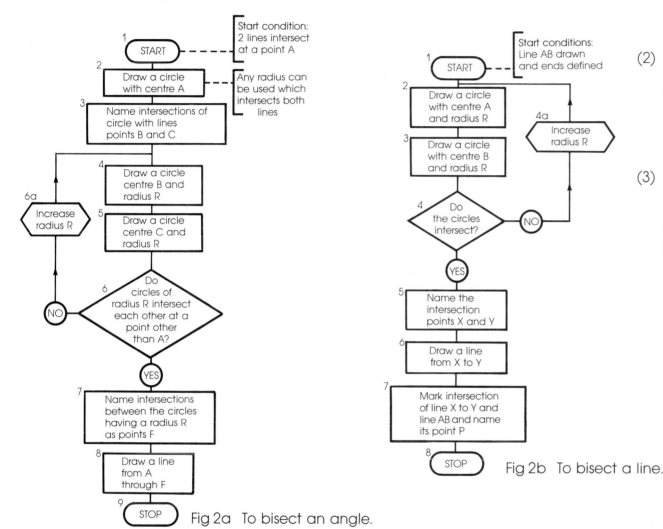

Fig 2a To bisect an angle.

Fig 2b To bisect a line.

Section No.	TITLE: **Flow networks.**	**Examples with flow charts.**	
T12			

351

Solutions to problems on previous page.

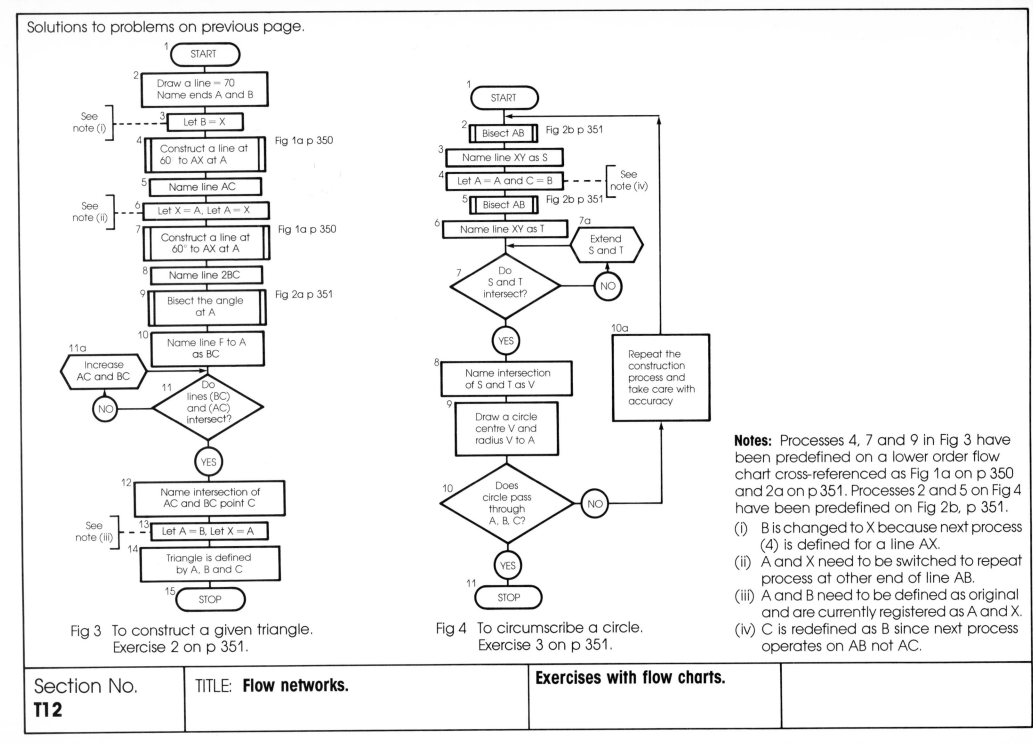

Fig 3 To construct a given triangle.
Exercise 2 on p 351.

Fig 4 To circumscribe a circle.
Exercise 3 on p 351.

Notes: Processes 4, 7 and 9 in Fig 3 have been predefined on a lower order flow chart cross-referenced as Fig 1a on p 350 and 2a on p 351. Processes 2 and 5 on Fig 4 have been predefined on Fig 2b, p 351.

(i)   B is changed to X because next process (4) is defined for a line AX.

(ii) A and X need to be switched to repeat process at other end of line AB.

(iii) A and B need to be defined as original and are currently registered as A and X.

(iv) C is redefined as B since next process operates on AB not AC.

Section No.	TITLE: **Flow networks.**	**Exercises with flow charts.**	
T12			

Flow charts can be used to organise and express our thoughts thus providing a useful tool in problem-solving. It can be quite difficult to explain how to arrive at a solution using written or verbal language but a flow diagram may help you to formulate, analyse and express your ideas. The flow chart shown in Fig 5 represents a strategy which can be used to solve problems, provide design solutions, write essays and even books!

Graphical representation of ideas is not only more economical and efficient than descriptive writing but also provides another dimension to aid the thinking process.

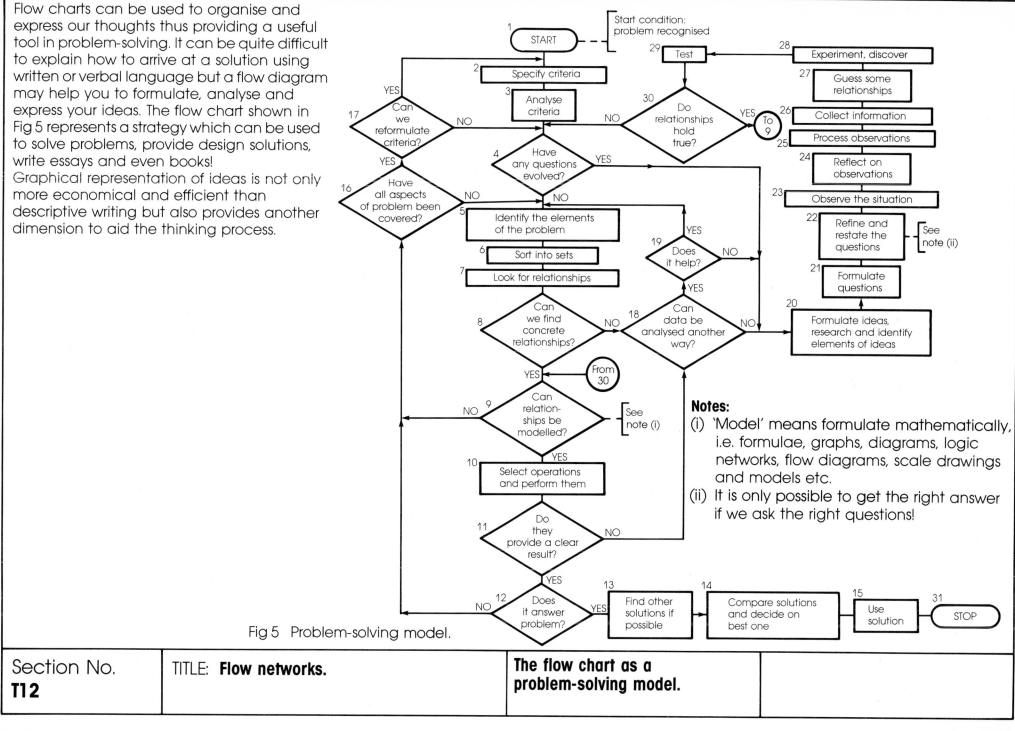

Fig 5 Problem-solving model.

Notes:
(i) 'Model' means formulate mathematically, i.e. formulae, graphs, diagrams, logic networks, flow diagrams, scale drawings and models etc.
(ii) It is only possible to get the right answer if we ask the right questions!

Section No. **T12**	TITLE: **Flow networks.**	**The flow chart as a problem-solving model.**	

353

Flow charts are used as a medium for communication of ideas to oneself or to others. Although much used in the preparation of computer programs, flow charts are not a programming language. They are a versatile tool used to clarify thinking when analysing systems, processes and problems. Flow charts provide a means of analysing, synthesising and communicating the ordered relationships of the minutest operations or process elements. They can be used to illustrate how several processes interact to form a system or how several systems interact with each other or with their environment.

The level and amount of detail shown on a flow chart needs to be sufficient to analyse or communicate the level of information being considered. The higher the level of flow chart the lower the level of detail which is generally shown. The highest level of flow chart is the block diagram or systems flow chart which shows how several independently functioning systems or processes can be interlinked to provide a desired output.

The block diagram shown in Fig 6 comprises

(a) a water heating system,
(b) a heat distribution system, and
(c) a space temperature control system etc.

This produces a domestic water and space heating system. Fig 6 is the highest level of flow diagram, i.e. Level 1. Each of the systems assembled to form the block diagram may be analysed and found to contain several processes or elements. The details of each of these systems and how their components relate to each other may be made more explicit by a second level flow chart (see Fig 8). A third level flow chart may be used to analyse one of the components of the system; e.g. Fig 9 analyses, at a Level 3, the fail safe device which is part of the water heating (boiler) system. Fig 9 does in fact analyse the logic of the device which is detailed in Fig 7. The lowest level of flow chart is reached when the logic itself is analysed.

This hierarchy enables one to gain a general view (overview) of a system prior to examining its constituent parts.

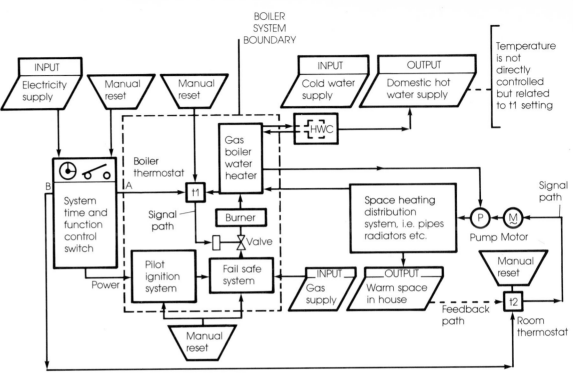

Fig 6   Block diagram of complete domestic heating system.

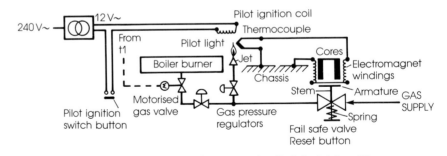

Fig 7   Fail safe system and pilot light ignition.

| Section No. **T12** | TITLE: **Flow networks.** | **Flow chart levels.** **Level 1: block diagram.** | |

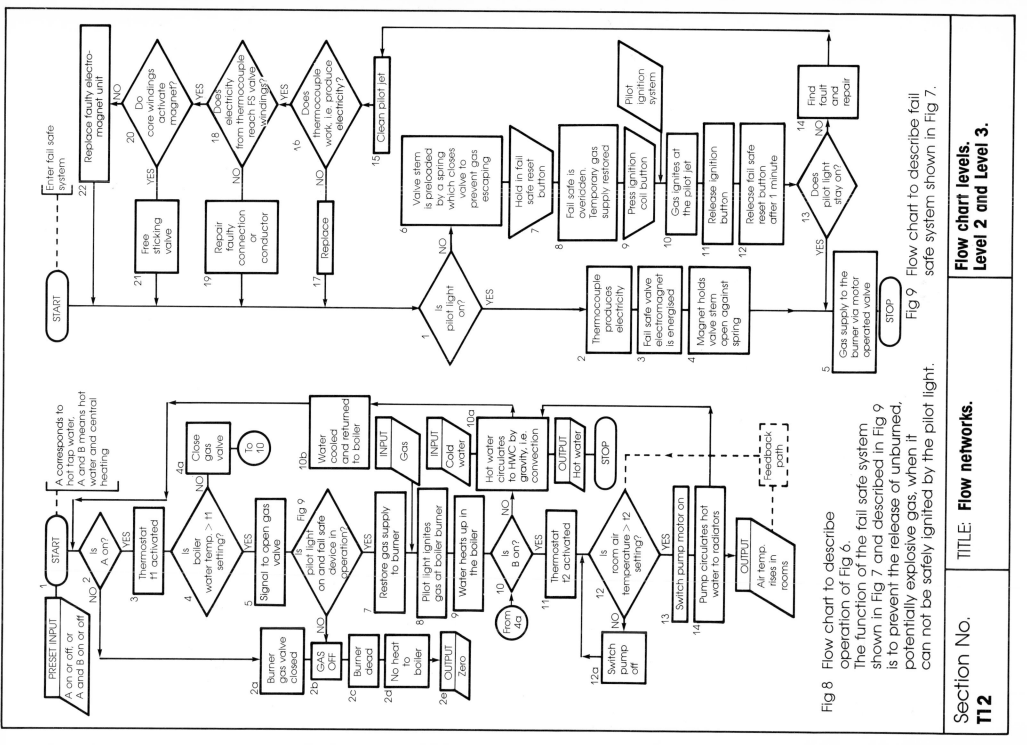

Fig 8 Flow chart to describe operation of Fig 6. The function of the fail safe system shown in Fig 7 and described in Fig 9 is to prevent the release of unburned, potentially explosive gas, when it can not be safely ignited by the pilot light.

Fig 9 Flow chart to describe fail safe system shown in Fig 7.

Flow chart levels. Level 2 and Level 3.

Section No.   TITLE: **Flow networks.**

T12

355

Networks used as in T12 relate a series of subtasks by the order in which they are performed during the completion of a task.

A subtask, or activity as it is often referred to, is represented by an arrow as shown in Fig 1a. The activity takes time, with the arrow being used as an arc as defined on p 328.

Event: This occurs on the completion of an activity and is represented by a circle which is termed a node similar to the definition used on p 328. The circle symbol for an event is shown in Fig 1b and it may be subdivided to display certain information which is located in the appropriate designated areas.

The task is complete when the final event or goal has been reached.

Dummy activity: This is a device which is used to relate or illustrate the dependence of one activity being started, to another being completed, when the activities are in parallel. The symbol used is a dotted arrow as shown in Fig 1c where the illustration also implies that the activity B cannot start until the activity C has been completed, i.e. until event 3 has been reached.

Dummy activities do not take time.

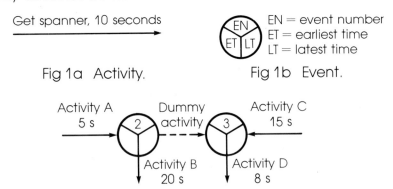

Get spanner, 10 seconds

Fig 1a Activity.

EN = event number
ET = earliest time
LT = latest time

Fig 1b Event.

Activity A
5 s
Dummy activity
Activity C
15 s
Activity B
20 s
Activity D
8 s

Fig 1c Dummy activity.

The production of a network diagram is a mathematical process. Its logical progress can be traced and the diagram drawn by asking 3 questions about each activity:

(a) What activity must be completed before the next one is started?
(b) What activity cannot start until this one is completed?
(c) What activity can be done at the same time as the activity being considered, these activities being shown in 'parallel'?

The critical path: This is the longest path through the network and any delay in completing any of the activities on the path will result in a delay in the task being completed or the goal being reached. The critical path provides the earliest time by which the whole process or task can be completed. The critical path is shown by a line on each side of the activity arcs as illustrated in Fig 2 and can follow dummy activity arcs where appropriate. The critical path in Fig 2 is given by the node order 1, 2, 4, 5, 7, 8, 9, 10, 11.

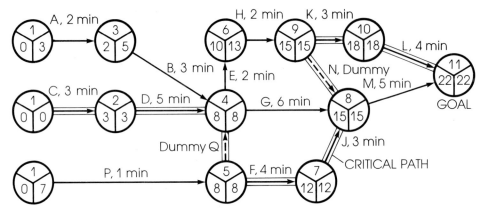

Note: Activity K cannot begin until H, G and J are complete since the dummy activity N shows that event 9 is dependent on event 8 being reached.

Fig 2

ET (earliest time): The earliest time for an event is not reached until all the activities leading to that event have been completed, e.g. ET for event 4 in Fig 2 is 3 min + 5 min = 8 min, since this route takes the longest time and finishes last. ET for event 7 is 8 min + 4 min = 12 min. (Activity F cannot start until both activities P and Q are complete, since Q is a dummy activity which shows that the start of F depends on event 4 being reached.)

LT (latest time): The time by which an event must be reached (if the process is to be kept on schedule) is derived by taking the last event and subtracting the time taken by the activity which occurs after the previous event. Where 2 or more activities lead to an event the shortest time is taken, e.g. LT for event 10 is 22 min − 4 min = 18 min.

| Section No. **T13** | TITLE: **Planning networks.** | **Task analysis and critical path analysis.** | |

Float or slack time: This is spare time and when this is at a minimum the network is at its most efficient. If there is spare time available then the activity may extend into the spare time without affecting the schedule (final time). Activity float equals LT of next event minus ET of previous event minus activity time; e.g. Float for activity H = 15 − 10 − 2 = 3 min. That is, activity H can take up to an extra 3 minutes without delay in the time at which the goal is reached.

EXAMPLE 1

The driver and navigator of a car, in preparing for a rally, decide to organise themselves for the task of replacing a wheel, should they have a puncture. They break the task down into a number of activities or sub-tasks and time each one individually, listing the times taken as shown in Table A below. Produce a network which organises the activities into a logical sequence for both car occupants to complete the task in the shortest possible time, bearing in mind the following procedure: Get the spare (which is held in place by a wing nut), jack, and combination hub cap lever/wheel nut spanner from the boot. Remove the hub cap and loosen the wheel nuts before jacking the car up (the wheel must be on the ground to enable the nuts to be loosened without the wheel rotating). The nuts and wheel are then removed and the spare fitted, together with the nuts which are nipped up. The jack is lowered, the nuts fully tightened and the hub cap replaced. The tools and faulty tyre are stored and the occupants return to their seats.

The first step in problem-solving is to simplify the problem — draw a picture.

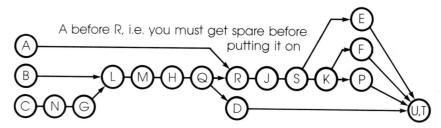

Fig 3   Network. This picture orders the activity sequence and illustrates the dependence of activities, i.e. which activity preceeds which.

Table A		
REF.	DESCRIPTION OF ACTIVITY	TIME
A	Get spare from boot	70 s
B	Get jack	20 s
C	Get spanner/lever combination	10 s
D	Put punctured wheel away	60 s
E	Put jack away	20 s
F	Put spanner/lever comb. away	10 s
G	Loosen nuts	40 s
H	Remove nuts	60 s
J	Replace nuts and nip them up	60 s
K	Tighten nuts	40 s
L	Place jack and take up slack	80 s
M	Lift car with jack	15 s
N	Remove hub cap	10 s
P	Replace hub cap	6 s
Q	Take punctured wheel off	2 s
R	Put spare wheel on	10 s
S	Lower jack and remove	50 s
T	Get in car	10 s
U	Get in car	10 s

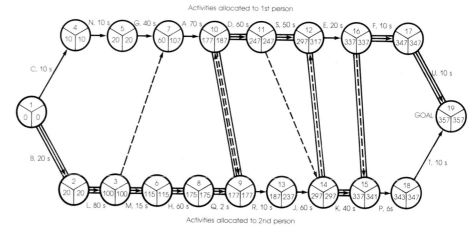

Fig 4   Network.

Section No. **T13**	TITLE: **Planning networks.**	**Example in critical path analysis.**	

357

A graph is a pictorial representation of a mapping.

Mapping: A mapping consists of 2 sets, i.e. a set X and a set Y, and a relationship or rule by which each element of the set X is assigned to an element or subset of elements which belong to the set Y. The rule relating the set X to the set Y can be expressed by a line or graph with any point on the line located using rectangular coordinates.

Rectangular coordinates: The line or graph (g) which expresses the rule of assignment is defined by the points which are the elements of the graph (g). These points (P) are defined by the intersection of the x ordinate and the y ordinate which locate them; see Fig 1. The x ordinates are shown as vertical ordinates and y ordinates are shown as horizontal ordinates in Fig 1. The x ordinate value is located along the horizontal axis and the y ordinate value along the vertical axis. Point (P) in Fig 1 is defined by (3, 5) with the x ordinate being given first, i.e. 3. P is a mapping indicated by the expression P:3 → 5.

The graph (g) which pictorially expresses the rule of assignment can also be expressed by an algebraic method as shown in Fig 2.

The graph (g) is defined by the set of points (0, 4) (1, 4) (2, 4) (3, 4) (4, 4) (5, 4) etc. g maps every x to 4,
i.e. g: x → 4 or $y = 4$
$y = c$ where c is a constant $= 4$.

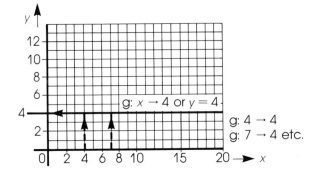

Fig 2a

The graph (g) is defined by the set of points (0, 0) (1, 1) (2, 2) (3, 3) (4, 4) (5, 5) (6, 6) etc. g maps every x to its own value, i.e. g: x → x, or $y = x$.

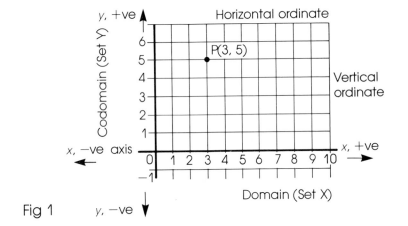

Fig 1

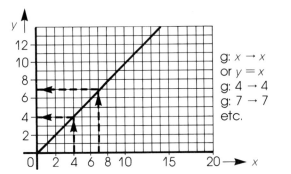

Fig 2b

Section No.	TITLE: **Graphs.**	**Rectangular coordinates and straight line graphs.**	
T14			

358

The graph (g) is defined by the set of points (0, 0) (3, 2) (6, 4) (9, 6) etc.
g maps x to $\frac{2}{3}$ of its own value,
i.e. g: $x \rightarrow \frac{2}{3}x$ or $y = \frac{2}{3}x$.

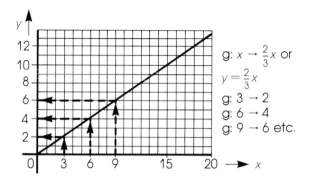

g: $x \rightarrow \frac{2}{3}x$ or

$y = \frac{2}{3}x$

g: 3 → 2
g: 6 → 4
g: 9 → 6 etc.

Fig 2c

The graph (g) is defined by the mapping g: $x \rightarrow \frac{2}{3}x + 4$ or $y = \frac{2}{3}x + 4$,
i.e. when $x = 6$ g: $x \rightarrow (\frac{2}{3} \times 6) + 4$
g: 6 → 8.

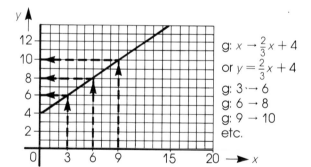

g: $x \rightarrow \frac{2}{3}x + 4$

or $y = \frac{2}{3}x + 4$

g: 3 → 6
g: 6 → 8
g: 9 → 10
etc.

Fig 2d

Fig 2d illustrates a graph of $y = \frac{2}{3}x + 4$ which is typical of a straight line graph. Since it is typical it can be expressed in the general form of $y = mx + c$ where m determines the angle or slope of the graph and c determines the intercept of the graph with the y axis and thus positions the graph vertically in relation to the x axis.

In Fig 2a $y = mx + c$ where $m = 0$ and $c = 4$ ∴ $y = 0x + 4$, i.e. $y = 4$
In Fig 2b $y = mx + c$ where $m = 1$ and $c = 0$ ∴ $y = 1x + 0$, i.e. $y = x$
In Fig 2c $y = mx + c$ where $m = \frac{2}{3}$ and $c = 0$ ∴ $y = \frac{2}{3}x + 0$, i.e. $y = \frac{2}{3}x$
In Fig 2d $y = mx + c$ where $m = \frac{2}{3}$ and $c = 4$ ∴ $y = \frac{2}{3}x + 4$

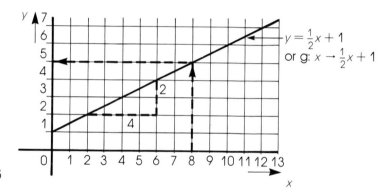

$y = \frac{1}{2}x + 1$
or g: $x \rightarrow \frac{1}{2}x + 1$

Fig 3

How is the slope m defined in the expression $y = mx + c$?

Fig 3 shows the graph of $y = \frac{1}{2}x + 1$ and it can be seen that the ratio of the vertical rise of the graph for a given horizontal translation is 2:4 or 2/4, i.e. $\frac{1}{2}$.

Note: c gives the intercept of the graph with the y axis, i.e. 1.

Section No.	TITLE: **Graphs.**	**Straight line graphs.**	
T14			

EXAMPLE 1

The temperature measured in degrees centigrade is directly related to the temperature in degrees Fahrenheit by the algebraic expression $F = \frac{9}{5}C + 32$ where F is the Fahrenheit temperature and C is the centigrade temperature. Since the relationship is a direct one and of the form $y = mx + c$ it can be represented by a straight graph.

(a) Draw the graph to illustrate the relationship for temperatures up to 240 °F.
(b) Determine from the graph the Fahrenheit temperature which corresponds to 60 °C and, using a reverse mapping, the centigrade equivalent to 212 °F.

Method (1)
Determine the constant in the equation $F = \frac{9}{5}C + 32$. The constant is 32. Mark this point on the F (vertical) axis as P_1. Determine the multiple, m, in the equation, i.e. $\frac{9}{5}$. This defines the slope of the graph, i.e. 9-to-5 or 90-to-50. Measure 50 horizontally from the constant marked on the vertical axis and then progress by 90 in the vertical direction to give P_2. The graph can now be drawn from P_1 through P_2.

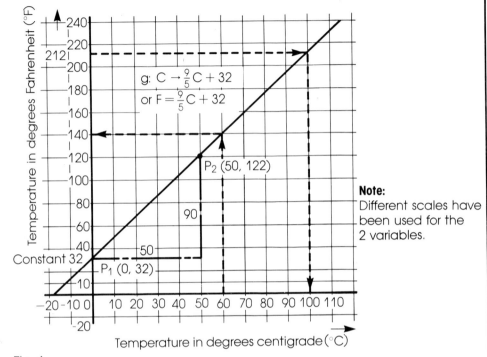

g: $C \to \frac{9}{5}C + 32$

or $F = \frac{9}{5}C + 32$

P_2 (50, 122)

90

50

Constant 32

P_1 (0, 32)

Temperature in degrees centigrade (°C)

Note:
Different scales have been used for the 2 variables.

Fig 4

Method (2)
Determine 2 pairs of coordinates by substitution,

i.e. when $C = 0$, $F = (\frac{9}{5} \times 0) + 32$

$C = 0$, $F = 32$ giving coordinates of (0, 32)

And when $C = 50$, $F = (\frac{9}{5} \times 50) + 32$

$C = 50$, $F = 122$ giving the coordinates of (50, 122).

Draw the graph through the coordinated points.

| Section No.

T14 | TITLE: **Graphs.** | **Straight line graphs.** | |

The normal convention used on graphs is positive (+ve) to the right of, and above, the origin (zero) and negative (−ve) to the left of, and below, the origin. The negative symbol is used to represent the opposite direction to the positive symbol.

The slope is considered to be +ve in Figs 5, 6 and 7, i.e. $+\frac{1}{2}$ and the graph rises from left to right. The slope is considered to be −ve in Figs 8 and 9, i.e. $-\frac{1}{2}$ and the graph falls from left to right.

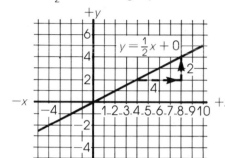

Fig 5

$$m = \frac{+2}{+4} = +\frac{1}{2}$$

Note direction of arrows.

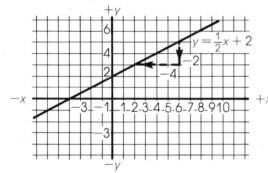

Fig 6

$$m = \frac{-2}{-4} = +\frac{1}{2}$$

Note direction of arrows.

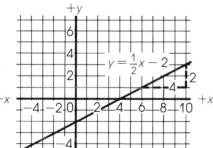

Fig 7

Note m is +ve, c −ve.

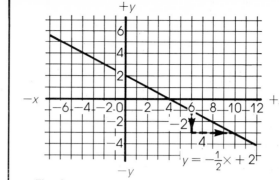

Fig 8

$$m = \frac{-2}{+4} = -\frac{1}{2}$$

Note direction of arrows.

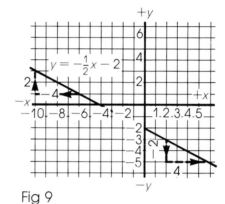

Fig 9

$$m = \frac{+2}{-4} \text{ or } \frac{-2}{+4} = -\frac{1}{2}$$

Note direction of arrows.

EXERCISE 1

The general expression for a straight line graph is $y = $ _____ . Determine the specific relationships of y to x for the graph shown in Fig 10.

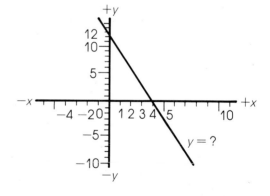

$y = ?$

Fig 10

ANS $y = -3x + 12$

Section No.	TITLE: **Graphs.**	**Slope.**	
T14			

Fig 11 shows 7 graphs (g1 to g7) illustrating the relative speeds of different modes of transport. It can be seen from the illustration that the faster the mode of transport the steeper is the slope of the graph; there is a relationship between the speed and the slope. Speed is the distance travelled in a unit of time, e.g. km/h. The graph g2 maps the distance of 150 km to 1 h using point P_2, therefore the slope of the graph $g2 = 150$ km/1 h, i.e. the speed of the train $= 150$ km/h. The graph g1 maps the distance of 200 km to $\frac{1}{4}$ h, g1 thus having a slope of $\dfrac{200 \text{ km}}{\frac{1}{4}\text{h}}$.

This gives a speed for the aircraft of 800 km/h. **Note:** P_1 was used in the solution.

Remember $y = mx + c$ where

$m = \text{slope} = \dfrac{y}{x}$.

Then in Fig 11, $s = vt + c$ where $v = \dfrac{s}{t}$,

v being the velocity or speed.

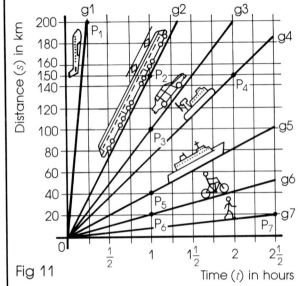

Fig 11

Time (t) in hours

EXAMPLE 2
Determine the slope and hence the speed for the other modes of transport illustrated in Fig 11.

Speed of car $=$ slope of g3 $= \dfrac{100 \text{ km}}{1 \text{ h}} = 100$ km/h

Speed of hovercraft $=$ slope of g4 $= \dfrac{150 \text{ km}}{2 \text{ h}} = 75$ km/h

Speed of ship $=$ slope of g5 $= \dfrac{40 \text{ km}}{1 \text{ h}} = 40$ km/h

Speed of bicycle $=$ slope of g6 $= \dfrac{20 \text{ km}}{1 \text{ h}} = 20$ km/h

Speed of pedestrian $=$ slope of g7 $= \dfrac{20 \text{ km}}{2\frac{1}{2} \text{ h}} = 8$ km/h

EXERCISE 2
The graph shown in Fig 12 illustrates that a ship has left port A at a speed of _ _ _ _ _ (use P_1). One hour later the hovercraft leaves the same port at a speed of _ _ _ _ _ (use P_2), and follows the same route as the ship, overtaking the ship _ h _ min after the hovercraft departed. The ship travelled _ _ km before it was overtaken.

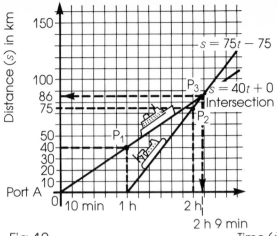

Fig 12

EXERCISE 3
The ship in Fig 13 heads for a port B which is _ _ _ _ km away from port A and _ _ min later a hovercraft leaves port B to follow the same route in reverse. The ship has been sailing for _ h _ min before it meets the hovercraft and has travelled _ _ km. The slope of the hovercraft graph is −ve because

_ _ _ _ _ _ _ _ _ _ .

ANS. TO EX. 2 (a) 40 km/h
(b) 75 km/h
(c) 1 h 9 min
(d) 86 km

ANS. TO EX. 3 (a) 180 km
(b) 45 min
(c) 2 h 3 min
(d) 82 km

S + from A. Start time of hovercraft $= +45$ min
Velocity of hovercraft is −ve compared with ship, i.e. in the opposite direction

Fig 13

| Section No. T14 | TITLE: **Graphs.** | **Interrelated graphs.** | |

A compound relationship is one where several graphs are added together to sum up the relationships expressed by the individual graphs.

EXAMPLE 3

A second-hand car is purchased for £2000 cash. Produce a graph which sums the following costs and illustrates the direct relationship between the distance travelled and the total cost of travel for the year. The following fixed costs are incurred regardless of any mileage covered by the car: £300 depreciation, since the car is only worth £1700 after one year; road fund licence and insurance £150 per year; and £200 notional interest which the £2000 would have yielded if invested at 10%. The cost of petrol varies directly to the mileage covered and is assessed at £50 per 1000 miles (approx. 32 miles/gallon) while the cost of servicing is assessed at £15 per 1000 miles, i.e. tyres, oil, brakes, plugs, etc. See Fig 14 for graph.

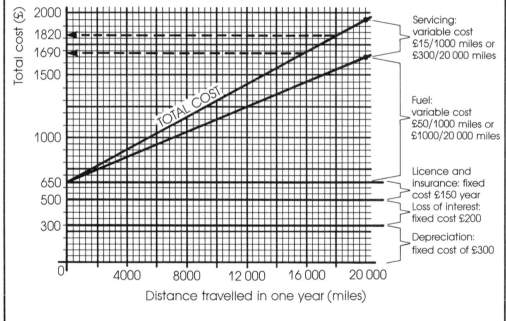

Fig 14

Another useful graph would be one which relates the cost per mile of travel to the distance travelled in one year. This graph may illustrate the information given in Example 3 and tell the story in a different way thus providing an alternative way fo analysing the information. See Fig 15 for this graph.

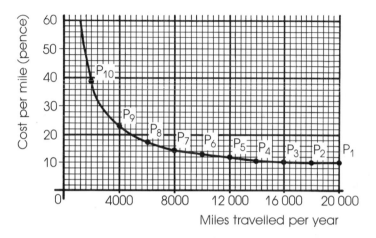

Fig 15

20 000 miles cost £1950 from Fig 14, i.e. cost per mile is
 £1950/20 000 = 9.7p/mile
 The coordinates for P_1 are
 (20 000, 9.7)

18 000 miles cost £1820 from Fig 14, i.e. cost per mile is
 £1820/18 000 = 10.1p/mile
 The coordinates for P_2 are
 (18 000, 10.1)

16 000 maps to £1690/16 000 = 10.6p/mile
14 000 maps to £1560/14 000 = 11.1p/mile
12 000 maps to £1430/12 000 = 11.9p/mile
 for P_3, P_4, P_5 etc.

The more miles the car is driven, the cheaper is the cost per mile since the fixed costs are distributed over more miles.

Section No.	TITLE: **Graphs.**	**Compound relationships.**	
T14			

Break-even charts: Graphical illustrations which compare the cost relationships of 2 or more processes by using the same axis. The break-even point is the intersection between the graphs expressing the relationships and illustrates where one process gains a cost advantage over the other. Example 4 and its solution in Fig 16 gives a demonstration of the use of a break-even chart in reaching a decision.

EXAMPLE 4

An engineering company has 2 processes to choose from when it considers the production of a component, (a) sand casting and, (b) die casting. The costs related to the 2 processes are as follows.

Sand casting: £300 fixed cost for the pattern, £2.50 per component for the metal and overheads and £4.50 per component for the production of the moulds, sand, moulding overheads and fettling.

Die casting: £2500 fixed cost for the manufacture of the die and £4.00 per component for the metal, die casting machine overheads and labour. Which process should be used if 400 components are required and which process would be used if 880 components are required?

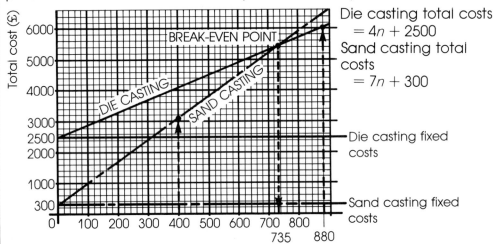

Die casting total costs
$$= 4n + 2500$$
Sand casting total costs
$$= 7n + 300$$

Die casting fixed costs

Sand casting fixed costs

Fig 16   Number of components (n)

The number of components maps to a lower cost using the sand casting graph until the number produced exceeds 735, i.e. the break-even point, where the die casting process then maps the number of components to the lower cost.

Fig 17 relates the 2 processes in Example 4 by illustrating the economy of scale of production for sand casting up to the break-even point and then changing to the die casting method.

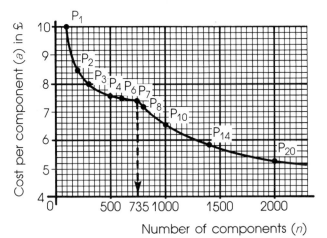

Fig 17

The graph between P_1 and P_7 is defined by $a = \dfrac{7n + 300}{n}$ where

a is the cost per component and n is the number of components.

The graph between P_7 and P_{20} is defined by $a = \dfrac{4n + 2500}{n}$.

To draw the graph first determine the coordinates, e.g. for P_2.

$$\text{If } n = 200, \ a = \frac{(7 \times 200) + 300}{200}$$

$$a = £8.50$$

∴ coordinates for P_2 are (200, 8.50)

Section No.	TITLE: **Graphs.**	**Break-even charts.**	
T14			

In a graph relating 2 sets, a further useful relationship may be obtained by examining the area under the graph.

The constant velocity (v) illustrated by the velocity-time graph in Fig 18a provides a relationship in which the area under the graph is directly proportional to the time, as shown in Fig 18b.

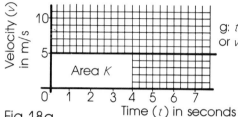

Fig 18a

The area under the graph in Fig 18a

g: $t \to 5$
or $v = 5$

after 1 s $= 5 \times 1 = 5$
after 2 s $= 5 \times 2 = 10$
after 3 s $= 5 \times 3 = 15$
after 4 s $= K = 5 \times 4 = 20$ etc.
i.e. $5t = s$

The coordinates of the points P_1, P_2, P_3, etc. in Fig 18b are (1, 5), (2, 10), (3, 15) etc.

To fully appreciate the area, K, under the graph in Fig 18a the units of the area should also be analysed:

$$K = vt = \frac{5 \text{ metres}}{\text{seconds}} \times 4 \text{ seconds} = 20 \text{ metres.}$$

Thus the area under the graph on Fig 18a represents a distance s in metres which forms the vertical axis of Fig 18b.

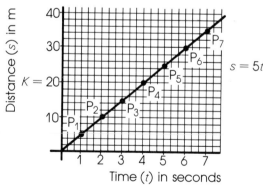

Fig 18b

Fig 19a illustrates that the velocity (v) increases at a uniform rate, i.e. the increase in velocity is directly proportional to time since the graph is a straight line graph. If the velocity of a car increases it is said to accelerate and if the rate of increase in velocity is uniform then the acceleration is also said to be uniform (UA).

The general form of a straight line graph can be expressed as $y = mx + c$ thus the graph in Fig 19a can be expressed as $v = mt + 0$ where $c = 0$ and m is the slope. In this case the slope $= v/t$ and since $v/t =$ acceleration (a) and $a = \frac{5}{2}$, then $v = \frac{5}{2}t = 2\frac{1}{2}t$,

i.e. $\quad\quad v = at \quad\quad$ (Equation 1)

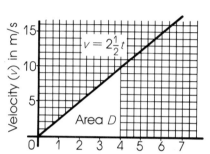

Fig 19a

In Fig 18a the area under the velocity-time graph was rectangular but in Fig 19a the area is triangular and the area of this triangle $= \frac{1}{2}vt$. Therefore the area under the graph in Fig 19a

after 1 s $= \frac{1}{2} \times 2.5 \times 1 = 1.25$
after 2 s $= \frac{1}{2} \times 5 \times 2 = 5.0$
after 3 s $= \frac{1}{2} \times 7.5 \times 3 = 11.25$
after 4 s $= D = \frac{1}{2} \times 10 \times 4 = 20.0$

i.e. $\quad\quad \frac{1}{2}vt = s \quad\quad$ (Equation 2)

Since $v = at$ (Equation 1) and $s = \frac{1}{2}vt$ (Equation 2) then substituting Equation 1 in Equation 2 we get

$$s = \frac{1}{2}at \times t = \frac{1}{2}at^2 \quad\quad \text{(Equation 3)}$$

An equation with a squared term in it is a quadratic and produces a graph having a parabolic form as shown in Fig 19b.

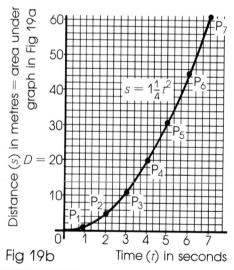

Fig 19b

| Section No. T14 | TITLE: **Graphs.** | **Introduction to parabolic relationships.** | |

Equation 3 arrived at a quadratic expression to describe the relationship between s and t in Fig 19b, this relationship being illustrated by a parabola. The general form of the equation for a parabola may contain 3 terms e.g. $y = ax^2 + mx + c$.

Note: in Equation 3 $c = 0$, $m = 0$ and the multiple of $t^2 = \frac{1}{2}a$.

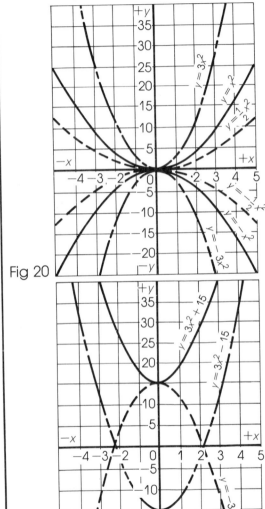

Fig 20

Fig 21

The contribution of each of the 3 terms to the shape, attitude and position of the parabola is now examined with reference to the axis.

A change of sign from $+x^2$ to $-x^2$ inverts the parabola (turns it upside down). When x^2 is increased or decreased by a constant multiplier, e.g. 3 or $\frac{1}{2}$, the rate at which the slope changes increases or decreases accordingly.

The addition or subtraction of a constant translates the parabola vertically upwards when the constant is positive, e.g. +15, and downwards when the constant is negative, e.g. −15.

When the x term in the general expression is positive, e.g. $+10x$, the parabola moves to the left but still passes through the origin, see $y = 3x^2 + 10x$. When the x term is negative, as in $y = 3x^2 - 10x$, the parabola moves to the right but still passes through zero.

When the quadratic contains all 3 terms the movement of the parabola becomes a compound one, i.e. $y = 3x^2 + 10x + 15$ rises and moves to the left whilst $y = 3x^2 - 10x - 15$ falls and moves to the right.

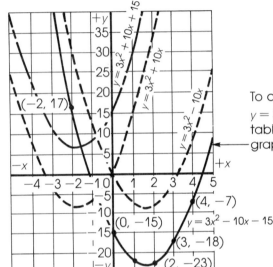

Fig 22

To determine the ordinates of $y = 3x^2 - 10x - 15$ produce the table shown below to draw the graph

x ordinate is	Substituting x ordinate in $y = 3x^2 - 10x - 15$	y ordinate is
−2	$3(-2)^2 - 10(-2) - 15 = 17$	+17
−1	$3(-1)^2 - 10(-1) - 15 = -2$	−2
0	$3(0)^2 - 10(0) - 15 = -15$	−15
+1	$3(+1)^2 - 10(+1) - 15 = -22$	−22
+2	$3(+2)^2 - 10(+2) - 15 = -23$	−23
+3	$3(+3)^2 - 10(+3) - 15 = -18$	−18
+4	$3(+4)^2 - 10(+4) - 15 = -7$	−7

Section No. T14	TITLE: **Graphs.**	**Introduction to parabolic relationships.**	

The areas of plane surfaces may be required for a number of reasons and when they are defined by boundaries having straight edges they become polygons. The area of a polygon can be found by reducing the polygon to a rectangle, as described in G8-10, and then calculating the area of the rectangle. If the area is bounded by a curve the problem becomes more involved but it can still be determined by one of the following methods.

(a) COUNTING SQUARES

This method can be rather laborious but with a little perception the task can be achieved quite quickly. The circle in Fig 1 has 4 equal quadrants thus it is only necessary to count up one quadrant and multiply by 4. Large, easily calculated areas may be taken out, e.g. area X, and the remainder counted up.

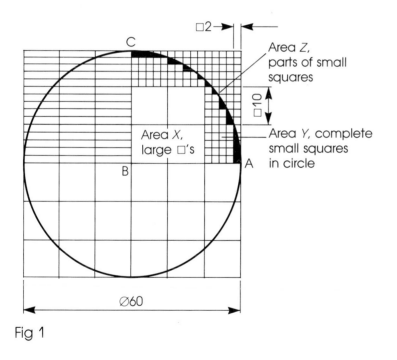

Fig 1

Area of circle in Fig 1 = 4 (area X + area Y + area Z)

Area $X = 10 \times 10 \times 4 = 400$ mm^2

Area Y = area of squares × no. of squares
$= 2 \times 2 \times 62 = 248$ mm^2

Area $Z = 2 \times 2 \times 14$ approx. (all black parts)
$= 56$ mm^2

Area of circle = 4(400 + 248 + 56) mm^2 = 2816 mm^2

The accuracy of the method can be checked through the use of the formula for the area of a circle = $\pi r^2 = 3.142 \times 30 \times 30 = 2829$ mm^2. Since the method provides a favourable result (accurate to 0.5%) it can prove a useful method for shapes with curved boundaries for which there is no formula.

(b) SIMPSON'S RULE

This uses the lengths of the ordinates in the formula

$$\text{Area} = \frac{A}{3}(B + 2C + 4D)$$

Where A = ordinate intervals or spacing size,

B = length of first + length of last ordinate,

C = sum of lengths of odd ordinates excluding first and last ones,

D = sum of lengths of even ordinates.

Section No.	TITLE: **Areas.**	**Plane surfaces with curved boundaries.**	
T15			

EXAMPLE 1

Construct an ellipse given major axis = 80 mm, minor axis = 50 mm, and determine its area. See Fig 2. G16-2 gives the construction method.

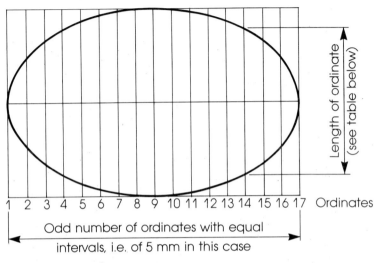

Fig 2

ORDINATE	1	2	3	4	5	6	7	8	9	10	11	12	13	14	15	16	17
MEASURED LENGTH	0	24	33	39	43	46	48	49	50	49	48	46	43	39	33	24	0

— Odd ordinates   — Even ordinates

Area $= \frac{5}{3}((0) + 2(\text{odd ordinates}) + \text{even ordinates})) = \frac{5}{3}(0 + 596 + 1264)$

Area = 3100 mm^2 by Simpson's Rule.

Again there is an exact formula which is specific for the ellipse,

i.e. area of ellipse $= \pi ab$ where a and b are $\frac{1}{2}$ the major and $\frac{1}{2}$ the minor axes respectively.

Area = $3.142 \times 25 \times 40 = 3142$ mm^2.

(c) MID-ORDINATE RULE

$$\text{Area} = \text{width across figure} \times \frac{\text{sum of lengths of mid-ordinates}}{\text{number of mid-ordinates}}$$

EXAMPLE 2

Draw the graph of $y = -\dfrac{x^2}{50} + 72$ between the ordinates $x = -60$ and

$x = +60$ and determine the area between the x axis and the parabola. See Fig 22 and table on p 366 for determination of coordinates to draw parabola.

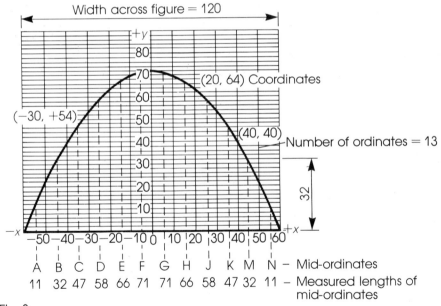

Fig 3

	A	B	C	D	E	F	G	H	J	K	M	N	— Mid-ordinates
	11	32	47	58	66	71	71	66	58	47	32	11	— Measured lengths of mid-ordinates

Section No.	TITLE: **Areas.**	**Plane surfaces with curved boundaries.**	
T15			

$$\text{Area} = 120\left(\frac{11 + 32 + 47 + 58 + 66 + 71 + 71 + 66 + 58 + 47 + 32 + 11}{12}\right)$$
$$= 5700 \text{ mm}^2$$

This can be checked using the formula specific to the parabola:

$$\text{Area} = \tfrac{2}{3} \text{ base} \times \text{height}$$
$$\text{Area} = \tfrac{2}{3}(120 \times 72) = 5760 \text{ mm}^2$$

The method is accurate to 2%.

EXAMPLE 3

Determine the area of the field which is shown to scale in Fig 4 and is bounded by a river, 2 straight hedges and a road. The curve is defined by the ordinates given in the table using the road line as a datum.

ORDINATE	1	2	3	4	5	6	7	8	9	10
LENGTH (m)	40	50	51.5	51.5	47.5	42.5	38	36	36.5	45

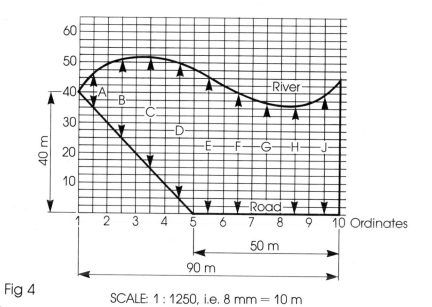

Fig 4

SCALE: 1 : 1250, i.e. 8 mm = 10 m

By measurement mid-ordinates are 12.5, 26, 36.5, 45, 46, 39, 36.5, 35.5, 38. Sum of mid-ordinates = 315 m.

$$\text{Area} = 90\left(\frac{315}{9}\right) = 3150 \text{ m}^2$$

Alternatively, using Simpson's Rule:

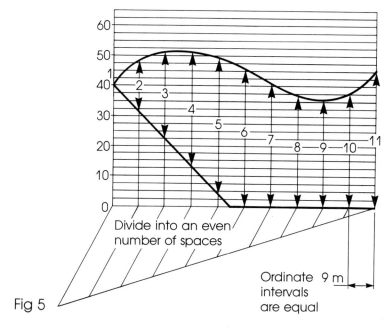

Fig 5

Divide into an even number of spaces

Ordinate intervals are equal

Ordinate 9 m

$$\text{Area} = \tfrac{9}{3}(45 + 2(149.5) + 4(175))$$
$$= 3132 \text{ m}^2$$

By measurement, first ordinate = 0, last ordinate = 45

Odd ordinates = 28.5, 45, 41, 35
Even ordinates = 16.5, 37.5, 46, 37, 38.

Section No.	TITLE: **Areas.**	**Plane surface with curved boundaries.**	
T15			

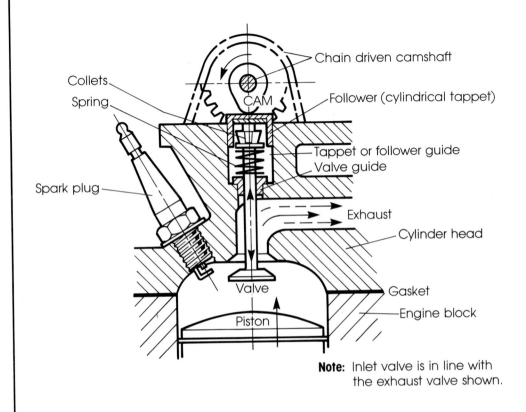

Chain driven camshaft

Collets

Spring

CAM

Follower (cylindrical tappet)

Spark plug

Tappet or follower guide

Valve guide

Exhaust

Cylinder head

Valve

Gasket

Piston

Engine block

Note: Inlet valve is in line with the exhaust valve shown.

Fig 1 Cam operated valve (in a car engine).

The cam synchronises the valve's displacement
to the position of the piston in the cylinder.
The piston's position is linked to the angular
displacement of the cam via the con-rod,
crankshaft, chain drive and camshaft.
Note that the valve's return depends upon the
compression of the return spring.

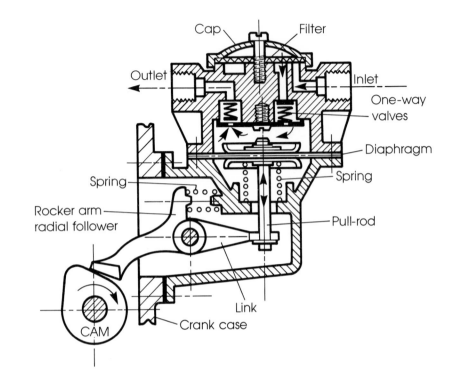

Cap

Filter

Outlet

Inlet

One-way
valves

Diaphragm

Spring

Rocker arm
radial follower

Pull-rod

Link

CAM

Crank case

Fig 2 Cam operated diaphragm pump (car fuel pump).

Here the cam is used to produce a displacement
in the pull-rod which displaces the diaphragm
and sucks fuel into the chamber through the
appropriate one-way valve. The diaphragm is then
returned by the spring thus forcing the petrol
through the other one-way valve and on to the
carburettor.

Section No. T16	TITLE: **Cams.**	**Uses of cams and eccentrics.**	

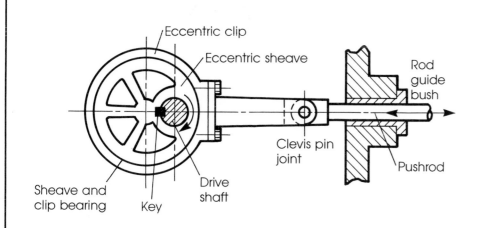

Fig 3 Eccentric drive.

The sheave is forced to rotate
about the drive shaft through the
key. The out-of-centre (eccentric)
rotation of the sheave is
transferred to the clip which
drives the rod.

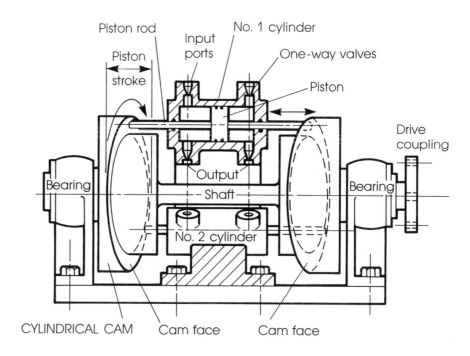

Fig 4 Cylindrical end, cam operated, axial pump
(3-cylinder double acting).

The pump has 3 cylinders usually spaced around the
axis of the shaft. The piston rods are located on end
faces of the cylindrical cams. The right-hand cam
drives the rods to the left and the left-hand cam
forces the rod and hence the piston to return, thus
providing a push and pull action on the rod. The pump is
double acting, i.e. the cylinder is both filling and
discharging at the same time.

Section No.	TITLE: **Cams.**	**Uses of cams and**	
T16		**eccentrics.**	

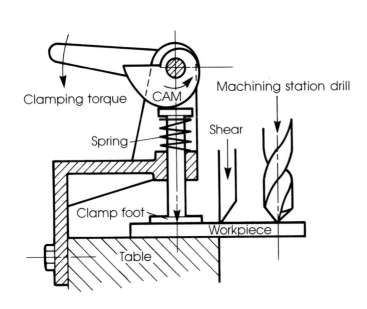

Fig 5 Cam operated clamp.

The rotation of the clamping handle produces a wedge action between the cam edge and the stem of the clamp. The spring is used to lift the foot automatically and clear the work when the cam pressure is released.

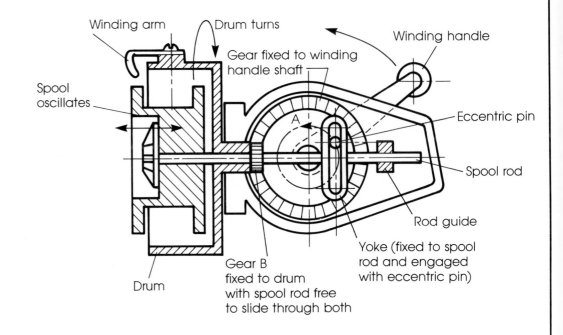

Fig 6 Fishing reel uses an eccentric.

The handle drives gear A to which the eccentric pin is fixed. The pin locates in the yoke attached to the spool rod and as the pin rotates with the gear A it causes the yoke and spool rod to oscillate with simple harmonic motion (SHM) when the handle turns with a constant speed. The rod is free to slide through the small gear B which rotates the drum and winding arm. As the spool oscillates it distributes the line being wound evenly along the spool.

| Section No.
T16 | TITLE: **Cams.** | **Uses of cams and eccentrics.** | |

Radial cam: Also referred to as a <u>disc</u> or <u>edge</u> cam. The cam imparts a positive motion to the follower in one direction only — away from the profile of the cam. In order to provide a return motion which is related to the profile of the cam the follower must be spring loaded to maintain the contact of the follower with the cam profile. The follower motion is related to the rotating profile of the cam.

Face cam: The cam imparts motion positively in both the lift and fall directions and thus eliminates the possibility of the follower bouncing. The follower motion is related to the shape of a groove machined in the face of a disc.

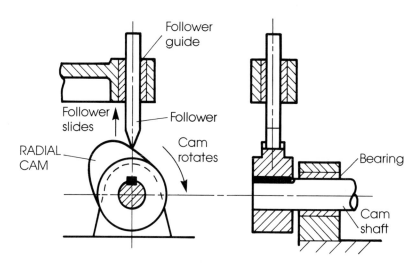

Fig 7   Radial cam.

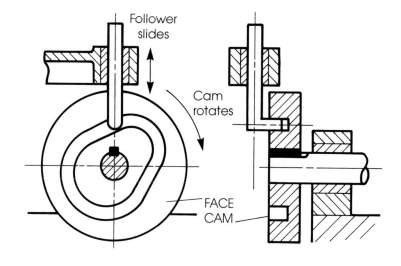

Fig 8   Face cam.

Cams can be used to provide a clamping action, a rocking motion or a sliding (linear) motion in another component termed the follower. Their most important function is to utilise a regular rotating motion to produce a desired defined motion in the follower. The follower motion is synchronised to the cam's rotation.

| Section No. **T16** | TITLE: **Cams.** | **Types of cam.** | |

Cylindrical cam: This cam also imparts motion positively to the follower in both the lift and fall directions. Note that the follower motion is parallel to the axis of the cam in this case. The motion of the follower is related to the form of the groove machined around a cylinder.

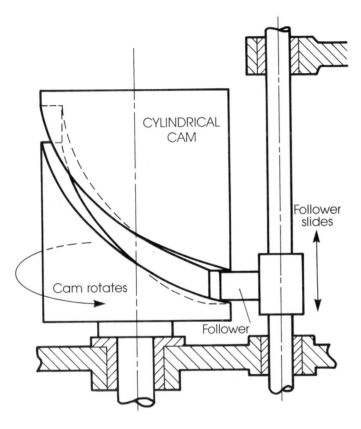

Fig 9   Cylindrical cam.

In-line followers

The <u>knife edge</u> follower can follow intricate cam profiles which include vee portions as at A in Fig 10a. The bearing surface of the knife edge is very small and it therefore wears very quickly. The friction forces tangential to the cam profile are applied to the follower and produce increased wear in the follower guides.

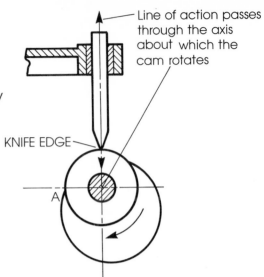

Fig 10a   Knife edge.

The <u>roller</u> follower reduces friction between the cam and the follower but the radius of the roller restricts the cam profile to a concave radius which must be greater than the roller radius, i.e. R_2 must be greater than R_1 in Fig 10b. The roller cannot make contact with the bottom of a vee as shown at A in Fig 10a.

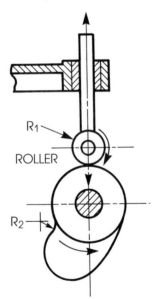

Fig 10b   Roller.

| Section No.
T16 | TITLE: **Cams.** | **Types of cam. Classification of followers.** | |

The flat-faced follower limits the cam profile to convex and tangent form only; the profile must not contain any vee or concave portion. The wear on the face is even and the restricted profile produces little side thrust on the follower, limiting guide wear.

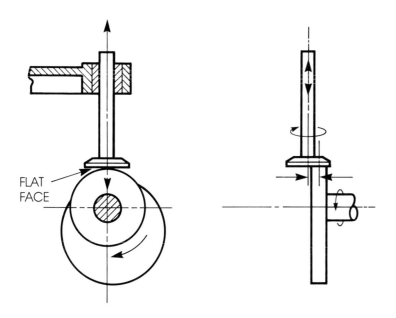

Fig 10c Flat-faced.

Offset followers
Each of the 3 types of follower previously described may be offset:

    (a) Offset roller (illustrated in Fig 11).
    (b) Offset knife edge.
    (c) Offset flat-faced

Offset followers tend to increase the side thrust on the follower and thus produce a corresponding increase in guide wear. They are useful, however, as a smoother follower action may be obtained.

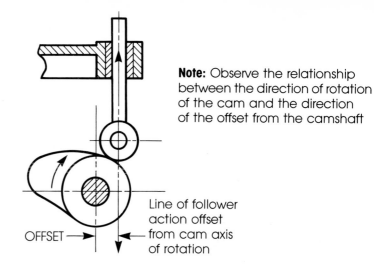

Note: Observe the relationship between the direction of rotation of the cam and the direction of the offset from the camshaft

Fig 11 Offset roller.

Radial followers
The 3 types may also be radial (Fig 12 shows the radial roller).

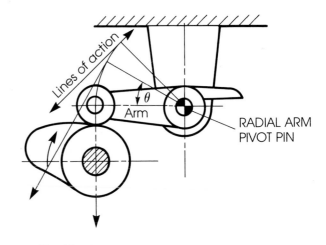

Fig 12 Radial roller

| Section No. T16 | TITLE: **Cams.** | **Classification of followers.** | |

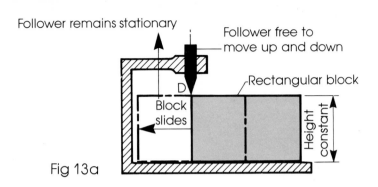

Fig 13a

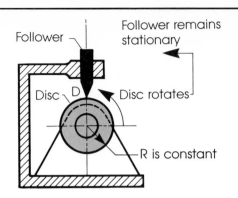

Fig 13b

When the block in Fig 13a slides under the point of the follower it transfers no movement to the follower since the height of the block is constant. Point D remains stationary.

When the disc rotates about its axis the point D of the follower remains stationary since the radius of the disc is constant. When the follower is stationary it is said to dwell.

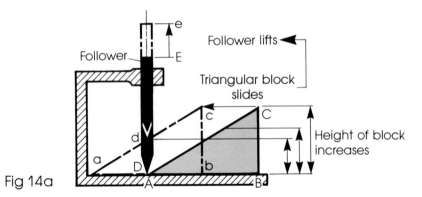

Fig 14a

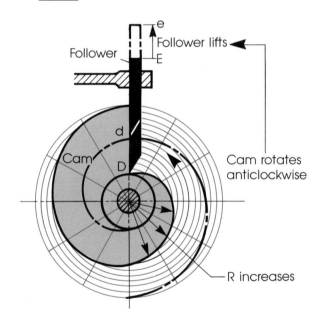

Fig 14b

When the triangular block in Fig 14a slides from its original position ABC to a new position, abc, the wedging action of the block forces the follower DE to rise or lift to a new position, de. The block or cam imparts motion to the follower.

When the cam rotates as indicated by the arrow the follower is pushed upwards from the initial position DE. A new position, de, is reached after the cam has rotated to the new position indicated in chain dot lines (after $\frac{1}{2}$ of a revolution).

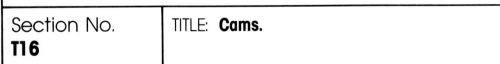

Section No. T16	TITLE: **Cams.**	**Dwell.**	

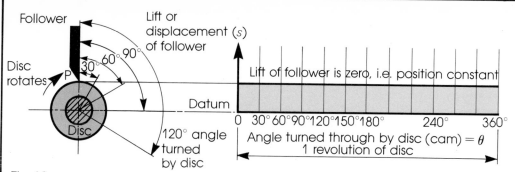

Fig 13c

The graph shows the relationship between the linear displacement of the follower and angular displacement of the cam.

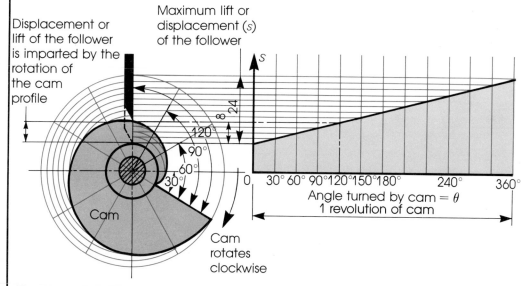

Displacement or lift of the follower is imparted by the rotation of the cam profile

Fig 14c

The graph shows the relationship between the follower displacement (s) and the angular displacement (θ) of the cam to be directly proportional. Do you recognise the straight line relationship and curve of the cam? See Fig 19a p 365 and G18-1 and G18-2.

Lift: The movement or displacement imparted to the follower by a rotation or angular displacement of the cam.

Linear displacement: (s) is the distance the follower moves in millimetres.

Dwell: The period when the continuing rotation or angular displacement of the cam maintains a constant displacement of the follower.

Angular displacement: (θ) is the angle through which the cam rotates in degrees or radians.

Uniform velocity: If the cam displacement, θ, is directly proportional ($\propto$) to the time t (e.g. the cam turns through 120° in 1 s, 240° in 2 s, 360° in 3 s), then the cam rotates with constant (uniform) angular velocity (ω) where $\omega = \theta/t$. If the rise of the cam profile is directly proportional to the angle through which the cam turns (e.g. $s = 8$ when $\theta = 120°$, $s = 16$ when $\theta = 240°$, $s = 24$ when $\theta = 360°$), i.e. $s \propto \theta$, since $\theta \propto t$ then $s \propto t$.
Linear velocity of follower $v = s/t$ which is directly related to $\theta/t = \omega$ and since ω is uniform then v must be uniform.
This is an important principle since the angular velocity of the cam is easily controlled to remain constant and thus restrict the follower's velocity to that defined by the cam profile.

Section No. T16	TITLE: **Cams.**	**Uniform velocity (UV).**	

377

EXAMPLE 1

Construct the profile of a radial (edge) cam which rotates with constant angular velocity in an anticlockwise direction and imparts motion to a knife edged follower as described in the specification.

Specification: Cam bowl 40 mm diameter,
cam shaft 16 mm diameter,
follower lifts 32 mm during 120° rotation of cam,
follower dwells between 120° and 240°,
follower falls 32 mm between 240° and 360°,
rise and fall with uniform velocity.

Note: Rotation of the cam is anticlockwise therefore the angular displacement is plotted clockwise. Point, a, rotates to the follower's vertical position first, followed by b then c, etc.

Action of follower is in line with axis of cam

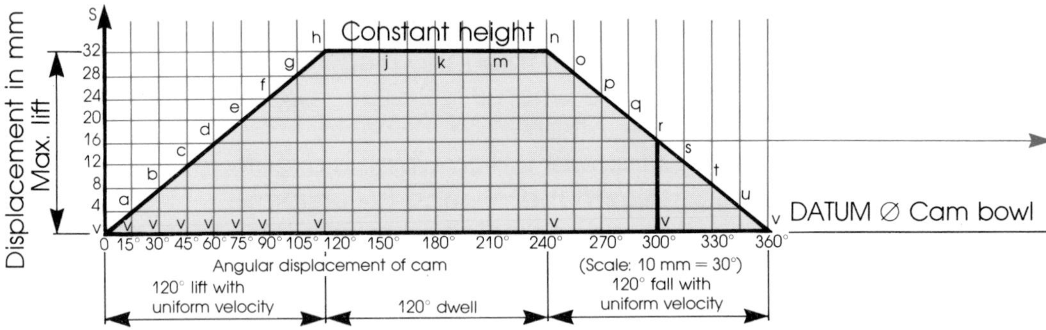

Fig 15a Cam graph.

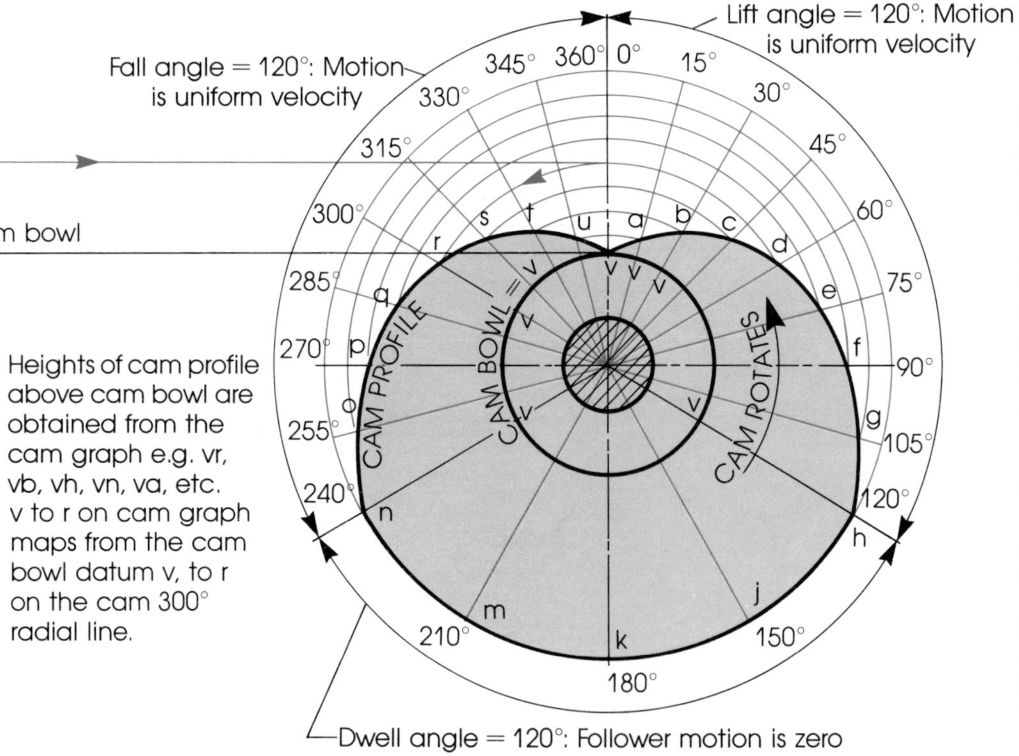

Lift angle = 120°: Motion is uniform velocity

Fall angle = 120°: Motion is uniform velocity

Heights of cam profile above cam bowl are obtained from the cam graph e.g. vr, vb, vh, vn, va, etc. v to r on cam graph maps from the cam bowl datum v, to r on the cam 300° radial line.

DATUM ∅ Cam bowl

Dwell angle = 120°: Follower motion is zero

Fig 15b Cam.

Section No.	TITLE: **Cams.**	**Examples using radial cams with uniform velocity and dwell.**	SCALE:
T16			

EXAMPLE 2

A radial cam which rotates in a clockwise direction with uniform angular velocity operates an in-line knife edged follower. Construct the cam profile to give the motion described relative to the cam's angular displacement. Cam turns 105° and the follower rises 14 mm with UV, the cam turns 45° and the follower dwells, the cam turns 60° and the follower rises 14 mm with UV, the cam turns 90° and the follower falls 28 mm with UV. Bowl diameter is 20 mm.

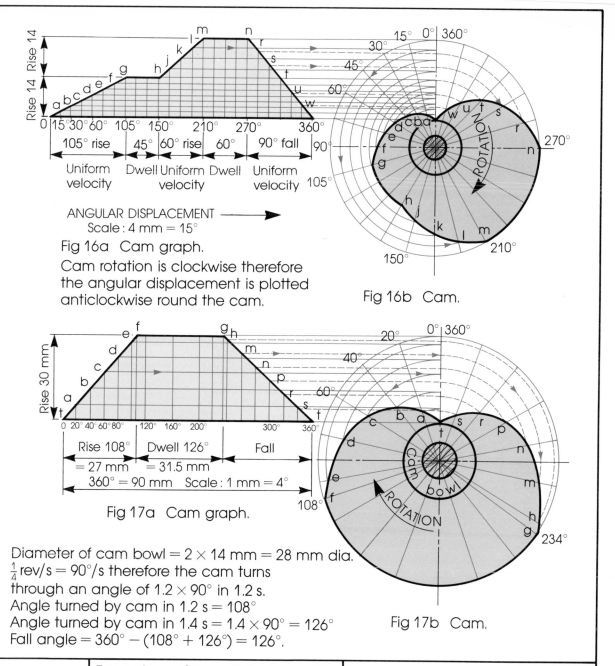

ANGULAR DISPLACEMENT ⟶
Scale : 4 mm = 15°

Fig 16a Cam graph.

Cam rotation is clockwise therefore the angular displacement is plotted anticlockwise round the cam.

Fig 16b Cam.

EXAMPLE 3

A radial cam rotates with uniform angular velocity $\omega = \pi/2$ rad/s, i.e. $\frac{1}{4}$ rev/s or 15 rev/min and is required to lift an in-line knife edged follower from a minimum position 14 mm above the cam axis to a maximum position of 44 mm above the cam axis in a time of 1.2 s with uniform velocity. The follower is then required to remain stationary for 1.4 s and return with uniform velocity to the minimum position during the remainder of the cam's cycle. The rotation of the cam is clockwise and the cam shaft diameter is 12 mm. Design the cam.

Fig 17a Cam graph.

Diameter of cam bowl = 2×14 mm = 28 mm dia.
$\frac{1}{4}$ rev/s = 90°/s therefore the cam turns through an angle of $1.2 \times 90°$ in 1.2 s.
Angle turned by cam in 1.2 s = 108°
Angle turned by cam in 1.4 s = $1.4 \times 90°$ = 126°
Fall angle = $360° - (108° + 126°) = 126°$.

Fig 17b Cam.

Section No.	TITLE: **Cams.**	**Examples using radial cams with uniform velocity and dwell.**	SCALE:
T16			0 10 20 30 40 50 60 70 80 mm

EXAMPLE 4

Produce the cam profile for a radial or edge cam which rotates with a clockwise uniform angular velocity and induces the motion described below to an in-line roller follower. The minimum distance of the roller centre to the cam axis is 30 mm and the roller diameter is 16 mm with the camshaft diameter 22 mm.

CAM DISPLACEMENT	FOLLOWER DISPLACEMENT
0° to 120°	Lift 30 mm with uniform velocity
120° to 210°	Dwell
210° to 360°	Fall 30 mm with uniform velocity

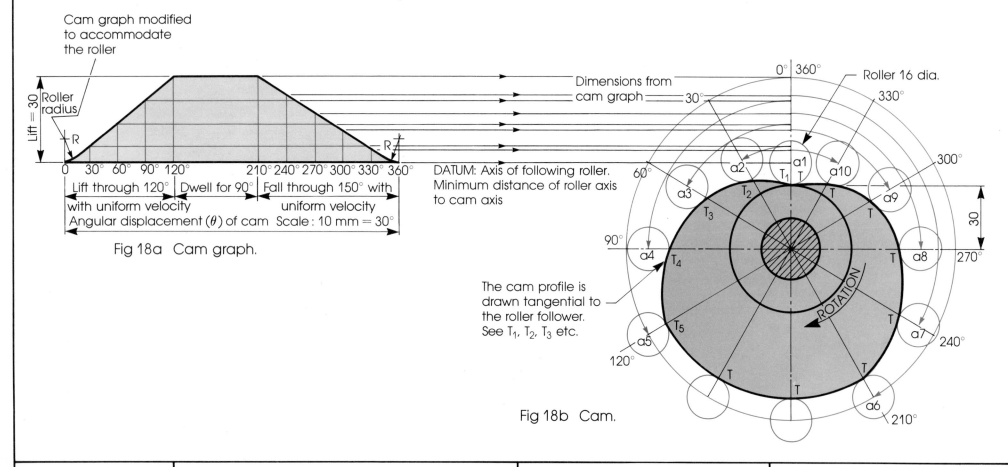

Cam graph modified to accommodate the roller

Lift = 30

Roller radius

Fig 18a Cam graph.

Lift through 120° with uniform velocity | Dwell for 90° | Fall through 150° with uniform velocity

Angular displacement (θ) of cam Scale : 10 mm = 30°

Dimensions from cam graph

DATUM: Axis of following roller. Minimum distance of roller axis to cam axis

The cam profile is drawn tangential to the roller follower. See T_1, T_2, T_3 etc.

Roller 16 dia.

ROTATION

Fig 18b Cam.

Section No. T16	TITLE: **Cams.**	**Example using in-line roller follower with uniform velocity and dwell.**	SCALE: 0 10 20 30 40 50 60 70 80 mm

EXAMPLE 5

Produce the cam profile for a radial cam which rotates with a uniform angular velocity in a clockwise direction and imparts the motion described below to an in-line flat-faced follower. The minimum distance of the follower face from the cam axis is 22 mm and the camshaft diameter is 20 mm.

CAM DISPLACEMENT	FOLLOWER DISPLACEMENT
0° to 180°	Lift 24 mm with uniform velocity
180° to 210°	Dwell
210° to 360°	Fall 24 mm with uniform velocity

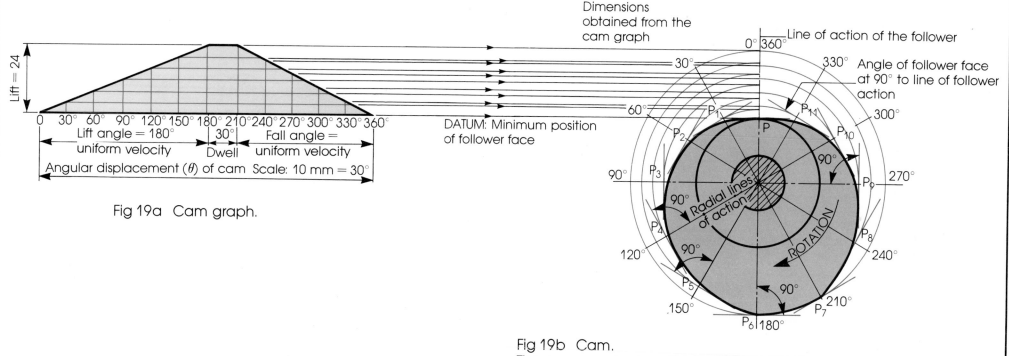

Fig 19a Cam graph.

Fig 19b Cam.

The cam graph gives the heights which the follower must attain to describe the given motion. The flat face must therefore attain the positions P_1, P_2, P_3, etc. with regard to the cam's axis and angle of rotation. The cam profile will therefore be a curve which is tangential to the follower's flat face.

Section No.	TITLE: **Cams.**	**Example using in-line flat-faced follower with uniform velocity and dwell.**	SCALE:
T16			

EXAMPLE 6

Produce the cam profile for a radial or disc cam which rotates with a clockwise uniform angular velocity and imparts the motion described below to an offset roller follower which is shown located with reference to the camshaft in Fig 20a.

CAM DISPLACEMENT	FOLLOWER DISPLACEMENT
0° to 120°	Lift 42 mm with uniform velocity
120° to 180°	Dwell
180° to 360°	Fall 42 mm with uniform velocity

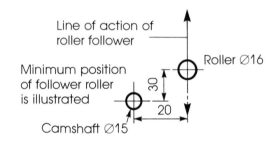

Fig 20a

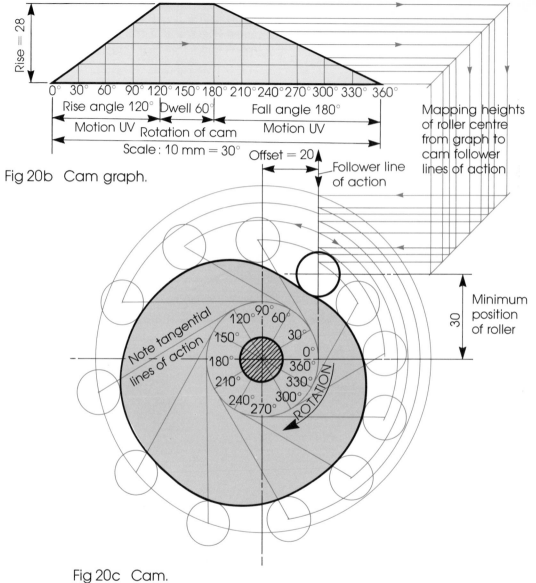

Rise = 28

0° 30° 60° 90° 120° 150° 180° 210° 240° 270° 300° 330° 360°

Rise angle 120° Dwell 60° Fall angle 180°

Motion UV Rotation of cam Motion UV

Scale : 10 mm = 30°

Offset = 20

Fig 20b Cam graph.

Mapping heights of roller centre from graph to cam follower lines of action

Follower line of action

Minimum position of roller

30

Note tangential lines of action

ROTATION

Fig 20c Cam.

Section No.	TITLE: **Cams.**	**Example using offset roller follower with uniform velocity and dwell.**	SCALE:
T16			

382

EXAMPLE 7

Produce the cam profile for a disc cam which rotates with uniform angular velocity in a clockwise direction and imparts an angular displacement of 30° to a radial arm roller follower located as shown in Fig 2a. The relative motion between the cam and follower is given below.

CAM DISPLACEMENT	FOLLOWER ANGULAR DISPLACEMENT
0° to 120°	Lift through 30° with uniform angular velocity
120° to 210°	Dwell
210° to 360°	Fall through 30° with uniform angular velocity

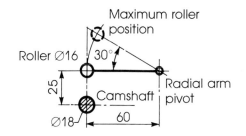

Fig 21a

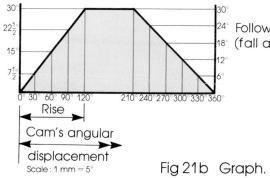

(Rise angles)

Follower angular displacement (fall angles) Scale : 1 mm = 1°

Rise

Cam's angular displacement
Scale : 1 mm = 5°

Fig 21b Graph.

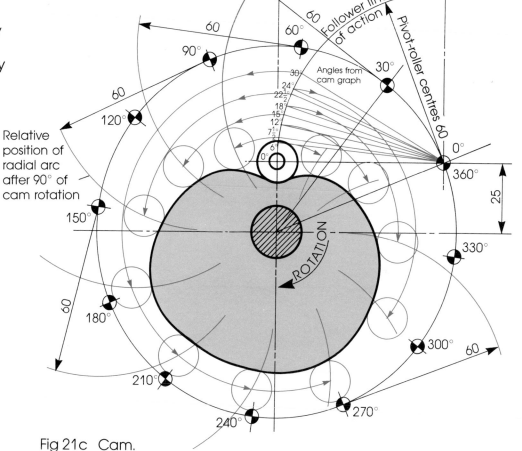

Relative position of radial arc after 90° of cam rotation

Fig 21c Cam.

| Section No. **T16** | TITLE: **Cams.** | **Example using a radial roller follower with uniform velocity and dwell.** | SCALE: |

383

Fig 18a p 380 illustrated a minor modification to the cam graph to accommodate the roller. This involved the inclusion of a radius at the start and finish of the cam graph similar to that shown at points W and Z in Fig 22 below.

Modification to the cam graph is also necessary for another important reason; to reduce or eliminate 'jerk'. Jerk is a sudden change in acceleration. If we refer to Fig 22 and examine the normal type of uniform velocity graph, which is shown by the dashed line, the follower has zero velocity during the dwell period between points X and Y. The follower however is expected to assume the velocity described by the sloping line in an infinitely small period of time. This sudden change in velocity would require an infinitely large acceleration in order to make the change in velocity from zero.

The jerk would be even more acute at points W and Z as the follower would be moving in one direction with a uniform velocity and suddenly in the next instant it would be travelling in the opposite direction with a different uniform velocity.

Fig 22 shows the cam graph modified at all points of change in velocity and this results in a slightly steeper slope thus producing a slight increase in velocity although the same average velocity is maintained. The modification would tend to a curved graph to minimise the jerk. A curve which describes <u>uniform acceleration</u> would produce a smoother operating follower, see Fig 25.

Acceleration (a) is defined as the rate of change of velocity (v) with time (t), i.e. $a = v/t$. Positive acceleration increases the velocity whilst negative acceleration (deceleration or retardation) decreases the velocity.

Uniform velocity $v = s/t$, i.e. $s = vt$ therefore s is proportional to t. For uniform acceleration $a = v/t$, i.e. $v = at$ therefore v is proportional to t. For constant or uniform acceleration, a is the rate of change of velocity when the velocity is directly proportional to the time. See Fig 23 for the direct or linear relationship between v and t when a is uniform.

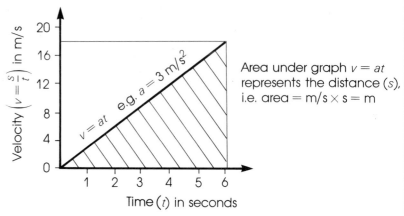

Area under graph $v = at$ represents the distance (s), i.e. area = m/s × s = m

Fig 23   Uniform increase in velocity.

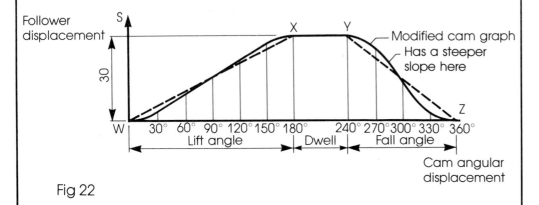

Fig 22

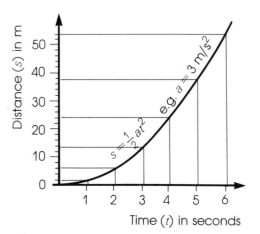

Fig 24   Uniform acceleration.

Section No.	TITLE: **Cams.**	**Cam graph modification to minimise 'jerk'. Uniform acceleration (UA).**	
T16			

Since the function relating v to t is the straight line illustrated in Fig 23 then the distance travelled (s) in a time (t) is the area under the graph which is given by the expression $s = \int v \, dt$. Since $v = at$, at can be substituted in the expression to give $s = \int at \, dt$ and this resolves to $s = \frac{1}{2} at^2$. Fig 24 illustrates this relationship between s and t which is of the quadratic, or parabolic, form. T14 pp 332–3 also gives the background to this relationship between s and t and since it is parabolic the construction shown in G17-3 can be used to construct the parabolic curve.

Note: The parabolic construction can be used to relate the linear displacement (s) to the angular displacement (θ) in Fig 25 since s is directly related to θ through the angular velocity (ω) $= \theta/t$, i.e. $\theta = \omega t$. The graph of $\theta = \omega t$ is a straight line (see pp 315–7).

EXAMPLE 8

Produce a cam graph for a cam which rotates with constant angular velocity (ω) and imparts the motion described below.

CAM DISPLACEMENT	FOLLOWER DISPLACEMENT
0° to 150°	Lift 48 mm with uniform acceleration
150° to 240°	Dwell
240° to 360°	Fall 48 mm with uniform acceleration

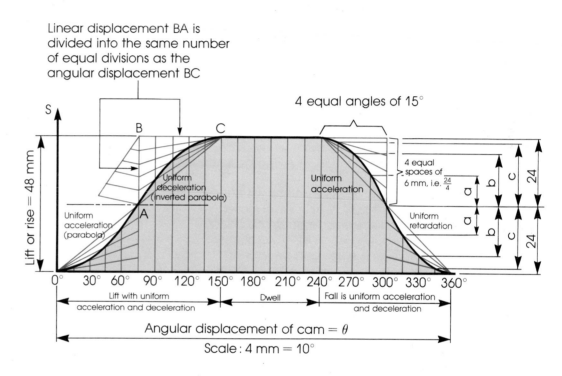

Fig 25　Cam graph construction involving uniform acceleration.

385

Simple harmonic motion is defined as motion in which the displacement or distance travelled (s) in relation to a fixed point is directly proportional to the acceleration (a).

The definition of simple harmonic motion is difficult to comprehend at this stage but it is the motion which occurs naturally in freely vibrating springs. See Fig 26a and 26b which illustrate a simple cantilever spring and a helical coil spring. The fixed point about which the spring's displacement takes place is the spring's normal position of rest. If either spring is disturbed to a position A and then released it will accelerate towards the rest position. Now since the extension (s) of the spring is directly proportional to the disturbing force (F) (Hooke's law) and force (F) = mass (m) × acceleration (a) (Newton's 2nd law) then s is directly proportional to the acceleration (a). i.e. $s \propto F$ and $F \propto a$ then $s \propto F \propto a$ therefore $s \propto a$. Note $F = m \times a$ and since m is constant then $F \propto a$. The momentum of the spring will increase on being released from position A and take the spring past its resting position, before the stiffness in the spring starts to retard the spring's motion, slowing it down until it momentarily comes to rest at the position B. The spring again accelerates back towards the rest position from where it decelerates until it reaches its original disturbed position at A. The cycle then repeats itself.

The spring will under normal circumstances come to rest after a period of time since the vibrations are not truly free. Internal friction together with the surrounding air damps out or absorbs some of the kinetic energy of the spring during each of its vibrations.

The SHM, which occurs naturally in springs, can be propagated by a disc which rotates with uniform angular velocity (i.e. constant speed). If the disc shown in Fig 27a, view X, rotates with a constant angular velocity (ω) then the movement of the pin P shown in view Y will appear to accelerate and decelerate with SHM. Fig 27b illustrates the relationship between distance travelled (s) about the fixed point (i.e. the axis of rotation) in view Y and the angle turned through by the disc. Since θ is proportional to the time (t) for constant angular velocity then Fig 27b also represents the relationship between s and t.

Note: It is important that when springs are used with cam followers the frequency of the cam's rotation should not coincide with the natural frequency of the spring nor should the simple harmonic motion induced to the follower by the cam profile. If the harmonics coincide the follower may 'bounce' and not follow the true motion proscribed by the cam profile.

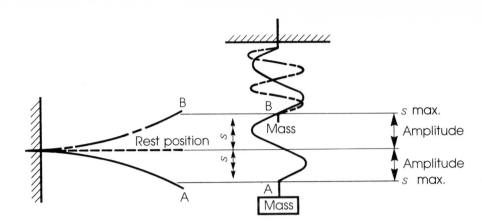

Fig 26a   Cantilever spring.   Fig 26b   Helical coil spring.

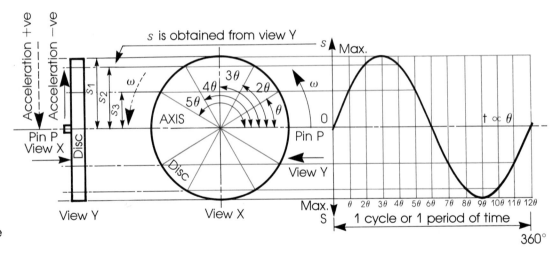

Fig 27a   Rotating disc.   Fig 27b   Displacement time or angle graph.

Have you seen curves of a similar form before? See the helix in G18-6 and the development of a cut cylinder in G34-7!

Section No.	TITLE: **Cams.**	**Simple harmonic motion (SHM).**	SCALE:

T16

EXAMPLE 9

Produce a cam graph for a cam which rotates with constant angular velocity (ω) and imparts the motion to a follower which is described below.

CAM DISPLACEMENT	FOLLOWER DISPLACEMENT
0° to 120°	Lift 40 mm with SHM
120° to 180°	Dwell
180° to 360°	Fall 40 mm with SHM

Both the lift and fall angles on the cam graph have the same number of divisions as propogating circle

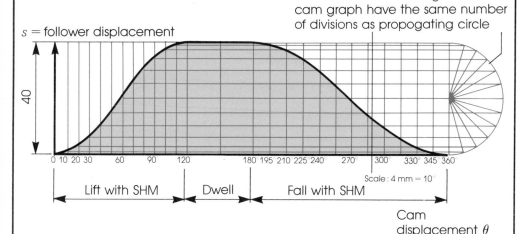

Scale : 4 mm = 10°

Lift with SHM — Dwell — Fall with SHM

Cam displacement θ

Fig 28

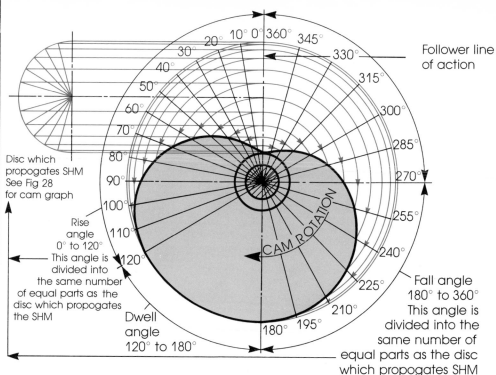

Disc which propogates SHM See Fig 28 for cam graph

Follower line of action

Rise angle 0° to 120°
This angle is divided into the same number of equal parts as the disc which propogates the SHM

Dwell angle 120° to 180°

Fall angle 180° to 360°
This angle is divided into the same number of equal parts as the disc which propogates SHM

CAM ROTATION

Fig 29 Cam described in Exercise 1.

EXERCISE 1

Construct the cam profile for a radial or disc cam which imparts motion to an in-line knife edged follower with the motion conforming to the cam graph drawn in Fig 28 above. The minimum follower position is 10 mm from the cam axis and the camshaft diameter is also 10 mm. Cam rotation is clockwise.

EXERCISE 2

Use the cam graph drawn in Fig 25 to construct the profile of a disc cam which rotates with uniform angular velocity and imparts the following motion to an in-line knife edge follower whose minimum distance to the cam axis is 12 mm and camshaft diameter is 12 mm. Cam rotation is anticlockwise.

CAM DISPLACEMENT	FOLLOWER DISPLACEMENT
0° to 150°	Lift 48 mm with uniform acceleration
150° to 240°	Dwell
240° to 360°	Fall 48 mm with uniform acceleration

Section No. T16	TITLE: **Cams.**	**Examples using UV, dwell, UA and SHM.**	SCALE:  mm

387

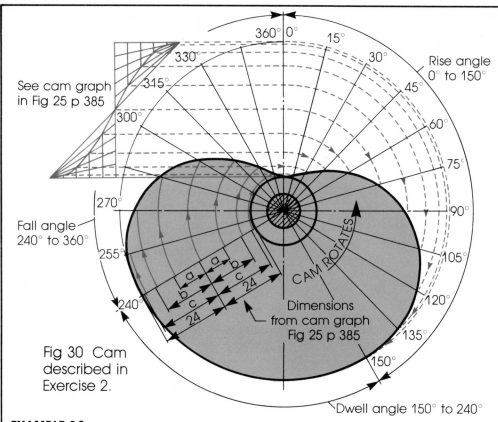

See cam graph in Fig 25 p 385

Rise angle 0° to 150°

Fall angle 240° to 360°

CAM ROTATES

Dimensions from cam graph Fig 25 p 385

Fig 30 Cam described in Exercise 2.

Dwell angle 150° to 240°

EXAMPLE 10

Construct the cam profile for a disc cam which rotates with clockwise uniform angular velocity and imparts motion to a follower as described in the table below. The follower is an in-line knife edge type and its minimum position relative to the cam axis is 25 mm and the camshaft has a diameter of 12 mm.

CAM'S ANGULAR DISPLACEMENT	FOLLOWER'S LINEAR DISPLACEMENT
0° to 150°	Lift 40 mm with uniform acceleration
150° to 200°	Dwell
200° to 250°	Fall 10 mm with uniform velocity
250° to 288°	Dwell
288° to 360°	Fall 30 mm with simple harmonic motion

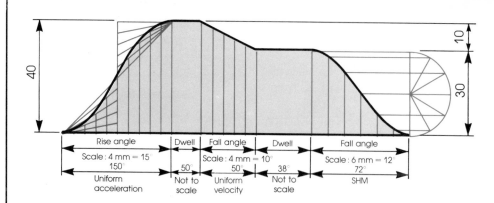

Fig 32 Cam graph.

Rise angle — Scale: 4 mm = 15° — 150° — Uniform acceleration
Dwell — 50° — Not to scale
Fall angle — Scale: 4 mm = 10° — 50° — Uniform velocity
Dwell — 38° — Not to scale
Fall angle — Scale: 6 mm = 12° — 72° — SHM

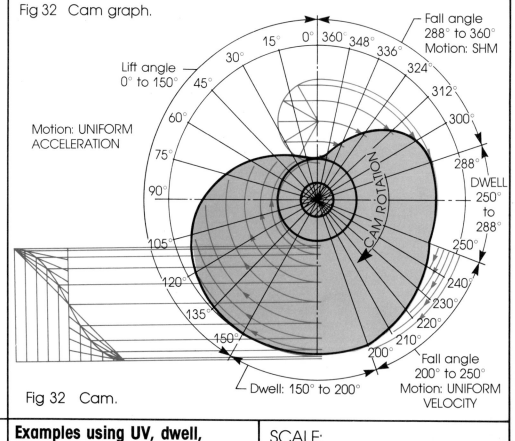

Lift angle 0° to 150°

Motion: UNIFORM ACCELERATION

Fall angle 288° to 360° Motion: SHM

DWELL 250° to 288°

Fall angle 200° to 250° Motion: UNIFORM VELOCITY

Dwell: 150° to 200°

CAM ROTATION

Fig 32 Cam.

Section No. **T16**

TITLE: **Cams.**

Examples using UV, dwell, UA and SHM.

SCALE:
0 10 20 30 40 50 60 70 80
mm

388

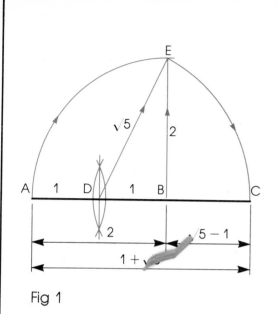

Fig 1

In the construction, AD = DB and DE = DC.
AB : AC = 1 : 1.618
Hence BC = 0.618
PROOF

$$DE^2 = DB^2 + BE^2 \text{ by Pythagoras}$$
$$DE^2 = 1^2 + 2^2$$
$$DE = \sqrt{5} \approx 2.236$$
now BC = $\sqrt{5} - 1$
$$BC \approx 1.236$$
AB : BC = 2 : 1.236
or   1 : 0.618

The proportions of AB to BC where AB : BC = 1 : 0.618 is known as the Divine or Golden Proportion.

Note: 1 : 0.618 = 1.618 : 1

'Divine Proportion', 'The Section', 'The Golden Section', 'The Golden Mean', are all names by which this particular proportion has been known. It has been known since Pythagoras, who preceded Euclid, and it is said to have been used in the design of the Parthenon. It was also familiar to the Egyptians and underlies many of the compositions of the Renaissance artists. Contemporary architecture and art have also been strongly influenced by the proportions, seen in works by Le Corbusier and paintings of the cubist period by Piet Mondrian.

Beauty is often visualised in terms of symmetrical proportions but these are not always the most interesting or most satisfying. Vitality and harmony of form often lies in repetition: in the ability of certain proportions to contain themselves, or be contained, time and time again. A simple numerical progression also provides an identical relationship eg.
1, 2, 3, 5, 8, 13, 21, 34, 55, . . . Can you see the geometric progression?
$\frac{1}{2} = 0.5$, $\frac{2}{3} = 0.666$, $\frac{3}{5} = 0.6$, $\frac{5}{8} = 0.625$, $\frac{8}{13} = 0.615$, $\frac{13}{21} = 0.619$, $\frac{21}{34} = 0.6178$, $\frac{34}{55} = 0.6182$ . . .

By taking successive pairs of numbers from the series and forming a fraction it is seen that the values oscillate and converge on the Golden Mean of 0.618. Where would you place a single chalice to give interest and balance to the fireplace, (a), (b) or (c)?

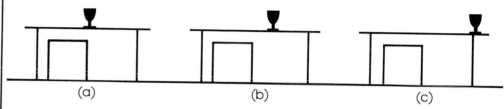

(a)   (b)   (c)

Fig 2

The brain recognises the proportions and is psychologically attracted to them when they are contained or are inherent in a structure. A square room feels boxed in and claustrophobic, a long room has positions of coldness or remoteness.

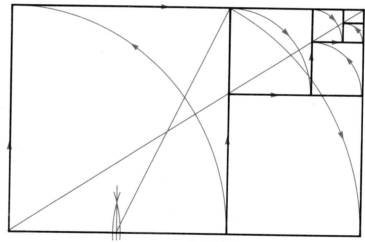

Fig 3

A room having divine proportions produces a feeling of warmth and harmony. Fig 3 illustrates the ability of the Golden rectangle to contain and regenerate its proportions.

Section No.	TITLE: **Golden proportions.**		
T17			

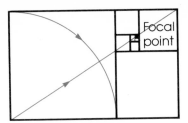

Fig 4a illustrates the convergence to a focal point.

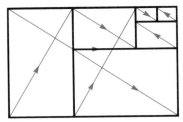

Fig 4b is an exercise to exploit the rhythm of repetition. (Note that right angles produced by diagonals also repeat.) Does the rectangle formed by the diagonals have golden proportions?

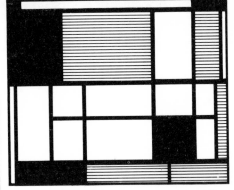

Fig 5 Asymmetrical composition by Piet Mondrian.

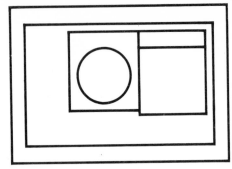

Fig 6 Asymmetrical composition by Ben Nicholson.

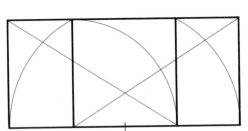

Fig 4c Proportions of the painting of 'The Last Supper' by Leonardo de Vinci. Where do you think the focal position is? Where do you think Christ was placed?

Symmetrical balance presents no major difficulty to the designer; he just reverses the one side to form a mirror image on the other side.

Asymmetrical balance is more complex and exciting, involving colour density or force of attraction, distance from the centre and the area or mass of a feature. A large dark shape some way from the centre may be balanced by a small dark shape close to centre.

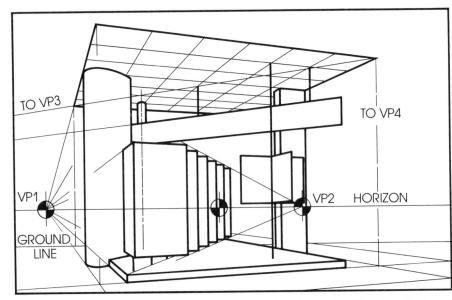

Fig 6 1930 building exhibition stand for Venesta Ltd by Le Corbusier (Olympia).

Exercise
See how many rectangles you can find in the three illustrations above, the rectangles to contain the golden proportions as in Figure 4a, b, c.

| Section No. **T17** | TITLE: **Golden proportions.** | | |

Fig 8 below illustrates that the diagonals of a pentagon cut each other into golden proportions, i.e. AB : BC = 1 : 0.618.

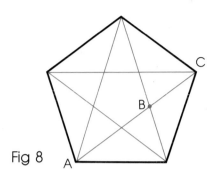

Fig 8

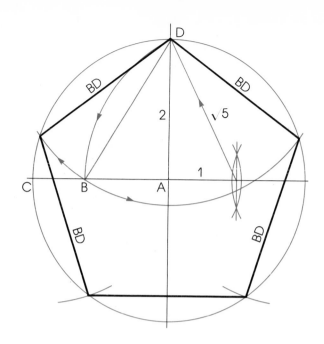

Fig 10   To construct a pentagon in a circle given the circle radius or to divide a line AC into the divine or golden proportions where AB : AC = 1 : 1.618.

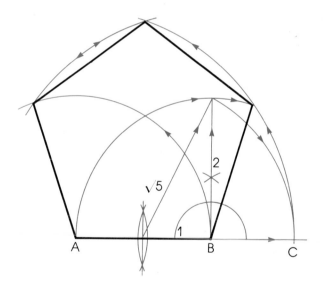

Fig 9   To construct a pentagon given the side or to determine a point C on a line AB produced, such that AC : AB = AB : BC.

Section No. **T17**	TITLE: **Golden proportion and the pentagon.**		

GLOSSARY OF TERMS

A/C, across corners: The measurement across the opposing corners of a regular polygon which has an even number of sides.

A/F, across flats: The measurement across the parallel sides of a regular polygon.

Altitude: The vertical height above a given datum.

Analyse: Separate into smaller parts so as to examine.

Angular velocity (uniform): Rotation about a fixed point at constant speed.

Apex: The top or highest point of a triangle in relation to its base.

Auxiliary elevation: An extra view taken at some angle other than 90° to a principle plane.

Axis: A line of symmetry or a line about which something revolves.

Bisect: To cut into 2 equal parts.

Cabinet oblique: A method of producing a pictorial view using half-size dimensions on the 45° lines and full-size dimensions on the vertical and horizontal lines.

Cavalier oblique: A method of producing a pictorial view using full size dimensions on the 45° lines and on the vertical and horizontal lines.

Cam: A mechanical device used to change motion from one form to another.

Centre of vision: The position from which all points are observed.

Circumscribe: To draw around a given figure, usually a circle which touches the corners.

Coordinates: Points described by 2 numbers.

Cross-section: The shape revealed across an object when cut by a plane surface.

Curve of interpenetration: } The curve produced by the meeting of 2 surfaces or solids.
Curve of intersection:

Cutting plane: A plane used to cut through a solid, usually to reveal the shape across the solid at that point.

Cylinder: A circular prism.

Datum: A point, line or surface to which other features are referenced or positioned.

Development: The unfolding or unwinding of the surface of a solid so that its surface can be contained on a plane or flat surface.

Dimension: Size or length of a feature.

Elevation: A view usually taken looking parallel with the horizontal plane.

EVP, end vertical plane: A principle plane erected at 90° to the horizontal plane and at 90° to the front vertical plane. See G22.

Escribe: To draw a circle which has one side of a triangle and the other 2 produced as tangents to the circle.

FVP, front vertical plane: A principle plane erected at 90° to both the horizontal and the end vertical plane. See G22.

Frustum: The part of a pyramid or cone which is left after the top has been cut off.

Ground line: A line parallel to the horizon on which the nearest corner of a solid, drawn in perspective, is located. Horizontal dimensions are set off on the ground line when using the measured point method of perspective drawing.

HP, horizontal plane: A flat or plane surface which is parallel to the ground. See G22.

HT, horizontal trace: The intersection of a line or plane with the horizontal plane.

Increment: A small change or step.

Inscribe: To draw one figure inside another. Usually a circle to touch the sides of a polygon.

Intersection: The point at which 2 lines meet, or the line producd where 2 surfaces meet.

Isometric: A method of drawing a pictorial view of a solid which uses axes at 30° to the horizontal and vertical.

Lamina: A wafer thin plane surface.

Linear velocity: Movement in a fixed direction at constant speed.

MP, measuring point: A point on the sight line or horizon used to determine the apparent lengths on a perspective drawing.

Normal: A line at 90° to a curve at its point of intersection with the curve. A line which passes through a circle and its centre.

Oblique: A method of producing a pictorial drawing. Also used to describe a line or plane which is at an obscure angle to the principle planes.

Ordinate: The vertical or horizontal distance from the origin of a graph. The horizontal distance, i.e. the x coordinate is also known as the abscissa.

Orthographic projection: A method of using more than one view to define a solid with the views being aligned or in projection and the sight line remaining normal to the principle planes as each corner is analysed. Only 2 dimensions can be seen in each view. See G22.

Perimeter: Distance all the way round a figure.

Perpendicular: Vertical or meeting at right angles, i.e. 90°.

Perspective: A method of drawing a pictorial view of a solid where its dimensions diminish as the solid recedes into the distance to give an illusion of space and depth. See T3.

Pictorial view: A view which illustrates all 3 dimensions of a solid as in a photograph.

Picture plane: The plane on to which the image of a solid is transferred.

Pivot: Turn about a fixed point.

Plan: A view of an object drawn looking directly from above.

Planometric: A pictorial method of representing a solid which utilises the plan view of the solid.

Polygon: A many sided plane figure. Usually more than 4 straight sides.

Principle planes: The horizontal, front vertical and end vertical planes on to which the normal orthographic views are transposed. See G22.

Prism: A body with similar parallel ends and of continuous cross-section.

Projection: Direct transfer of a position in one view to a position in another.

Revolution: A circle. Turn through 360° about a fixed point.

Right cone: A body generated by a right-angled triangle as it rotates about a vertical side.

Right square pyramid: A square pyramid with its apex above the centre of the base.

Schematic diagram: A diagram to organise and represent a scheme or idea.

Sight line: The horizon or horizontal line which represents the viewing level.

Sphere: A circular solid as in a cricket ball.

Stimulus response: The reaction generated by some input or occurrence.

Symmetry: The exact correspondence between the opposite halves of a figure, form or line on either side of an axis or centre.

Synthesise: To make up by combining parts or elements into a complex whole.

Tangent: A straight line which touches a curve at a single point and if produced does not cut through it. A line at 90° to the Normal.

Trace: The intersection of a line or plane or a line or plane produced with one of the principle planes.

Triangulation: To divide into triangles to facilitate the location of points.

True length: The real or actual length as opposed to the apparent or projected length.

True shape: The real or actual shape.

VP, vanishing point: The point on a perspective drawing located on the horizon where the diminishing dimensions would become infinitely small.

VT, vertical trace: The point at which a line or plane would, if produced, meet the vertical plane.